INTRODUCTION
TO MATHEMATICS

FRANK M. HUDSON and **DONALD W. ADLONG**
State College of Arkansas

ADDISON-WESLEY PUBLISHING COMPANY
Reading, Massachusetts · Menlo Park, California · London · Don Mills, Ontario

This book is in the
ADDISON-WESLEY SERIES
IN INTRODUCTORY MATHEMATICS

Gail S. Young and Richard S. Pieters
Consulting Editors

To Sandii and Paula

PREFACE

In writing this book we have worked toward achieving three basic goals. These are:

1 To reveal to the reader the structure of pure mathematics.

2 To provide the reader with a mathematical background which will enable him to appreciate the present elementary school mathematics curriculum.

3 To introduce the reader to some of those topics that are important to him in his day-to-day activities.

The reader is immediately introduced to the methods of pure mathematics in Chapter 1 by a general discussion of mathematical systems. These methods are used in the development of the number systems in Chapters 4 and 5. In Chapter 4 the natural numbers and their basic properties are assumed. The integers are defined as ordered pairs of natural numbers, and the basic properties of the integers are derived from the assumed properties of the natural numbers. The development of the number systems, through the complex numbers, is continued in Chapter 5. Chapter 8 presents the same type of development from a more abstract point of view through a discussion of groups and fields. Chapter 7 on modular arithmetic has been included to provide examples for Chapter 8 and to present some topics which we have found to interest the majority of our students in the past. Throughout the book emphasis is placed on concepts rather than on techniques.

In reference to the second goal, Chapter 2 on sets, Chapter 3 on numeration systems, Chapter 4 on natural numbers and integers, Chapter 5 on real and complex numbers, Chapter 7 on modular systems, and Chapter 9 on geometry could be used as the nucleus for a first course for elementary teachers. Certainly this treatment would be more than adequate to give the reader an appreciation of the mathematics curriculum in the elementary grades.

As to the third goal, we have included Chapter 10 on probability and statistics, Chapter 11 on interest and annuities, and Chapter 12 on computers and computer programming. Chapter 6 on functions and graphs includes a discussion of statistical graphs frequently encountered by the reader.

This book contains enough material to be used as a text for a two-semester course for liberal arts majors. With certain limitations, the chapters of the book are independent, so the material can be used with considerable flexibility as the text for a one-semester course. As we noted in a previous paragraph, the book also contains those topics essential to a course for elementary teachers.

We have assumed little previous mathematical experience; two years of high school mathematics should be sufficient for any course taught from the text. We have not attempted to review high school mathematics to any great degree. Our primary aim has been to include those topics which we have found to be interesting to a nontechnical mathematics student.

With the exception of Chapters 11 and 12, Chapters 1 and 2 are essential for a study of every chapter of the book. The language of sets is introduced in Chapter 2 and is used throughout the next eight chapters. Chapters 4 and 5 can be omitted, provided the reader is familiar with the basic properties of a number field (that is, associativity, commutativity, distributivity, etc.). The instructor who wishes to include Chapter 8 in his course will probably want to discuss the first two sections of Chapter 6 on relations and functions. The remainder of Chapter 6 is not essential to the chapters which follow and may be omitted if desired. The first five sections of Chapter 7 are prerequisites for Chapter 8. All chapters following Chapter 8 are independent of one another, allowing the instructor to cover those topics of particular interest to him and his class.

The majority of the material in this book has been classroom-tested at some time during the past two years in the authors' basic mathematics classes at State College of Arkansas. Much of the material has also been used in classes taught by Miss Dorothy Long, and we would like to express our appreciation for the many helpful suggestions she has made.

The manuscript was typed by Gayle Joyner, Jimmie Anne Mitchum, and Loretta McElroy. Gail S. Young of Tulane University and Dorothy Schrader of Southern Connecticut State College made many helpful suggestions in the preparation of the manuscript. We wish to thank all these people for the valuable assistance they have given us in completing our writing project.

Conway, Arkansas
January 1970

F. M. H.
D. W. A.

CONTENTS

CHAPTER 5   RATIONAL, REAL, AND COMPLEX NUMBERS

CHAPTER 6   FUNCTIONS AND GRAPHS

CHAPTER 7 MODULAR ARITHMETIC AND APPLICATIONS

CHAPTER 8 MATHEMATICAL SYSTEMS

CHAPTER 9 GEOMETRY

Chapter 1

INTRODUCTION

1.1 WHAT IS MATHEMATICS?

The meaning mathematics has for people varies from person to person. To many people mathematics is merely the art of calculation and measurement or a study of mysterious manipulations. One of the major objectives of this book is to bring the student to a clearer and more complete understanding of mathematics.

In recent years more and more people have been studying mathematics as an entity in itself, and for this reason mathematics can be considered an art. For years people thought that mathematics should be used only as a tool for the study of other disciplines, but today many study mathematics irrespective of its applications. Of course one doesn't listen to mathematics as he does to music, nor does one look at mathematics as he would a painting, but certainly the pure mathematician creates mathematics that is pleasing to himself and others. Even though much of mathematics is created without motivation from the physical world, it often happens that this mathematics can be used in studying the physical world.

When mathematics can be used to study some physical situation, it becomes a tool. Certainly the chemist, physicist, biologist, engineer, and people in many other professions must be able to use mathematics as a tool in their work. When mathematics is used in this way, it is sometimes referred to as "applied mathematics." Notice in this case that it is not a matter of developing mathematics, but one of using mathematics already developed.

Through the use of mathematics one is able to communicate with any person having an understanding of mathematics. To a person in China, π is the ratio of the circumference of a circle to its diameter just as it is to a person in Africa. Not only is mathematics a language, but it is one of the more exact languages. For convenience, the mathematician makes use of many symbols in his work. Frequently a person is impressed by the ability of another to interpret the symbols used in mathematics, but remember, these symbols are only a shorthand for the mathematician and they carry no meaning within themselves.

Mathematics is sometimes classed with the sciences, since the mathematician uses some of the methods of the scientist. However, it should be pointed out that the truths of natural science are probable truths. The natural scientist bases his theories on observations of phsyical objects. Through the years, many stated theories have been changed due to the fact that further observations showed them to be incorrect. The truths of mathematics are relative truths, in that the mathematician is concerned with whether or not his conclusions follow logically from a given hypothesis. For example, if $2 = 7$, then $5 = 10$. The conclusion that $5 = 10$ follows from the assumption that $2 = 7$ by the addition of 3 to each member of the equation. Hence, $5 = 10$ relative to the assumption that $2 = 7$.

1.2 MATHEMATICAL SYSTEMS

A mathematical system consists of undefined terms, defined terms, axioms and theorems. In this section we shall discuss each of these and how they are related.

Not all things can be defined, and therefore, mathematicians have agreed to accept some notions to be primitive concepts and leave them undefined. For example, "point" and "line" are usually accepted as undefined terms in geometry. The concept of a set, to be discussed in Chapter 2, is another concept that we do not define.

A *proposition* is a statement which makes an assertion that may be either true or false. Just as one cannot define each term, one cannot prove or disprove every proposition. A proposition which we accept without proof is called an *axiom*. An axiom is not a self-evident truth, but merely an accepted proposition. From system to system the set of axioms might differ. It has been said that, "One man's axiom is another's theorem." Since axioms are propositions that the mathematician accepts without proof, one might be inclined to assume that all propositions are true and, thus, leave nothing to prove. However, the mathematician wishes to keep the number of axioms to a minimum. Furthermore, he wants to make sure no axiom contradicts another axiom and that each axiom is independent in the sense that it cannot be proved using other axioms.

The first step in developing a mathematical system is to compile a list of undefined terms and axioms and agree on the laws of logic that are to be used. This is not to say that all undefined terms and axioms to be used in the development are listed at the beginning. As the need arises, other undefined terms and other axioms will be added to the original list. Using these undefined terms and axioms, one then formulates definitions for terms to be used in the study. Once a term is defined, it may be used in defining other terms. Caution must be taken to avoid the assumption that the everyday meaning of a term is the same as the meaning of the term in a mathematical discussion. For example, the word "group" has a definite meaning to the mathematician (Chapter 8) which differs significantly from the everyday meaning of the word. It is no easy task to formulate a good definition and care must be taken. The definition of a term must completely characterize the term. Consider the following examples.

"A square is a parallelogram,"

but this statement does not completely characterize a square because some parallelograms are not squares.

"A square is a rectangle,"

but this statement does not completely characterize a square because some rectangles are not squares. Therefore, neither of the above statements defines a square. A statement that does completely characterize a square is the statement,

"A square is a rectangle with two adjacent sides equal."

In order to use this statement as the definition of a square, the meaning of the terms "rectangle," "adjacent sides," and "equal" must be agreed on before they are used in the statement of the definition. A good definition should also be concise. For example, the statement,

"A square is a quadrilateral with four right angles and all sides equal"

completely characterizes a square. This statement would not be considered as good a definition as the previous one because it contains more informaton than is necessary to characterize a square.

A *theorem* is a proposition that can be proved using undefined terms, defined terms, axioms, and the laws of logic. The last and perhaps most important step in the study of a mathematical system is the stating and proving of theorems. A mathematician is primarily concerned with the theorems he can prove from a given set of axioms.

Problems

1 Without the use of a dictionary, define "chair." Does your definition completely characterize a chair? Without telling your roommate what you have defined, ask him whether he can tell what your definition defines.

2 Repeat Problem 1 for the word "automobile."

3 Repeat Problem 1 for the word "table."

4 Are the following probable truths or relative truths?
   a) The sun will rise in the east tomorrow.
   b) If $x = 2$, then $2x = 4$.
   c) If an apple falls from a tree, then it will fall on the ground.
   d) If $3 = 2$, then $5 = 4$.
   e) If two triangles are congruent, then they have the same area.

5 In Problem 4, which parts would be of concern to a scientist? a mathematician?

1.3 MATHEMATICAL PROOF

In the previous section mention was made of proving theorems. Just what is involved in proving something? Perhaps a simple definition would be that proof is a convincing argument. This may seem too simple, and yet if we follow certain rules, our statement would fairly well describe the concept of proof. If a man says he can eat ten apple pies and proceeds to do so, then he has certainly proved his statement. Scientists have proved that a rocket can be shot to the moon by doing it. These are both examples of proof by performance. Proof by performance is not mathematical proof. *Inductive reasoning* involves observing a number of objects and then stating a conclusion about all future objects of the observed type. One must be careful to avoid inductive reasoning in mathematical proof. In mathematics we cannot prove a proposition by listing examples for which the proposition is true unless the proposition can be verified for all possible cases. However, one example for which a proposition is not true, called a *counterexample*, is sufficient to disprove the proposition. We might be inclined to state that all prime numbers are odd, because we can certainly list as many odd prime numbers as desired. However, the prime number 2 is a counterexample of the above statement. Note that 2 is the only counterexample; nevertheless we must conclude it is not true that all prime numbers are odd. *Deductive reasoning* involves showing that a statement is true logically. Mathematical proof is proof by deduction. The rules to be used are the laws of logic. In this book we will not dwell on the formal laws of logic but will give some examples of different types of mathematical proofs

Most theorems are of the "if–then" form. For example, "If two angles of a triangle are equal, then the sides opposite these angles are equal." In this statement the mathematician is concerned with accepting as a fact that he has a triangle with two equal angles and proving that the sides opposite these angles are equal by using a sequence of logical statements. The part of the statement he accepts is called the *hypothesis* and the part he proves the *conclusion*. Again, the mathematician is not concerned with the truth of the hypothesis, but only with whether or not the conclusion can be arrived at logically from the hypothesis. Many theorems that are not stated in the "if–then" form can be converted to this form. As an example consider the following theorem from plane geometry: "Two lines perpendicular to the same line are parallel." This theorem can be stated in the "if–then" form in the following way: "If two lines are perpendicular to the same line, then the two lines are parallel." One of the advantages of stating a theorem in the "if–then" form is that the hypothesis and the conclusion of the theorem are easily recognized.

1.4 DIRECT PROOF

Suppose H represents the hypothesis and C the conclusion of a theorem, and we wish to prove the theorem "If H, then C." Another way of stating this is to prove "H implies C," written $H \rightarrow C$. The basis for the direct proof is the use of the *transitive property of implication*. This can be stated as "If $H \rightarrow C$ and $C \rightarrow D$, then $H \rightarrow D$." The meaning of the transitive property of implication can be illustrated by considering the following: "If Bob makes 60 on the final exam, then he will pass the course. If Bob passes the course then he will maintain his scholarship." By use of the transitive property of implication, we conclude that if Bob makes 60 on the final exam, then he will maintain his scholarship. At this point we shall assume that implication has the property of being transitive.

We now return to the original problem of proving $H \rightarrow C$. Suppose we can show

$$H \rightarrow C_1, \ C_1 \rightarrow C_2, \ C_2 \rightarrow C_3, \ \ldots, \ C_{n-1} \rightarrow C_n, \ C_n \rightarrow C,$$

where $C_1, C_2, \ldots, C_n$, and C are different conclusions. Then we can conclude by a repeated use of the transitive property of implication that $H \rightarrow C$.

Perhaps one of the simplest examples of a direct proof is that of solving an equation.

Example 1 Solve the equation $3x - 5 = x + 7$.

Solution

$$3x - 5 = x + 7,$$
$$3x = x + 12,$$
$$2x = 12,$$
$$x = 6.$$

Now this can be considered as the theorem "If $3x - 5 = x + 7$, then $x = 6$." To prove this theorem we used the following implications:

If $3x - 5 = x + 7$, then $3x = x + 12$.
If $3x = x + 12$, then $2x = 12$.
If $2x = 12$, then $x = 6$.
Therefore, if $3x - 5 = x + 7$, then $x = 6$.

Note that each step in the proof (finding a solution for the equation) is justifiable by some definition, axiom, or previously proved fact.

Another important thing to note is that we have not proved the theorem "If $x = 6$, then $3x - 5 = x + 7$." The question might arise as to how these two theorems are related. The latter of the two is obtained by interchanging the hypothesis and the conclusion of the first. The result of this interchange is called the *converse* of the original theorem. Our steps in the proof of the converse involve the following sequence of implications:

> If $x = 6$, then $2x = 12$.
> If $2x = 12$, then $3x = x + 12$.
> If $3x = x + 12$, then $3x - 5 = x + 7$.
> Therefore, if $x = 6$, then $3x - 5 = x + 7$.

If the steps of a direct proof are reversible, as in the above example, then the theorem and its converse are both true. If $H \rightarrow C$ and $C \rightarrow H$, then we say "*H if and only if C*," and write $H \leftrightarrow C$. Thus, to prove $H \leftrightarrow C$ we must prove $H \rightarrow C$ and $C \rightarrow H$. In the above example, we can write

$$(3x - 5 = x + 7) \leftrightarrow (x = 6)$$

because

$$(3x - 5 = x + 7) \rightarrow (x = 6) \quad \text{and} \quad (x = 6) \rightarrow (3x - 5 = x + 7).$$

If $\sqrt{x + 1} = -1$, then we can prove $x = 0$. However, we cannot prove the theorem "If $x = 0$, then $\sqrt{x + 1} = -1$." Hence, the converse of the theorem "If $\sqrt{x + 1} = -1$, then $x = 0$" is not true and we cannot write

$$(\sqrt{x + 1} = -1) \leftrightarrow (x = 0).$$

It should be pointed out that the "if and only if" expression is frequently used in stating a definition. For example, if a statement B defines a statement A, we will frequently write "*A if and only if B.*"

Example 2 Prove that if $7x + 3 = 2x + 28$, then $x = 5$.
Proof

> If $7x + 3 = 2x + 28$, then $7x = 2x + 25$.
> If $7x = 2x + 25$, then $5x = 25$.
> If $5x = 25$, then $x = 5$.
> Therefore, if $7x + 3 = 2x + 28$, then $x = 5$.

We mention here that the terms *positive integer* and *negative integer* will be used from time to time. The term "positive integers" will refer to the numbers 1, 2, 3, ..., and the term "negative integers" will refer to the numbers -1, -2, -3, ... A complete discussion of these terms will be given in Chapter 4.

Problems

1 Using the direct method of proof, prove that if $2x - 5 = x + 3$, then $x = 8$.

2 Using the direct method of proof, prove that if $3x - 4 = x + 8$, then $x = 6$.

3 Using the direct method of proof, prove that if $5x + 4 = x + 8$, then $x = 1$.

4 What is the hypothesis and what is the conclusion of the theorem in Problem 1?

5 What is the hypothesis and what is the conclusion of the theorem in Problem 2?

6 What is the hypothesis and what is the conclusion of the theorem in Problem 3?

7 State the converse of the theorem in Problem 1. Is it true? Prove your answer.

8 State the converse of the theorem in Problem 2. Is it true? Prove your answer?

9 State the converse of the theorem in Problem 3. Is it true? Prove your answer?

10 Find a counterexample to disprove each of the following propositions.

a) If a person lives in the United States, then he lives in Wisconsin.

b) If $x^2 + 1 = 5$, then $x = 4$.

c) If $2x - 3 = x + 5$, then $x = 1$.

d) If a line L_1 is perpendicular to a line L_2 and the line L_2 is perpendicular to a line L_3, then L_1 is perpendicular to L_3.

11 Consider the theorem: "If a person lives in Chicago, then he lives in North America." What is the hypothesis of this theorem? What is the conclusion? State the converse. Is the converse true? Justify your answer to the last question.

12 Restate the following theorem in the "if–then" form: "Two lines parallel to the same line are parallel."

13 What is the hypothesis and what is the conclusion of the theorem in Problem 12?

14 Using the direct method, prove that the product of two odd positive integers is odd. [*Hint:* Any odd positive integer may be expressed as $2n + 1$, where n is some positive integer or zero.]

15 Using the direct method, prove that if either of two positive integers is even, then the product is even. [*Hint:* Any even positive integer may be expressed as $2n$, where n is some positive integer.]

16 If we are willing to accept that $1 = 2$, can we prove that $4 = 5$? Explain.

1.5 INDIRECT PROOF

Since it is not always easy to establish a list of implications and then apply the transitive property, the direct method of proof is sometimes quite difficult. Frequently, it is easier to establish the desired implication indirectly. The logical basis for this type of proof hinges on the assumption that a true hypothesis cannot imply a false conclusion. The procedure in the indirect proof is to accept the hypothesis, assume that the conclusion is false, and then arrive at a contradiction of the hypothesis or some other truth. For this reason the indirect proof is sometimes called *proof by contradiction* or *reductio ad absurdum*. The following examples will illustrate this method.

Example 1 Use an indirect proof to prove that if the product of two positive integers is odd, then both integers are odd.

Proof Suppose the product of two positive integers is odd. Then both of the integers are odd or at least one is even. If one integer is even, then the product must also be even by Problem 15 of Section 1.4. However, this statement contradicts our hypothesis that the given product is odd. Thus we must reject the assumption that at least one of the integers is even and conclude that both are odd.

Example 2 A *prime number* is a positive integer p greater than 1 whose only factors are $\pm p$ and ± 1. For example, the first five prime numbers are 2, 3, 5, 7, and 11. The following proof that the set of prime numbers is infinite is credited to Euclid.

Proof The set of prime numbers is either finite or it is infinite. We will assume that there is only a finite number of primes and denote them $p_1, p_2, \ldots, p_n$. Now consider the number

$$Q = p_1 \times p_2 \times \cdots \times p_n + 1.$$

If this new number Q is not a prime number, then it must be divisible by one of the primes $p_1, p_2, \ldots, p_n$. However, we observe that when Q is divided by any one of these numbers, the remainder is 1. Thus, the number Q is divisible only by itself and 1 and must be a prime number. Clearly Q is not one of the n prime numbers listed above. We now have $n + 1$ different prime numbers, which contradicts our assumption that there are only n such numbers. Therefore, we reject the assumption that the set of prime numbers is finite. We have now but to conclude that the set of prime numbers is infinite.

Problems

1 Rooms 101, 102, and 103 are located at the end of a hall. Bill is in room 102. If a person knows only that Bill is in one of these three rooms, how can he use the indirect method of proof to prove that Bill is in room 102?

2 Prove by using the indirect method that if the product of two positive integers is even, at least one of the integers is even.

3 Suppose the square of a positive integer is even. Prove by the indirect method that the integer must also be an even integer.

4 Suppose the square of a positive integer is odd. Prove by the indirect method that the integer must also be odd.

5 Prove by using the indirect method that if x is an even positive integer, then x^3 is an even positive integer.

6 Prove by using the indirect method that if x is an odd positive integer, then x^3 is an odd positive integer.

1.6 MATHEMATICAL INDUCTION

One of the most important methods of mathematical proof is mathematical induction. Mathematical induction is usually used in proving a proposition which makes some statement about every positive integer. As an example, suppose we wish to prove the statement that the sum of the first n odd positive integers is n^2, for every positive integer n. It is fairly easy to verify that this statement is true if the value of n is small.

For example

If $n = 1$, the sum is 1.
If $n = 2$, the sum is $1 + 3 = 4 = 2^2$.
If $n = 3$, the sum is $1 + 3 + 5 = 9 = 3^2$.

However, one would have considerable difficulty in showing this statement to be true if n is a large positive integer such as 3,000,000. By the above procedure it would be impossible to prove the statement true for every positive integer n.

One could relate a proof by mathematical induction to the childhood game of setting up a row of dominoes in such a fashion that when the first domino is pushed over, all the others fall in turn. In this game the dominoes are placed in a row so that if the domino in a given position falls, the domino in the next position must also fall. Thus, if the domino in the first position is pushed over, the second domino and eventually all the rest must fall. There-fore, there are two conditions necessary to ensure that all dominoes will fall. The first domino must be knocked over and, any time a domino is knocked over, it must knock over the next domino. Under these conditions we can be assured that all the dominoes will fall regardless of the number involved.

A proof by mathematical induction involves two steps.

1 The statement must be verified for the positive integer 1.

2 On the assumption that the statement is true for any positive integer k, it must be shown that the statement is true for the positive integer $k + 1$.

If these two conditions are satisfied, then the statement is true for all positive integers by mathematical induction.

Let us examine the significance of these steps. In step 2 we show that the statement is true for the positive integer $k + 1$ whenever it is true for any positive integer k. Using this and step 1, which verifies that the statement is true for the positive integer 1, we conclude that the statement is true for the positive integer 2. Then using step 2 again, we conclude that the statement is true for the positive integer 3. By repeated use of step 2, we now see that the statement is true for all positive integers. Thus, step 1 guarantees that the statement is true for the first positive integer, and step 2 guarantees that any time the statement is true for a positive integer, it is true for the next positive integer.

Example 1 Prove by mathematical induction that the sum of the first n odd positive integers is n^2.

Proof

1 If $n = 1$, then clearly the sum of the first n odd integers is 1. But n^2 is also 1. Thus the statement is true if $n = 1$.

2 Assume that the statement is true for any positive integer k, that is assume

$$1 + 3 + 5 + \cdots + (2k - 1) = k^2.$$

We now wish to show that the sum of the first $k + 1$ positive integers is $(k + 1)^2$. The $(k + 1)$st positive odd integer is $2k + 1$. Thus we want to prove that

$$1 + 3 + 5 + \cdots + (2k - 1) + (2k + 1) = (k + 1)^2.$$

From our assumption, we have

$$1 + 3 + 5 + \cdots + (2k - 1) = k^2.$$

If we add $(2k + 1)$ to both sides of this equation then we have

$$1 + 3 + 5 + \cdots + (2k - 1) + (2k + 1) = k^2 + 2k + 1 = (k + 1)^2.$$

Thus, if the statement is true for any positive integer k, it must also be true for the positive integer $k + 1$. The theorem is now established by mathematical induction.

Problems

1 Prove by mathematical induction that the sum of the first n positive integers is $n(n + 1)/2$.

2 Prove by mathematical induction that the sum of the first n positive even integers is $n(n + 1)$.

3 Prove by mathematical induction that each of the following is true for every positive integer n.

a) $1 + 4 + 7 + \cdots + (3n - 2) = \dfrac{n(3n - 1)}{2}$

b) $1 + 3 + 6 + \cdots + \dfrac{n(n + 1)}{2} = \dfrac{n(n + 1)(n + 2)}{6}$

c) $1 \cdot 2 + 2 \cdot 3 + 3 \cdot 4 + \cdots + n(n + 1) = \dfrac{n(n + 1)(n + 2)}{3}$

d) $4 + 8 + 12 + \cdots + 4n = 2n(n + 1)$

e) $1^2 + 2^2 + 3^2 + \cdots + n^2 = \dfrac{n(n + 1)(2n + 1)}{6}$

f) $2 + 2^2 + 2^3 + \cdots + 2^n = 2^{n+1} - 2$

4 Can we prove that the sun will rise in the east tomorrow observing that it has always risen in the east? Explain.

Chapter 2

SETS

2.1 SETS AND SET NOTATION

One of the most important concepts of mathematics is the concept of a *set*. Although it is one of the undefined terms mentioned in Chapter 1, its meaning is clear because of its frequent use in everyday situations. For example, the concept of a set is used when one speaks of a covey of quail, a herd of cattle, a bouquet of roses, a set of dishes, or a galaxy of stars. The term "set" will be used in much the same way in reference to numbers, points, etc. The concept of a set was first considered by Georg Cantor (1845–1918).

One of the most commonly used methods for describing a set is to state a property which each element of the set must possess. Each of the following properties could describe a set:

1. The people in the United States under the age of 21
2. The books in the Library of Congress
3. All mountain peaks in North America with elevations over 30,000 feet
4. All triangles having an area of 9 square feet

If a set is described in this manner, the property must be precisely stated. The property must characterize the elements of the set, so that not only each element of the set possesses the property, but if an object possesses the property, it is in the set. A set cannot be described by stating that it consists of all tall trees. One must be more precise and specify how tall a tree must be in order that it be considered a tall tree. A set is described by stating that it consists of all trees over 20 feet tall. This more precise statement of the property now makes it possible to determine whether a given tree can be considered a tall tree.

We do not want to interpret the preceding remarks of this section to mean that all the elements of a set must be the same kind of object. That is, the elements of a set need not all be birds, or roses, or mountain peaks, etc. A set may be composed of totally unrelated objects. For example, we may wish to consider a set which consists of a giraffe, a candle, and a cherry pie. These objects are related to each other only in the sense that they belong to the same set.

If the number of elements in a set is small, the set can be described by naming the elements and enclosing these names in braces. For example, the set consisting of the numbers 1, 2, 3, 4, 5 could be described by writing $\{1, 2, 3, 4, 5\}$. This method is called the *roster* or *listing method*. It is possible for a set to have no elements at all. For example, the set of all mountain peaks in North America higher than 30,000 feet has no elements. Such a set is called the *empty set* and is usually denoted by the symbol $\{\ \}$ or by the symbol $\varnothing$. The empty set is frequently encountered both in mathematics and everyday affairs.

A modification of the roster method can also be used for certain sets having a large number of elements. The set of letters of the alphabet could be described by writing $\{a, b, c, \ldots, x, y, z\}$. Here we employed the symbol $\ldots$, called *ellipsis*. This symbol, used after the letter c, means that the remaining letters of the alphabet through the letters x, y and z are included in the set although they are not listed. As a further example, the set consisting of the first 1000 positive integers is the set $\{1, 2, 3, \ldots, 999, 1000\}$.

Many sets cannot be conveniently described by enclosing the elements of the set in braces. The set of all apples in the state of Washington would be difficult to describe by this method. It would be impossible to describe the set of all numbers between 0 and 1 in this manner. In situations such as this a set is frequently described by writing $\{x \mid x$ has a given property$\}$. This is read "the set of all x such that x has a given property." The symbol x (or any other symbol such as y or z) represents an element of the set. The vertical bar, $\mid$, which is read "such that," separates the symbol x from the statement of the property of the object x. Using this method, the set of all apples in the state of Washington could be described by writing $\{x \mid x$ is an apple in the state of Washington$\}$. The set of numbers between 0 and 1 would be the set $\{x \mid x$ is a number between 0 and 1$\}$. This method is the one most commonly used for describing sets in mathematics.

In working with sets it will be convenient to have some kind of notation for denoting sets and elements of sets. It is customary in mathematics to use capital letters to denote sets and lower-case letters for elements of sets. For example, a set may be represented by one of the letters $A, B, C, \ldots$, and an element of the set by one of the letters $a, b, c, \ldots$. If a is an element of the set A, then we write $a \in A$; if a is not an element of the set A, we write $a \notin A$. The following examples will demonstrate the meaning of this notation.

Example 1 $4 \in \{1, 2, 3, 4, 5\}$, but $6 \notin \{1, 2, 3, 4, 5\}$.

Example 2

$$\tfrac{1}{2} \in \{x \mid x \text{ is a number between 0 and 1}\}, \quad \text{but}$$

$$5 \notin \{x \mid x \text{ is a number between 0 and 1}\}.$$

If each element of a set A is also an element of a set B, A is said to be a *subset* of B. If A is a subset of B, then we write $A \subset B$. For instance, if $A = \{a, b\}$ and $B = \{a\ b, c\}$, then $A \subset B$. However, B is not a subset of A since the set B has the element c, which is not in the set A. In this case, we write $B \not\subset A$. We may also remark at this point that a set A is called a *proper subset* of a set B if A is a subset of B and B has at least one element which does not belong to A. Thus the set A in the above example is a proper subset of the set B.

An interesting problem is that of finding all the subsets of a given set. Suppose we consider the set $B = \{a, b, c\}$. The subsets of B having one element are the sets $\{a\}$, $\{b\}$, and $\{c\}$. The subsets of B having two elements are the sets $\{a, b\}$, $\{a, c\}$, and $\{b, c\}$. One also observes that B is a subset of itself, and furthermore, the empty set is a subset of B. In fact, the empty set is a subset of every set. The condition that each element of $\{\ \}$ be an element of B (or any set for that matter) is certainly satisfied since the set $\{\ \}$ has no elements. We now conclude that the set B has 8 subsets if we count $\{\ \}$ and B. We observe that $2^3 = 8$ and remark that the number of subsets of a set with n elements is always 2^n. The student can verify this claim for sets having a small number of elements.

Two sets A and B are equal if they have the same elements. This means that each element of A must be an element of B and each element of B must be an element of A. Thus *the set A is equal to the set B if and only if $A \subset B$ and $B \subset A$*. It should be noted at this point that the sets $\{a, b, c\}$ and $\{c, a, b\}$ are equal according to this definition. A set is not affected by the order in which its elements appear nor by the number of times any one element appears. It should be clear from the definition of equality of sets that the two sets $\{a, b, c\}$ and $\{a, b, c, a\}$ are equal. In the second set the element a has simply been listed twice. This does not change the fact that this is the set with the three elements a, b, and c.

Problems

1 Describe the following sets in two different ways:
   a) The members of your immediate family
   b) The positive integers which are between 5 and 10
   c) The positive integers greater than 50
   d) The numbers x which have the property that $x^2 = 1$
   e) The women who have served as president of the United States

2 Describe the following sets in two different ways:

a) The days of the week   b) The months of the year

c) The first 1000 positive integers

d) The set of positive integers x which have the property that $x^2 = -1$

e) The set of even positive integers less than 21

3 Give an example of a set with just two elements; one element; no elements; infinitely many elements.

4 If $A = \{1, 2, 3, 4, 5, 6, 7, 8, 9, 10\}$, $B = \{2, 3, 4\}$, and $C = \{2, 4, 5\}$, which of the following are true?

a) $A \subset B$ b) $B \subset C$

c) $B \subset A$ d) $C \subset A$

e) $\emptyset \subset B$ f) $A \subset A$

g) $B = C$

5 Is $\{1, 2, 3, 3\} = \{1, 2, 3\}$? Explain.

6 Is $\{1, 2, 3, 4, 5\} = \{2, 4, 1, 3, 5\}$? Explain.

7 If A, B and C are the sets in Problem 4, answer the following:

a) What is the set with elements common to A and B?

b) What is the set with elements either in B or C?

c) What is the set with elements common to A, B, and C?

8 If $A = \{a, b, c\}$, find all sets B such that $\{a\} \subset B$, $B \subset A$, and $A \neq B$.

9 If $S = \{1, 4, 7, 11\}$, which of the following are true?

a) $4 \in S$ b) $4 \subset S$

c) $\{4\} \in S$ d) $\{4\} \subset S$

e) $\emptyset \subset S$ f) $\emptyset \in S$

g) $4 \in \{4\}$ h) $4 \subset \{4\}$

i) $1 \in S$ j) $\{4, 11, 1, 1\} \subset S$

10 If $S = \{1, \{2\}, 3\}$, which of the following are true?

a) $1 \in S$ b) $2 \in S$ c) $\{2\} \subset S$

d) $\{2\} \in S$ e) $\{\{2\}\} \subset S$ f) $S = \{1, 2, 3\}$

11 If $S = \{1, 2, \{2, 3\}\}$, which of the following are true?

a) $1 \subset S$ b) $2 \in S$ c) $\{2\} \subset S$

d) $\{2, 3\} \subset S$ e) $\{2, 3\} \in S$ f) $3 \in S$

g) $\{3\} \subset S$ h) $\{\{2, 3\}\} \subset S$ i) $S = \{1, 2, 3\}$

12 Suppose $p \in X$, $q \in Y$, $X \subset Z$, and $Y \subset Z$.

a) Is $p \in Z$?   b) Is $q \in Z$?

c) Is $p \in Y$?   d) Does $X = Y$?

e) Could there be an element in X not in Y?

f) Could there be an element in Y not in X?

13 List all the subsets of $\emptyset$.

14 List all the subsets of $\{1\}$.

13 List all the subsets of the set $\{1, 2\}$.

16 List all the subsets of the set $\{1, 2, 3, 4\}$.

17 List all the subsets of $\{1, \{2\}, 3\}$.

2.2 SPECIAL SETS

It is always possible to choose a set U which has the property that every set used in a given discussion is a subset of U. Such a set U is called a *universal set* relative to the discussion. If a universal set is of particular significance, one generally specifies what it is to be. The examples which follow will further illustrate the meaning of this concept.

Example 1 In a discussion about oranges, a California orange grower wishes to consider the set of oranges he has grown. Then the set of all oranges grown in California could serve as a universal set, since all his oranges are California oranges. The set of all oranges grown in the United States, the set of all California citrus fruit, or the set of all California fruit could serve equally as well as a universal set in this discussion.

Example 2 Let $P = \{x \mid x$ is a President of the United States elected since 1900$\}$. P could be chosen as a universal set for a discussion of the Presidents still alive at this time. P could not be chosen as a universal set for a discussion of all Presidents who remained in office for two consecutive terms, since George Washington served two consecutive terms but is not an element of the set P.

Example 3 Suppose we wish to discuss the set of all solutions of the equation $2x + 1 = x + 3$. We may choose any set as a universal set for this discussion. For example, the sets $\{1, 2, 3, \ldots, 10\}$, $\{-3, 6, 4, 2\}$, $\{1, 3, 4, 5\}$, $\{x \mid x$ is a positive integer$\}$, or the set of real numbers could serve as a universal set. However, if we choose $\{1, 3, 4, 5\}$ as a universal set for a discussion of this problem, we must say that the equation has no solution in the given set. Thus, whether or not an equation has a solution depends on the choice of a universal set. The desire to solve equations will motivate us to develop a sequence of number systems in Chapters 4 and 5.

The set of real numbers is frequently chosen as the universal set for elementary mathematical discussions. The reader probably has at least a vague understanding of the meaning of the term "real number." This concept will be discussed in Chapter 5.

Let U be the universal set for a given discussion and let A be a subset of U. Then the set of all elements in U which are not in A is called the *complement* of A and is denoted by A'. Thus

$$A' = \{x \mid x \in U \text{ and } x \notin A\}.$$

Example 4 If $U = \{1, 2, 3\}$ and $A = \{1, 3\}$, then $A' = \{2\}$.

Example 5 If U is the set of all oranges grown in the United States and A is the set of all oranges grown in California, then

$A' = \{x \mid x \text{ is an orange grown in the United States but not in California}\}.$

The student will observe that the complement of a universal set U is $\emptyset$, and the complement of $\emptyset$ is U.

One may also discuss the complement of a set A relative to a set B. The *complement of A relative to B* is the set of all elements in B which are not in A. This set is denoted $B - A$. Thus

$$B - A = \{x \mid x \in B \text{ and } x \notin A\}.$$

Example 6 If $B = \{\$, \#, *, @, ?\}$ and $A = \{\$, *, @\}$, then

$$B - A = \{\#, ?\} \qquad \text{and} \qquad A - B = \emptyset.$$

Example 7 If $A = \{a, b, c, d\}$ and $B = \{b, e\}$, then

$$A - B = \{a, c, d\} \qquad \text{and} \qquad B - A = \{e\}.$$

From the definition of the complement of A relative to B, it is easy to verify that $A - \emptyset = A$ and $A - A = \emptyset$.

Let $A = \{\#, \$, @\}$ and $B = \{\cent, \$, \#, \%\}$. The set $C = \{\#, \$, @, \cent, \%\}$ has the property that each of its elements is an element of either A or B. The elements $\#$ and $\$$ appear in both sets. This new set C is called the *union* of A and B and is denoted by the symbol $A \cup B$. One can construct another set from A and B by choosing those elements which have membership in both sets. This set is called the *intersection* of A and B and is denoted by the symbol $A \cap B$. $\#$ and $\$$ are the only elements that belong to both A and B. Thus, $A \cap B = \{\#, \$\}$.

For two arbitrary sets A and B, the union is defined to be the set obtained by choosing those elements which have membership in A or B or in both A and B. Thus,

$$A \cup B = \{x \mid x \in A \text{ or } x \in B\}.$$

The intersection of A and B is defined to be the set of elements which belong to both A and B. Thus,

$$A \cap B = \{x \mid x \in A \text{ and } x \in B\}.$$

Example 8   Let $A = \{\text{Mary, Bob, Jane, Bill}\}$ and $B = \{\text{Tom, Alice, Bob, Ann}\}$. Then

$$A \cup B = \{\text{Mary, Bob, Jane, Bill, Tom, Alice, Ann}\},$$

and

$$A \cap B = \{\text{Bob}\}.$$

Example 9   Let $A = \{3, 4\}$ and $B = \{1, 2, 3, 4, 5\}$. Then

$$A \cup B = \{1, 2, 3, 4, 5\} = B \quad \text{and} \quad A \cap B = \{3, 4\} = A.$$

Example 10   Let

$$A = \{x \mid x \text{ is a letter in the word "Mississippi"}\}$$

and

$$B = \{y \mid y \text{ is a letter in the word "blue"}\}.$$

Then

$$A \cup B = \{\text{m, i, p, s, b, l, u, e}\} \quad \text{and} \quad A \cap B = \varnothing.$$

If the intersection of two sets is the empty set, then the sets are said to be *disjoint*. Thus two sets are disjoint if they have no elements in common. For example, the sets defined in Example 10 are disjoint sets.

If A is an arbitrary set, then $A \cup A = A$ and $A \cap A = A$. We also observe that $A \cup \varnothing = A$ and $A \cap \varnothing = \varnothing$.

If $A \subset B$, then $A \cup B = B$ and $A \cap B = A$.   These two results are illustrated by the sets of Example 9.

Problems

1   Specify each of the following sets by the roster method and in each case give an appropriate universal set.

a)   The set of courses you are taking for credit

b)   The digits in your street number

c)   The positive integers which are greater than 5 but less than 12

d)   The digits of your social security number

2.   Specify each of the following sets by the roster method and in each case give an appropriate universal set.

a)   The set of letters used to spell your last name

b)   The set of positive integers greater than 100

c) The set of different colors in the American flag

d) The set of all states of the United States whose area is greater than 100,000 square miles

3 If the universal set is the set of positive integers, which of the following equations have solutions?

a) $2x - 2 = 4$

b) $2x - 1 = 2$

c) $x - 2 = 1$

d) $x = 2 - 2$

4 If the universal set is the set of all even positive integers, which of the following equations have solutions?

a) $3x + 4 = 13$

b) $2x + 1 = 5$

c) $5x - 3 = 17$

d) $4x - 2 = 10$

5 Give three examples of sets that could be used as universal sets for a discussion of the set $S = \{1, \{2\}, 3\}$.

6 Given $A = \{1, 2, 3, 4, 5\}$, $B = \{4, 5, 6\}$, and $C = \{6, 7, 8, 9\}$. Find:

a) $A \cup B$

b) $A \cap B$

c) $C - A$

d) $A \cup C$

e) $A \cap C$

f) $B - \varnothing$

g) $A - B$

h) $A \cup \varnothing$

i) $(A \cup C) \cap B$

7 Given $U = \{1, 2, 3, 4, 5, 6, 7, 8, 9\}$, $A = \{1, 2, 3, 4, 5\}$, $B = \{2, 3, 4, 5\}$, $C = \{4, 5, 6\}$, $D = \{6, 7, 8, 9\}$. Find:

a) $A \cup B$

b) $B \cup C$

c) $D \cup \varnothing$

d) $A - C$

e) $A \cap D$

f) $B \cap C$

g) $C \cap \varnothing$

h) B'

i) $A - B$

j) $(B \cap C)'$

k) $(A \cup D')'$

l) $(A \cap \varnothing)'$

8 Given $U = \{a, b, c, d, e, f, g\}$, $A = \{a, c, e, g\}$, $B = \{a, e\}$, $C = \{b, c, d, f, g\}$. Find:

a) $A \cup B$

b) $A \cap B$

c) $B \cup C$

d) $B \cap C$

e) B'

f) $B' \cup A$

g) $C' - A$

h) $C \cap C'$

i) $A \cup \varnothing$

j) $(A')'$

k) $(A \cap B)'$

l) $(A \cup B)'$

9 Given

$U = \{x \mid x$ is a letter in the English alphabet$\}$,

$V = \{v \mid v$ is a vowel$\}$,

$C = \{c \mid c$ is a consonant$\}$,

$F = \{y \mid y$ is f or one of the next five letters in the English alphabet$\}$.

Find:

a) $V \cup C$

b) $V \cap F$

c) $V \cap C$

d) $V \cup F$

e) C'

f) $F - \{i\}$

g) $(V \cap C)'$

h) $(V \cup \varnothing)'$

i) $(V \cup C) \cap F$

10 Give three different examples of disjoint sets.

11 Let X be any subset of a universal set U. Find:

a) $X \cap U$ b) $X \cup X'$ c) $X \cup \varnothing$

d) $X \cap \varnothing$ e) $X \cap X$ f) $X \cup X$

g) $X \cap X'$ h) $U \cap \varnothing$ i) $U \cup \varnothing$

12 Let A and B be subsets of a universal set U. Under what conditions on the sets A and B will the following statements be true ?

a) $A \cup B = \varnothing$ b) $A \cap B = \varnothing$ c) $A \cup \varnothing = \varnothing$

d) $A \cap \varnothing = \varnothing$ e) $A \cup U = U$ f) $A \cup \varnothing = U$

g) $A \cap B = A$ h) $A \cup B = B$ i) $A \cup U = \varnothing$

j) $A \cap U = \varnothing$ k) $B \cap B' = \varnothing$ l) $B \cap A' = U$

13 If A and B are any two sets, which of the following statements are always true ?

a) $A \subset (A \cup B)$ b) $A \subset (A \cap B)$

c) $(A \cup B) \subset B$ d) $(A \cap B) \subset B$

2.3 ONE-TO-ONE CORRESPONDENCE

Suppose one walks into a classroom and observes that each chair in the room is occupied and no students are standing. Although the set of chairs and the set of students are not equal, the two sets certainly have something in common. The elements of the two sets can be paired in such a way that each chair in the room corresponds to one and only one student and each student corresponds to one and only one chair. This type of pairing is called a *one-to-one correspondence*. As another example, we note that each state in the United States has one and only one capital. Also, corresponding to each capital there is one and only one state. Thus there exists a one-to-one correspondence between the states of the union and their capitals. We summarize these remarks with the following definition.

Definition 2.1 A *one-to-one correspondence* from a set A to a set B is a pairing of the elements of the sets which has the following properties:

1) Each element of set A is paired with a unique element of set B.
2) Each element of set B is paired with a unique element of set A.

If there exists a one-to-one correspondence from A to B, we say that A is *equivalent* to B and write $A \leftrightarrow B$. If $a \in A$ and $b \in B$, we define $a \leftrightarrow b$ to mean that a is paired with b.

Example 1 Let

$$A = \{a, b, c\} \quad \text{and} \quad B = \{\$, *, \#\}.$$

We can define a one-to-one correspondence from A to B as follows:

$$a \leftrightarrow \$,$$
$$b \leftrightarrow *,$$
$$c \leftrightarrow \#.$$

Thus A is equivalent to B. This is not, however, the only one-to-one correspondence from A to B. Both of the pairings,

$$\left.\begin{matrix} a \leftrightarrow \$ \\ b \leftrightarrow \# \\ c \leftrightarrow * \end{matrix}\right\} \quad \text{and} \quad \left\{\begin{matrix} a \leftrightarrow * \\ b \leftrightarrow \$ \\ c \leftrightarrow \# \end{matrix}\right.$$

also define one-to-one correspondences from A to B.

An interesting problem is to determine the total number of one-to-one correspondences between the two sets of Example 1. If we start with the element a, we observe that we can pair any one of the three elements $\$$, $*$, and $\#$ with it. However, we can only pair b with one of the two remaining elements of B. This leaves only one possible element to pair with c. Thus we see that the elements of A can be paired with the elements of B in $3 \cdot 2 \cdot 1 = 6$ different ways. The student should verify this result for Example 1 by listing the other possibilities. Other problems of this type will appear in the problems at the end of this section.

Example 2 Let $A = \{$Joe, Bill, Bob, Jim$\}$ and let $B = \{$Mary, Alice, Ann, Sue$\}$. The pairings

$$\left.\begin{matrix} \text{Joe} \leftrightarrow \text{Sue} \\ \text{Bill} \leftrightarrow \text{Alice} \\ \text{Bob} \leftrightarrow \text{Mary} \\ \text{Jim} \leftrightarrow \text{Ann} \end{matrix}\right\} \quad \text{and} \quad \left\{\begin{matrix} \text{Joe} \leftrightarrow \text{Ann} \\ \text{Bill} \leftrightarrow \text{Alice} \\ \text{Bob} \leftrightarrow \text{Sue} \\ \text{Jim} \leftrightarrow \text{Mary} \end{matrix}\right.$$

are just two of the 24 one-to-one correspondences from the set A to the set B.

Example 3 Let $A = \{$a, b, c$\}$ and $B = \{1, 2\}$. We see in this case that it is impossible to define a one-to-one correspondence from A to B. For if we pair a with one of the elements of B, then we must pair with b the remaining element of B. This leaves no element of B to be paired with element c.

If two sets can be placed in one-to-one correspondence, they are said to have the same *number*. Thus number is an abstract property common to equivalent sets. We notice that the sets of Example 1 have the same number and the sets of Example 2 have the same number, but the sets of Example 3 do not. The concept of number and counting will be discussed in more detail in Chapter 4.

Sometimes a set can be placed in a one-to-one correspondence with a *proper* subset of itself. If this can be done, the set is said to be an *infinite* set. On the basis of this definition we can now prove that the set $\{1, 2, 3, \ldots, n, \ldots\}$, the set of positive integers, is an infinite set. The set of even positive integers is a proper subset of the set of positive integers, and a one-to-one correspondence between the sets can be established as follows:

$$
\begin{array}{ccccc}
1 & 2 & 3 & \ldots & n \ldots \\
\updownarrow & \updownarrow & \updownarrow & & \updownarrow \\
2 & 4 & 6 & \ldots & 2n \ldots
\end{array}
$$

We have paired with the positive integer n the even positive integer $2n$. Thus, we observe that the set of positive integers can be placed in a one-to-one correspondence with a proper subset of itself, and hence the set of positive integers is an infinite set. The reader may remember that a one-to-one correspondence could be established between the two sets of Examples 1 and 2 in several different ways. It is also possible to define in many other ways a one-to-one correspondence between the two sets of the present discussion.

As a second example, we remark that the set $S = \{10, 20, 30, \ldots\}$ of multiples of 10 is also an infinite set, since it can be placed in a one-to-one correspondence with the set $T = \{30, 60, 90, \ldots\}$, and T is a proper subset of S.

The most natural way to define a *finite* set is to say that we can count the elements of the set and get a definite number. Thus the set of fingers on my hand is finite, because I can count them: "1, 2, 3, 4, 5." We now ask a question that appears foolish at first sight: "Can a finite set be infinite?" This is not foolish, because we did not define "infinite" as being not-finite. The answer is *no*, but it is not easy to prove. Roughly speaking, if a set A is finite and has n elements, its proper subsets have less than n elements, and cannot be paired one-to-one with A.

Problems

1 Explain the difference between $A \leftrightarrow B$ and $A = B$.

2 Exhibit all the different one-to-one correspondences from the set A to the set B if $A = \{1, 2\}$ and $B = \{3, 4\}$.

3 Exhibit three different one-to-one correspondences from the set A to the set B if

$$A = \{\text{Tom, Bob, Bill}\} \quad \text{and} \quad B = \{\text{Mary, Jane, Alice}\}.$$

4 How many one-to-one correspondences can one establish from the set $A = \{a, b, c\}$ to the set $B = \{b, d, e\}$? List all of them.

5 How many one-to-one correspondences can one establish from the set $A = \{a, b, c, d\}$ to the set $B = \{1, 2, 3, 4\}$? List three of them.

6 Exhibit three different one-to-one correspondences from the set A to the set B if

$$A = \{a, b, c, d, e\} \quad \text{and} \quad B = \{\#, \$, @, ¢, *\}.$$

How many one-to-one correspondences can be established from A to B?

7 Can one construct a one-to-one correspondence from the set A to the set B if

$$A = \{1, 2\} \quad \text{and} \quad B = \{\#, \$, ¢, *\}?$$

Explain.

8 Prove that the set $\{3, 6, 9, 12, \ldots\}$, the set of multiples of 3, is an infinite set.

9 Prove that the set of multiples of 5 is an infinite set.

10 If line segment m is 1 in. long and line segment n is 2 in. long, which line segment has the most points? Prove your answer. [*Hint:* Show a one-to-one correspondence from the points on line segment m to the points on line segment n.]

11 For each of the sets listed below, tell which is finite and which is infinite.

a) The set of odd positive integers less than 5

b) The set of odd positive integers

c) The set of letters in the word "mathematics"

d) The set of all living people

e) The set of all grains of sand on earth

f) The set of all real numbers between 1 and 2

12 For the sets listed below, tell which are equivalent and which are equal.

a) The set of letters in the word "Mississippi"

b) The set of letters in the word "wasp"

c) The set of letters in the word "swap"

d) The set of time zones in the United States

e) $\{1, 2, 3, 4, 1, 2, 3, 4, 1, 2, 3, 4\}$

f) The set of letters in the word "imps"

2.4 VENN DIAGRAMS

A useful device for picturing sets and illustrating relationships between sets is a figure called a *Venn diagram*. In a Venn diagram the universal set U is usually represented by the set of points enclosed by a rectangle. A subset A of the universal set can then be represented by the set of points enclosed by

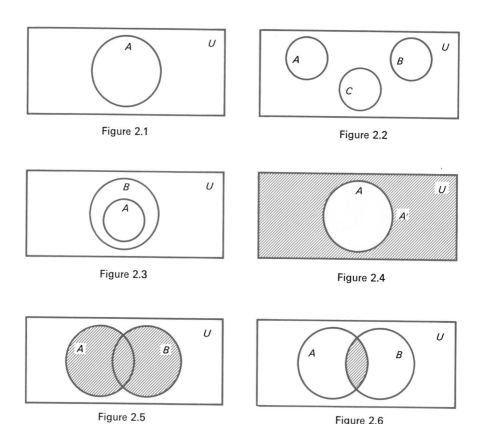

Figure 2.1

Figure 2.2

Figure 2.3

Figure 2.4

Figure 2.5

Figure 2.6

a circle or some other geometrical figure drawn inside the rectangle. Figure 2.1 is an example of a Venn diagram illustrating the universal set U and an arbitrary subset A of U.

Two or more sets may be represented in the same manner. Figure 2.2 shows three disjoint sets A, B, and C.

In Fig. 2.3 the set A is a subset of the set B.

The shaded portion of the rectangle in Fig. 2.4 represents the complement, A', of the set A.

The shaded region of Fig. 2.5 represents the union of two sets A and B, whereas the shaded region in Fig. 2.6 represents the intersection of A and B.

When two or more sets are involved, the Venn diagram is usually drawn to indicate the maximum number of subsets. For example, in Figs. 2.5 and 2.6 the two circles are drawn so that the two sets have some elements in common, each set has some elements which are not elements of the other, and the universal set has elements which are in neither of the two sets.

Example 1 Draw a Venn diagram to represent the set $(A \cup B)'$.

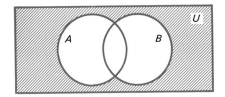

Figure 2.7

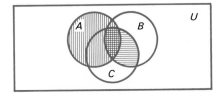

Figure 2.8

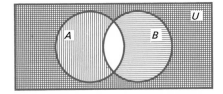

Figure 2.9

Figure 2.10

Solution We want to shade the region of the rectangle which represents the set of points *not* in $A \cup B$. This set is represented by the shaded region in Fig. 2.7.

Example 2 Draw a Venn diagram to represent the set $(A \cap B) \cap C$.

Solution Since $A \cap B$ is enclosed by parentheses, we are directed to first find $A \cap B$ and then take the intersection of this set with C. In Fig. 2.8, $A \cap B$ is shaded horizontally and C is shaded vertically. Since $(A \cap B) \cap C$ is the set of objects in both $A \cap B$ and C, it is represented by the region of Fig. 2.8 which is shaded both horizontally and vertically.

Example 3 Draw a Venn diagram to represent the set $A \cup (B \cap C)$.

Solution In Fig. 2.9, the region representing $B \cap C$ is shaded horizontally and the region representing A is shaded vertically. The set $A \cup (B \cap C)$ is then represented by the region of the rectangle shaded horizontally, vertically, or both horizontally and vertically.

Example 4 Draw a Venn diagram to represent the set $A' \cap B'$.

Solution In Fig. 2.10, A' is shaded horizontally and B' is shaded vertically. Since $A' \cap B'$ is the set of objects in both A' and B', it is represented by the region of Fig. 2.10 which is shaded both horizontally and vertically.

Note that Figs. 2.7 and 2.10 represent the same region. This would suggest (but not prove) that

$$(A \cup B)' = A' \cap B'.$$

2.4 VENN DIAGRAMS

25

Similarly, if we draw Venn diagrams for the sets $A \cap (B \cap C)$ and $(A \cup B) \cap (A \cup C)$, we will find that these diagrams represent regions identical to those represented by Figs. 2.8 and 2.9, respectively. This suggests the following equations:

$$(A \cap B) \cap C = A \cap (B \cap C), \qquad A \cup (B \cap C) = (A \cup B) \cap (A \cup C).$$

Each of these equations could be proved using the definition of equal sets. The first equation tells us that the operation of intersection on sets is *associative*. From the second equation we are able to say that the operation $\cup$ *distributes* over the operation $\cap$. The terms "associative" and "distributive" will be discussed in greater detail in Chapters 4 and 5.

Problems

1 Use a Venn diagram to illustrate each of the following sets; U denotes the universal set.

a) $A \cap B'$ 　　　　　　b) $A - B$ 　　　　　　c) $A' \cup B$

d) $A \cap (B \cap C)$ 　　e) $(A \cup B) \cap (A \cup C)$ 　　f) $U \cap A'$

g) $A \cap (B \cup C)$ 　　h) $(A' \cup B)'$ 　　　　i) $\varnothing'$

2 Use a Venn diagram to illustrate each of the following sets; U denotes the universal set.

a) $A \cup A$ 　　　　　　b) $B - A$ 　　　　　　c) $A \cap C$

d) $C \cap (A - B)$ 　　e) $C \cup (A - C)$ 　　f) $A \cup (B \cap C)'$

g) $A - B'$ 　　　　　　h) $A' - B'$ 　　　　i) $(A' \cup C)'$

3 Use a Venn diagram to illustrate the set $A \cup B$. Do the same thing for $B \cup A$. What is your conclusion?

4 Use a Venn diagram to illustrate the set $A \cup (B \cup C)$. Do the same thing for $(A \cup B) \cup C$. What is your conclusion?

5 Use the procedure of Problems 3 and 4 to suggest the equality of the sets $(A \cap B)'$ and $A' \cup B'$.

6 Using a Venn diagram illustrate that $(A \cap B) \subset A$ and $(A \cap B) \subset B$.

7 Let $A = \{a, b, c, d, e\}$, $B = \{f, g, h\}$, and $C = \{b, d, g\}$. Locate each of the elements of the sets A, B, and C in the proper region of a Venn diagram.

2.5 THE CARTESIAN PRODUCT

An *ordered set* is a set in which the order of the elements is specified. An ordered set with two elements is called an *ordered pair*. If the first element is x and the second element is y, then the ordered pair is denoted (x, y). We observe that $(x, y) \neq (y, x)$, although $\{x, y\} = \{y, x\}$. Two ordered sets (*a, b*) and (*c, d*) are *equal* if and only if *a* = *c* and *b* = *d*. That is, the sets must consist of the same elements and these elements must be listed in the same order.

A person can travel from Little Rock to New York by auto, plane, or bus and from New York to London by plane or ship. The ways a person can travel from Little Rock to New York and on to London could be described by ordered pairs, with the first element of each ordered pair denoting the means of transportation from Little Rock to New York and the second element of each ordered pair denoting the means of transportation from New York to London. For example, the ordered pair (auto, plane) indicates that a person travels from Little Rock to New York by auto and on to London by plane. The diagram in Fig. 2.11 gives us a systematic method for tabulating the various possibilities. The set of possibilities is the set

$$T = \{(\text{auto, plane}), (\text{auto, ship}), (\text{plane, plane}), (\text{plane, ship}), (\text{bus, plane}),$$
$$(\text{bus, ship})\}.$$

The set *T* can be more compactly described if we let *A* = {auto, plane, bus}, *B* = {plane, ship}, and write

$$T = \{(a, b) \mid a \in A \text{ and } b \in B\}.$$

In view of these remarks we state the following definition.

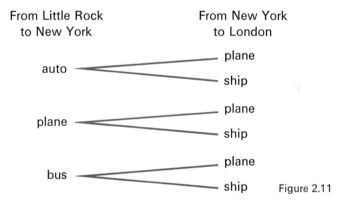

From Little Rock to New York

From New York to London

auto   plane / ship

plane   plane / ship

bus   plane / ship

Figure 2.11

Definition 2.2 The *Cartesian product* of two sets *X* and *Y*, denoted *X* × *Y*, is defined by the equation

$$X \times Y = \{(x, y) \mid x \in X \text{ and } y \in Y\}.$$

The Cartesian product of two sets *X* and *Y* is the set of all ordered pairs which can be formed by choosing the first element from *X* and the second element from *Y*. Note that *X* × *Y* is a set of sets.

Example 1 Let $A = \{\#, \$\}$ and $B = \{1, 2, 3\}$. Then

$$A \times B = \{(\#, 1), (\#, 2), (\#, 3), (\$, 1), (\$, 2), (\$, 3)\}$$

and

$$B \times A = \{(1, \#), (1, \$), (2, \#), (2, \$), (3, \#), (3, \$)\}.$$

We observe that $A \times B \neq B \times A$.

Example 2 Let $A = \{1, 2, 3, 4\}$ and $B = \{4, 5\}$. Then

$$A \times B = \{(1, 4), (1, 5), (2, 4), (2, 5), (3, 4), (3, 5), (4, 4), (4, 5)\}$$

and

$$B \times A = \{(4, 1), (4, 2), (4, 3), (4, 4), (5, 1), (5, 2), (5, 3), (5, 4)\}.$$

Although these two product sets have a common element, $A \times B \neq B \times A$.

The reader may have observed that in each of these examples, the number of elements in $A \times B$ is equal to the number of elements in A times the number of elements in B. In Chapter 4 we will relate the Cartesian product of two sets and the product of two natural numbers. We will also refer to the Cartesian product of two sets in Chapter 6 in discussing the graph of a function.

Problems

1 Let $A = \{a, b\}$ and $B = \{r, s, t\}$. Find the sets $A \times B$ and $B \times A$.

2 Let $R = \{1, 2, 3\}$ and $S = \{3, 4\}$. Find the sets $R \times S$ and $S \times R$.

3 Let $X = \{5\}$ and $Y = \{a, b, c\}$. Find the sets $X \times Y$ and $Y \times X$.

4 Let $A = \{\$, \#\}$ and $B = \{\cent, @, *\}$. Find $A \times B$ and $B \times A$.

5 Let $A = \{\$, \#, \cent, @\}$ and $B = \{\cent, *\}$. Find $A \times B$ and $B \times A$.

6 Let $A = \{1, 2, \cent\}$ and $B = \{\ \}$. Find $A \times B$ and $B \times A$.

7 Let $A = \{\#, \cent, *\}$. Find $A \times A$.

8 Let $A = \{a, b, c, d\}$. Find $A \times A$.

9 Let $A = \{1, 2\}, B = \{3, 4\}$, and $C = \{5\}$. Find $(A \times B) \times C$.

10 Let $A = \{1, 2\}, B = \{a, b, c\}$, and $C = \{\#, *\}$. Find $A \times (B \times C)$.

11 Suppose in remodeling a room, a person may choose white, yellow, or blue paint for the walls and green or brown carpet for the floor. Define two sets A and B for which $A \times B$ is the set of all possible color combinations for decorating the room. List the elements of $A \times B$.

12 A person can travel from city A to city B by railroad, car, bus, or plane. He can return from B to A by car, bus, or boat. Define a product set whose elements will be the various possibilities of traveling from A to B and returning. List the elements of this product set.

13 Under what conditions on the sets A and B will $A \times B = B \times A$?

Chapter 3

SYSTEMS
OF NUMERATION

3.1 NUMBER AND NUMERAL

In Chapter 2 we stated that sets which can be placed in one-to-one correspondence are said to have the same number. Thus number is an abstract
property common to equivalent sets. Since number is an abstract concept,
we need some physical representation for a number. A symbol used to
represent a number is called a *numeral*. Often the term "number" is used in
reference to both the concepts of number and numeral, and even though the
distinction between these is frequently overlooked, we will make it whenever
it adds to the clarity of the presentation.

A *system of numeration* is a set of symbols used according to some
scheme to represent a set of numbers. It is our purpose in this chapter to
study some of the early numeration systems and the numeration system we
use today, the Hindu-Arabic system. Some computational work will be done
in each of the systems studied in order to point out advantages of the Hindu-
Arabic system. We hope that the reader will become aware that the Hindu-
Arabic system is one of the more recent ones. It is a highly sophisticated
system which has evolved over many centuries.

Every numeration system has a symbol for the number one. In some
systems other numbers are represented by a repeated use of this symbol,
at least until the notation becomes bulky or inconvenient; then a new symbol
is introduced to replace a given collection of symbols representing the
number one. In other systems unique symbols are used to represent subsequent numbers up to a certain number, then a number is represented by
two or more of these symbols. In some systems the position of a symbol in
the representation of a number is significant, whereas in other systems it is not.

Most, but not all, numeration systems are based on the number ten.
Early numeration systems were developed for the purpose of counting, and a
person's fingers are perhaps the most convenient reference set for the

process. We can speculate that if man had twelve fingers, then most numeration systems would be based on the number twelve.

The development of early numeration systems was hindered primarily by the lack of writing materials and printing processes. The invention of the printing press tremendously enhanced the further development of numeration systems.

3.2 THE EGYPTIAN SYSTEM

An example of a very early numeration system is the Egyptian system, which was used as early as 3400 B.C. An insight into the Egyptian system was obtained through the deciphering of the Egyptian hieroglyphics, or picture writing. This system was based on the number ten. Table 3.1 is a partial list of the symbols used in the Egyptian system.

TABLE 3.1

1	|	vertical staff
10	∩	heel bone
100	૭	scroll
1,000	⌇	lotus flower
10,000	⌒	pointing finger
100,000	∾	burbot fish
1,000,000	⚐	man in astonishment

Numerals were sometimes written vertically, sometimes right to left, and sometimes left to right. A number was represented by repeating each basic symbol the required number of times. The role of the number ten in this system is quite evident. The symbol for one was used repeatedly to represent numbers one through nine, and then a new symbol was introduced for ten. Combinations of these two symbols were used to represent numbers through ninety-nine, and then a new symbol was introduced for one hundred. To write larger numbers the Egyptians followed a similar procedure. In no instance was a given symbol used in a numeral more than nine times.

Example 1

ⵁⵁ૭∩∩∩||||

means

1000 + 1000 + 100 + 10 + 10 + 10 + 1 + 1 + 1 + 1 = 2134.

Example 2 1435 = ⵁ૭૭૭૭∩∩∩|||||.

Example 3

$$||\cap??§\Gamma$$

means

$$1 + 1 + 10 + 100 + 100 + 1000 + 10,000 = 11,212.$$

Addition and subtraction using Egyptian numerals are quite easy. The process of addition is as simple as counting the number of times each basic symbol is used. The following examples will illustrate the operations of addition and subtraction.

Example 4 Add

$$??\cap\cap || \quad \text{and} \quad §?\cap|||.$$

Solution To find this sum, we list each basic symbol the total number of times it is used in the two numerals. Thus the solution is

$$§???\cap\cap\cap|||||.$$

Example 5 Add

$$?\cap||||||| \quad \text{and} \quad \cap|||||.$$

Solution We must remember that in representing a number no basic symbol is used more than nine times. In this problem we find the symbol for one used a total of eleven times. We will, therefore, exchange ten of the symbols for one for the symbol $\cap$, which represents the number ten. This is similar to the process of carrying in our own numeration system. Thus, the solution is

$$?\cap\cap\cap|.$$

Example 6 Subtract

$$?\cap\cap| \quad \text{from} \quad ??\cap\cap\cap\cap|||.$$

Solution To find this difference, we list each basic symbol the number of times it occurs in the second numeral, called the *minuend*, decreased by the number of times it occurs in the first numeral, called the *subtrahend*. Thus, the solution is

$$?\cap\cap||.$$

Example 7 Subtract

$$?\cap\cap||| \quad \text{from} \quad ??\cap\cap||.$$

Solution Since the minuend has only two symbols for the number one and the subtrahend has three symbols for the number one, we must use the borrowing process. That is, we will exchange one of the symbols for the number ten in the minuend for ten symbols for the number one. After we have done this, the minuend will have only one symbol for the number ten and the subtrahend will have two. Thus we borrow again and exchange one symbol for the number one hundred for ten symbols for the number ten. Our problem is now equivalent to subtracting

$$?∩∩|||$$

from

$$?∩∩∩∩∩∩∩∩∩∩∩∩|||||||||||$$

and, subtracting in the usual way, we have

$$∩∩∩∩∩∩∩∩∩|||||||| .$$

Problems

1 Express the following in Egyptian numerals.

    a) 516   b) 3487   c) 45

    d) 75,153   e) 96,135   f) 8962

2 What number does each of the following represent?

    a) 𒈙??∩∩∩|||| c) ||∩??   e) ??????∩∩||||||

    b) ⌐⌐∩|||||| d) 𒈙∩| f) ⌐𒈙∩∩∩∩∩∩|||

3 Convert 523 and 261 to Egyptian numerals and add.

4 Convert 945 and 347 to Egyptian numerals and add.

5 Convert 3425 and 2716 to Egyptian numerals and add.

6 Convert 568 and 327 to Egyptian numerals and subtract the second from the first.

7 Convert 356 and 147 to Egyptian numerals and subtract the second from the first.

8 Add

    ||∩∩∩∩???

   and

    𒈙𒈙𒈙??????????∩∩∩∩∩∩∩| .

9 Add

    ?????∩∩∩∩∩∩|||||||

   and

    𒈙𒈙????????∩∩∩∩∩|||||| .

10 Subtract

    ?∩∩∩||||

   from

    𒈙???∩∩∩∩∩∩|||||||| .

11 Subtract

$$???\cap\cap\cap\cap II$$

from

$$\text{ᶻ}\cap\cap\cap\cap\cap\cap I.$$

12 Subtract

$$??\cap\cap\cap\cap\cap IIIII$$

from

$$?????\cap\cap I.$$

13 Is there any way to represent zero in the Egyptian system?

3.3 THE ROMAN SYSTEM

The Roman numeral system dates back to the time of ancient Rome. Roman numerals were commonly used in Europe as late as the eighteenth century. The invention of the printing press helped to bring about a rapid change from this system to the Hindu-Arabic numerals. The student is probably more familiar with the Roman system than with any of the other early systems. In fact, we see limited use of Roman numerals today. Even though there are Roman numerals to represent the numbers 5, 50, and 500, the Roman numeral system is based on the number ten. Table 3.2 lists the symbols used in the Roman system.

TABLE 3.2

1	I
5	V
10	X
50	L
100	C
500	D
1000	M

The procedure for representing a number in the Roman system is very similar to the procedure used in the Egyptian system.

Example 1

DCCLVIII   means $500 + 100 + 100 + 50 + 5 + 1 + 1 + 1 = 758.$

Example 2   3857 = MMMDCCCLVII.

Just as the order of the symbols used in representing a number was unimportant in the Egyptian system, the order was unimportant to the early users of the Roman system. Later, the Romans frequently placed a symbol for a smaller number to the left of the symbol for a larger number to represent the difference of the two numbers. For example, the numeral IV represents the same number as the numeral IIII. This procedure is called the *subtractive principle*, and when it was introduced, the order in which the symbols were written became quite important. Table 3.3 gives the symbol combinations used with the subtractive principle.

TABLE 3.3

IV	= IIII	XC	= LXXXX
IX	= VIIII	CD	= CCCC
XL	= XXXX	CM	= DCCCC

Example 3   Without using the subtractive principle

549 = DXXXXVIIII,

whereas, using the subtractive principle, we have

549 = DXLIX.

Example 4   431 = CCCCXXXI = CDXXXI.

Note that the subtractive principle shortens the representation of some numbers, but it necessitates ordering the symbols to avoid improper interpretation.

Addition and subtraction in the Roman system are very similar to addition and subtraction in the Egyptian system.

Example 5   Add MDCCVII and CLXIII.

Solution We must list each basic symbol the total number of times it occurs in the two numerals. In the Roman system no symbol need be used more than four times, since any symbol used five times can be exchanged for a new symbol. Thus the solution is MDCCCLXX.

Consider the following examples in which the subtractive principle is used.

Example 6   Add XCVIII and LXIV.

Solution Since the X in the first numeral implies subtraction of X, it nullifies one of the X's in the second numeral. Similarly, since the I in the second numeral implies subtraction of I, it nullifies one of the I's in the first numeral. Thus the solution is CLXII.

SYSTEMS OF NUMERATION

Example 7 Subtract LXIV from XCVIII.

Solution The subtractive symbols can be handled quite effectively in a subtraction problem by adding the same number to both the subtrahend and minuend, a process which does not change the difference. If XI is added to both the subtrahend and minuend, the above problem is then equivalent to subtracting LXXV from CVIIII. To solve this problem one must resort to the borrowing process discussed in Example 7, Section 3.2. Using this procedure, one finds that the solution is XXXIV.

Problems

1 Express the following in Roman numerals.

a) 3617   b) 999   c) 449

d) 787   e) 4356   f) 807

2 What number does each of the following represent?

a) MCMXLVII   b) DCCLIX   c) CLXIV

d) DXIX   e) MMCCCXLIV   f) CMLXXIV

3 Add: 4 Add:

MCXVI   DCCXCIV
CLXI   CCXXIV

5 Add: 6 Subtract:

CXLIV   MCCXXVIII
DXIX   CCXII

7 Subtract: 8 Subtract:

XCLIV   DCXLVII
LXXIX   CLIX

9 What Roman numeral would be placed on a building erected this year?

10 Is there any way to represent the number zero in the Roman system?

11 Express the Egyptian numeral

as a Roman numeral.

12 Express the Egyptian numeral

as a Roman numeral.

13 Convert 437 and 189 to Roman numerals and add; subtract.

14 Convert 935 and 462 to Roman numerals and add; subtract.

3.4 THE GREEK SYSTEM

The Greek numeration system can be traced as far back as 450 B.C. It is an example of a system in which the letters of the alphabet were used to represent numbers. The use of this system necessitated memorization of twenty-seven symbols. Because of the larger number of symbols, numbers could be represented more compactly than in the Egyptian and Roman systems. Table 3.4 gives a modern adaptation of the symbols used in the Greek system.

TABLE 3.4

A = 1	G = 7	M = 40	S = 100	Y = 700
B = 2	H = 8	N = 50	T = 200	Z = 800
C = 3	I = 9	O = 60	U = 300	# = 900
D = 4	J = 10	P = 70	V = 400	
E = 5	K = 20	Q = 80	W = 500	
F = 6	L = 30	R = 90	X = 600	

The Greek system, which is older than the Roman system, approached one characteristic which is essential in the Hindu-Arabic system. Unique symbols were used to represent the successive numbers from one through nine, rather than the repetitive principle used in the Egyptian and Roman systems. However, the real value of this idea escaped the Greeks; F was used for six ones, but their scheme did not allow for the use of F to represent six tens or six hundreds.

Example 1

$$976 = \#PF, \quad 355 = UNE, \quad 47 = MG.$$

The Greek system enabled its users to represent numbers through 999 without difficulty. The numbers 1000, 2000, . . . , 9000 could be represented by placing primes on the symbols for 1, 2, . . . , 9. Thus 5000 could be represented by E' and the number 6285 by F'TQE. Using this procedure, the Greeks could represent numbers through 9999.

Example 2

$$8750 = H'YN, \quad 3972 = C'\#PB.$$

The addition and multiplication combinations had to be memorized. For example, to learn that $5 \times 8 = 40$, the Greeks had to know that $E \cdot H = M$; for $50 \times 8 = 400$, that $N \cdot H = V$. Even though the large number of symbols allowed more compact representation of numbers, it made computational work more difficult.

SYSTEMS OF NUMERATION

Example 3

$$WQB + KG = XI, \qquad PI + KA = S;$$
$$M \cdot J = V, \qquad D \cdot G = KH.$$

The fact that the letters of a word had numerical equivalents led to a pseudo science called *gematria* which still has adherents today. The last verse of Chapter 13 of Revelation of the Bible is perhaps the best known example of gematria. "Here is wisdom. Let him that hath understanding count the number of the beast; for it is the number of a man; and his number is six hundred three score and six." Gematria addicts have been proving that their enemies had the number 666 for years. Among those established by someone as bearing the number of the beast are Martin Luther, Adolph Hitler, and a number of Popes. When a boy and girl have names whose corresponding numbers are the same, the student of gematria would say they are a perfect match. For a further discussion of the science of numerology, the reader is referred to E. T. Bell's book, *Numerology*.

Problems

1 What number does each of the following Greek numerals represent?

   a) VPH   *478*   b) H'#K   c) XRA

2 Represent the following numbers in the Greek system.

   a) 463   b) 976   c) 9999

3 Complete the following in the Greek system.

   a) $N + H =$ b) $QH + KF =$ c) $XNH + MC =$

4 Complete the following in the Greek system.

   a) $G \cdot H =$ b) $D \cdot F =$ c) $C \cdot QE =$

5 If TARAH wants a happy marriage, should she marry HARRY, DICK, or TOM?

6 Is there any way to represent the number zero in the Greek system?

7 Write the following Roman and Egyptian numerals in the Greek system.

   a) MCMXLIX   b) DCCLVI

   c) ₤???∩∩ || d) ₤₤??? |

3.5 INTEGRAL EXPONENTS

In the remaining sections of this chapter we will frequently encounter products which are formed by the repeated use of a single factor. For example, the number 1000 can be written $10 \cdot 10 \cdot 10$ and the number 64 has the factored form $2 \cdot 2 \cdot 2 \cdot 2 \cdot 2 \cdot 2$. When the factors of a product are equal, the product is called a *power* of the repeated factor. For example, 1000 is a power of the number 10, and we shall denote this product by the symbol 10^3. The superscript 3 indicates that 10 is used as a factor 3 times. The number 64 is a power of 2, and using the notation of the preceding example, we write $64 = 2^6$. We now generalize the foregoing remarks in the following definition.

Definition 3.1 If n is a positive integer and a is any number, then a^n is called the nth *power of a* and is defined by the equation

$$a^n = \underbrace{a \cdot a \cdot a \cdot \,\cdots\, \cdot a.}_{n \text{ factors of } a}$$

In the symbol a^n, a is called the *base* and n is called the *exponent* of the power.

Example 1 $125 = 5^3$ because $125 = 5 \cdot 5 \cdot 5$. Thus 125 is the third power of the number 5. 5 is the base and 3 is the exponent of this power.

Because $a^4 = a \cdot a \cdot a \cdot a$ and $a^3 = a \cdot a \cdot a$, we have

$$a^4 \cdot a^3 = (a \cdot a \cdot a \cdot a) \cdot (a \cdot a \cdot a).$$

Hence, by Definition 3.1, we may write $a^4 \cdot a^3 = a^7$ and, in general, we have the following theorem.

Theorem 3.1 If m and n are positive integers and a is any number, then

$$a^m \cdot a^n = a^{m+n}.$$

Proof

$$a^m \cdot a^n = \underbrace{(a \cdot a \cdot a \cdot \,\cdots\, \cdot a)}_{m \text{ factors}} \cdot \underbrace{(a \cdot a \cdot a \cdot \,\cdots\, \cdot a)}_{n \text{ factors}}$$

$$= \underbrace{a \cdot a \cdot a \cdot \,\cdots\, \cdot a}_{m + n \text{ factors}}$$

$$= a^{m+n}.$$

To illustrate this theorem, the student can easily verify the results of the next example.

Example 2

$$2^3 \cdot 2^4 = (2 \cdot 2 \cdot 2) \cdot (2 \cdot 2 \cdot 2 \cdot 2) = 2^7 = 128,$$
$$5^2 \cdot 5^3 = (5 \cdot 5) \cdot (5 \cdot 5 \cdot 5) = 5^5 = 3125.$$

By definition $a^3 = a \cdot a \cdot a$. Thus

$$(a^3)^4 = (a^3) \cdot (a^3) \cdot (a^3) \cdot (a^3)$$
$$= (a \cdot a \cdot a) \cdot (a \cdot a \cdot a) \cdot (a \cdot a \cdot a) \cdot (a \cdot a \cdot a),$$

SYSTEMS OF NUMERATION

and since a is repeated as a factor 12 times, we conclude from Definition 3.1 that $(a^3)^4 = a^{12}$. This observation is generalized in the following theorem. The proof will be left as an exercise for the student.

Theorem 3.2 If m and n are positive integers and a is any number, then

$$(a^m)^n = a^{mn}.$$

To complete our work on numeration systems, we need two additional definitions for exponents. If a is any nonzero number, then we define

$$a^0 = 1.$$

Furthermore, if n is a positive integer and $a \neq 0$, we define

$$a^{-n} = \frac{1}{a^n}.$$

We shall return to a more detailed discussion of exponents in Chapter 6. At this time, we are content to illustrate these definitions by a few examples.

Example 3 $3^0 = 1$.

Example 4

$$10^{-3} = \frac{1}{10^3} = \frac{1}{10 \cdot 10 \cdot 10} = \frac{1}{1000}.$$

Example 5

$$2^{-4} = \frac{1}{2^4} = \frac{1}{2 \cdot 2 \cdot 2 \cdot 2} = \frac{1}{16}.$$

Problems

1 Perform the indicated operations by using the theorems and definitions involving exponents.

a) $a^2 \cdot a^5$ b) $(x^3)^6$ c) $a^0 \cdot a^7$

d) $(a^4)^6$ e) $(a^3)^0$ f) $x^3 \cdot x^4$

g) $(y^9)^6$ h) $y^{19} \cdot y^{47}$ i) $b^2 \cdot b^3 \cdot b^4$

2 Evaluate the following numbers.

a) 10^{-2} b) 10^{-5} c) 2^{-5}

d) $10^4 \cdot 10^3$ e) $(2^3)^4$ f) $3^2 \cdot 3^4$

g) $5^0 \cdot 5^4$ h) $(14^6)^0$ i) 3^{-3}

3 Prove Theorem 3.2.

4 Explain why Definition 3.1 cannot be used to define a^0 or a^{-n}, where n is a positive integer.

3.6 THE BABYLONIAN SYSTEM

In each of the numeration systems we have studied so far, with the exception of the Greek system, the repetitive principle was used to represent a number. In each of these systems a number was represented by a combination of certain basic symbols, and if the subtractive principle was not used, the position of these symbols in the representation was unimportant. However, in some numeration systems the value of a basic symbol in the representation of a number depends on the position of the symbol in the representation. This procedure for representing numbers is called the *positional principle*. To illustrate this we call on the reader's familiarity with the Hindu-Arabic system, which will be discussed in detail later. The numeral 5 can be used to represent 5 ones, 5 tens, 5 hundreds, etc., depending on its position in the representation of a number.

The Babylonian numeration system, which evolved sometime between 3000 and 2000 B.C., offers an example of a numeration system which makes use of both the repetitive principle and the positional principle. The Babylonian system was based on the number 60. Numbers through 59 were represented by use of the repetitive principle. These 59 numerals could then be used to represent a number of ones, sixties, thirty-six hundreds, etc., depending on their positions in the representation of a number. Although this system contained some of the essential features of the Hindu-Arabic system, it had serious shortcomings and was very cumbersome. Lacking suitable writing materials, the Babylonians wrote on soft clay with a stick called a stylus. This fact suggests the simplicity of the basic symbols listed below. In order to preserve their writings, the clay was baked to form tablets. The numbers one through nine were represented as follows.

$$I, \ II, \ III, \ \begin{matrix} III \\ I \end{matrix}, \ \begin{matrix} III \\ II \end{matrix}, \ \begin{matrix} III \\ III \end{matrix}, \ \begin{matrix} III \\ III \\ I \end{matrix} \ \begin{matrix} III \\ III \\ II \end{matrix} \ \begin{matrix} III \\ III \\ III \end{matrix}.$$

The symbol for the number ten was $<$. Thus the number 42 is represented by

$$\begin{matrix} <<< \\ < \end{matrix} \ II \ ;$$

the number 37 by

$$<<< \begin{matrix} III \\ \\ I \end{matrix} .$$

The Babylonians used the symbol ● to represent the absence of quantity, or zero. In representing a number, this symbol always occurred as an interior symbol, never at the end, and apparently was not used in computational work. The occurrence of this symbol is what makes possible the use of the positional principle. The procedure for representing a number larger than 60 is best explained by considering some examples.

Example 1 Express 4357 as a Babylonian numeral.
Solution

$$4357 = 3600 + 720 + 37$$
$$= 1 \times 60^2 + 12 \times 60 + 37$$
$$= |\ <|| \ <<<|||.$$

It should be clear from the above example that care must be taken in representing numbers in this system if misinterpretation is to be avoided. The symbols must be spaced so that we can clearly recognize where the set of symbols in one position ends and the set in the next position begins. Note that the first set of symbols, from the right, represents the number of ones; the second, the number of 60's; the third, the number of 60^2 or 3600's, etc.

Example 2 What number does $<<$ ● ||| represent?
Solution

$$<<\ ●\ ||| = 20 \times 60^2 + 0 \times 60 + 3$$
$$= 72{,}000 + 3$$
$$= 72{,}003.$$

Example 3 Express 56,375 as a Babylonian numeral.
Solution

$$56{,}375 = 15 \times 3600 + 39 \times 60 + 35$$

$$= <\genfrac{}{}{0pt}{}{|||}{||} \quad <<<\genfrac{}{}{0pt}{}{|||}{|||} \quad <<<\genfrac{}{}{0pt}{}{|||}{||}.$$

Problems

1 Express each of the following as a Babylonian numeral.

   a) 52   b) 623   c) 425

   d) 507   e) 7647   f) 1320

2 What number does each of the following represent?

a) | <<< || <<<|||
    <   << |||

b) <|| <<< |||
    <<

c) <<< ||| | <| <<<||
    <<

3 Change the Roman numeral MCMLXI to a Babylonian numeral.

4 Change the Roman numeral CXLIV to a Babylonian numeral.

5 Change the Egyptian numeral $\mathcal{L} \cap \cap \cap ||||$ to a Babylonian numeral.

6 Change the Egyptian numeral $\mathcal{L L L} 9 9 9 \cap |||||||$ to a Babylonian numeral.

7 Without using the symbol ●, represent the number 60 in the Babylonian system.

8 If we could use the symbol ● as the last symbol in representing a number in the Babylonian system, how could we represent the number 60 using this symbol?

3.7 THE MAYAN SYSTEM

The Mayan numeration system apparently was developed independently from any other numeration system. It was uncovered by the early sixteenth-century Spanish expeditions into Yucatan, but its date of origin is unknown.

The Mayan system was a positional system based on the number 20. Table 3.5 is a list of the symbols used for the numbers 0 through 19.

Numerals were written vertically in the Mayan system. Reading from the bottom up, the set of symbols in the first position represented the number of units or ones; the set of symbols in the second position represented the

TABLE 3.5

0	⬯	5	—	10	=	15	≡
1	·	6	⊹	11	≐	16	≝
2	··	7	⁚⁚	12	≑	17	≞
3	···	8	⁞⁞	13	≡	18	≣
4	····	9	⁞⁞⁞	14	≣	19	≣

number of 20's; the set of symbols in the third position represented the number of 18×20's or 360's; the set of symbols in the fourth position represented the number of 18×20^2 or 7200's. With the exception of the first and second positions, the nth position in the Mayan numeration system had the value $18 \times 20^{n-2}$. Consider the following examples of representing numbers in the Mayan system and note that care must be taken in spacing the symbols in different positions to avoid misinterpretation.

Example 1 What number does the following Mayan numeral represent?

$$\overset{\cdot\cdot}{=} \;\; \mathrel{||}$$

$$\overset{\cdot}{=}$$

$$\overset{\equiv}{=}$$

Solution The symbol $\equiv$ in the first position represents sixteen 1's; the symbol $\overset{\cdot}{=}$ in the second position represents six 20's; the symbol $=$ in the third position represents ten 18×20's and the symbol $\cdot\cdot$ in the fourth position represents two 18×20^2's. Hence this numeral represents the number

$$16(1) + 6(20) + 10(18 \times 20) + 2(18 \times 20^2)$$
$$= 16 + 6(20) + 10(360) + 2(7200)$$
$$= 16 + 120 + 3600 + 14{,}400 = 18{,}136.$$

Example 2 The Mayan numeral $\overset{\cdot}{\underset{\cdot\cdot}{\overset{\cdot\cdot}{\ominus}}}$ represents the number

$$2(1) + 0(20) + 7(18 \times 20) + 1(18 \times 20^2) = 2 + 0 + 2520 + 7200$$
$$= 9722.$$

Example 3 Express 4652 as a Mayan numeral.
Solution $4652 = 12(360) + 16(20) + 12$

$$= \quad \overset{\cdot\cdot}{\underset{\equiv}{=}} \;\; \overset{\cdot}{\underset{\equiv}{=}} \;\; \overset{\cdot\cdot}{=} \; .$$

The Mayas had a highly developed concept of a positional system, but their choice of using the factor 18, instead of another factor of 20 in the third position, hindered computational work in their system. The choice of the factor 18 was probably due to the fact that their calendar year was divided into 18 divisions with 20 days in each division.

Problems

1 Represent the following numbers in the Mayan system.

    a) 752   b) 365   c) 4336   d) 35,476

2 What number does each of the following Mayan numerals represent?

   a)   b)   c)   d)

3 Add: and   4 Add: and

5 Add: and   6 Subtract: from

7 Subtract: from   8 Subtract: from

3.8 THE HINDU-ARABIC SYSTEM

The numeration system presently used in the United States, the Hindu-Arabic system, originated in India, probably in the third century B.C. The Hindu-Arabic numeration system is named after the Hindus, who invented it, and after the Arabs, who brought the system to western Europe. The earliest preserved examples of these numerals are found on some stone columns erected in India about 250 B.C. by King Asoka. These early examples did not contain a zero and did not employ positional notation. Positional notation and zero must have been introduced sometime before 800 A.D., since the Arab mathematician al-Khowarizma described a Hindu system with these characteristics in a book he wrote about 825 A.D.

It is not possible to say with certainty how the Hindu-Arabic numerals reached the countries of Western Europe. In all probability they were carried by merchants and travelers of the Mediterranean region. There is also evidence to indicate that these numerals may have been introduced in Spain during the Arab invasion of 711 A.D. Scholars who later studied in Spain helped to spread the numerals to other countries of Europe.

The Italian mathematician Fibonacci (1170–1250) was the first European to write an extensive discussion of the Hindu-Arabic numerals. His publication, *Liber Abaci*, which appeared in 1202, contains a detailed treatment of these numerals and their uses. Fibonacci probably came in contact with the Hindu-Arabic numeration system while his father served as a commercial agent in northern Africa. Fibonacci later studied in Constantinople and in Spain and was one of the foremost mathematicians of his time.

The Hindu-Arabic numerals did not achieve immediate popularity with people concerned with computations. It was not until around 1500 that something resembling our present rules in computing became widely used in European countries. The Hindu-Arabic numerals were more slowly adopted wherever the abacus was popular. In Italy, where the use of the abacus was less prevalent, Hindu-Arabic numerals were possibly in common use for as long as a century before they were commonly employed in France and Germany.

The Hindu-Arabic numeration system is a positional system with a symbol for zero. The base of the system is 10 and it utilizes the symbols 0, 1, 2, 3, 4, 5, 6, 7, 8, and 9, referred to as digits, to represent numbers. A number is represented by a sequence of these symbols, and this sequence is interpreted as the sum of the products obtained by multiplying these symbols by the appropriate power of ten. The appropriate power of ten is determined by the position of the symbol relative to a reference point, called a *decimal* point. The first digit to the left of the decimal point is multiplied by 10^0 or 1, the second digit by 10^1 or 10, the third digit by 10^2 or 100, the fourth digit by 10^3 or 1000, etc. In writing whole numbers, the decimal point is usually omitted, but its position is understood to be immediately to the right of the sequence of digits. As an aid to reading large sequences of digits, a comma is often used to group the digits in groups of three, starting from the decimal point.

Example 1

$$283 = 2 \cdot 10^2 + 8 \cdot 10^1 + 3 \cdot 10^0$$
$$= 2(100) + 8(10) + 3(1).$$

In words, the numeral 283 represents 2 hundreds, 8 tens, and 3 ones, or two hundred eighty-three.

Example 2

$$560,871 = 5 \cdot 10^5 + 6 \cdot 10^4 + 0 \cdot 10^3 + 8 \cdot 10^2 + 7 \cdot 10^1 + 1 \cdot 10^0$$
$$= 5(100,000) + 6(10,000) + 0(1000) + 8(100) + 7(10) + 1(1).$$

In words, the numeral 560,871 represents 5 hundred thousands, 6 ten thousands, 8 hundreds, 7 tens, and 1 one, or five hundred sixty thousand eight hundred seventy-one.

Because of the small number of symbols and positional notation, the Hindu-Arabic system is especially convenient for computation. In the following two examples we will take a close look at the procedure for adding and multiplying whole numbers.

Example 3 Add 385 and 572.

Solution These two numbers are written in expanded form in the array in Fig. 3.1. To find the sum of the two numbers we first add ones, then tens, and then hundreds. Our work is summarized in the figure. The steps are:

1) Add $5 \cdot 10^0$ to $2 \cdot 10^0$ to get $7 \cdot 10^0$.

2) Record $7 \cdot 10^0$.

3) Add $8 \cdot 10^1$ to $7 \cdot 10^1$ to get $15 \cdot 10^1 = 1 \cdot 10^2 + 5 \cdot 10^1$.

4) Record $5 \cdot 10^1$ and carry $1 \cdot 10^2$.

5) Add $3 \cdot 10^2$, $5 \cdot 10^2$, and $1 \cdot 10^2$, which was carried from the previous step, to obtain $9 \cdot 10^2$.

6) Record $9 \cdot 10^2$.

Thus the sum of 385 and 572 is

$$9 \cdot 10^2 + 5 \cdot 10^1 + 7 \cdot 10^0, \text{ or } 957.$$

$$385 = 3 \cdot 10^2 + 8 \cdot 10^1 + 5 \cdot 10^0$$
$$572 = 5 \cdot 10^2 + 7 \cdot 10^1 + 2 \cdot 10^0$$
$$\overline{957 = 9 \cdot 10^2 + 5 \cdot 10^1 + 7 \cdot 10^0}$$

Figure 3.1

Example 4   Multiply 38 by 43.

Solution We write 38 and 43 in expanded form in the array in Fig. 3.2. To multiply these numbers, we must multiply each term of the expression $3 \cdot 10^1 + 8 \cdot 10^0$ by each term of the expression $4 \cdot 10^1 + 3 \cdot 10^0$. Our work is summarized in the figure. The steps are:

1) Multiply $8 \cdot 10^0$ by $3 \cdot 10^0$ to get $24 \cdot 10^0$.

2) $24 \cdot 10^0 = 2 \cdot 10^1 + 4 \cdot 10^0$, so record $4 \cdot 10^0$ and carry $2 \cdot 10^1$.

3) Multiply $3 \cdot 10^1$ by $3 \cdot 10^0$ obtaining $9 \cdot 10^1$ and add $2 \cdot 10^1$, which was carried from the previous step, to get $11 \cdot 10^1$.

4) $11 \cdot 10^1 = 1 \cdot 10^2 + 1 \cdot 10^1$, so record $1 \cdot 10^1$ and carry $1 \cdot 10^2$.

5) Record $1 \cdot 10^2$.

6) Multiply $8 \cdot 10^0$ by $4 \cdot 10^1$ to get $32 \cdot 10^1$.

7) $32 \cdot 10^1 = 3 \cdot 10^2 + 2 \cdot 10^1$, so record $2 \cdot 10^1$ and carry $3 \cdot 10^2$.

8) Multiply $3 \cdot 10^1$ by $4 \cdot 10^1$ to get $12 \cdot 10^2$ and add $3 \cdot 10^2$, which was carried from the previous step, to obtain $15 \cdot 10^2$.

9) $15 \cdot 10^2 = 1 \cdot 10^3 + 5 \cdot 10^2$, so record $5 \cdot 10^2$ and carry $1 \cdot 10^3$.

10) Record $1 \cdot 10^3$.

11) Add the numbers $1 \cdot 10^2 + 1 \cdot 10^1 + 4 \cdot 10^0$ and $1 \cdot 10^3 + 5 \cdot 10^2 + 2 \cdot 10^1$ to obtain $1 \cdot 10^3 + 6 \cdot 10^2 + 3 \cdot 10^1 + 4 \cdot 10^0$.

SYSTEMS OF NUMERATION

Hence the result of multiplying 38 by 43 is

$$1 \cdot 10^3 + 6 \cdot 10^2 + 3 \cdot 10^1 + 4 \cdot 10^0, \text{ or } 1634.$$

$$
\begin{array}{rr}
38 = & 3 \cdot 10^1 + 8 \cdot 10^0 \\
43 = & 4 \cdot 10^1 + 3 \cdot 10^0 \\
\hline
& 1 \cdot 10^2 + 1 \cdot 10^1 + 4 \cdot 10^0 \\
1 \cdot 10^3 + 5 \cdot 10^2 + 2 \cdot 10^1 & \\
\hline
1 \cdot 10^3 + 6 \cdot 10^2 + 3 \cdot 10^1 + 4 \cdot 10^0 &
\end{array}
$$

Figure 3.2

The procedure in Example 4 may seem rather complicated when we make comparison with the customary procedure for multiplying two numbers. For example, we usually find the product of 38 and 43 by constructing the array

$$
\begin{array}{r}
38 \\
43 \\
\hline
114 \\
152 \\
\hline
1634
\end{array}
$$

This array of numbers is merely a shorthand form of the procedure used in Example 4 and is called an algorithm. We shall examine other algorithms for multiplying two numbers in Section 3.11.

It was not until the sixteenth century that Hindu-Arabic notation was extended to the right of the decimal point to denote fractions. Simon Stevin (1548–1620), a Dutch mathematician, was the first to give a systematic treatment of decimal fractions. In representing fractions, we multiply the first digit to the right of the decimal point by 10^{-1} or $\frac{1}{10}$, the second digit by 10^{-2} or $\frac{1}{100}$, the third digit by 10^{-3} or $\frac{1}{1000}$, etc. We then add these products to the products associated with the digits to the left of the decimal point to find the number represented.

Example 5

$$
\begin{aligned}
32.427 &= 3 \cdot 10^1 + 2 \cdot 10^0 + 4 \cdot 10^{-1} + 2 \cdot 10^{-2} + 7 \cdot 10^{-3} \\
&= 3(10) + 2(1) + 4(\tfrac{1}{10}) + 2(\tfrac{1}{100}) + 7(\tfrac{1}{1000}).
\end{aligned}
$$

The digits 0, 1, 2, 3, 4, 5, 6, 7, 8, and 9 have evolved over a period of many centuries and they only slightly resemble the symbols originally used by the Hindus. These symbols are by no means standard even today, as their appearance may vary from region to region.

Problems

1 Write each of the following numerals in expanded form.

a) 476   b) 3.404   c) 8096

d) 9871   e) 4893   f) 0.00052

g) 651.63   h) 0.612   i) 4,020,316.22

2 Write the Hindu-Arabic numeral for:

a) $9(10^3) + 6(10^2) + 3(10^1) + 1(10^0)$

b) $7(10^4) + 6(10^3) + 0(10^2) + 0(10^1) + 9(10^0)$

c) $7(10^5) + 3(10^1) + 6(10^0)$

d) $9(10^3) + 1(10^1)$

e) $7(10^6) + 6(10^4) + 3(10^1) + 1(10^0)$

3 Write each of the following pairs of numerals in expanded form and add by the method of this section.

a) 96 and 78   b) 328 and 415   c) 675 and 882

d) 4763 and 9118   e) 3005 and 468   f) 2162 and 5162

4 Write each of the following pairs of numerals in expanded form and multiply by the method of this section.

a) 47 and 52   b) 18 and 94   c) 26 and 85

d) 328 and 415   e) 63 and 39   f) 847 and 669

3.9 BASES OTHER THAN TEN

Most of the numeration systems studied in this chapter have had the number 10 as their base. We have pointed out that the choice of 10 is a natural choice, since a person's fingers provide him with a very convenient reference set. Although it may seem that 10 is the only logical number to choose as the base of a numeration system, any other positive integer would serve the purpose equally well, and some better. We are prejudiced in favor of 10 because of our long practice with a numeration system having 10 as a base.

Let b denote a positive integer and let us consider a positional numeration system with base b. In this system a number will be represented by a sequence of symbols for the numbers 0, 1, 2, 3, ..., b-2, and b-1. This sequence will be interpreted as the sum of the products obtained by multiplying these symbols by the appropriate power of the base b. The appropriate power is determined by the position of the symbol relative to a fixed point called the reference point (it is only called the decimal point if $b = 10$). The first symbol to the left of the reference point is multiplied by b^0, the second by b^1, the third by b^2, the fourth by b^3, etc. For example, if a number N is represented by the sequence 243 using base 5, then

$$N = 2 \cdot 5^2 + 4 \cdot 5^1 + 3 \cdot 5^0.$$

If 243 is a numeral in a base five numeration system, it is customary to write 243_5, using the subscript 5 to indicate the base of the system, to avoid confusion with numerals using another base. If no subscript appears on a numeral, it will be understood that the numeral is written in base ten notation. The reference point is usually omitted when working with whole numbers and, as before, it is understood to be located immediately to the right of the sequence of digits.

Base 0 1 1 2 3 4 5 6
5 0 1 1 2 3 4 10 11

Example 1   Write 4023_5 as a numeral in base ten.

Solution

$$\begin{aligned} 4023_5 &= 4 \cdot 5^3 + 0 \cdot 5^2 + 2 \cdot 5^1 + 3 \cdot 5^0 \\ &= 4 \cdot 125 + 0 \cdot 25 + 2 \cdot 5 + 3 \cdot 1 \\ &= 500 + 0 + 10 + 3 \\ &= 513. \end{aligned}$$

Example 2   Write 5162_7 as a numeral in base ten.

Solution

$$\begin{aligned} 5162_7 &= 5 \cdot 7^3 + 1 \cdot 7^2 + 6 \cdot 7^1 + 2 \cdot 7^0 \\ &= 5 \cdot 343 + 1 \cdot 49 + 6 \cdot 7 + 2 \cdot 1 \\ &= 1715 + 49 + 42 + 2 \\ &= 1808. \end{aligned}$$

Example 3   Write 1100101_2 as a numeral in base ten.

Solution

$$\begin{aligned} 1100101_2 &= 1 \cdot 2^6 + 1 \cdot 2^5 + 0 \cdot 2^4 + 0 \cdot 2^3 + 1 \cdot 2^2 + 0 \cdot 2^1 + 1 \cdot 2^0 \\ &= 1 \cdot 64 + 1 \cdot 32 + 0 \cdot 16 + 0 \cdot 8 + 1 \cdot 4 + 0 \cdot 2 + 1 \cdot 1 \\ &= 64 + 32 + 4 + 1 \\ &= 101. \end{aligned}$$

If the base of our system is 12, then we have some notational problems to overcome. We cannot use the symbols 0, 1, 2, 3, 4, 5, 6, 7, 8, 9, 10, 11 to construct base 12 numerals because the use of the symbols 10 and 11 would result in an ambiguity. For example, it is not possible to determine from its use in a numeral whether 10 is a single symbol or the two symbols 1 and 0. This problem can be overcome by using t in place of 10 and e in place of 11. Similar problems will be encountered anytime the base of a system exceeds 10.

Example 4   Write $t096e_{12}$ as a numeral in base ten.

Solution

$$t096e_{12} = 10 \cdot 12^4 + 0 \cdot 12^3 + 9 \cdot 12^2 + 6 \cdot 12^1 + 11 \cdot 12^0$$
$$= 10 \cdot 20736 + 9 \cdot 144 + 6 \cdot 12 + 11 \cdot 1$$
$$= 207{,}360 + 1296 + 72 + 11$$
$$= 208{,}739.$$

All our examples so far have been examples illustrating the conversion of a numeral in a base other than ten to a numeral in base ten. The following examples will illustrate the conversion process from base ten to some other base.

Example 5   Write 247 as a numeral in base five.

Solution   Our goal is to express the numeral 247 in the form

$$a_0 5^n + a_1 5^{n-1} + \cdots + a_{n-1} 5^1 + a_n 5^0.$$

The powers of 5 are 1, 5, 25, 125, 625, 3125, ... The power $5^4 = 625$ is larger than our number 247 and 247 is in turn larger than the power $5^3 = 125$. Thus, our base five numeral will have four symbols. The symbol in the position at the far left is obtained by determining the number of times 125 is "contained" in 247. This answer, 1, is found by dividing 247 by 125. The remainder, 122, is now divided by 25 to determine the next symbol. The remainder of this division problem is divided by 5 to determine the next symbol, and the process is continued until the remainder is smaller than 5. The last remainder is the final symbol in our numeral.

$$
\begin{array}{ccc}
1 & 4 & 4 \\
125\overline{)247} & 25\overline{)122} & 5\overline{)22} \\
\underline{125} & \underline{100} & \underline{20} \\
R_1 = 122 & R_2 = 22 & R_3 = 2
\end{array}
$$

Our work can be summarized by writing

$$247 = 1 \cdot 5^3 + 4 \cdot 5^2 + 4 \cdot 5^1 + 2 \cdot 5^0.$$

Therefore $247 = 1442_5$.

Example 6   Write 1289 as a numeral in base twelve.

Solution   We wish to express the numeral 1289 in the form

$$a_0 12^n + a_1 12^{n-1} + \cdots + a_{n-1} \cdot 12^1 + a_n \cdot 12^0.$$

The powers of 12 are 1, 12, 144, 1728, ... 1728 is larger than 1289, and 1289 is larger than 144, so the desired numeral in base twelve will have three symbols. These symbols are determined by long division, as in Example 5. The process will be terminated when we first obtain a remainder smaller than 12.

$$
\begin{array}{r}
8 \\
144\overline{)1289} \\
1152 \\
\hline
R_1 = 137
\end{array}
\qquad
\begin{array}{r}
11 = e \\
12\overline{)137} \\
132 \\
\hline
R_2 = 5
\end{array}
$$

We summarize our work by writing

$$1289 = 8 \cdot 12^2 + 11 \cdot 12^1 + 5 \cdot 12^0.$$

Thus $1289 = 8e5_{12}$.

Problems

1 Write the numerals 1, 2, 3, 4, . . . , 30, using base five numerals.

2 Write the numerals 1, 2, 3, 4, . . . , 30, using base twelve numerals.

3 Write the numerals 1, 2, 3, 4, . . . , 30, using base two numerals.

4 Convert each of the following numerals to a base ten numeral.

    a) 11001_2 b) 413_5 c) $t18_{12}$

    d) 7614_8 e) $e00t_{12}$ f) 2104_5

    g) 623_7 h) 10101010_2 i) 40000_5

5 Write each of the following as a numeral in base two.

    a) 73   b) 102   c) 617

6 Write each of the following as a numeral in base five.

    a) 65   b) 386   c) 1281

7 Write each of the following as a numeral in base twelve.

    a) 45   b) 1571   c) 33,400

8 Change $t13_{12}$ to base five.

9 Change 7614_8 to base seven.

10 Change 1101101_2 to base five.

11 For what values of b, if any, will 42_b be an even integer when converted to a base ten numeral? Answer the same question for the numeral 41_b.

12 Arrange the following numerals in order from smallest to largest.

    a) $et1_{12}$ b) 8716_9 c) 11011100111_2

3.10 COMPUTATION IN OTHER BASES

Computation in numeration systems using a base different from ten can be carried out by adopting the same method used in the Hindu-Arabic system. In this section we consider some examples of addition, subtraction, and multiplication using a variety of bases different from ten. In these problems we will depend to some extent on the student's knowledge of the Hindu-Arabic system.

Example 1   Add 134_5 and 243_5.

Solution In the array in Fig. 3.3 we have written the two numerals in expanded form. To find the sum of these numbers, we will first add ones, then fives, and then twenty-fives. The array in the figure will be used to keep track of our steps and summarize our work. Our steps are:

1) Add $4 \cdot 5^0$ to $3 \cdot 5^0$ to get $7 \cdot 5^0 = 1 \cdot 5^1 + 2 \cdot 5^0$.
2) Record $2 \cdot 5^0$ and carry $1 \cdot 5^1$.
3) Add $3 \cdot 5^1$, $4 \cdot 5^1$, and $1 \cdot 5^1$, which was carried from the previous step, to obtain $8 \cdot 5^1 = 1 \cdot 5^2 + 3 \cdot 5^1$.
4) Record $3 \cdot 5^1$ and carry $1 \cdot 5^2$.
5) Add $1 \cdot 5^2$, $2 \cdot 5^2$, and $1 \cdot 5^2$, which was carried from the previous step, to obtain $4 \cdot 5^2$.
6) Record $4 \cdot 5^2$.

Therefore the sum of 134_5 and 243_5 is 432_5.

$$134_5 = 1 \cdot 5^2 + 3 \cdot 5^1 + 4 \cdot 5^0$$
$$243_5 = 2 \cdot 5^2 + 4 \cdot 5^1 + 3 \cdot 5^0$$
$$\overline{432_5 = 4 \cdot 5^2 + 3 \cdot 5^1 + 2 \cdot 5^0}$$

Figure 3.3

Example 2   Add $6e8_{12}$ and 851_{12}.

Solution Our work is summarized in Fig. 3.4. The steps are:

1) Add $8 \cdot 12^0$ to $1 \cdot 12^0$ to obtain $9 \cdot 12^0$.
2) Record $9 \cdot 12^0$.
3) Add $11 \cdot 12^1$ to $5 \cdot 12^1$ to get $16 \cdot 12^1 = 1 \cdot 12^2 + 4 \cdot 12^1$.
4) Record $4 \cdot 12^1$ and carry $1 \cdot 12^2$.
5) Add $6 \cdot 12^2$, $8 \cdot 12^2$, and $1 \cdot 12^2$, which was carried from the previous step, to obtain $15 \cdot 12^2 = 1 \cdot 12^3 + 3 \cdot 12^2$.
6) Record $3 \cdot 12^2$ and carry $1 \cdot 12^3$.
7) Record $1 \cdot 12^3$.

Therefore the sum of $6e8_{12}$ and 851_{12} is 1349_{12}.

$$6e8_{12} = \qquad 6 \cdot 12^2 + 11 \cdot 12^1 + 8 \cdot 12^0$$
$$851_{12} = \qquad 8 \cdot 12^2 + 5 \cdot 12^1 + 1 \cdot 12^0$$
$$\overline{1349_{12} = 1 \cdot 12^3 + 3 \cdot 12^2 + 4 \cdot 12^1 + 9 \cdot 12^0} \qquad \text{Figure 3.4}$$

Example 3   Subtract 265_8 from 717_8.

Solution   Our work is summarized in Fig. 3.5. The steps are:

1) Subtract $5 \cdot 8^0$ from $7 \cdot 8^0$ to get $2 \cdot 8^0$.
2) Record $2 \cdot 8^0$.
3) Borrow $1 \cdot 8^2$ and then subtract $6 \cdot 8^1$ from $9 \cdot 8^1 = 1 \cdot 8^2 + 1 \cdot 8^1$ to obtain $3 \cdot 8^1$.
5) Record $3 \cdot 8^1$.
6) Subtract $2 \cdot 8^2$ from $6 \cdot 8^2$ (recall that we borrowed one 8^2 in the previous step) to get $4 \cdot 8^2$.
7) Record $4 \cdot 8^2$.

Therefore $717_8 - 265_8 = 432_8$.

$$717_8 = 7 \cdot 8^2 + 1 \cdot 8^1 + 7 \cdot 8^0$$
$$265_8 = 2 \cdot 8^2 + 6 \cdot 8^1 + 5 \cdot 8^0$$
$$\overline{432_8 = 4 \cdot 8^2 + 3 \cdot 8^1 + 2 \cdot 8^0} \qquad \text{Figure 3.5}$$

Example 4   Subtract 1101_2 from 11010_2.

Solution   Our work is summarized in Fig. 3.6. The steps are:

1) Borrow $1 \cdot 2^1$ and then subtract $1 \cdot 2^0$ from $2 \cdot 2^0 = 1 \cdot 2^1 + 0 \cdot 2^0$ to obtain $1 \cdot 2^0$.
2) Record $1 \cdot 2^0$.
3) Subtract $0 \cdot 2^1$ from $0 \cdot 2^1$ (remembering that we borrowed $1 \cdot 2^1$ in the previous step) to get $0 \cdot 2^1$.
4) Record $0 \cdot 2^1$.
5) Borrow $1 \cdot 2^3$ and then subtract $1 \cdot 2^2$ from $2 \cdot 2^2 = 1 \cdot 2^3 + 0 \cdot 2^2$ to get $1 \cdot 2^2$.
6) Record $1 \cdot 2^2$.
7) Borrow $1 \cdot 2^4$ and then subtract $1 \cdot 2^3$ from $2 \cdot 2^3 = 1 \cdot 2^4 + 0 \cdot 2^3$ to obtain $1 \cdot 2^3$.
8) Record $1 \cdot 2^3$.

We conclude that $11010_2 - 1101_2 = 1101_2$.

$$11010_2 = 1 \cdot 2^4 + 1 \cdot 2^3 + 0 \cdot 2^2 + 1 \cdot 2^1 + 0 \cdot 2^0$$
$$1101_2 = 1 \cdot 2^3 + 1 \cdot 2^2 + 0 \cdot 2^1 + 1 \cdot 2^0$$

$$1101_2 = 1 \cdot 2^3 + 1 \cdot 2^2 + 0 \cdot 2^1 + 1 \cdot 2^0 \qquad \text{Figure 3.6}$$

Example 5 Multiply 46_7 by 34_7.

Solution Our work is summarized in Fig. 3.7. The steps are:

1) Multiply $6 \cdot 7^0$ by $4 \cdot 7^0$ to get $24 \cdot 7^0$.
2) $24 \cdot 7^0 = 3 \cdot 7^1 + 3 \cdot 7^0$, so record $3 \cdot 7^0$ and carry $3 \cdot 7^1$.
3) Multiply $4 \cdot 7^1$ by $4 \cdot 7^0$ to obtain $16 \cdot 7^1$ and add $3 \cdot 7^1$, which was carried from the previous step, to get $19 \cdot 7^1$.
4) $19 \cdot 7^1 = 2 \cdot 7^2 + 5 \cdot 7^1$, so record $5 \cdot 7^1$ and carry $2 \cdot 7^2$.
5) Record $2 \cdot 7^2$.
6) Multiply $6 \cdot 7^0$ by $3 \cdot 7^1$ to get $18 \cdot 7^1$.
7) $18 \cdot 7^1 = 2 \cdot 7^2 + 4 \cdot 7^1$, so record $4 \cdot 7^1$ and carry $2 \cdot 7^2$.
8) Multiply $4 \cdot 7^1$ by $3 \cdot 7^1$ to get $12 \cdot 7^2$ and add $2 \cdot 7^2$, which was carried from the previous step, to obtain $14 \cdot 7^2$.
9) $14 \cdot 7^2 = 2 \cdot 7^3 + 0 \cdot 7^2$, so record $0 \cdot 7^2$ and carry $2 \cdot 7^3$.
10) Record $2 \cdot 7^3$.
11) Add the numbers $2 \cdot 7^2 + 5 \cdot 7^1 + 3 \cdot 7^0$ and $2 \cdot 7^3 + 0 \cdot 7^2 + 4 \cdot 7^1$.

The result of multiplying 46_7 by 34_7 is 2323_7.

$$46_7 = 4 \cdot 7^1 + 6 \cdot 7^0$$
$$34_7 = 3 \cdot 7^1 + 4 \cdot 7^0$$

$$253_7 = 2 \cdot 7^2 + 5 \cdot 7^1 + 3 \cdot 7^0$$
$$2040_7 = 2 \cdot 7^3 + 0 \cdot 7^2 + 4 \cdot 7^1$$

$$2323_7 = 2 \cdot 7^3 + 3 \cdot 7^2 + 2 \cdot 7^1 + 3 \cdot 7^0 \qquad \text{Figure 3.7}$$

Our primary goal in this section is to obtain a better understanding of the arithmetic operations in our own numeration system, which has base ten. Because we have been working with our system for such a long time, we normally go through the steps of adding, subtracting, and multiplying without giving any thought to the significance of these steps. However, using a base different from ten, we must analyze each step and, therefore, we gain insight into the arithmetic process.

Problems

1 Find the following sums.

   a) $101_2 + 110_2$ b) $10011_2 + 1101_2$ c) $314_5 + 443_5$

   d) $7482_9 + 5853_9$ e) $5t61_{12} + e9t3_{12}$ f) $314_7 + 652_7 + 435_7$

2 Find the following differences.

   a) $413_5 - 241_5$ b) $1100_2 - 1010_2$ c) $6134_8 - 2655_8$

   d) $3854_{12} - 1te6_{12}$ e) $3112_5 - 1324_5$ f) $1001_2 - 110_2$

3 Find the following products.

   a) $24_5 \times 32_5$ b) $20_3 \times 22_3$ c) $t5_{12} \times 68_{12}$

   d) $76_8 \times 63_8$ e) $234_5 \times 344_5$ f) $653_7 \times 400_7$

4 For what value of b would:

   a) $31_b + 24_b = 110_b$?   b) $26_b + 17_b = 45_b$?

   c) $65_b - 13_b = 52_b$?   d) $4_b \times 5_b = 26_b$?

   e) $7_b \times 12_b = 106_b$?

3.11 ALGORITHMS

An *algorithm* is a special procedure for solving a certain type of problem. For example, to multiply 38 by 43 we use the algorithm in Fig. 3.8 to obtain the answer 1634. The student is undoubtedly familiar with the algorithms that we use for finding sums, differences, and quotients. In the Hindu-Arabic system many algorithms have been used to perform the basic arithmetic operations of addition, subtraction, multiplication, and division, with our present algorithms having evolved over a period of several centuries. Algorithms were also used in the other numeration systems studied in this chapter. It is the purpose of this section to study a few examples of these earlier algorithms.

$$
\begin{array}{r}
38 \\
43 \\
\hline
114 \\
152 \\
\hline
1634
\end{array}
$$
   Figure 3.8

The Egyptians usually performed multiplication and division by a sequence of *doubling* operations. Their method was based on the fact that any number can be expressed as a sum of powers of 2. Suppose, for example, that we wish to find the product 37×48. We can write $37 = 1 + 4 + 32$ and 37×48 can be found by adding the products 1×48, 4×48, and 32×48.

This work can be accomplished by using the array in Fig. 3.9.

*1	48
2	96
*4	192
8	384
16	768
*32	1536
	1776

Figure 3.9

This array consists of two columns headed by the numbers 1 and 48, respectively. In each of the two columns, each number after the first is obtained by doubling the preceding number. The product is found by adding the appropriate multiples of 48, i.e., those which are indicated by an asterisk.

The procedure of doubling, used by the Egyptians, could also be used to find quotients. To illustrate this method, we will divide 703 by 37. We will again use an array, Fig. 3.10, consisting of two columns, one headed by the number 1 and the other headed by the divisor 37. The numbers in these columns are doubled until the number in the divisor's column exceeds the dividend 703. Because

$$703 = 592 + 111$$
$$= 592 + 74 + 37,$$

the quotient is found by adding the numbers in the first column marked by an asterisk. Thus $703 \div 37 = 19$.

*1	37
*2	74
4	148
8	296
*16	592
32	1184
19	

Figure 3.10

The Egyptian method for multiplying and dividing was convenient because it did not require the memorization of a multiplication table. The procedure was also easily performed on an abacus.

Another method for multiplying numbers is called the *gelosia* or *lattice* method. The word "gelosia" means jealousy and the method was so named because the array resembles a grating that was at one time placed on Venetian windows to provide a degree of privacy for the lady of the house. This method will be used to find the product of 248 and 653.

The numbers 248 and 653 are placed at the top and to the right, respectively, of the lattice in Fig. 3.11. To find the numbers in the square in the lower right-hand corner we multiply 8 by 3 to get 24 ; 4 is placed in the lower half of the square and 2 is carried to the upper half of the square. All the other numbers of the array are found in a similar manner. The numbers below and to the left of the square are obtained by adding the numbers along the diagonals of the square, starting in the lower right-hand corner, and carrying to the diagonal above, if necessary. For example, the number 9 below the lower left-hand square of the lattice is obtained by adding 8, 4, 0, 1 and 6 (note that no number is carried from the diagonal below). This sum is 19, so we record 9 and carry 1 to the diagonal immediately above. The product of 248 and 653 is found by reading in a counterclockwise sense the numbers to the left and below the lattice. The product is 161,944.

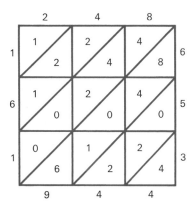

Figure 3.11

The lattice method can be used to multiply two whole numbers of any size. This method was still in use even after Columbus discovered America in 1492.

We will illustrate one other algorithm called the *scratch method*. This method was used in several countries of western Europe almost to the exclusion of all others, and it was not until the beginning of the eighteenth century that it was replaced in England. It originated with the Hindus, who made their computations on a sand- or dust-covered surface. The name "scratch method" is derived from the fact that the Hindus erased a figure by scratching it out. We illustrate the process by multiplying 43 by 26 (see Fig. 3.12).

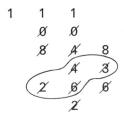

Figure 3.12

We start by writing the unit's digit of 26 directly beneath the ten's digit of 43. In Fig. 3.12, the original 26 and 43 are enclosed by a line. Then we multiply 4 by 2, placing the result 8 above 2. The 2 of 26 is then scratched. Next, we multiply 4 by 6 to get 24. The 4 is recorded over the 4 of 43 and we carry 2 to the left and add to 8. We have $8 + 2 = 10$, so we scratch the 8, replace it by 0, and carry 1 to the next column to the left. We now scratch the 6 of the multiplier and the 4 of the multiplicand 43. We next move 26 one space to the right, with the digit 2 being written beneath the 6 of the original 26 and the digit 6 being written one space to the right and one space above the digit 2. The foregoing process is repeated, using the digit 3 of 43 as the multiplicand. When we have finished using a digit, it is scratched. The number that remains, reading from the top left, is the product of 43 and 26. Thus, $43 \times 26 = 1118$.

Problems

1 Find the following products by using the Egyptian method.

   a) $17 \cdot 44$ b) $34 \cdot 63$ c) $74 \cdot 93$ d) $147 \cdot 281$

2 Find the following quotients by using the Egyptian method.

   a) $696 \div 29$ b) $1776 \div 24$

   c) $950 \div 38$ d) $8466 \div 83$

3 Find the following products by using the gelosia method.

   a) $38 \cdot 45$ b) $64 \cdot 91$ c) $543 \cdot 83$

   d) $396 \cdot 518$ e) $43 \cdot 987$ f) $5496 \cdot 3877$

4 Find the following products by the "scratch" method.

   a) $23 \cdot 34$ b) $86 \cdot 47$ c) $59 \cdot 36$ d) $493 \cdot 48$

5 Find the product $465_7 \times 505_7$, using the gelosia method.

6 Find the product $4326_8 \times 567_8$, using the gelosia method.

7 Find the product $43_5 \times 32_5$, using the scratch method.

8 Find the product $542_6 \times 43_6$, using the scratch method.

Chapter 4

THE NATURAL NUMBERS AND INTEGERS

4.1 COUNTING AND THE NATURAL NUMBERS

Since the concept of number and the process of counting evolved before the time of recorded history, we can only conjecture as to their beginnings. We have some idea how the primitive man first counted. Suppose he wished to count the number of sheep in his flock. In the morning as his sheep left the pen, he placed a pebble in a pile, one for each sheep. In the evening as the sheep returned to the pen, he would remove a pebble for each sheep, as it entered the pen. If after the last sheep had entered, he had some pebbles left, he knew some of his sheep were missing. If he ran out of pebbles before all the sheep were in the pen, he knew he had gained some sheep, perhaps his neighbor's, during the day. Of course, if the pebbles and sheep corresponded one-to-one, then he knew that all his sheep were in the pen. In this latter case he had established a one-to-one correspondence between the set of sheep and the set of pebbles. From this method alone we can see that primitive man had some notion about the concept of numbers. Even though no numbers were needed in this counting, he acquired the concepts of "more than" and "less than."

Obviously, this method proved to be uncertain and inaccurate. What happened if the sheep began to run into the pen and the sheep herder was unable to ascertain how many sheep were entering at a time? Or suppose he kept his pebbles in a bag during the day, and he lost the bag? Through the years man developed the idea of a set of words for a reference set and, later, he used a set of symbols to represent his reference set. It was at this time that he probably realized that a set of five sheep and a set of five pebbles have something in common.

Example 1 Consider the following sets:

$$A = \{\#, \$, \%, *, \&\},$$
$$B = \{X, (, Q, @, +\}.$$

Clearly we see that $A \neq B$, but the two sets do have something in common. We can certainly establish a one-to-one correspondence between the two sets.

As we learned in Section 2.3, the sets A and B in Example 1 have a common property called their *number*. Any other set that can be placed in one-to-one correspondence with either of these sets is a representative of the same number. Thus number is a property common to equivalent sets.

Example 2   At first glance the sets

$$A = \{\text{Jane, Bob, Harry}\},$$
$$B = \{X, Y, Z\},$$
$$C = \{1, 2, 3\}$$

seem to have nothing in common. Clearly, no element appears in more than one set. Yet, if we look again, we can see that there exist one-to-one correspondences between each pair of the three sets. Therefore, as reference sets, each represents the same number.

Since many different sets could act as a reference set for a given number, there should be some agreement as to which set to use. The symbol "0" represents the number of the empty set. The symbol "1" represents the number of every set equivalent to the set $\{0\}$. Likewise, the symbol "2" represents the number of every set equivalent to the set $\{0, 1\}$. Similarly we have the numerals 3, 4, . . ., n with corresponding reference sets

$$\{0, 1, 2\}, \{0, 1, 2, 3\}, \ldots, \{0, 1, 2, 3, \ldots, n-1\}.$$

The set of numbers represented by the numerals 0, 1, 2, 3, . . . is called the set of *natural numbers*. The symbols used to denote the natural numbers are arbitrary. We will use the letter N to denote the set of natural numbers.

Example 3   The symbol "5" represents the number of every set which can be placed in one-to-one correspondence with the set $\{0, 1, 2, 3, 4\}$. The symbol "100" represents the number of every set which can be placed in one-to-one correspondence with the set $\{0, 1, 2, 3, 4, \ldots, 99\}$.

Counting a set is simply the process of establishing a one-to-one correspondence between the set being counted and the appropriate reference set. When we say a set A has six elements, we mean that there is a one-to-one correspondence between the set A and the set $\{0, 1, 2, 3, 4, 5\}$, the reference set of six elements.

Example 4 Count the letters in the word "math." To count the letters in the set {m, a, t, h} we will begin by exhibiting the following one-to-one correspondence between this set and the set {0, 1, 2, 3}.

$$m \leftrightarrow 0$$
$$a \leftrightarrow 1$$
$$t \leftrightarrow 2$$
$$h \leftrightarrow 3$$

Thus, the reference set used is the set {0, 1, 2, 3}, and the set {m, a, t, h} has 4 elements, since 4 represents the number of every set equivalent to {0, 1, 2, 3}.

The one-to-one correspondence used in finding the number of the set in Example 4 is just one of twenty-four possibilities. Any one of the other twenty-three could have been used to show that the set {m, a, t, h} has 4 elements.

Natural numbers can be used in two different ways in the counting process. Perhaps the most frequent use of a number is to tell how many elements are in a set. When a number is used in this manner, we say it is a *cardinal number*. The cardinal number of a set A is denoted $n(A)$. If a set is ordered, each element of the set has an *ordinal number* to specify its position in the set. We recall from Section 2.5 that an ordered set is a set in which the order of elements is specified. Since we chose to enclose the elements of an ordered pair (an ordered set with two elements) by parentheses to distinguish it from a nonordered set, we use the same notation for ordered sets with more than two elements.

The children in a family are Bill, Sue, Mary, Tom, and Joe. If C represents this set of children, then C = {Bill, Sue, Mary, Tom, Joe} and $n(C)$ = 5 regardless of the order in which the elements of the set appear. However, if we are told that the children are listed according to age, the oldest being listed first, the next oldest second, etc., then the set becomes an ordered set. In this case we denote the set by C = (Bill, Sue, Mary, Tom, Joe). Thus, we say Bill is first, Sue second, Mary third, Tom fourth, and Joe fifth. Note that the ordinal number of the last element is the cardinal number of the set.

Example 5 Examples of cardinal numbers:

a) Susan is 5 feet tall.

b) Bill has 3 brothers.

c) There are 12 months in a year.

In each part of this example the number is used to tell how many.

Example 6 Examples of ordinal numbers:

a) Susan is in the 5th grade.

b) Bill wears size 7 shoes.

c) October is the 10th month of the year.

In each part of this example the number is used to specify order or to tell which one.

Example 7 In the following tell whether each number is used as a cardinal number or as an ordinal number.

a) James bought 2 pairs of size 7 shoes.

b) The 12th month of the year has 31 days.

c) On the 23rd day of May, he will have his 40th birthday.

Solution

a) 2 — Cardinal   b) 12 — Ordinal   c) 23 — Ordinal

   7 — Ordinal   31 — Cardinal   40 — Ordinal

Problems

1 Let M represent the set of months of a year. Denote M so that it is an ordered set; an unordered set.

2 In how many ways can the set $\{\nabla, \$, \#, *\}$ be counted? What is the cardinal number of this set?

3 Count the set of letters in the word "number." What is the cardinal number of this set? What reference set was used in counting this set?

4 Count the set of letters in the word "problem." What is the cardinal number of this set? What reference set was used in counting this set?

5 What is the cardinal number of each of the following sets?

   a) The set of letters in the alphabet.

   b) The set of days in a week.

   c) The set of states in the United States with a population of more than 50 million.

   d) $A = \{1, \{2, 3, 4\}, 5\}$.

6 What is the cardinal number of the empty set $\varnothing$? What is the cardinal number of the set $\{\varnothing\}$?

7 Let S be the set of states of the United States. What is $n(S)$? If we order S according to area, with the largest first, what is the ordinal number of Alaska? of Texas? Give another way to order S.

8 Suppose sets A and B have cardinal numbers 8 and 15, respectively. What can be said about the cardinal number of $A \cup B$? What about the cardinal number of $A \cap B$?

9 Let $A = \{a, b, c\}$ and $B = \{\#, *\}$. What is the cardinal number of $A \times B$? How does this compare with $n(A) \times n(B)$?

10 Consider the ordered set $A = (a, c, m, n, t)$. What is $n(A)$? What is the ordinal number of m?

11 Classify each of the following numbers as cardinal or ordinal.

a) We won our 4th game by a margin of 6 points.

b) There are 4 girls and 2 boys sitting in the 7th row.

c) October has 31 days and it is the 10th month of the year.

d) Jim is the 5th child in a family of 7 boys and 4 girls.

e) It was a 12-page assignment ending on page 147.

f) Channel 7 showed 3 comedies 4 days in a row.

4.2 ADDITION OF NATURAL NUMBERS

We will continue the development of the natural number system by considering operations on the set of natural numbers. Surely the reader can add, subtract, multiply, and divide natural numbers, but the ability to do so has most likely come from memorization of certain arithmetic facts. In this book we will be more concerned with how these facts are obtained than with the facts themselves. We might begin this section by asking ourselves two questions:

1 What is addition of natural numbers?

2 How are the basic facts about addition (i.e., the addition table) derived?

The operation of addition is simply a counting process. To add the numbers 3 and 5, we are in fact counting the union of two disjoint sets, one with three elements and one with five elements. In view of Section 4.1, it should be clear that this union can be placed in one-to-one correspondence with the set $\{0, 1, 2, 3, 4, 5, 6, 7\}$ and, therefore, it is a set with 8 elements. On the basis of this observation, we say that addition of the number 3 and the number 5 yields the number 8. The number 8, or any result of an addition, is called the *sum*, whereas the numbers being added, 3 and 5, are called *addends*. Hence the sum of two natural numbers a and b is the cardinal number of the union of two disjoint sets A and B, where $n(A) = a$ and $n(B) = b$. If the sum of two numbers a and b is the number c, we write $a + b = c$. The equals sign, "$=$," simply means that $a + b$ and c are two different symbols for the same number. The properties of equality will be discussed in Section 4.5.

Example 1 Add the natural numbers 4 and 7.

Solution Let

$$A = \{a, b, c, d\} \quad \text{and} \quad B = \{\#, \$, \%, \&, !, (,)\}.$$

Then $n(A) = 4$, $n(B) = 7$, and A and B are disjoint. The set

$$A \cup B = \{a, b, c, d, \#, \$, \%, \&, !, (,)\}$$

has cardinal number 11 since it can be placed in one-to-one correspondence with the set

$$\{0, 1, 2, 3, 4, 5, 6, 7, 8, 9, 10\}.$$

Hence we say that the sum of 4 and 7 is 11, and we write $4 + 7 = 11$.

Example 2 Bill has a bag containing 2 apples, and Jane has a bag containing 4 apples. How many apples do Bill and Jane have together?

Solution One might be concerned with the fact that both of the sets in this example have the same kind of elements. However, these sets are disjoint, since no apple is common to both sets. At this point we remark that in the solution to this problem, we are adding numbers and not apples. The union of the two above sets would have cardinal number 6. Thus, $2 + 4 = 6$. Therefore, Bill and Jane together have 6 apples.

These two examples suggest that if we memorize certain facts about addition, we will be able to solve similar problems in the future.

A *binary operation* on a set S is a rule that associates with each pair of elements in S a uniquely determined element. As we have defined it, addition on the set of natural numbers is a binary operation because it associates with each pair of natural numbers a unique natural number. Since the sum of two natural numbers is also a natural number, we say that the set of natural numbers is *closed* under the operation of addition and thus we state our first property for addition of natural numbers.

Property A1 The set of natural numbers is closed under addition.

We might remark before proceeding that we can prove that the set of even natural numbers is also closed under addition; i.e., the sum of any two even natural numbers is an even natural number. However, the set of odd natural numbers is not closed under addition because 3 and 5 are odd, but $3 + 5 = 8$, which is even.

Since addition is a binary operation by our definition, how can we find the sum of more than two numbers? Suppose we wish to find the sum $3 + 2 + 6$. If we consider this as a counting problem, we could first count the union of two disjoint sets having cardinal numbers 3 and 2, respectively. The cardinal number of the union of these sets is 5, and to this number we want to add 6. We next consider the union of two disjoint sets having cardinal numbers 5 and 6, respectively. The cardinal number of this union is easily seen to be 11. We can now summarize the remarks of this paragraph by stating that

$$3 + 2 + 6 = (3 + 2) + 6 = 11.$$

THE NATURAL NUMBERS AND INTEGERS

The parentheses, or grouping symbols, are used here to indicate that we first added 3 and 2 and then added 6 to this sum.

We could also solve this problem by first adding 2 and 6 to get the sum 8. If this sum is added to 3, we again get 11 for the sum $3 + 2 + 6$. In this case we have

$$3 + 2 + 6 = 3 + (2 + 6) = 11.$$

We now conclude that

$$(3 + 2) + 6 = 3 + (2 + 6).$$

Thus we can group the numbers in either of these two ways. These numbers must be grouped in some fashion, since we can add only two numbers at a time. Note that it is important to know that the set of natural numbers is closed under addition. In order to carry out the second addition in both of these cases, we must know that the first addition yields a natural number. The property observed in the preceding example is called the *associative property of addition*.

Property A2 Addition on the set of natural numbers is associative. That is, if a, b, and c are natural numbers, then

$$(a + b) + c = a + (b + c).$$

Example 3   Verify: $(3 + 5) + 7 = 3 + (5 + 7)$.
Solution

$$(3 + 5) + 7 = 8 + 7 = 15,$$
$$3 + (5 + 7) = 3 + 12 = 15.$$

Example 4   Verify: $[(2 + 1) + 3] + 5 = 2 + [1 + (3 + 5)]$.
Solution

$$[(2 + 1) + 3] + 5 = (3 + 3) + 5 = 6 + 5 = 11,$$
$$2 + [1 + (3 + 5)] = 2 + (1 + 8) = 2 + 9 = 11.$$

Ask any first grader and he will verify that $2 + 3$ and $3 + 2$ both have the value 5. This suggests that the order in which these numbers are added is not important. It should be observed at this point that there is a difference between $2 + 3$ and $3 + 2$, but the difference is not the sum of the two numbers. The expression $2 + 3$ means to add 3 to 2, whereas the expression $3 + 2$ means to add 2 to 3. If we add 2 and 3, in either order, it amounts to counting the union of two disjoint sets with 2 and 3 elements, and the sum is 5. Therefore, $2 + 3 = 3 + 2$. This property is called the *commutative property of addition*.

Property A3 Addition on the set of natural numbers is commutative. That is, if a and b are natural numbers, then $a + b = b + a$.

There is one more property we need to state for addition on the set of natural numbers. This property is called the *cancellation property for addition*.

Property A4 If $a + c = b + c$ for natural numbers a, b, and c, then $a = b$.

At this time we wish to take note of a very important property of the natural number 0. If n is any natural number, observe that $0 + n = n + 0 = n$. The number 0 is called an *identity element*. More specifically, it is called an *additive identity* for the set of natural numbers, since it is an identity for the operation of addition. We remark that no other natural number has this property.

As we study these properties, the reader is probably inclined to say, "I know all these things are true. Why do I have to study them?" or "I've been doing that all my life." Because the nature of this discussion is quite basic, we will naturally mention some concepts the reader has studied before. In Chapter 8 we will study several examples of operations on sets for which some of these familiar properties do not hold.

Problems

1 Use the counting process to find the following sums.
   a) $2 + 3$ b) $4 + 6$ c) $5 + 7 + 2$

2 In finding the sum $2 + 3$ we count the union of two disjoint sets, one having cardinal number 2 and the other having cardinal number 3. Show by example that we will not get the correct answer if the two sets are not disjoint.

3 If a and b denote natural numbers, what is the difference in meaning between the expressions $a + b$ and $b + a$? Does $a + b = b + a$? Why?

4 Verify the following:
   a) $1 + (2 + 3) = (1 + 2) + 3$
   b) $(5 + 7) + 2 = 5 + (7 + 2)$
   c) $6 + (1 + 3) = (6 + 1) + 3$
   d) $(10 + 21) + 35 = 10 + (21 + 35)$
   e) $7 + [4 + (3 + 1)] = [(7 + 4) + 3] + 1$

5 Verify the following:
   a) $6 + 7 = 7 + 6$ b) $13 + 3 = 3 + 13$
   c) $(6 + 3) + (7 + 1) = (7 + 1) + (6 + 3)$
   d) $17 + (5 + 3) = (5 + 3) + 17$

6 Which property of addition is used in each of the following statements?
Each symbol represents a natural number.

a) $3 + 5 = 5 + 3$

b) If $x + z = y + z$, then $x = y$.

c) $(2 + 3) + 8 = 2 + (3 + 8)$

d) $(a + b) + (c + d) = a + [b + (c + d)]$

e) $(a + b) + c = (b + a) + c$

f) $[(5 + 6) + 7] + 8 = (5 + 6) + (7 + 8)$

7 Which of the following is associative?

a) (Iced tea + lemon) + sugar

b) (Putting on socks + putting on shoes) + putting on a tie

c) $(100 \div 10) \div 5$

8 Which of the following is commutative?

a) Putting on your shoes and socks

b) Starting the engine and driving a car

c) Putting sugar and lemon in tea

9 Is the set $S = \{0, 1\}$ closed under the operation of addition? Justify
your answer.

10 Use the properties of addition to prove that

$$a + b + c = a + c + b$$

for all natural numbers a, b, and c.

11 Use the properties of addition to prove

$$[(a + b) + c] + d = a + [b + (c + d)]$$

for all natural numbers a, b, c, and d.

12 Verify the equality expressed in Problem 11 for $a = 2$, $b = 4$, $c = 3$,
and $d = 8$.

4.3 MULTIPLICATION OF NATURAL NUMBERS

Another operation with which the reader is familiar is that of multiplication.
To introduce a procedure for multiplying two natural numbers, suppose we
have 3 sacks with 4 apples in each sack. The total number of apples in these
3 sacks could be interpreted as the result of multiplying 4 by 3. One can find
the total number of apples by evaluating the sum $4 + 4 + 4$, since we have
3 sets with 4 elements in each set. By performing two additions, we can

easily find that this sum is 12 and, therefore, we accept 12 as the result of multiplying 4 by 3. This simple example suggests that we define multiplication in terms of addition.

If m and n denote natural numbers, then the result of multiplying n by m is the total number of elements in m sets, each having n elements. Thus the answer can be obtained by evaluating the sum, $n + n + \cdots + n$, having m terms. This result is called the *product* of the two numbers m and $n;$ m is called the *multiplier* and n is called the *multiplicand*. The numbers m and n are frequently called *factors* of their product.

If n multiplied by m has product p, then we write $m \times n = p$. Because we might confuse the times sign, "$\times$," with the symbol x in a given problem, we sometimes use the dot notation, or $m \cdot n = p$. Furthermore, using *juxtaposition*, we have $mn = p$. Juxtaposition is often employed when letters are used to represent numbers. The choice of notation for denoting products is usually determined by what is most suitable for a given problem.

We shall find that multiplication on the set of natural numbers has basically the same properties as addition. For example, the product of two natural numbers is a natural number. We now state our first property for multiplication.

Property M1 The set of natural numbers is closed under multiplication.

We must solve the problem of how to find the product of three or more numbers, because like addition, multiplication is a binary operation. For example, how do we evaluate the product $2 \times 3 \times 4$? We have two choices. We can evaluate the product 2×3 to get 6 and then multiply 4 by 6 to get an answer of 24. On the other hand, we can first evaluate the product 3×4 to get 12 and then multiply 12 by 2 to again get the answer of 24. Thus we conclude that the answer to this problem is 24 and summarize these results by writing

$$2 \times 3 \times 4 = (2 \times 3) \times 4 = 2 \times (3 \times 4) = 24.$$

This result suggests our second property for multiplication.

Property M2 Multiplication on the set of natural numbers is associative. That is, if a, b, and c are natural numbers, then

$$(a \times b) \times c = a \times (b \times c).$$

Example 1

a) $(2 \times 3) \times 6 = 2 \times (3 \times 6) = 36;$

b) $(5 \cdot 4) \cdot 3 = 5 \cdot (4 \cdot 3) = 60;$

c) $a(bc) = (ab)c = abc$ for natural numbers, a, b and c.

The next question that arises is, "What about commutativity?" For example, is $3 \times 4 = 4 \times 3$? Referring to the first paragraph of this section, we see that these two expressions, 3×4 and 4×3, represent two different problems. As a sum, the expression 4×3 would be $3 + 3 + 3 + 3$, whereas the expression 3×4 would be $4 + 4 + 4$. The expression 3×4 means that we are to consider 3 sets, each with 4 elements, whereas the expression 4×3 means that we are to consider 4 sets, each with 3 elements. We note that the products are equal, and this suggests that multiplication is commutative.

Property M3 Multiplication on the set of natural numbers is commutative. That is, if a and b are natural numbers, then

$$a \times b = b \times a.$$

Example 2

a) $3 \times 2 = 2 \times 3 = 6$;

b) $6 \cdot 7 = 7 \cdot 6 = 42$;

c) $ab = ba$ for natural numbers a and b.

We also state the cancellation property for the operation of multiplication.

Property M4 If $ac = bc$ for natural numbers a, b, and c with $c \neq 0$, then $a = b$.

At this time we wish to take note that the natural number 1 has the same property with respect to multiplication that the natural number 0 has with respect to addition. If n is any natural number, observe that $1 \times n = n \times 1 = n$. The number 1 is called a *multiplicative identity* for the set of natural numbers since it is an identity for the operation of multiplication. No other natural number has this property.

From our discussion of multiplication we see that for any natural number n, $n \cdot 0$ is the sum $0 + 0 + 0 + \cdots + 0$, having n terms. Since 0 is the additive identity, it follows that $n \cdot 0 = 0$. Furthermore, multiplication on the set of natural numbers is commutative, and thus $n \cdot 0 = 0 \cdot n = 0$ for every natural number n.

There is a second method frequently used to find the answer to a multiplication problem. Suppose we wish to multiply 3 times 2. Let A and B be sets such that A has cardinal number 3 and B has cardinal number 2. Then, $A \times B$ has cardinal number 6. This suggests that we could define the product of two natural numbers a and b to be the cardinal number of the Cartesian product of two sets A and B, where A has cardinal number a, and B has cardinal number b.

Example 3 Find the product 3×4.

Solution Let $A = \{a, b, c\}$ and $B = \{\#, \$, \%, @\}$.

Clearly, A has cardinal number 3 and B cardinal number 4. Further,

$A \times B = \{(a, \#), (a, \$), (a, \%), (a, @), (b, \#), (b, \$), (b, \%), (b, @),$
$$(c, \#), (c, \$), (c, \%), (c, @)\}$$

and $A \times B$ has cardinal number 12. Thus $3 \times 4 = 12$.

Problems

1 Use addition to find the following products.

a) 3×2 b) 5×6 c) 2×4

d) 3×7 e) 1×6 f) 4×0

2 If a and b denote natural numbers, what is the difference between the expressions ab and ba? Does $ab = ba$? Why?

3 Verify the following:

a) $1 \times (2 \times 3) = (1 \times 2) \times 3$

b) $(5 \times 7) \times 2 = 5 \times (7 \times 2)$

c) $6 \times (1 \times 3) = (6 \times 1) \times 3$

d) $(10 \times 21) \times 35 = 10 \times (21 \times 35)$

e) $7 \times [4 \times (3 \times 1)] = [(7 \times 4) \times 3] \times 1$

4 Verify the following:

a) $6 \times 7 = 7 \times 6$ b) $13 \times 3 = 3 \times 13$

c) $(6 \times 3) \times (7 \times 1) = (7 \times 1) \times (6 \times 3)$

d) $17 \times (5 \times 3) = (5 \times 3) \times 17$

5 Which property of multiplication is used in each of the following statements? Each symbol represents a natural number.

a) $2 \cdot (3 \cdot 5) = (2 \cdot 3) \cdot 5$ b) $6 \cdot 14 = 14 \cdot 6$

c) $2 \times 5 \times 3 \times 6 \times 4 = (2 \times 5) \times (3 \times 6) \times 4$

d) $[a \times (b \times c)] \times d = d \times [a \times (b \times c)]$

e) $[a \times (b \times c)] \times d = a \times [(b \times c) \times d]$

6 Is the set $\{0, 1\}$ closed under the operation of multiplication? Justify your answer.

7 Find the product 5×3 by taking the Cartesian product of two sets, one set having 5 elements and the other having 3 elements. Must the two sets be disjoint?

8 If $4x = 4y$, prove that $x = y$. Justify each step by quoting a property of multiplication of natural numbers.

9   Use the properties of multiplication to prove

$$a \times b \times c = a \times c \times b.$$

10 Use the properties of multiplication to prove

$$[(a \times b) \times c] \times d = a \times [b \times (c \times d)].$$

11 Verify the equality expressed in Problem 10 for $a = 2$, $b = 4$, $c = 3$, and $d = 8$.

12 Use the properties of multiplication to prove

$$a \times b \times c = c \times b \times a.$$

4.4 THE DISTRIBUTIVE PROPERTY

Referring to the properties in Sections 4.2 and 4.3, we note that each property pertains to only one operation, addition or multiplication. When a set has two operations defined on it, these operations are sometimes related by a property called the *distributive property*. In Section 2.4 we observed that the operations $\cup$ and $\cap$ on sets were related by the equation

$$A \cup (B \cap C) = (A \cup B) \cap (A \cup C)$$

for all sets A, B, and C. At the time we remarked that the operation $\cup$ distributes over the operation $\cap$. One can also establish that $\cap$ distributes over $\cup$, or that

$$A \cap (B \cup C) = (A \cap B) \cup (A \cap C)$$

for all sets A, B, and C. We now state a similar property relating multiplication and addition on the set of natural numbers. The reader has used this property many times in doing ordinary arithmetic.

Property D In the set of natural numbers, multiplication distributes over addition. That is, if a, b, and c are natural numbers, then

$$a \times (b + c) = (a \times b) + (a \times c).$$

Example 1

$$2 \times (3 + 4) = 2 \times 7 = 14,$$
$$(2 \times 3) + (2 \times 4) = 6 + 8 = 14.$$

Therefore,

$$2 \times (3 + 4) = (2 \times 3) + (2 \times 4).$$

Example 2 Evaluate $5 \times [6 + (3 + 1)]$.

Solution

$$5 \times [6 + (3 + 1)] = (5 \times 6) + 5 \times (3 + 1)$$
$$= 30 + [(5 \times 3) + (5 \times 1)]$$
$$= 30 + (15 + 5)$$
$$= 30 + 20$$
$$= 50.$$

When the distributive property is stated as in property D, it is sometimes called the *left distributive property*. We could have chosen to state the *right distributive property*. That is, we could have stated that

$$(b + c) \times a = (b \times a) + (c \times a)$$

for all natural numbers a, b, and c. Since multiplication is commutative, we can prove either of these properties assuming the other. Therefore, we prove the right distributive property as a theorem.

Theorem 4.1 If a, b, and c are natural numbers, then

$$(b + c) \times a = (b \times a) + (c \times a).$$

Proof

$(b + c) \times a = a \times (b + c)$	Commutative property of multiplication
$a \times (b + c) = (a \times b) + (a \times c)$	Distributive property
$(a \times b) + (a \times c) = (b \times a) + (c \times a)$	Commutative property of multiplication

Therefore, $(b + c) \times a = (b \times a) + (c \times a)$.

Example 3

$$(4 + 7) \times 5 = 11 \times 5 = 55,$$
$$(4 \times 5) + (7 \times 5) = 20 + 35 = 55.$$

Therefore, $(4 + 7) \times 5 = (4 \times 5) + (7 \times 5)$.

We observe that addition does not distribute over multiplication by considering the following example.

Example 4 If addition distributes over multiplication, then

$$a + (b \times c) = (a + b) \times (a + c)$$

for all natural numbers a, b, and c. However, if $a = 6$, $b = 3$, and $c = 2$, then

$$6 + (3 \times 2) = 6 + 6 = 12$$

and

$$(6 + 3) \times (6 + 2) = 9 \times 8 = 72.$$

Thus

$$6 + (3 \times 2) \neq (6 + 3) \times (6 + 2),$$

and we have exhibited a counterexample to prove that addition does *not* distribute over multiplication.

The distributive property can be a useful aid in mental arithmetic. Consider the problem of multiplying 23 by 9. If we express 23 as $20 + 3$ and use the distributive property, we have

$$9 \times 23 = 9 \times (20 + 3) = (9 \times 20) + (9 \times 3).$$

By using the distributive property, we have reduced our problem to one of finding the sum of two familiar products. These two products are 180 and 27, and their sum is 207. Thus $9 \times 23 = 207$.

Example 5 Use the distributive property to find the following products.

a) 7×62,   b) 13×22,   c) 8×113.

Solution

a) $7 \times 62 = 7 \times (60 + 2)$
$= (7 \times 60) + (7 \times 2)$
$= 420 + 14$
$= 434.$

b) $13 \times 22 = 13 \times (20 + 2)$
$= (13 \times 20) + (13 \times 2)$
$= 260 + 26$
$= 286.$

c) $8 \times 113 = 8 \times (110 + 3)$
$= (8 \times 110) + (8 \times 3)$
$= 8 \times (100 + 10) + (8 \times 3)$
$= (8 \times 100) + (8 \times 10) + (8 \times 3)$
$= 800 + 80 + 24$
$= 904.$

Problems

1 Verify the following:
  a) $3 \cdot (2 + 5) = 3 \cdot 2 + 3 \cdot 5$
  b) $7 \cdot (6 + 3) = 7 \cdot 6 + 7 \cdot 3$
  c) $4 \cdot (3 + 7) = 4 \cdot 3 + 4 \cdot 7$

2 Use the distributive property to rewrite the following numbers. Each symbol denotes a natural number.

a) $3(x + y)$ b) $5x + 10y$ c) $10^2(10^0 + 10^1)$

d) $xy + x^2z$ e) $3 \cdot 10^3 + 4 \cdot 10^3$ f) $5x + xy$

3 Since $6 + 16 \cdot 9 = 6 \cdot 16 + 6 \cdot 9 = 150$, is it true that $a + b \cdot c = ab + ac$ for all natural numbers a, b, and c? Explain.

4 Find another set of values for a, b, and c which will satisfy the equation in Problem 3.

5 Show how one could use the distributive law to find the following products mentally.

a) $5 \cdot 35$ b) $7 \cdot 42$

c) $15 \cdot 25$ d) $4 \cdot 136$

6 Find a counterexample different from the one in Example 4 to prove that addition does not distribute over multiplication.

7 The fact that addition does not distribute over multiplication does not mean that there are no natural numbers a, b, and c such that

$$a + (b \times c) = (a + b) \times (a + c).$$

Find three such numbers.

8 Prove that $(b + c)a = ac + ab$ for all natural numbers a, b, and c.

9 Prove that $a(b + c + d) = ab + ac + ad$ for all natural numbers a, b, c, and d.

10 Prove that $(a + b)(c + d) = ac + bc + ad + bd$ for all natural numbers a, b, c, and d.

4.5 THE EQUALITY RELATION

We have used the equal sign, $=$, to denote that two symbols represent the same number. In general the equal sign can be read, "is the same as." For example, we write $3 + 5 = 8$ to mean "$3 + 5$ is the same as 8." Rather than dwell on the basic idea of equality, we will point out specifically the properties for the relation of equality on a set S.

Property E1 For every element a in S,

$$a = a. \quad \text{(The \textit{reflexive property})}$$

Property E2 For all elements a and b in S,

$$\text{if } a = b, \text{ then } b = a. \quad \text{(The \textit{symmetric property})}$$

Property E3 For all elements *a*, *b*, and *c* in *S*,

$$\text{if } a = b \text{ and } b = c, \text{ then } a = c. \qquad \text{(The } \textit{transitive property}\text{)}$$

Any relation on a set *S* that has the reflexive, symmetric, and transitive properties is called an *equivalence relation* on *S*. Hence, the relation of equality is an equivalence relation on any set *S*. Other examples of equivalence relations follow.

Example 1 Consider a set *T* of triangles and the relation of similarity on this set, denoted by the symbol "∼." Thus, if $t \in T$ and $s \in T$, then $t \sim s$ means "*t* is similar to *s*." Now observe that any triangle $t \in T$ is similar to itself, and thus $t \sim t$ for every *t* in *T*. Likewise, if *t* and *s* are two triangles in *T* such that *t* is similar to *s*, then *s* is similar to *t*. That is, if $t \sim s$, then $s \sim t$. Also, if *r*, *s*, and *t* are triangles in *T* with the relationship that *r* is similar to *s* and *s* is similar to *t*, then *r* is similar to *t*. This can be summarized by writing:

$$\text{If } r \sim s \text{ and } s \sim t, \text{ then } r \sim t.$$

Therefore, the similarity relation on the set of triangles is an equivalence relation, since it has the reflexive, symmetric, and transitive properties.

Example 2 Consider the following relation defined on the set of students at a given college. Student *A* is related to student *B* if *A* lives in the same dormitory as *B*. If *A* lives in the same dormitory as *B*, we will write *A r B*. It is clear that *A r A*, since every person lives in the same dormitory with himself. If *A* lives in the same dormitory as *B*, then *B* lives in the same dormitory as *A*. Thus, if *A r B*, then *B r A*. If *A* lives in the same dormitory as *B*, and *B* lives in the same dormitory as *C*, then certainly *A* lives in the same dormitory as *C*. Thus, if *A r B* and *B r C*, then *A r C*. Therefore, the relation is an equivalence relation.

Before leaving the discussion of an equivalence relation, we will give an example of a relation that is not an equivalence relation. Let us consider student *A* to be related to student *B* if *A* is taking a course with *B*. It can be verified that this relation is reflexive and symmetric, but not transitive. Hence, the relation is not an equivalence relation.

We now state two other properties of equality.

Property E4 *Addition Property.* If $a = b$ and $c = d$, then $a + c = b + d$.

Property E5 *Multiplication Property.* If $a = b$ and $c = d$, then $a \times c = b \times d$.

Finally, we shall state that any quantity may be substituted in any expression for an equal quantity.

A statement that two expressions are equal is called an *equation*. The properties of the equality relation are used extensively in the discussion of equations. An equation which is true for all permissible values of the variables involved (that is, all values for which the equation is defined) is called an *identity*. As an example, the equation $2x = x + x$ is an identity because it is true for all values of x. An equation which is true for some but not all permissible values of the variables involved in called a *conditional equation*. Thus, the equation $2x = 10$ is a conditional equation since it is true only if x has the value 5. Of these two types of equations, we are more often concerned with conditional equations and in finding values for the variables which will make such an equation true. Any set of values for which an equation is true is called a *solution* of the equation, and the set of all solutions is called the *solution set* of the equation. Any element of the solution set is said to *satisfy* the equation. Finding the solution set is called *solving* the equation.

Problems

1 If $6 = 3x$, then $3x = 6$. Which property of the equality relation has been used to rearrange this equation?

2 If

$$x + y = z \quad \text{and} \quad z = u + v,$$

then

$$x + y = u + v.$$

Which property of the equality relation is used to reach this conclusion?

3 In proving Theorem 4.1, which property for equality was used to reach the desired conclusion?

4 In writing $a = b$, must a and b always represent numbers? Explain.

5 Student A is related to student B if A is taking a course with B. This relation is reflexive and symmetric but not transitive. Show by example that this relation is not transitive.

6 Let person A be related to person B if A is an ancestor of B. Is this relation reflexive? symmetric? transitive? an equivalence relation?

7 Let line n be related to line m if n is parallel to m. Show that this relation is an equivalence relation.

8 Find an example of a relation that is reflexive and transitive but not symmetric.

9 Find an example of a relation that is not reflexive, symmetric, or transitive.

10 Tell whether each of the following is an identity or a conditional equation.

a) $5x = x + 4$

b) $x + 2 = 2x + 2 - x$

c) $6x + 7 = x + 4x + 7 + x$

d) $\frac{1}{2}x - 3 = 12$.

4.6 THE ORDER RELATION

In Section 4.1 we mentioned that primitive man must have had some concept of "less than" and "more than." We now define these relations on the set of natural numbers.

Definition 4.1 Let a and b denote natural numbers. If there exists a nonzero natural number n such that $a + n = b$, then we say that a is less than b and write

$$a < b.$$

If a is not less than b, we write

$$a \not< b.$$

The natural number a is greater than the natural number b if b is less than a. If a is greater than b, we write

$$a > b.$$

Example 1 $2 < 6$ because we can find a nonzero natural number n, namely 4, such that $2 + n = 6$.

$5 < 11$ because $5 + 6 = 11$.

$6 > 3$ because $3 < 6$.

$7 \not< 4$ because we cannot find a natural number n such that $7 + n = 4$.

Intuitively, we see that the "less than" relation is a way of comparing the "sizes" of two natural numbers. To compare any two natural numbers by "size" we need the following property.

Property O *The Trichotomy Law.* If m and n are any two natural numbers, then exactly one of the following must be true:

$$1)\ m = n,$$
$$2)\ m < n,$$
$$3)\ m > n.$$

Let us consider in more detail the relation "less than" defined on the set of natural numbers. We readily observe that no natural number a has the property that $a < a$. Hence, the relation "$<$" is not reflexive. If a and b are natural numbers such that $a < b$, then certainly $b \not< a$, since this would contradict the Trichotomy Law. The following theorem shows that the relation "$<$" has the transitive property.

Theorem 4.2 Let a, b, and c denote natural numbers. If $a < b$ and $b < c$, then $a < c$.

Proof By hypothesis, $a < b$ and $b < c$. Hence, there exist nonzero natural numbers k and p such that

$$a + k = b \quad \text{and} \quad b + p = c.$$

If we add p to both sides of the first equation, then

$$(a + k) + p = b + p.$$

However, $b + p = c$. Consequently,

$$(a + k) + p = a + (k + p) = c.$$

Because $k + p$ is a nonzero natural number, it follows by definition that $a < c$.

The relation "$<$" is obviously not an equivalence relation as it has only one of the properties required of an equivalence relation.

One can also prove the following theorems concerning the relation "$<$."

Theorem 4.3 Let a and b denote natural numbers. Then for every natural number c, $a < b$ if and only if $a + c < b + c$.

Theorem 4.4 Let a and b denote natural numbers. Then for every nonzero natural number c, $a < b$ if and only if $ac < bc$.

Theorem 4.5 Let a, b, c, and d denote natural numbers. If $a < b$ and $c < d$, then

1) $a + c < b + d$,

2) $ac < bd$.

We frequently write $a \leqq b$. This is read "a is less than or equal to b" and means $a < b$ or $a = b$. For example, if x is a natural number and $x \leqq 2$, then x is 0, 1, or 2. On many occasions we shall also write $a < x < b$, which means $a < x$ and $x < b$. For example, if x is a natural number and $3 < x < 7$, then x is 4, 5, or 6.

Problems

1 Verify each of the following by using the definition of the appropriate relation.

a) $6 < 15$ b) $1 < 7$ c) $8 > 5$ d) $4 \not< 3$

e) $1 \leqq 5$ f) $10 > 8$ g) $6 < 7$ h) $0 < 5$

THE NATURAL NUMBERS AND INTEGERS

2 In each of the following find all values of x in the set of natural numbers which will satisfy the relationship.

a) $x + 3 < 5$ b) $x > 10$ c) $2x < 5$

d) $x > 3$ and $x < 9$ e) $2x + 3 \leqq 9$ f) $4 < 2x \leqq 12$

3 Let x denote a natural number and define $A = \{x \mid 3 < x\}$ and $B = \{x \mid x < 12\}$. List the elements of A and B. Find $A \cap B$ and $A \cup B$.

4 Let x denote a natural number and define $A = \{x \mid 5 \leqq x \leqq 9\}$ and $B = \{x \mid 7 < x < 13\}$. List the elements of A and B. Find $A \cap B$ and $A \cup B$.

5 If $8 < 12$ and x denotes a natural number, how is $8 + x$ related to $12 + x$?

6 If $8 < 12$ and x denotes a natural number with $x \neq 0$, how is $8x$ related to $12x$? Can you draw this same conclusion if $x = 0$? Explain.

7 Does the relation ">" defined on the set of natural numbers have the reflexive property? the symmetric property? the transitive property? Is the relation ">" an equivalence relation?

8 Prove Theorem 4.3.

9 Prove Theorem 4.4. [*Hint:* Use the Trichotomy Law.]

10 Prove Theorem 4.5, using Theorems 4.2, 4.3, and 4.4.

4.7 A SUMMARY OF THE PROPERTIES OF THE NATURAL NUMBERS

We are now prepared to compile a list of properties of the natural numbers. The reader should familiarize himself with this list since we shall frequently refer to the properties listed.

Property A1 The set of natural numbers is closed under addition.

Property A2 Addition on the set of natural numbers is associative. That is, if a, b, and c are natural numbers, then $(a + b) + c = a + (b + c)$.

Property A3 Addition on the set of natural numbers is commutative. That is, if a and b are natural numbers, then $a + b = b + a$.

Property A4 If $a + c = b + c$ for natural numbers a, b, and c, then $a = b$.

Property M1 The set of natural numbers is closed under multiplication.

Property M2 Multiplication on the set of natural numbers is associative. That is, if a, b, and c are natural numbers, then $(a \times b) \times c = a \times (b \times c)$.

Property M3 Multiplication on the set of natural numbers is commutative. That is, if a and b are natural numbers, then $a \times b = b \times a$.

Property M4 If $ac = bc$ for natural numbers a, b, and c with $c \neq 0$, then $a = b$.

Property D In the set of natural numbers, multiplication distributes over addition. That is, if a, b, and c are natural numbers, then $a \times (b + c) = (a \times b) + (a \times c)$.

Property O *The Trichotomy Law.* If m and n are any two natural numbers, then exactly one of the following must be true:

$$1) \ m = n,$$
$$2) \ m < n,$$
$$3) \ m > n.$$

Theorem 4.2 Let a, b, and c denote natural numbers. If $a < b$ and $b < c$, then $a < c$.

Theorem 4.3 Let a and b denote natural numbers. Then for every natural number c, $a < b$ if and only if $a + c < b + c$.

Theorem 4.4 Let a and b denote natural numbers. Then for every nonzero natural number c, $a < b$ if and only if $ac < bc$.

Theorem 4.5 Let a, b, c, and d denote natural numbers. If $a < b$ and $c < d$, then

$$1) \ a + c < b + d,$$
$$2) \ ac < bd.$$

We complete our list of properties with the remark that 0 is the additive identity and 1 is the multiplicative identity for the set of natural numbers. That is, if n is any natural number, then

$$0 + n = n + 0 = n,$$

and

$$1 \cdot n = n \cdot 1 = n.$$

The following examples will illustrate how these properties are used to prove theorems concerning the natural numbers.

Example 1 Prove that $a(b + c + d) = ab + ac + ad$ for all natural numbers $a, b, c,$ and d.

Proof

$$a(b + c + d) = a[b + (c + d)] \qquad \text{Associative property of addition}$$
$$= ab + a(c + d) \qquad \text{Distributive property}$$
$$= ab + (ac + ad) \qquad \text{Distributive property}$$
$$= ab + ac + ad \qquad \text{Associative property of addition}$$

Example 2 Prove that $x + y + z = z + y + x$ for all natural numbers x, y, and z.

Proof

$$x + y + z = x + (y + z) \qquad \text{Associative property of addition}$$
$$= x + (z + y) \qquad \text{Commutative property of addition}$$
$$= (z + y) + x \qquad \text{Commutative property of addition}$$
$$= z + y + x \qquad \text{Associative property of addition}$$

Example 3 Prove that $(a + b)(c + d) = ac + bc + ad + bd$ for all natural numbers a, b, c, and d.

Proof

$$(a + b)(c + d) = (a + b)c + (a + b)d \qquad \text{Distributive property}$$
$$= (ac + bc) + (ad + bd) \qquad \text{Theorem 4.1}$$
$$= ac + bc + ad + bd \qquad \text{Associative property of addition}$$

Problems

1 In the following, each symbol represents a natural number. State the property that justifies each part.

a) $3 + 5 = 5 + 3$

b) $(x + 6) + y = x + (6 + y)$

c) $6(x + 3) = 6 \cdot x + 6 \cdot 3$

d) $x \cdot y + a = y \cdot x + a$

e) $(x + 6)(y + 7) = (y + 7)(x + 6)$

f) $7 + 3 \cdot 5 = 3 \cdot 5 + 7$

g) $a + c$ is a natural number

h) $(x + 3)(x + 5) = (3 + x)(x + 5)$

i) If $(ab)c = (de)c$ and $c \neq 0$, then $ab = de$.

j) $xyz = (xy)z$

2 If a, b, and c denote natural numbers, then

$$[(a + b) + c] = [c + (a + b)].$$

To justify this statement we should quote two properties of addition. One property is the commutative property. What is the other?

3 In the following, each symbol represents a natural number. Prove each part, justifying every step of the proof.

a) $(x + y) + z = x + (z + y)$

b) $m \cdot (n \cdot p) = (m \cdot p) \cdot n$

c) $(a + b) + (c + d) = (a + d) + (c + b)$

d) $(a + b)^2 = a^2 + 2ab + b^2$

4 Let a and b denote natural numbers. Prove that if $ab = 0$ and $b \neq 0$, then $a = 0$. [*Hint:* Write $0 = 0b$.]

4.8 THE NATURAL NUMBERS AND SUBTRACTION

Having discussed the properties of the natural numbers relative to the operations of addition and multiplication, we turn to the operation of subtraction on the set of natural numbers.

Definition 4.2 Let a and b denote natural numbers. $a - b = x$ if and only if $a = b + x$. The expression "$a - b$" can be read, "a minus b," "a subtract b," or "b subtracted from a." In this expression the number a is called the *minuend,* and the number b is called the *subtrahend.* The number x is called the *difference.*

Example 1 Find $6 - 2$.

Solution $6 - 2 = x$ if and only if $6 = 2 + x$. To satisfy the latter equation we see that x must have the value 4. Hence $6 - 2 = 4$.

Example 2 Find 7 subtract 5.

Solution $7 - 5 = x$ if and only if $7 = 5 + x$. We see that x must have the value 2. Hence $7 - 5 = 2$.

From the above examples, we see that the solution of a subtraction problem is found by solving an equation of the form $a = b + x$. If a and b each represent a natural number, is there always a natural number x such that $a = b + x$? Indeed not! Consider the following example.

Example 3 Find $3 - 7$.

Solution $3 - 7 = x$ if and only if $3 = 7 + x$. Because $7 > 3$, there is no natural number which satisfies the equation $3 = 7 + x$.

From this example it is clear that the set of natural numbers is not closed under subtraction. Likewise, if the universal set is the set of natural numbers, then there are equations of the form $a = b + x$ which do not have a solution relative to this universal set. Clearly, the only cases in which solutions to these equations exist are the cases in which $a \geq b$. It is important that we be able to solve every equation of the form $a = b + x$. Because a solution is not always available in the system of natural numbers, we will develop a system of numbers in which a solution can always be found.

Problems

1 Using the definition of subtraction, find the following:

   a) $12 - 7$ b) $6 - 3$ c) $47 - 22$ d) $15 - 8$

   e) $38 - 15$ f) $8 - 0$ g) $0 - 0$ h) $92 - 17$

2 If subtraction is associative, then $(a - b) - c = a - (b - c)$ for all natural numbers a, b, and c. Evaluate $(15 - 8) - 3$ and $15 - (8 - 3)$. Is subtraction associative? Explain your answer.

3 If subtraction is commutative, then $a - b = b - a$ for all natural numbers a and b. Is subtraction commutative? Explain your answer.

4 Which of the following equations have a solution in the set of natural numbers? Give the solution for those equations which have one.

   a) $5 = 3 + x$ b) $3 = 7 + x$ c) $6 + x = 11$

   d) $6 + x = 2$ e) $27 - 13 = x$ f) $46 - 50 = x$

5 Verify the following:

   a) $6(3 - 1) = 6(3) - 6(1)$ b) $5(7 - 2) = 5(7) - 5(2)$

   c) $8(11 - 6) = 8(11) - 8(6)$

6 Problem 5 suggests that whenever subtraction is possible, multiplication distributes over subtraction in the set of natural numbers. Prove $a(b - c) = ab - ac$ whenever $b \geq c$. [*Hint:* If $b \geq c$, then $b - c = x$ and $b = c + x$, for some natural number x. Now multiply both members of the latter equation by a.]

4.9 INTEGERS

We now turn our attention to the development of a number system which we call the *system of integers*. In this development we will be guided by our experience with the natural numbers and we will often use the properties of the system of natural numbers in our work with the integers. Consequently, it should not be surprising to find that the operations on the set of integers will have all the properties of the corresponding operations on the set of natural numbers. In fact, we will be able to say, at least in a sense, that the set of natural numbers is a subset of the set of integers.

There is no point in developing the system of integers unless we can solve problems in this system which cannot be solved in the system of natural numbers. The development of the integers is motivated by our desire to have a system of numbers in which every equation of the form $a = b + x$, where a and b are in the system, has a solution x in the system. As we saw in the previous section, this is not true in the system of natural numbers. Clearly, $x = a - b$ is a solution of this equation, but our problem is due to the fact that $a - b$ is not always a natural number. This would suggest that we define an integer to be the difference of two natural numbers, and intuitively this is how we shall think of an integer. Furthermore, this intuitive interpretation of an integer will be used to motivate certain definitions in the system of integers. However, for the development of the system of integers it will be convenient to use the ordered pair (a, b) to represent the integer $x = a - b$. An ordered pair is used to represent the difference $a - b$ since it is not always the same as the difference $b - a$.

Definition 4.3 If a and b are natural numbers, the ordered pair (a, b) is called an *integer*.

We shall use the letter I to denote the set of integers. Hence

$$I = \{(a, b) \mid a \text{ and } b \text{ are natural numbers}\}.$$

It is easy to define operations on the set of integers using the notation of Definition 4.3, and this notation is also well suited to proving properties of these operations. However, we shall revert to the familiar notation 0, ± 1, ± 2, ± 3, . . . , for the integers whenever it is convenient. In fact, these familiar symbols will be used exclusively when the development of the system of integers has been completed. As we have already pointed out, the reader can relate these two methods for denoting integers by thinking of the ordered pair (a, b), intuitively, as the difference $a - b$. For instance, one can think of $(3, 8)$, intuitively, as $3 - 8 = -5$. Other examples are:

$(5, 2)$ corresponds to the difference $5 - 2 = 3$.
$(5, 7)$ corresponds to the difference $5 - 7 = -2$.
$(3, 3)$ corresponds to the difference $3 - 3 = 0$.

We also observe that there are many ways of writing the integer $(3, 8)$ using ordered pairs of natural numbers. Some of these are $(4, 9)$, $(10, 15)$, $(19, 24)$, and $(36, 41)$. This integer corresponds, intuitively, to the difference -5. The ordered pairs $(4, 1)$, $(6, 3)$, $(41, 38)$, and $(116, 113)$ all represent the integer which corresponds to the difference 3. The reader can do the same thing for other integers. Since a given integer can be represented in many different ways as an ordered pair of natural numbers, we must have some method for determining whether two integers are equal. Using the difference representation for the integers (a, b) and (c, d), the statement that $(a, b) = (c, d)$ is equivalent to stating that $a - b = c - d$. The equation

$a - b = c - d$ is equivalent to the equation $a + d = b + c$. This suggests the following definition.

Definition 4.4 Two integers (a, b) and (c, d) are equal if and only if $a + d = b + c$.

Example 1

$$(3, 8) = (14, 19) \quad \text{because} \quad 3 + 19 = 8 + 14.$$
$$(8, 8) = (10, 10) \quad \text{because} \quad 8 + 10 = 8 + 10.$$
$$(5, 1) = (6, 2) \quad \text{because} \quad 5 + 2 = 1 + 6.$$
$$(5, 1) = (16, 12) \quad \text{because} \quad 5 + 12 = 1 + 16.$$

In Chapter 1 we mentioned the terms *positive integer* and *negative integer*. The meaning of these terms is given in the following definition.

Definition 4.5 Let (a, b) be an integer with $a \neq b$. If $a > b$, then (a, b) is called a *positive integer.* If $a < b$, then (a, b) is called a *negative integer.*

Example 2

$$(5, 2) \quad \text{is a positive integer because} \quad 5 > 2.$$
$$(2, 7) \quad \text{is a negative integer because} \quad 2 < 7.$$

As the reader knows, it is customary to represent the positive and negative integers by the symbols $+1, +2, +3, \ldots$ and $-1, -2, -3, \ldots$, respectively. If a is any natural number, the integer (a, a) will be represented by the symbol 0. We remark that zero is neither a positive integer nor a negative integer.

In the remaining sections of this chapter, an ordered pair is to be interpreted as an ordered pair of natural numbers.

We said at the beginning of this section that, in a sense, the set of natural numbers would be a subset of the set of integers. Because an integer is an ordered pair of natural numbers, we would not expect the set of natural numbers, as such, to be a subset of the set of integers. However, the following one-to-one correspondence identifies with each natural number a non-negative integer.

0	1	2	3	$\cdots$	n	$\cdots$
$\updownarrow$	$\updownarrow$	$\updownarrow$	$\updownarrow$		$\updownarrow$	
$(0, 0)$	$(1, 0)$	$(2, 0)$	$(3, 0)$	$\cdots$	$(n, 0)$	$\cdots$

We could say a great deal more about this one-to-one correspondence, but the reader can see, intuitively at least, that the set of natural numbers is to be found in some form in the set of integers.

Problems

1 Write each of the following integers using the conventional notation 0, ±1, ±2, ±3, ...

   a) (3, 6)   b) (8, 2)   c) (0, 7)

   d) (21, 28)   e) (5, 5)   f) (16, 3)

   g) (10, 0)   h) (0, 0)   i) (14, 51)

2 Write each of the following integers as ordered pairs of natural numbers in three other ways.

   a) (15, 4)   b) (7, 11)   c) (9, 22)

   d) (3, 3)   e) (6, 0)   f) (69, 87)

   g) (91, 23)   h) (17, 17)   i) (3, 31)

3 In each of the following use the definition of equality of two integers to find the natural number x for which the integer $(x, 12)$ is equal to the given integer.

   a) (1, 8)   b) (5, 2)   c) (7, 7)

   d) (19, 30)   e) (5, 6)   f) (106, 52)

4 Determine whether the following integers are positive integers or negative integers.

   a) (3, 7)   b) (1, 8)   c) (10, 2)

   d) (43, 78)   e) (3, 4)   f) (9, 4)

4.10 ADDITION OF INTEGERS

Having defined the integers, we are now prepared to discuss operations on the set of integers. If we take the intuitive approach and consider the integers (a, b) and (c, d) to be the differences $a - b$ and $c - d$, respectively, then

$$(a, b) + (c, d) = (a - b) + (c - d)$$
$$= (a + c) - (b + d).$$

Intuitively, this last difference corresponds to the integer $(a + c, b + d)$, and this leads to the following definition for addition of integers.

Definition 4.6 Addition of integers is defined by the equation

$$(a, b) + (c, d) = (a + c, b + d).$$

Example 1 Find the sum $(5, 7) + (3, 8)$.

Solution

$$(5, 7) + (3, 8) = (5 + 3, 7 + 8)$$
$$= (8, 15).$$

                                            THE NATURAL NUMBERS AND INTEGERS

We now investigate the properties of the operation of addition on the set of integers. From Definition 4.6, we see that the sum of two integers (ordered pairs of natural numbers) is an ordered pair. Further, we notice that each element of the ordered pair is the sum of two natural numbers. Since the set of natural numbers is closed under addition, each element of the ordered pair is a natural number and the ordered pair is an integer. Therefore, we have proved the following theorem.

Theorem 4.6 The set of integers is closed under addition.

If addition on the set of integers is associative, then we must have $(x + y) + z = x + (y + z)$ for all integers x, y, and z. This is proved in the following theorem.

Theorem 4.7 Addition on the set of integers is associative.

Proof Let x, y, and z be integers. Then there exist natural numbers a, b, c, d, e, and f such that

$$x = (a, b), \qquad y = (c, d), \qquad \text{and} \qquad z = (e, f).$$

It now follows that

$(x + y) + z = [(a, b) + (c, d)] + (e, f)$	Substitution
$= (a + c, b + d) + (e, f)$	Definition of addition for integers
$= ((a + c) + e, (b + d) + f)$	Definition of addition for integers
$= (a + (c + e), b + (d + f))$	Associative property of addition for natural numbers
$= (a, b) + (c + e, d + f)$	Definition of addition for integers
$= (a, b) + [(c, d) + (e, f)]$	Definition of addition for integers
$= x + (y + z)$	Substitution

Therefore, addition on the set of integers is associative.

If addition on the set of integers is commutative, then we must have $x + y = y + x$ for all integers x and y. This property is proved in the following theorem.

Theorem 4.8 Addition on the set of integers is commutative.

Proof Let x and y be integers. Then there exist natural numbers a, b, c, and d such that $x = (a, b)$ and $y = (c, d)$.

$$
\begin{aligned}
x + y &= (a, b) + (c, d) && \text{Substitution} \\
&= (a + c, b + d) && \text{Definition of addition for integers} \\
&= (c + a, d + b) && \text{Commutative property of addition for natural numbers} \\
&= (c, d) + (a, b) && \text{Definition of addition for integers} \\
&= y + x && \text{Substitution}
\end{aligned}
$$

Therefore, addition on the set of integers is commutative.

We now wish to show that the set of integers contains an additive identity. That is, we wish to show there is an integer which has the same property with respect to addition of integers that the natural number 0 has with respect to addition of natural numbers (Section 4.2). If (c, d) is any integer, consider the following:

$$
\begin{aligned}
(0, 0) + (c, d) &= (c, d) + (0, 0) \\
&= (c + 0, d + 0) \\
&= (c, d).
\end{aligned}
$$

We have proved the following theorem.

Theorem 4.9 The integer $(0, 0)$ is an additive identity for the set of integers.

It can be shown that every integer of the form (a, a) is an additive identity for the set of integers. However, it is clear that for every natural number a, $(a, a) = (0, 0)$ because $a + 0 = a + 0$. We choose $(0, 0)$ to represent the additive identity simply because of our previous knowledge and familiarity with the properties of the natural number 0. The symbol 0 will also be used to denote the additive identity for the set of integers. Although we will not do so here, it is possible to prove that the additive identity is unique except for the way it is represented. That is, there is one and only one additive identity.

The integer x is called an *additive inverse* of the integer y if and only if

$$
x + y = y + x = 0.
$$

For example, the additive inverse of $(3, 2)$ is $(2, 3)$ because

$$
(3, 2) + (2, 3) = (2, 3) + (3, 2) = (5, 5) = (0, 0).
$$

We now prove the following theorem.

Theorem 4.10 Every integer has an additive inverse. To be more specific, the additive inverse of (a, b) is (b, a).

Proof

$$(b, a) + (a, b) = (a, b) + (b, a)$$
$$= (a + b, b + a)$$
$$= (a + b, a + b)$$
$$= (0, 0).$$

We state here without proof that the additive inverse of an integer is unique.

Example 2 The additive inverse of $(4, 9)$ is $(9, 4)$ because

$$(9, 4) + (4, 9) = (4, 9) + (9, 4) = (4 + 9, 9 + 4) = (13, 13) = (0, 0).$$

0 is its own inverse under addition because

$$(0, 0) + (0, 0) = (0 + 0, 0 + 0) = (0, 0).$$

If (a, b) is any integer, we will denote the additive inverse of (a, b) by $-(a, b)$. Thus, $-(a, b) = (b, a)$. For example, $-(3, 4) = (4, 3)$ and $-(5, 2) = (2, 5)$. If a single symbol, such as x, is used to represent an integer, then the additive inverse of the integer x will be denoted by $-x$.

We conclude this section with a sketch of the proof of the cancellation property for addition.

Theorem 4.11 If x, y, and z are integers such that $x + z = y + z$, then $x = y$.

Proof If x, y, and z are integers, then there exist natural numbers a, b, c, d, e, and f such that $x = (a, b)$, $y = (c, d)$, and $z = (e, f)$. By hypothesis, we have

$$(a, b) + (e, f) = (c, d) + (e, f).$$

If we add the integer (f, e) to both members of the equation and apply the appropriate properties of addition, we will have the desired result. The reader should supply the details.

Problems

1 Use the definition of addition for integers to find the following sums.

   a) $(4, 2) + (7, 3)$ b) $(5, 2) + (4, 8)$ c) $(6, 11) + (12, 4)$

   d) $(7, 15) + (4, 9)$ e) $(11, 3) + (3, 11)$ f) $(5, 9) + (17, 20)$

2 Use the definition of addition for integers to verify the associative property in each of the following.

   a) $[(3, 4) + (5, 8)] + (11, 7) = (3, 4) + [(5, 8) + (11, 7)]$

   b) $[(13, 11) + (3, 7)] + (12, 8) = (13, 11) + [(3, 7) + (12, 8)]$

   c) $[(6, 12) + (5, 2)] + (23, 15) = (6, 12) + [(5, 2) + (23, 15)]$

3 Use the definition of addition for integers to verify the commutative property in each of the following.

   a) $(5, 3) + (7, 6) = (7, 6) + (5, 3)$

   b) $(9, 12) + (12, 5) = (12, 5) + (9, 12)$

   c) $(0, 4) + (8, 3) = (8, 3) + (0, 4)$

4 Find the additive inverse for each of the following integers.

   a) $(7, 7)$ b) $(15, 11)$ c) $(9, 6)$ d) $(3, 6)$

5 Find a value for x such that $(x, 8) + (4, 7) = (5, 11) + (6, 2)$.

6 The additive inverse of 0 can be denoted -0. Is -0 a negative integer? Explain.

7 $-(a, b)$ denotes the additive inverse of the integer (a, b). Prove that $-(-(a, b)) = (a, b)$.

8 Let x and y denote integers. If $-x$ and $-y$ denote the additive inverses of x and y, respectively, prove that $-(x + y) = -x + (-y)$. [*Hint:* The integer a is an additive inverse of the integer b if $a + b = 0$.]

9 Supply the details for the proof of Theorem 4.11.

10 Prove that the additive identity for the set of integers is unique. [*Hint:* Let 0 and 0′ be two additive identities and use the property of an additive identity to conclude that $0 = 0'$.]

4.11 SUBTRACTION OF INTEGERS

In keeping with the definition of subtraction for natural numbers in Section 4.8, we state the following definition of subtraction for integers.

Definition 4.7 If (a, b) and (c, d) are integers, then

$$(a, b) - (c, d) = (x, y) \quad \text{if and only if} \quad (a, b) = (c, d) + (x, y).$$

Example 1   Find $(8, 3) - (7, 5)$.

Solution

$(8, 3) - (7, 5) = (x, y)$ if and only if

$$(8, 3) = (7, 5) + (x, y)$$
$$= (7 + x, 5 + y).$$

$(8, 3) = (7 + x, 5 + y)$ if and only if

$$8 + (5 + y) = 3 + (7 + x),$$
$$13 + y = 10 + x,$$
$$3 + y = x.$$

If we let $x = 3$ and $y = 0$, we obtain one solution for the equation $3 + y = x$. Thus, $(8, 3) - (7, 5) = (3, 0)$. For every integer (x, y) such that $3 + y = x$, $(8, 3) = (7, 5) = (x, y)$. However, every such integer (x, y) is simply another representation for the integer $(3, 0)$.

Suppose (a, b), (c, d), and (x, y) are integers, such that $(a, b) - (c, d) = (x, y)$. Then

$$(a, b) - (c, d) = (x, y)$$

if and only if

$(a, b) = (c, d) + (x, y)$	Definition of subtraction for integers
$\qquad = (c + x, d + y)$	Definition of addition for integers

Now

$$(a, b) = (c + x, d + y)$$

if and only if

$a + (d + y) = b + (c + x)$	Definition of equality for integers
$(a + d) + y = (b + c) + x$	Associative property of addition for natural numbers
$(a + d, b + c) = (x, y)$	Definition of equality for integers
$(a, b) + (d, c) = (x, y)$	Definition of addition for integers

We have now proved that subtracting (c, d) from (a, b) is equivalent to adding the additive inverse of (c, d) to (a, b). That is, $(a, b) - (c, d) = (a, b) + (d, c)$. For this reason, subtraction is called the inverse operation of addition.

Example 2 Find $(8, 3) - (7, 5)$ by using the additive inverse of $(7, 5)$.

Solution

$$(8, 3) - (7, 5) = (8, 3) + (5, 7)$$
$$= (13, 10).$$

By comparing Example 1 with Example 2, we see that the procedure in Example 2 is much easier. We now use this equivalent method for subtraction to prove that the set of integers is closed under subtraction. In order to subtract any integer (c, d) from an integer (a, b), it is sufficient to know that (c, d) has an additive inverse and the set of integers is closed under addition. Since both of these properties were proved in Section 4.10, we have proved that the set of integers is closed under subtraction.

We now consider the problem of solving equations of the form $a = b + x$ in the system of integers. From the definition of subtraction, $a = b + x$ is equivalent to stating that $x = a - b$. Hence $x = a - b$ is a solution of the equation $a = b + x$; $a - b$ is an integer because the set of integers is closed under subtraction. Consequently, all equations of the form $a = b + x$ have the solution $x = a - b$ in the system of integers.

Example 3 Solve the equation

$$(5, 4) + (x, y) = (2, 3) \qquad \text{for} \qquad (x, y).$$

Solution From the preceding discussion we know that the difference $(2, 3) - (5, 4)$ is a solution of the equation. Hence

$$(x, y) = (2, 3) - (5, 4) = (2, 3) + (4, 5) = (6, 8).$$

Example 4 We now present another method of solving the equation given in the second example of this section. This method will be useful in solving equations of a more complicated nature.

Solution

$$(5, 4) + (x, y) = (2, 3),$$
$$(4, 5) + [(5, 4) + (x, y)] = (4, 5) + (2, 3),$$
$$[(4, 5) + (5, 4)] + (x, y) = (4, 5) + (2, 3),$$
$$0 + (x, y) = (4, 5) + (2, 3),$$
$$(x, y) = (4, 5) + (2, 3),$$
$$(x, y) = (6, 8).$$

By exhibiting counterexamples we now show that subtraction is neither associative nor commutative. As a first example,

$$[(5, 3) - (6, 2)] - (1, 2) = [(5, 3) + (2, 6)] - (1, 2)$$
$$= (7, 9) - (1, 2)$$
$$= (7, 9) + (2, 1)$$
$$= (9, 10)$$

and

$$(5, 3) - [(6, 2) - (1, 2)] = (5, 3) - [(6, 2) + (2, 1)]$$
$$= (5, 3) - (8, 3)$$
$$= (5, 3) + (3, 8)$$
$$= (8, 11).$$

THE NATURAL NUMBERS AND INTEGERS

These two results are obviously not the same, and therefore subtraction is not associative. As a second example,

$$(6, 7) - (8, 10) = (6, 7) + (10, 8) = (16, 15)$$

and

$$(8, 10) - (6, 7) = (8, 10) + (7, 6) = (15, 16).$$

Because these two results are not the same, subtraction is not commutative.

Problems

1 Find the following differences.

a) $(3, 4) - (7, 2)$ b) $(8, 5) - (11, 3)$

c) $(3, 7) - (4, 11)$ d) $(14, 7) - (5, 6)$

e) $(12, 5) - (6, 6)$ f) $(16, 5) - (3, 13)$

2 Using the definition of subtraction for integers, find $(5, 7) - (11, 8)$.

3 The equation $a = b + x$ is equivalent to the equation $b + x = a$. What property of the relation "$=$" can we quote to justify this statement?

4 Justify each step in solving the equation in Example 4.

5 Solve the following equations and check your solution.

a) $(7, 4) + (x, y) = (5, 9)$ b) $(9, 16) + (x, y) = (6, 6)$

c) $(8, 3) + (x, y) = (9, 7)$ d) $(12, 2) + (x, y) = (12, 2)$

e) $(x, y) + (3, 3) = (4, 9)$ f) $(14, 5) + (2, 5) = (x, y)$

6 Even though subtraction on the set of integers is not associative, there exist integers a, b, and c such that $a - (b - c) = (a - b) - c$. Find three such integers.

7 Under what conditions on the integers a and b will $a - b = b - a$?

4.12 MULTIPLICATION OF INTEGERS

We observe that our definitions of integer and addition of integers have preserved all the properties that the natural numbers have with respect to addition. Furthermore, the set of integers is closed under subtraction. Our next question is, "What about multiplication?" If we proceed intuitively and consider the integers (a, b) and (c, d) as the respective differences $a - b$ and $c - d$, then we have

$$(a, b) \cdot (c, d) = (a - b)(c - d)$$
$$= (ac + bd) - (bc + ad).$$

This last difference corresponds intuitively to the integer $(ac + bd, bc + ad)$. This suggests the following definition.

Definition 4.8 If (a, b) and (c, d) are integers, we define multiplication by the equation

$$(a, b) \cdot (c, d) = (ac + bd, bc + ad).$$

Example 1   Find the product $(3, 7) \cdot (5, 2)$.

Solution
$$
\begin{aligned}
(3, 7) \cdot (5, 2) &= (3 \cdot 5 + 7 \cdot 2, 7 \cdot 5 + 3 \cdot 2) \\
&= (15 + 14, 35 + 6) \\
&= (29, 41).
\end{aligned}
$$

Using the familiar notation for integers, the integers $(3, 7)$ and $(5, 2)$ would be written -4 and 3, respectively. The product of -4 and 3 is -12, which agrees with the result in Example 1.

From the definition, we see that the product of two integers is an ordered pair. Furthermore, since the set of natural numbers is closed under the operations of addition and multiplication, the product is an ordered pair of natural numbers. Thus we have proved the theorem:

Theorem 4.12   The set of integers is closed under multiplication.

We now prove that multiplication on the set of integers is commutative.

Theorem 4.13   Multiplication on the set of integers is commutative.

Proof   Let x and y be integers. Then there exist natural numbers $a, b, c,$ and d such that $x = (a, b)$ and $y = (c, d)$.

$xy = (a, b)(c, d)$	Substitution
$= (ac + bd, bc + ad)$	Definition of multiplication for integers
$= (ca + db, cb + da)$	Commutative property of multiplication for natural numbers
$= (ca + db, da + cb)$	Commutative property of addition for natural numbers
$= (c, d)(a, b)$	Definition of multiplication for integers
$= yx$	Substitution

The proof of the following theorem will be left as an exercise for the reader.

Theorem 4.14   Multiplication on the set of integers is associative. That is, if $x, y,$ and z are integers, then $(xy)z = x(yz)$.

THE NATURAL NUMBERS AND INTEGERS

In Section 4.3 we observed that 1 is the multiplicative identity for the system of natural numbers. Do we have a similar property for the system of integers? That is, does there exist an integer e such that $e \cdot x = x \cdot e = x$ for every integer x? For every integer (a, b), we have

$(1, 0)(a, b) = (a, b)(1, 0)$ Commutative property of multiplication for integers

$\qquad = (a \cdot 1 + b \cdot 0, b \cdot 1 + a \cdot 0)$ Definition of multiplication for integers

$\qquad = (a + 0, b + 0)$ Properties of multiplication by the natural numbers 1 and 0

$\qquad = (a, b)$ Property of addition of the natural number 0

The foregoing remarks are summarized in the following theorem.

Theorem 4.15 The integer $(1, 0)$ is a multiplicative identity for the set of integers.

If a is any natural number, it can be shown that every integer of the form $(a + 1, a)$ is a multiplicative identity for the set of integers. However, it is clear that every such integer is equal to $(1, 0)$. The symbol 1 will also be used to denote the multiplicative identity for the set of integers. It can be proved that the multiplicative identity for the set of integers is unique.

We know from previous experience with integers that the product of any integer and zero is zero. We now establish this as a theorem.

Theorem 4.16 If (c, d) is any integer, then

$$(0, 0)(c, d) = (c, d)(0, 0) = (0, 0).$$

Proof

$$(0, 0)(c, d) = (c, d)(0, 0)$$
$$= (c \cdot 0 + d \cdot 0, d \cdot 0 + c \cdot 0)$$
$$= (0 + 0, 0 + 0)$$
$$= (0, 0)$$

Although we will not do so here, it is possible to prove the cancellation property for multiplication. The statement of this property is contained in the next theorem.

Theorem 4.17 Let x, y, and z denote integers with $z \neq 0$. If $xz = yz$, then $x = y$.

If the product of two numbers is 0, then at least one of the numbers is 0. The reader has used this property many times in his work in mathematics. With the use of the cancellation law, we are able to prove this as a theorem for the set of integers.

Theorem 4.18 Let a and b be integers such that $ab = 0$. If $a \neq 0$, then $b = 0$.

Proof By hypothesis, $ab = 0$. From Theorem 4.16, we have $a \cdot 0 = 0$. Hence

$$ab = a \cdot 0$$

and by the commutative property of multiplication for integers

$$ba = 0 \cdot a.$$

Thus, by the cancellation property for multiplication, we have $b = 0$.

Problems

1 Use the definition of multiplication for integers to find the following products.
   a) $(6, 3)(7, 2)$ b) $(7, 3)(4, 11)$ c) $(8, 12)(11, 3)$
   d) $(7, 9)(3, 1)$ e) $(13, 156)(2, 2)$ f) $(15, 21)(21, 15)$

2 Use the familiar notation for integers (that is, $0, \pm1, \pm2, \ldots$) to find the products in Problem 1.

3 Use the definition of multiplication for integers to verify the associative property in each of the following.
   a) $[(5, 7)(3, 11)](6, 2) = (5, 7)[(3, 11)(6, 2)]$
   b) $[(3, 7)(9, 5)](8, 2) = (3, 7)[(9, 5)(8, 2)]$

4 Use the definition of multiplication for integers to verify the commutative property in each of the following.
   a) $(11, 7)(5, 3) = (5, 3)(11, 7)$ b) $(17, 3)(12, 7) = (12, 7)(17, 3)$

5 State the property that is needed to justify each of the following statements. Each symbol represents an integer.
   a) $a(bc) = (ab)c$ b) If $2b = 0$, then $b = 0$.
   c) $1 \cdot a = a$ d) $(ab)(cd) = (cd)(ab)$
   e) $a + b$ is an integer.   f) If $2x = 2y$, then $x = y$.

6 What conditions must be placed on x and y for (x, y) to satisfy the equation $(x, y)(4, 7) = (5, 3) + (3, 5)$?

7 Prove Theorem 4.14.

8 Prove that the multiplicative identity 1 for the set of integers is unique. [*Hint:* Assume 1 and $1'$ are multiplicative identities and show that $1 = 1'$.]

4.13 THE DISTRIBUTIVE PROPERTY

We only need to establish one more property for addition and multiplication on the set of integers to show that these operations have all the general properties of addition and multiplication on the set of natural numbers. We now prove that multiplication distributes over addition in the set of integers.

Theorem 4.19 Multiplication distributes over addition in the set of integers. That is, if x, y, and z are integers, then

$$x(y + z) = xy + xz.$$

[*Note:* We will prove this theorem by showing that both members of the equation represent the same number.]

Proof Let x, y, and z be integers. Then there exist natural numbers a, b, c, d, e, and f such that $x = (a, b)$, $y = (c, d)$, and $z = (e, f)$.

$x(y + z)$

$= (a, b)[(c, d) + (e, f)]$	Susbstitution
$= (a, b)(c + e, d + f)$	Definition for addition for integers
$= (a(c + e) + b(d + f), b(c + e) + a(d + f))$	Definition of multiplication for integers
$= ((ac + ae) + (bd + bf), (bc + be) + (ad + af))$	Distributive property for natural numbers
$= (ac + ae + bd + bf, bc + be + ad + af)$	Associative property for addition for natural numbers

$xy + xz$

$= (a, b)(c, d) + (a, b)(e, f)$	Substitution
$= (ac + bd, bc + ad) + (ae + bf, be + af)$	Definition of multiplication for integers
$= ((ac + bd) + (ae + bf), (bc + ad) + (be + af))$	Definition of addition for integers
$= (ac + ae + bd + bf, bc + be + ad + af)$	Several applications of the associative and commutative properties of addition for natural numbers

We now conclude that $x(y + z) = xy + xz$. Therefore multiplication distributes over addition in the set of integers.

By using the commutative property of multiplication one can now prove that $(x + y)z = xz + yz$. We shall also refer to this property as the distributive property.

The reader has often heard the familiar rule, "The product of a negative number and a positive number is negative." Or to put it another way, $(-x)(y) = -(xy)$ for all numbers x and y. Using the distributive property, we shall now prove that multiplication has this property in the set of integers. When we write $(-x)(y) = -(xy)$, we are saying that the additive inverse of xy is $(-x)(y)$ and to prove this property, we must show that

$$xy + (-x)(y) = 0.$$

This can be done as follows:

$$xy + (-x)(y) = [x + (-x)]y \quad \text{The distributive property}$$
$$= 0 \cdot y \quad \text{Definition of the additive inverse}$$
$$= 0 \quad \text{Theorem 4.16}$$

Thus we may write $(-x)(y) = -(xy)$.

The other familiar rules for multiplying "signed numbers" are:

1) $(x)(-y) = -(xy)$,
2) $(-x)(-y) = xy$.

It can be proved that multiplication on the set of integers has these two properties. The proofs will be listed as problems at the end of this section.

Example 1 Using the rule for multiplying "signed numbers," we have:

a) $(-2)(3) = -6$ \qquad\qquad b) $(-2)(-3) = 6$

c) $(-6)(-8) = 48$ \qquad\qquad d) $(4)(-5) = -20$

Problems

1 Find each of the following numbers.

a) $(-8)(2)$ \qquad\qquad b) $(0)(-3)$

c) $(-7)(-8)$ \qquad\qquad d) $(3)(-6)$

e) $(-10)(-2)$ \qquad\qquad f) $(-3)[5 + (-7)]$

g) $(-2)(-3)(-4)$ \qquad\qquad h) $(-5)(6)(-7)$

i) $-[(4)(-3)]$

2 Prove that $(x + y)z = xz + yz$ for all integers x, y, and z.

3 Prove that $(a)(-b) = -(ab)$ for all integers a and b.

4 Prove that $(-a)(-b) = ab$ for all integers a and b. [*Hint:* Write $(-a)(-b) = -(a)(-b)$.]

4.14 THE INTEGERS AND ORDER

In Section 4.6 we discussed the order relation and the properties of order on the set of natural numbers. Considering the integers (a, b) and (c, d) to be the respective differences $a - b$ and $c - d$, we find that the statement $(a, b) < (c, d)$ corresponds intuitively to the statement $a - b < c - d$. If $a - b < c - d$, it follows that $a + d < b + c$. This result motivates the following definition for the "less than" relation on the set of integers. The definition for "greater than" is analogous to the corresponding definition in Section 4.6.

Definition 4.9 $(a, b) < (c, d)$ if and only if $a + d < b + c$.

Example 1

$$(4, 3) < (7, 2) \quad \text{since} \quad 4 + 2 < 3 + 7.$$
$$(5, 7) < (6, 4) \quad \text{since} \quad 5 + 4 < 7 + 6.$$
$$(2, 9) < (13, 4) \quad \text{since} \quad 2 + 4 < 9 + 13.$$

Theorem 4.20 *Transitive Property.* If $(a, b) < (c, d)$ and $(c, d) < (e, f)$, then $(a, b) < (e, f)$.

Proof By hypothesis $(a, b) < (c, d)$ and $(c, d) < (e, f)$. Hence, by definition of the relation "$<$," we have

$$a + d < b + c \text{ and } c + f < d + e.$$

By Theorem 4.5

$$(a + d) + (c + f) < (b + c) + (d + e),$$

and after several applications of the associative and commutative properties of addition for natural numbers, we have

$$(a + f) + (d + c) < (b + e) + (d + c).$$

By Theorem 4.3, $a + f < b + e$. Therefore, by definition, $(a, b) < (e, f)$.

The remaining properties of the relation "$<$" on the set of integers can be established by using Definition 4.9 and the properties of the relation "$<$" on the set of natural numbers. However, some of the properties can be more easily established by using previously proved properties of the relation "$<$" on the set of integers. Theorem 4.24 will be proved using the latter approach. The other theorems will be stated without proof.

In the remainder of this section integers will be represented by a single symbol instead of an ordered pair. This notation will be used exclusively in the next chapter.

Theorem 4.21 *The Trichotomy Law.* If x and y are integers, then exactly one of the following must be true:

$$1) \ x = y,$$
$$2) \ x < y,$$
$$3) \ x > y.$$

Theorem 4.22 Let x and y denote integers. Then for every integer z,

$$x < y \quad \text{if and only if} \quad x + z < y + z.$$

Theorem 4.23 Let x and y denote integers. Then

1) For every integer $z > 0$, $x < y$ if and only if $xz < yz$.
2) For every integer $z < 0$, $x < y$ if and only if $xz > yz$.

Theorem 4.24 Let x, y, z, and w denote integers. If $x < y$ and $z < w$, then $x + z < y + w$.

Proof

If $x < y$, then $x + z < y + z$.	Theorem 4.22
If $z < w$, then $z + y < w + y$ and	Theorem 4.22
$y + z < y + w$.	Commutative property of addition for integers

Thus, if $x < y$ and $z < w$, we have

$$x + z < y + z \quad \text{and} \quad y + z < y + w.$$

Therefore,

$$x + z < y + w. \qquad \text{Theorem 4.20}$$

Theorem 4.25 Let x, y, z, and w be positive integers. If $x < y$ and $z < w$, then $xz < yw$.

Problems

1 Verify each of the following, using Definition 4.9.
   a) $(3, 7) < (7, 2)$ b) $(4, 11) < (2, 8)$
   c) $(11, 4) < (13, 2)$ d) $(15, 3) < (20, 6)$

2 In each of the following find all values of x in the set of natural numbers which will make the relationship true.
   a) $(x, 5) < (3, 1)$ b) $(9, x) > (7, 2)$
   c) $(x, 6) < (11, 2)$ d) $(7, x) > (15, 10)$

3   Use the roster method to list the elements in each of the following sets. In each case the symbol x represents an integer.

a) $A = \{x \mid -2 \leq x \leq 8\}$ b) $B = \{x \mid -3 < x < 5\}$

c) $C = \{x \mid x^2 = 16\}$ d) $D = \{x \mid x^2 = -1\}$

e) $E = \{x \mid x + 2 = 6\}$ f) $F = \{x \mid x = -x\}$

4   Referring to the sets of Problem 3, find

a) $A \cup B$ b) $A \cap B$ c) $A - B$

d) $C \cup D$ e) $B \cap F$ f) $A \cup F$

5   Is there a smallest positive integer? What is it?

6   If x is an integer such that $x \leq 0$ and $-x \leq 0$, what is x? Justify your answer.

7   Prove Theorem 4.22.

8   Prove Theorem 4.25.

4.15 THE INTEGERS AND DIVISION

Before beginning a discussion of division, we admonish the reader to review the properties of the integers found in Sections 4.9 through 4.14. It should be observed that the operations on the set of integers have all the properties of the corresponding operations on the set of natural numbers. Furthermore, the set of integers is closed under subtraction, and every equation of the form $a = b + x$ has a solution in the system of integers.

We begin the discussion of division, the last of the four familiar operations of arithmetic, with the following definition.

Definition 4.10 If x and y are integers, then $x \div y = z$ if and only if $x = yz$ and z is unique. The expression "$x \div y$" can be read, "x divided by y." In this expression, the number x is called the *dividend* and the number y is called the *divisor*. The number z is called the *quotient*.

Example 1   Find $6 \div 2$.

Solution $6 \div 2 = x$ if and only if $6 = 2x$. To satisfy the latter equation we see that x must have the value 3. Hence, $6 \div 2 = 3$.

Example 2   Find $-12 \div 3$.

Solution $-12 \div 3 = x$ if and only if $-12 = 3x$. We see that x must have the value -4. Hence, $-12 \div 3 = -4$.

If ordered pair notation is used in Definition 4.10, we have $(a, b) \div (c, d) = (x, y)$ if and only if $(a, b) = (c, d)(x, y)$, and (x, y) is unique. We will use this notation in reworking Example 1.

Example 3 Find $(12, 6) \div (4, 2)$.

Solution

$$(12, 6) \div (4, 2) = (x, y)$$

if and only if

$$(12, 6) = (4, 2)(x, y)$$
$$= (4x + 2y, 2x + 4y).$$
$$(12, 6) = (4x + 2y, 2x + 4y)$$

if and only if

$$12 + 2x + 4y = 6 + 4x + 2y,$$

and by the cancellation property of addition for natural numbers, if and only if

$$6 + 2y = 2x.$$

We readily observe that $x = 6$ and $y = 3$ is one solution to this equation. Thus

$$(12, 6) \div (4, 2) = (6, 3).$$

For every integer (x, y) such that $6 + 2y = 2x$,

$$(12, 6) \div (4, 2) = (x, y).$$

However, every such integer (x, y) is simply another representation for the integer $(6, 3)$.

From the above example, we see that the solution of a division problem is found by solving an equation of the form $a = bx$. If a and b represent integers, is there always an integer x such that $a = bx$? Consider the following example.

Example 4 Find $7 \div 2$.

Solution $7 \div 2 = x$ if and only if $7 = 2x$. Because there is no integer x such that $7 = 2x$, we cannot solve this equation nor can we find $7 \div 2$ in the set of integers.

From this example it is clear that the set of integers is not closed under division. Likewise, if the universal set is the set of integers, then not every equation of the form $a = bx$ has a solution in the universal set. Clearly, the only equations of this form which have solutions are those for which b is a factor of a. The fact that we cannot solve every equation of the form $a = bx$ in the system of integers is a serious shortcoming of the system. In the next chapter we will develop a system of numbers in which a solution can always be found provided $b \neq 0$.

THE NATURAL NUMBERS AND INTEGERS

In Example 4 we noted that the quotient $7 \div 2$ cannot be found in the set of integers. However, 7 and 2 can be related by the equation

$$7 = 2 \cdot 3 + 1.$$

This example illustrates an important theorem called the *division algorithm*.

The Division Algorithm If m and n are integers with $n > 0$, then there exist unique integers q and r such that

$$m = nq + r$$

and $0 \leqq r < n$.

We will not attempt to prove the division algorithm. Instead, we will illustrate the theorem by the following examples.

Example 5 If $m = 23$ and $n = 5$, find integers q and r, satisfying the conditions of the division algorithm, such that $m = nq + r$.

Solution By the usual process of long division, we have

$$
\begin{array}{r}
4 \\
5\overline{)23} \\
20 \\
\hline
3
\end{array}
$$

Thus, $23 = 5 \cdot 4 + 3$ and q and r have the values 4 and 3, respectively. We observe that $0 \leqq r < 5$.

Example 6 Follow the instructions of Example 5 for $m = -47$ and $n = 13$.

Solution We are looking for integers q and r such that

$$-47 = 13q + r$$

and $0 \leqq r < 13$. We can solve this problem by making some educated guesses. If we set $q = -3$, we have $13q = -39$, but -47 cannot be expressed as the sum of -39 and an integer r satisfying the condition that $0 \leqq r < 13$. However, if we set $q = -4$, $13q = -54$ and $-54 + 7 = -47$. Thus the desired integers are $q = -4$ and $r = 7$.

We note that if the quotient $m \div n$ can be found in the set of integers, then the number r in the division algorithm will always be 0.

Before leaving this section, we wish to discuss the use of the integer 0 in division problems. If $a \neq 0$, let us consider the following.

$$1) \ 0 \div a,$$
$$2) \ a \div 0,$$
$$3) \ 0 \div 0.$$

$0 \div a = x$ if and only if $0 = ax$. Since $a \neq 0$, by Theorem 4.18, we conclude that $x = 0$. Therefore, $0 \div a = 0$.

$a \div 0 = x$ if and only if $a = 0 \cdot x$. By Theorem 4.16, $0 \cdot x = 0$ for every integer x. Since $a \neq 0$, the equation $a = 0 \cdot x$ has no solution. Hence, $a \div 0$ is undefined.

$0 \div 0 = x$ if and only if $0 = 0 \cdot x$. We cannot find a unique solution for this equation, since it is true for every integer x (Theorem 4.16). Hence $0 \div 0$ is undefined. We summarize these remarks by saying that division by 0 is impossible. However, 0 divided by any nonzero integer is always 0.

Problems

1 Find the following quotients if they exist in the set of integers. Use Definition 4.10.

   a) $14 \div 7$ b) $15 \div 2$ c) $0 \div 3$

   d) $3 \div 2$ e) $-18 \div 6$ f) $16 \div -4$

   g) $7 \div 0$ h) $24 \div 10$ i) $-30 \div -15$

2 Using ordered pair notation, find $(8, 2) \div (3, 6)$.

3 Which of the following equations have solutions in the set of integers? Give the solution for those equations which have one.

   a) $2x + 5 = 21$ b) $3x - 7 = 23$ c) $4x - 2 = -11$

   d) $7x - 21 = 42$ e) $5x + 1 = 8$ f) $2x - 1 = -3$

   g) $x + 5 = 2$ h) $(-2)x + 3 = 9$

4 For each of the following values of m and n, find integers q and r, satisfying the conditions of the division algorithm, such that $m = nq + r$.

   a) $m = 15$ and $n = 6$ b) $m = 138$ and $n = 15$

   c) $m = 48$ and $n = 12$ d) $m = -31$ and $n = 7$

   e) $m = 294$ and $n = 23$ f) $m = -508$ and $n = 63$

   g) $m = 672$ and $n = 56$ h) $m = -69$ and $n = 5$

   i) $m = 177$ and $n = 42$ j) $m = -445$ and $n = 8$

4.16 THE FUNDAMENTAL THEOREM OF ARITHMETIC

Definition 4.11 An integer c is *divisible* by an integer a, $a \neq 0$, if there is an integer b such that $c = a \cdot b$. If c is divisible by a, we say that a is a *divisor* of c (or a divides c) and that c is a *multiple* of a.

It is clear from Definition 4.11 and Section 4.3 that if an integer a divides the integer c, then a is a *factor* of c. Thus a divisor of an integer is a nonzero factor of the integer. As an example, $12 = 3 \cdot 4$, and thus 3 and 4 both divide 12 and are both factors of 12. Since $n = n \cdot 1$ for any integer n, it follows by definition that 1 divides n and if $n \neq 0$, n divides n. Furthermore, $n \cdot 0 = 0$ for every integer n, and thus, if $n \neq 0$, then n divides 0.

Definition 4.12 An integer p greater than 1 whose only divisors are ± 1 and $\pm p$ is called a *prime number*. An integer greater than 1 which is not prime is called a *composite number*.

Some examples of prime numbers are 2, 3, 5, 7, 11, and 13, whereas 4, 6, 8, 9, 10, and 12 are composite numbers. Note that Definition 4.12 separates the integers greater than 1 into two sets, the prime numbers and the composite numbers. Also, note that 0 and 1 are neither prime numbers nor composite numbers. With a minor adaptation one can extend the concept of primeness to negative integers less than -1, but we will not do so here.

We are now prepared to discuss a fundamental property of integers. Observe the following different ways to express the integer 72, or a product of integers.

$$72 = 72 \cdot 1,$$
$$72 = 36 \cdot 2,$$
$$72 = 24 \cdot 3,$$
$$72 = 18 \cdot 4,$$
$$72 = (-12) \cdot (-6),$$
$$72 = 9 \cdot 8,$$
$$72 = 18 \cdot 2 \cdot 2,$$
$$72 = (-3) \cdot 4 \cdot 3 \cdot (-2),$$
$$72 = 3 \cdot 3 \cdot 2 \cdot 2 \cdot 2.$$

Each of these products is called a *factorization* of 72. The above list of factorizations does not include all possible factorizations. Note that the last factorization gives 72 as a product of prime numbers. This is called the *prime factorization* of 72. This leads us to state, but not prove, the following theorem.

Theorem 4.26 *The Fundamental Theorem of Arithmetic.* Any integer different from 0, 1, or -1 can be expressed as a product of prime numbers and ± 1 in one and only one way, except for the order in which the factors occur.

With reference to the integer 72, the factorization $2 \cdot 2 \cdot 2 \cdot 3 \cdot 3$ is the unique factorization of 72 into the product of primes. The Fundamental Theorem of Arithmetic is sometimes called the Unique Factorization Theorem.

Example 1 Express 105 as a product of primes and ± 1.

Solution To express 105 as a product of primes and ± 1, we first determine that we will use the factor $+1$, since 105 is a positive integer. The next step is to find the prime divisors of 105. Perhaps the best-organized procedure for doing this is to start with the smallest prime, 2, and check to see whether it is a factor of 105. Since 2 does not divide 105, we then try the next prime, which is 3. We find $105 = 3 \cdot 35$. Thus we have 105 written as the product of two integers, one of which is prime. The next step is to express 35 as a product of primes. Clearly, the factorization desired is $35 = 5 \cdot 7$. Therefore, we have

$$105 = 3 \cdot 35$$
$$= 3 \cdot 5 \cdot 7.$$

Example 2 Express -660 as a product of primes and ± 1.

Solution We first note that $-660 = (-1) \cdot 660$. We next find that 2 is a factor of 660 and we can write $-660 = (-1)2 \cdot 330$. Before going to the next prime we check to see whether 2 is also a factor of 330. It is, so we have $-660 = (-1) \cdot 2 \cdot 2 \cdot 165$. Since 2 is not a factor of 165, we try the next prime, which is 3. Continuing in this manner we obtain the desired factorization. Our work is summarized below.

$$-660 = (-1) \cdot 660$$
$$= (-1) \cdot 2 \cdot 330$$
$$= (-1) \cdot 2 \cdot 2 \cdot 165$$
$$= (-1) \cdot 2 \cdot 2 \cdot 3 \cdot 55$$
$$= (-1) \cdot 2 \cdot 2 \cdot 3 \cdot 5 \cdot 11.$$

Example 3 Express 97 as a product of primes and ± 1.

Solution Following the procedure of Example 1, we find that none of the prime numbers 2, 3, 5, or 7 are factors of 97. Thus, the only prime factors that 97 can have must be greater than or equal to 11. However, the product of two such numbers would be greater than 97, and this leads us to conclude that 97 is itself a prime. In fact, whenever we use the procedure in Example 1 to express a positive integer x as a product of primes, we need not proceed beyond the prime number p such that $p^2 > x$.

In Chapter 1 we proved that there are infinitely many primes. Even though there are infinitely many primes, it can be shown that the prime numbers do begin to "thin out." To illustrate this, we need the symbol $n!$, which is read "n factorial." For any positive integer n,

$$n! = n \cdot (n - 1) \cdot (n - 2) \cdot \ \cdots \ \cdot (2) \cdot (1).$$

For example,

$$4! = 4 \cdot 3 \cdot 2 \cdot 1 = 24 \quad \text{and} \quad 3! = 3 \cdot 2 \cdot 1 = 6.$$

THE NATURAL NUMBERS AND INTEGERS

Using the factorial notation, we can readily see that for any positive integer n, the n consecutive integers

$$(n + 1)! + 2, (n + 1)! + 3, \ldots, (n + 1)! + n + 1$$

are all composite numbers. To verify this assertion we observe that

$$(n + 1)! + 2 = 2[(n + 1) \cdot (n) \cdot (n - 1) \cdot \cdots \cdot 3 \cdot 1] + 2$$
$$= 2[(n + 1) \cdot (n) \cdot (n - 1) \cdot \cdots \cdot 3 \cdot 1 + 1],$$
$$(n + 1)! + 3 = 3[(n + 1) \cdot (n) \cdot (n - 1) \cdot \cdots \cdot 4 \cdot 2 \cdot 1] + 3$$
$$= 3[(n + 1) \cdot (n) \cdot (n - 1) \cdot \cdots \cdot 4 \cdot 2 \cdot 1 + 1],$$
$$\vdots$$
$$(n + 1)! + n + 1 = (n + 1)n! + (n + 1) = (n + 1)(n! + 1).$$

From these equations we see that $(n + 1)! + 2$ has a factor of 2, $(n + 1)! + 3$ has a factor of 3, etc. Therefore, each of these numbers is a composite number. Using this procedure, we can find 100, 1,000,000, or any desired number of consecutive composite numbers. As an example, suppose we wish to find five consecutive composite numbers. From the above remarks we have

$$(5 + 1)! + 2 = 6! + 2 = 722,$$
$$(5 + 1)! + 3 = 6! + 3 = 723,$$
$$(5 + 1)! + 4 = 6! + 4 = 724,$$
$$(5 + 1)! + 5 = 6! + 5 = 725,$$
$$(5 + 1)! + 6 = 6! + 6 = 726.$$

Problems

1 List all the positive divisors of 20.

2 List all the positive divisors of 72.

3 Since $3 \cdot 0 = 0$, 0 is a multiple of 3 and a multiple of 0. Furthermore, 3 divides 0. Does 0 divide 0? Why?

4 Determine whether the following numbers are prime or composite. Express those that are composite as the product of prime factors.

   a) 280   b) 493   c) 101

   d) 311   e) 252   f) 211

5 Express the following as the product of prime factors.

   a) 144,000   b) 13,013   c) 6409

6 List all the prime numbers less than 100.

7 How many prime numbers are even? Explain.

8 List all pairs of consecutive integers which are prime. Explain how you know your list is complete.

9 Two consecutive odd primes are called prime twins. For example, 3 and 5 are prime twins as are 5 and 7. List three other prime twins.

10 Find five consecutive composite numbers less than 100.

11 Find six consecutive composite numbers by the process described in this section.

4.17 THE GREATEST COMMON DIVISOR AND THE LEAST COMMON MULTIPLE

Because the number 2 divides both 24 and 60, we say that 2 is a *common divisor* of 24 and 60 Other common divisors are 3, 4, 6, and 12. The number 12 has special significance in this situation because it is the largest positive integer which divides both 24 and 60; 12 is called the *greatest common divisor* of these two numbers.

Definition 4.13 A positive integer d is a *greatest common divisor* (GCD) of the integers a and b if

1) d divides both a and b, and

2) every integer c which divides both a and b also divides d.

If one of the integers a and b is not zero, the division algorithm can be used to prove that the greatest common divisor always exists and is unique.

The Fundamental Theorem of Arithmetic can also be used to find the greatest common divisor of two integers. The greatest common divisor of two integers can be found by taking the product of all the prime factors *common* to both prime factorizations, each factor being repeated the minimum number of times it appears in either of the integers. This procedure will be illustrated by the following examples.

Example 1 Find the greatest common divisor of 24 and 60.

Solution We first find the prime factorizations for the integers 24 and 60:

$$24 = 2 \cdot 2 \cdot 2 \cdot 3,$$
$$60 = 2 \cdot 2 \cdot 3 \cdot 5.$$

The factors 2 and 3 are common to both factorizations. The number 2 is used as a factor three times in 24 and only twice in 60. Hence, it will appear as a factor twice in the greatest common divisor of 24 and 60. The number 3 is used as a factor only once in each of the integers 24 and 60 and will appear only once in the GCD. We now conclude that the GCD of 24 and 60 is $2 \cdot 2 \cdot 3 = 12$.

Example 2 Find the GCD of 18 and 175.

Solution The prime factorizations of 18 and 175 are

$$18 = 2 \cdot 3 \cdot 3 \quad \text{and} \quad 175 = 5 \cdot 5 \cdot 7.$$

We observe that 18 and 175 have no common prime factors. However, the positive integer 1 divides both 18 and 175. Hence the GCD of 18 and 175 is the positive integer 1.

If the GCD of two integers is 1, the integers are said to be *relatively prime*. Thus, in Example 2, the integers 18 and 175 are relatively prime.

The GCD of three or more integers is defined as a positive integer *d* which divides each of the integers and has the additional property that if *c* also divides each of the integers, then *c* divides *d*. The GCD of three or more integers can be found by the same method used to find the GCD of two integers. Consider the following example.

Example 3 Find the GCD of 18, 24, and 36.

Solution The prime factorizations of 18, 24, and 36 are

$$18 = 2 \cdot 3 \cdot 3,$$
$$24 = 2 \cdot 2 \cdot 2 \cdot 3,$$
$$36 = 2 \cdot 2 \cdot 3 \cdot 3.$$

The prime factors common to 18, 24, and 36 are the factors 2 and 3. We see that 2 appears only once as a factor in 18 and 3 is listed only once as a factor in 24. Hence the GCD of 18, 24, and 36 is $2 \cdot 3 = 6$.

Because 72 is a multiple of both 12 and 18, we say that 72 is a *common multiple* of 12 and 18. Other common multiples of 12 and 18 are 36, 108, and 216. However, 36 is the least positive integer which is a multiple of both 12 and 18 and is called their *least common multiple*.

Definition 4.14 A positive integer *m* is a *least common multiple* (LCM) of the integers *a* and *b*, provided

1) *m* is a multiple of both *a* and *b*, and

2) if *k* is a multiple of *a* and *b*, then *k* is also a multiple of *m*.

The least common multiple of two integers can be found by taking the product of all *different* prime factors of the two integers, each listed as a factor the maximum number of times it appears in either of the integers. The following examples will illustrate this procedure.

Example 4 Find the LCM of 12 and 18.

Solution The prime factorizations of 12 and 18 are

$$12 = 2 \cdot 2 \cdot 3 \quad \text{and} \quad 18 = 2 \cdot 3 \cdot 3.$$

The LCM of 12 and 18 is $2 \cdot 2 \cdot 3 \cdot 3$, or 36.

Example 5 Find the LCM of 99 and 350.

Solution The prime factorizations of 99 and 350 are

$$99 = 3 \cdot 3 \cdot 11 \quad \text{and} \quad 350 = 2 \cdot 5 \cdot 5 \cdot 7.$$

The LCM of 99 and 350 is found to be $2 \cdot 3 \cdot 3 \cdot 5 \cdot 5 \cdot 7 \cdot 11$ or 34,650.

In Example 5 the numbers 99 and 350 had no common prime factors. If two integers a and b have no common prime factors, their LCM is the product ab.

The LCM of three or more integers is defined to be a positive integer m which is a multiple of each of the integers and has the property that if k is a multiple of each of the integers, then k is a multiple of m. The LCM of three or more integers can be found by the same method used to find the LCM of two integers.

Example 6 Find the LCM of 6, -24, 28, and 35.

Solution Factoring each of these integers into a product of primes and ± 1, we have

$$\begin{aligned}
6 &= 2 \cdot 3, \\
-24 &= (-1) \cdot 2 \cdot 2 \cdot 2 \cdot 3, \\
28 &= 2 \cdot 2 \cdot 7, \\
35 &= 5 \cdot 7.
\end{aligned}$$

The LCM of the four integers is then $2 \cdot 2 \cdot 2 \cdot 3 \cdot 5 \cdot 7$ or 840. The fact that one of the four integers is negative makes no difference in finding the LCM. Remember that the LCM of two or more numbers is a positive integer.

In adding fractions one is often concerned with finding a least common denominator. It should be observed that the least common denominator is the LCM of the denominators. Thus the procedure outlined in the preceding examples can be very helpful when we have to add fractions.

Problems

1 List the set of positive divisors common to 24 and 72. What is the greatest common divisor of 24 and 72?

2 List the set of positive divisors common to 18 and 60. What is the greatest common divisor of 18 and 60?

THE NATURAL NUMBERS AND INTEGERS

3 Find the GCD and the LCM in each of the following:

   a) 48, 918

                       b) 381, −216

   c) 24, 96, 216

                       d) 28, 35, 84

4 If p and q are distinct prime numbers, then what is GCD of p and q? Explain.

5 Give an example of two composite numbers which are relatively prime.

6 If a and b are positive integers, it can be shown that the product of the GCD and LCM of a and b is ab. Verify this for the integers 24 and 50.

7 The integer 6 is called a perfect number because all of its positive divisors (except itself) add to the number itself, i.e., 1, 2, and 3 are the positive divisors of 6 and $1 + 2 + 3 = 6$. There is another perfect number between 20 and 30. What is it?

Chapter 5

RATIONAL, REAL, AND COMPLEX NUMBERS

5.1 RATIONAL NUMBERS

In Chapter 4 we observed that the system of natural numbers did not possess all the properties which a mathematician would like. This motivated us to develop the system of integers. The discussion in Section 4.15 motivates us to develop another system, called the rational number system, in which every equation of the form $a = bx$, where a and b are in the system with $b \neq 0$, has a solution in the system. Clearly, $x = a \div b$ or $x = a/b$ is a solution, but $a \div b$ is not always an integer. However, this suggests that we define a rational number to be the quotient of two integers, and intuitively this is how we shall think of a rational number. Although this intuitive interpretation will be most helpful in motivating certain definitions, we will continue the pattern established in the development of the integers and use ordered pair notation. The ordered pair of integers (a, b) will be used to represent the rational number $x = a \div b$.

Definition 5.1 If a and b are integers such that $b \neq 0$, then the ordered pair (a, b) is called a *rational number*. We shall use the letter Q to denote the set of rational numbers. Hence

$$Q = \{(a, b) \mid a \in I, b \in I, \text{ and } b \neq 0\}.$$

The development of the rational number system will be very similar to that of the system of integers. We will be guided by our experience with the integers. We will observe that the operations of addition and multiplication on the set of rational numbers will have all the general properties of the corresponding operations on the set of integers. Furthermore, the set of integers can be identified with a proper subset of the set of rational numbers. Even though we shall develop the rational numbers from the integers, we remark that rational numbers were in use long before negative integers. The early Babylonians and Egyptians worked with fractions, but it was not until the seventeenth century that negative numbers were freely used.

After completing the development of the system of rational numbers, we shall abandon the ordered pair notation in favor of the familiar fractional notation. As we have already pointed out, the reader can relate these two methods for denoting rational numbers by thinking of the ordered pair (a, b) intuitively as the quotient $a \div b$ or the fraction a/b. Other examples are:

$(1, 2)$ corresponds to the quotient $1 \div 2$ or the fraction $\frac{1}{2}$.
$(-3, 5)$ corresponds to the quotient $-3 \div 5$ or the fraction $-\frac{3}{5}$.
$(0, 7)$ corresponds to the quotient $0 \div 7$ or the fraction 0.

We have just observed that $(1, 2)$ corresponds to the fraction $\frac{1}{2}$. However, the rational numbers $(2, 4)$, $(3, 6)$, and $(4, 8)$ also correspond to the fraction $\frac{1}{2}$, and we are led to think that the numbers $(1, 2)$, $(2, 4)$, $(3, 6)$, and $(4, 8)$ are related in some way. Actually all four ordered pairs represent the same rational number. A rational number can be represented as an ordered pair of integers in many different ways, and thus we must have some method for determining whether two rational numbers are equal. Using the fractional representation for the rational numbers (a, b) and (c, d), the statement that $(a, b) = (c, d)$ is equivalent to stating that

$$\frac{a}{b} = \frac{c}{d}.$$

The equation

$$\frac{a}{b} = \frac{c}{d}$$

is equivalent to the equation $ad = bc$. These observations lead us to state the following definition.

Definition 5.2 Two rational numbers (a, b) and (c, d) are equal if and only if

$$ad = bc.$$

Example 1

$(5, 7) = (10, 14)$,	because	$5 \cdot 14 = 7 \cdot 10$.
$(-3, 4) = (9, -12)$,	because	$(-3)(-12) = 4 \cdot 9$.
$(12, 6) = (2, 1)$,	because	$12 \cdot 1 = 6 \cdot 2$.

Earlier in this section, we said the set of integers could be identified with a proper subset of the set of rational numbers. Let us observe the following one-to-one correspondence from the set of integers to a proper subset of the set of rational numbers.

$$\cdots, \quad -n, \quad \cdots, \quad -2, \quad -1, \quad 0, \quad 1, \quad 2, \quad \cdots, \quad n, \quad \cdots$$
$$\updownarrow \qquad\qquad \updownarrow \qquad \updownarrow \quad \updownarrow \quad \updownarrow \quad \updownarrow \qquad\qquad \updownarrow$$
$$\cdots, (-n, 1), \cdots, (-2, 1), (-1, 1), (0, 1), (1, 1), (2, 1), \cdots, (n, 1), \cdots$$

It should now be clear that each integer is identified with a rational number whose second element is 1. Thus the set of integers can be identified with a proper subset of the set of rational numbers.

An immediate consequence of Definition 5.2 is the following theorem.

Theorem 5.1 If (a, b) is any rational number and k is any nonzero integer, then $(ka, kb) = (a, b)$.

Proof By Definition 5.2, $(a, b) = (ka, kb)$ if and only if $a(kb) = b(ka)$. The latter equation can be verified by use of the associative and commutative properties of multiplication for integers. Therefore, $(a, b) = (ka, kb)$.

The reader should recognize that Theorem 5.1 is the justification for the familiar process of reducing fractions to lowest terms.

Example 2 Use Theorem 5.1 to simplify the rational numbers $(24, 12)$ and $(25, -45)$.

Solution $(24, 12) = (12 \cdot 2, 12 \cdot 1)$, and by Theorem 5.1 we have $(24, 12) = (2, 1)$. If we interpret $(24, 12)$ as the fraction $\frac{24}{12}$, we are stating that $\frac{24}{12} = \frac{2}{1} = 2$.

As to $(25, -45)$, we can write

$$(25, -45) = (5 \cdot 5, 5(-9)).$$

Thus, by Theorem 5.1,

$$(25, -45) = (5, -9).$$

If $(25, -45)$ is interpreted as the fraction $25/-45$, we are stating that $25/-45 = 5/-9$.

Until further notice, an ordered pair is to be interpreted as an ordered pair of integers.

Problems

1 Write each of the following rational numbers as ordered pairs of integers in three other ways.

a) $(5, 6)$ b) $(-3, 4)$ c) $(0, 8)$
d) $(-7, -8)$ e) $(11, -13)$ f) $(7, 4)$

2 In each part of Problem 1, write the rational number as a quotient and as a fraction.

3 In each of the following, use Definition 5.2 to find the integer x for which $(x, 12)$ is equal to the given rational number.

a) $(3, 4)$ b) $(-3, 4)$ c) $(1, -3)$
d) $(-1, -6)$ e) $(0, 5)$ f) $(2, 3)$

4 In each of the following, use Theorem 5.1 to find the integer x such that $(x, 18)$ is equal to the given rational number.

a) $(1, 3)$ b) $(-2, 9)$ c) $(5, -6)$

d) $(9, -2)$ e) $(1, 1)$ f) $(6, 3)$

5 Use Theorem 5.1 to simplify each of the following rational numbers as in Example 2 of this section.

a) $(45, 9)$ b) $(3, 12)$ c) $(90, -27)$

d) $(0, 50)$ e) $(-21, 49)$ f) $(48, 36)$

6 Interpret each of the rational numbers in Problem 5 as fractions and write the results in lowest terms.

7 Since $(-3)(-4) = 4 \cdot 3 = 12$, then $(-3, 4) = (3, -4)$. What generalization does this suggest?

8 Since $3 \cdot (-4) = 4 \cdot (-3) = -12$, then $(3, 4) = (-3, -4)$. What generalization does this suggest?

9 Does the ordered pair of integers $(5, 0)$ represent a rational number? Explain.

10 Consider the intuitive interpretation of an ordered pair of integers and explain why in Definition 5.1 we insist that $b \neq 0$.

11 The following is a one-to-one correspondence from the set of integers to a proper subset of the set of rational numbers.

$$\cdots, \quad -n, \quad \cdots, \quad -2, \quad -1, \quad 0,$$
$$\updownarrow \qquad\qquad \updownarrow \qquad \updownarrow \qquad \updownarrow$$
$$\cdots, (n, -1), \cdots, (2, -1), (1, -1), (0, -1),$$

$$1, \qquad\qquad 2, \qquad \cdots, \qquad n, \qquad \cdots$$
$$\updownarrow \qquad\qquad \updownarrow \qquad\qquad\qquad \updownarrow$$
$$(-1, -1), (-2, -1), \cdots, (-n, -1), \cdots$$

Is this one-to-one correspondence really different from the one described in this section? Explain.

5.2 ADDITION AND SUBTRACTION OF RATIONAL NUMBERS

The familiar formula for adding two fractions suggests the following definition.

Definition 5.3 Addition of rational numbers is defined by the equation

$$(a, b) + (c, d) = (ad + bc, bd).$$

Example 1 Find the sum $(3, 8) + (2, 3)$.

Solution

$$(3, 8) + (2, 3) = (3 \cdot 3 + 8 \cdot 2, 8 \cdot 3)$$
$$= (9 + 16, 24)$$
$$= (25, 24).$$

Example 2 Find the sum $(-3, 4) + (-1, 3)$.

Solution

$$(-3, 4) + (-1, 3) = ((-3) \cdot 3 + 4 \cdot (-1), 4 \cdot 3)$$
$$= (-9 + (-4), 12)$$
$$= (-13, 12).$$

The following example will suggest that Definition 5.3 is consistent with the familiar procedure of adding fractions.

Example 3 Find the sum $\frac{3}{8} + \frac{2}{3}$.

Solution Note this is the same problem that was encountered in Example 1.

$$\frac{3}{8} + \frac{2}{3} = \frac{3 \cdot 3}{8 \cdot 3} + \frac{2 \cdot 8}{3 \cdot 8}$$

$$= \frac{9}{24} + \frac{16}{24}$$

$$= \frac{9 + 16}{24}$$

$$= \frac{25}{24}.$$

Since the rational number $(25, 24)$ corresponds to the fraction $\frac{25}{24}$, we see that the results of Examples 1 and 3 are the same except for notation.

We now investigate the properties of addition on the set of rational numbers. The proofs of several of these properties will be left as exercises for the reader.

Theorem 5.2 The set of rational numbers is closed under addition.

Proof The proof of this theorem follows from an inspection of Definition 5.3. Clearly, the sum is an ordered pair. Furthermore, since the integers are closed under addition and multiplication, the sum is an ordered pair of integers. Therefore, the sum of two rational numbers is also a rational number and the theorem is established.

Theorem 5.3 Addition on the set of rational numbers is associative.

Proof The proof is left as an exercise for the reader.

RATIONAL REAL, AND COMPLEX NUMBERS

Theorem 5.4 Addition on the set of rational numbers is commutative.

Proof Let x and y denote rational numbers. Then there exist integers a, b, c, and d with $b \neq 0$ and $d \neq 0$, such that $x = (a, b)$ and $y = (c, d)$.

$$\begin{aligned}
x + y &= (a, b) + (c, d) & &\text{Substitution} \\
&= (ad + bc, bd) & &\text{Definition of addition for rational numbers} \\
&= (da + cb, db) & &\text{Commutative property of multiplication for integers} \\
&= (cb + da, db) & &\text{Commutative property of addition for integers} \\
&= (c, d) + (a, b) & &\text{Definition of addition for rational numbers} \\
&= y + x & &\text{Substitution}
\end{aligned}$$

Therefore, addition on the set of rational numbers is commutative.

If (c, d) is any rational number, we have

$$\begin{aligned}
(0, 1) + (c, d) &= (c, d) + (0, 1) & &\text{Commutative property of addition for rational numbers} \\
&= (c \cdot 1 + d \cdot 0, d \cdot 1) & &\text{Definition of addition for rational numbers} \\
&= (c + d \cdot 0, d) & &\text{1 is the multiplicative identity for the set of integers} \\
&= (c + 0, d) & &\text{Property of multiplication by 0} \\
&= (c, d) & &\text{0 is the additive identity for the set of integers}
\end{aligned}$$

Thus $(0, 1)$ is an additive identity for the set of rational numbers, and we have proved the following theorem.

Theorem 5.5 The rational number $(0, 1)$ is an additive identity for the set of rational numbers.

Just as the additive identity for the set of integers is unique, the additive identity for the set of rational numbers is also unique except for the way it is represented. Any rational number in which the first element is 0 represents the additive identity. When ordered-pair representation is used, we will represent the additive identity by the ordered pair $(0, 1)$. Otherwise, it will be represented simply by the symbol 0.

We now turn our discussion to additive inverses for rational numbers. As the reader might expect, the discussion will rely on the existence of additive inverses for integers. Suppose (a, b) is any rational number and $-a$ is the additive inverse of the integer a. Then we have

$$(-a, b) + (a, b) = (a, b) + (-a, b)$$ Commutative property of addition for rational numbers

$$= (ab + b(-a), bb)$$ Definition of addition for rational numbers

$$= (ba + b(-a), bb)$$ Commutative property of multiplication of integers

$$= (b(a + (-a)), bb)$$ Distributive property for integers

$$= (b \cdot 0, bb)$$ Property of the additive inverse for integers

$$= (0, bb)$$ Property of multiplication by the integer 0.

$$= (0, 1)$$

Therefore, we state the following theorem.

Theorem 5.6 Every rational number has an additive inverse. To be more specific, an additive inverse of (a, b) is $(-a, b)$.

We state without proof that the additive inverse of a rational number is unique.

Example 4 The additive inverse of $(2, 3)$ is $(-2, 3)$ because

$$\begin{aligned}(2, 3) + (-2, 3) &= (2 \cdot 3 + 3(-2), 3 \cdot 3) \\ &= (6 + (-6), 9) \\ &= (0, 9) \\ &= (0, 1).\end{aligned}$$

Example 5 The additive inverse of $(0, 1)$ is $(0, 1)$ because

$$\begin{aligned}(0, 1) + (0, 1) &= (0 \cdot 1 + 1 \cdot 0, 1 \cdot 1) \\ &= (0 + 0, 1) \\ &= (0, 1).\end{aligned}$$

Therefore, $(0, 1)$ is its own additive inverse.

In Theorem 5.6 we proved that $-(a, b) = (-a, b)$. Stating this result in fractional form, we have

$$-\frac{a}{b} = \frac{-a}{b}.$$

RATIONAL, REAL, AND COMPLEX NUMBERS

By Theorem 5.1, $(-a, b) = (a, -b)$, using $k = -1$. Hence $-(a, b)$ $= (a, -b)$ and stating this result in fractional form we have

$$-\frac{a}{b} = \frac{a}{-b}.$$

In summary we may write

$$-\frac{a}{b} = \frac{-a}{b} = \frac{a}{-b}.$$

The reader perhaps recognizes this as a familiar rule for operating with fractions.

The cancellation property for addition on the set of rational numbers can be easily verified, and we leave this as an exercise for the reader.

The definition of subtraction for rational numbers is analogous to the definition of subtraction for integers.

Definition 5.4 If (a, b) and (c, d) are rational numbers, the following equations define subtraction.

$(a, b) - (c, d) = (x, y)$ if and only if $(a, b) = (c, d) + (x, y)$.

Example 6 Find $(7, 8) - (1, 4)$.

Solution

$(7, 8) - (1, 4) = (x, y)$ if and only if
$$\begin{aligned}
(7, 8) &= (1, 4) + (x, y) \\
&= (1 \cdot y + 4 \cdot x, 4y) \\
&= (y + 4x, 4y).
\end{aligned}$$

$(7, 8) = (y + 4x, 4y)$ if and only if
$$\begin{aligned}
7(4y) &= 8(y + 4x) \\
28y &= 8y + 32x \\
20y &= 32x \\
5y &= 8x.
\end{aligned}$$

If we let $x = 5$ and $y = 8$, we obtain one solution for the equation $5y = 8x$. Thus $(7, 8) - (1, 4) = (5, 8)$. For every rational number (x, y) such that $5y = 8x$, $(7, 8) - (1, 4) = (x, y)$. However, every such rational number (x, y) is simply another representation for the rational number $(5, 8)$.

It can be shown by a procedure similar to that in Section 4.11, that to subtract (c, d) from (a, b) is equivalent to adding the additive inverse of (c, d) to (a, b). That is,

$$(a, b) - (c, d) = (a, b) + (-c, d).$$

We have observed that each rational number has an additive inverse and that the set of rational numbers is closed under addition. Hence, it follows from the above equation that the set of rational numbers is closed under subtraction.

Example 7   Find $(7, 8) - (1, 4)$.

Solution

$$(7, 8) - (1, 4) = (7, 8) + (-1, 4)$$
$$= (7 \cdot 4 + 8 \cdot (-1), 8 \cdot 4)$$
$$= (28 - 8, 32)$$
$$= (20, 32)$$
$$= (5, 8).$$

Problems

1 Use the definition of addition for rational numbers to find the following sums.

a) $(1, 2) + (1, 3)$ b) $(3, 4) + (-7, 8)$

c) $(2, 3) + (5, 6)$ d) $(-4, 7) + (2, 14)$

e) $(1, -9) + (-2, -3)$ f) $(3, 8) + (4, 12)$

2 Use fractional notation for rational numbers to find each of the sums in Problem 1.

3 Use the definition of addition for rational numbers to verify the associative property in each of the following.

a) $[(5, 8) + (2, 3)] + (3, 4) = (5, 8) + [(2, 3) + (3, 4)]$

b) $[(-2, 3) + (5, -7)] + (2, 9) = (-2, 3) + [(5, -7) + (2, 9)]$

4 Use the definition of addition for rational numbers to verify the commutative property in each of the following.

a) $(-3, 8) + (7, 3) = (7, 3) + (-3, 8)$

b) $(9, 27) + (1, 3) = (1, 3) + (9, 27)$

5 Find the additive inverse for each of the following rational numbers.

a) $(3, 7)$ b) $(-2, 3)$ c) $(-6, -9)$ d) $(11, -13)$

6 Find a value for x such that

$$(x, 7) + (3, 14) = (2, 7) + (14, 28).$$

7 Find the following differences, using ordered-pair notation.

a) $(3, 7) - (2, 14)$ b) $(1, 2) - (2, 3)$

c) $(-5, 8) - (3, 4)$ d) $(-5, 16) - (3, -8)$

e) $(7, 16) - (-7, -8)$ f) $(3, 32) - (1, 16)$

8 Use fractional notation for rational numbers to find each of the differences in Problem 7.

9 Let x denote a rational number. If x is its own additive inverse, what is x?

10 $-(a, b)$ denotes the additive inverse of the rational number (a, b). Prove that
$$-(-(a, b)) = (a, b).$$

11 Let x and y denote rational numbers. If $-x$ and $-y$ denote the additive inverses x and y, respectively, prove that $-(x + y) = -x + (-y)$. [*Hint*: a is an additive inverse of b if $a + b = 0$.]

12 Prove that the additive identity for the set of rational numbers is unique. [*Hint*: Assume that 0 and $0'$ are two additive identities and show that $0 = 0'$.]

13 Prove Theorem 5.3.

14 State and prove the cancellation property of addition for rational numbers.

5.3 MULTIPLICATION OF RATIONAL NUMBERS

The familiar formula for multiplying two fractions suggests the following definition.

Definition 5.5 Multiplication of rational numbers is defined by the equation
$$(a, b)(c, d) = (ac, bd).$$

Example 1 Find the product $(2, 3)(5, 7)$.

Solution
$$\begin{aligned}(2, 3)(5, 7) &= (2 \cdot 5, 3 \cdot 7) \\ &= (10, 21).\end{aligned}$$

Example 2 Find the product $(-3, 4)(5, 8)$.

Solution
$$\begin{aligned}(-3, 4)(5, 8) &= (-3 \cdot 5, 4 \cdot 8) \\ &= (-15, 32).\end{aligned}$$

A comparison of the following example with Example 1 should suggest to the reader that Definition 5.5 is consistent with the familiar procedure for multiplying fractions.

Example 3 Find the product $\frac{2}{3} \cdot \frac{5}{7}$.

Solution
$$\frac{2}{3} \cdot \frac{5}{7} = \frac{2 \cdot 5}{3 \cdot 7} = \frac{10}{21}.$$

Since the set of integers is closed under multiplication, it is clear from Definition 5.5 that the set of rational numbers is closed under multiplication, and we have the following theorem.

Theorem 5.7 The set of rational numbers is closed under multiplication.

Theorem 5.8 Multiplication on the set of rational numbers is associative.

Proof Let x, y, and z denote rational numbers. Then there exist integers a, b, c, d, e, and f with $b \neq 0$, $d \neq 0$, and $f \neq 0$ such that

$$x = (a, b), y = (c, d) \text{ and } z = (e, f).$$

$(x \cdot y) \cdot z = [(a, b)(c, d)](e, f)$	Substitution
$= (ac, bd)(e, f)$	Definition of multiplication for rational numbers
$= ((ac)e, (bd)f)$	Definition of multiplication for rational numbers
$= (a(ce), b(df))$	Associative property of multiplication for integers
$= (a, b)(ce, df)$	Definition of multiplication for rational numbers
$= (a, b)[(c, d)(e, f)]$	Definition of multiplication for rational numbers
$= x \cdot (y \cdot z)$	Substitution

Thus multiplication on the set of rational numbers is associative.

Theorem 5.9 Multiplication on the set of rational numbers is commutative.

Proof The proof is left as an exercise for the reader.

Theorem 5.10 The rational number $(1, 1)$ is a multiplicative identity for the set of rational numbers.

Proof Let (c, d) be any rational number. Then

$(1, 1)(c, d) = (c, d)(1, 1)$	Commutative property of multiplication for rational numbers
$= (c \cdot 1, d \cdot 1)$	Definition of multiplication for rational numbers
$= (c, d)$	1 is the multiplicative identity for the set of integers

Thus $(1, 1)$ is a multiplicative identity for the set of rational numbers.

RATIONAL, REAL, AND COMPLEX NUMBERS

Again we state without proof that the multiplicative identity is unique except for the way it is represented. When ordered-pair representation is used, we will represent the multiplicative identity by the ordered pair $(1, 1)$. Otherwise, it will be represented simply by the symbol 1.

Up to this point in our discussion of number systems we have not mentioned the existence of multiplicative inverses. The reason for this is simple; few numbers have multiplicative inverses in either the system of natural numbers or the system of integers. However, we will show in the following theorem that every rational number, except 0, has a multiplicative inverse.

Theorem 5.11 Every rational number, except 0, has a multiplicative inverse. To be more specific, a multiplicative inverse of the nonzero rational number (a, b) is (b, a).

Proof Let (a, b) be any nonzero rational number. Then $a \neq 0$, and (b, a) is a rational number. It now follows that

$$
\begin{aligned}
(b, a)(a, b) &= (a, b)(b, a) && \text{Commutative property of multiplication} \\
& && \text{for rational numbers} \\
&= (ab, ba) && \text{Definition of multiplication for} \\
& && \text{rational numbers} \\
&= (ab, ab) && \text{Commutative property of multiplication} \\
& && \text{for integers} \\
&= (1, 1) && \text{Theorem 5.1}
\end{aligned}
$$

Therefore, a multiplicative inverse for the nonzero rational number (a, b) is the rational number (b, a).

Example 4 Find a multiplicative inverse of $(2, 3)$.

Solution $(3, 2)$ is a multiplicative inverse of $(2, 3)$ because

$$
\begin{aligned}
(2, 3)(3, 2) &= (2 \cdot 3, 3 \cdot 2) \\
&= (6, 6) \\
&= (1, 1).
\end{aligned}
$$

We remark that the multiplicative inverse of a nonzero rational number is unique. If (a, b) is any nonzero rational number, we will denote the multiplicative inverse of (a, b) by $(a, b)^{-1}$. Thus, $(a, b)^{-1} = (b, a)$. For example, $(3, 4)^{-1} = (4, 3)$ and $(-3, 5)^{-1} = (5, -3)$. If a single symbol, such as x, is used to represent a nonzero rational number, then the multiplicative inverse of the rational number x will be denoted by x^{-1}.

The reader may be somewhat concerned with the fact that we have not exhibited a multiplicative inverse for the rational number 0. Before explaining this omission, we remark that theorems analogous to Theorems 4.16 through

4.18 can be proved in the system of rational numbers. These will be left as exercises at the end of this section.

Suppose 0 has a multiplicative inverse x in the set of rational numbers. Then $0 \cdot x = 1$. However, the counterpart of Theorem 4.16 for rational numbers states that $0 \cdot x = 0$ for all rational numbers x. If we state the existence of a multiplicative inverse for the rational number 0, then we have a contradiction of this theorem. Hence, we do not exhibit a multiplicative inverse for the rational number 0.

To conclude this section, we state without proof that multiplication distributes over addition in the system of rational numbers.

Theorem 5.12 Multiplication distributes over addition in the set of rational numbers.

Problems

1 State the property that is needed to justify each of the following statements. Each symbol represents a rational number.

a) $(a + b)c = c(a + b)$ b) $(a + b)c = ac + bc$

c) $a + (b + c) = a + (c + b)$ d) ab is a rational number

e) $(ab)(cd) = a(b(cd))$ f) $(a + bc) + d = a + (bc + d)$

2 Use the definition of multiplication for rational numbers to find the following products.

a) $(2, 3)(3, 4)$ b) $(-5, 7)(4, 3)$

c) $(7, 8)(3, 10)$ d) $(-8, 9)(-7, 11)$

e) $(3, 5)(-5, 6)$ f) $(0, 7)(1, 3)$

3 Use the familiar notation for rational numbers to find the products in Problem 2.

4 Use the definition of multiplication for rational numbers to verify the associative property in each of the following.

a) $[(3, 8)(-2, 8)](2, 5) = (3, 8)[(-2, 8)(2, 5)]$

b) $[(7, 9)(3, 3)](0, 2) = (7, 9)[(3, 3)(0, 2)]$

5 Use the definition of multiplication for rational numbers to verify the commutative property in each of the following.

a) $(3, 8)(-5, 7) = (-5, 7)(3, 8)$

b) $(11, 13)(9, 22) = (9, 22)(11, 13)$

6 Use the appropriate definitions to verify the distributive property in each of the following.

a) $(5, 6)[(3, 8) + (9, 12)] = (5, 6)(3, 8) + (5, 6)(9, 12)$

b) $(1, 2)[(-3, 5) + (7, -8)] = (1, 2)(-3, 5) + (1, 2)(7, -8)$

7 Find the multiplicative inverse for each of the following.

   a) (2, 7)   b) (−3, 8)   c) (−4, −11)   d) (8, 1)

8 If a rational number x is its own multiplicative inverse, what is x?

9 Prove Theorem 5.9.

10 Prove that for any rational number z, $z \cdot 0 = 0$.

11 Let x, y, and z denote rational numbers with $z \neq 0$. Prove that $xz = yz$ implies $x = y$. This is the cancellation property for multiplication.

12 Let x and y be rational numbers such that $xy = 0$. Prove that $x \neq 0$ implies $y = 0$.

13 Let x denote a nonzero rational number. Prove that the multiplicative inverse of x is unique. [*Hint:* Assume that y and z are multiplicative inverses of x and show $y = z$.]

14 All the rules for multiplying signed numbers (see Section 4.13) apply to the rational numbers. For example, prove that $(−a)(b) = −(ab)$ for rational numbers a and b.

5.4 DIVISION OF RATIONAL NUMBERS

In keeping with the definition of division for integers in Section 4.15, we state the following definition of division for rational numbers.

Definition 5.6 If (a, b) and (c, d) are rational numbers, then $(a, b) \div (c, d) = (x, y)$ if and only if $(a, b) = (c, d)(x, y)$, and (x, y) is unique.

Example 1 Find the quotient $(3, 8) \div (1, 4)$.

Solution

$$(3, 8) \div (1, 4) = (x, y)$$

if and only if

$$(3, 8) = (1, 4)(x, y)$$
$$= (1 \cdot x, 4 \cdot y)$$
$$= (x, 4y).$$

From the definition of equality for rational numbers,

$$(3, 8) = (x, 4y)$$

if and only if

$$3(4y) = 8x,$$
$$12y = 8x,$$
$$3y = 2x.$$

If we let $x = 3$ and $y = 2$, we obtain one solution for the equation $3y = 2x$.

Thus $(3, 8) \div (1, 4) = (3, 2)$. For every rational number (x, y) such that $3y = 2x$, $(3, 8) \div (1, 4) = (x, y)$. However, every such rational number (x, y) is simply another representation for the rational number $(3, 2)$.

In Section 4.11 we observed that subtraction, when it can be performed, is the inverse operation of addition. We will show presently that division, when it can be performed, is the inverse operation of multiplication. To do this we must show that to divide (a, b) by the nonzero rational number (c, d) is equivalent to multiplying the multiplicative inverse of (c, d) by (a, b). For rational numbers (a, b) and (c, d), we have

$$(a, b) \div (c, d) = (x, y)$$

if and only if

$(a, b) = (c, d)(x, y)$ Definition of division for rational numbers

$ = (cx, dy)$ Definition of multiplication for rational numbers

Now

$$(a, b) = (cx, dy)$$

if and only if

$a(dy) = b(cx)$ Definition of equality for rational numbers

$(ad)y = (bc)x$ Associative property of multiplication for integers

$(ad, bc) = (x, y)$ Definition of equality for rational numbers

$(a, b)(d, c) = (x, y)$ Definition of multiplication for rational numbers

Thus, for rational numbers (a, b) and (c, d),

$$(a, b) \div (c, d) = (a, b)(d, c).$$

Example 2   Find the quotient $(3, 8) \div (1, 4)$.

Solution

$$
\begin{aligned}
(3, 8) \div (1, 4) &= (3, 8)(4, 1) \\
&= (12, 8) \\
&= (3, 2).
\end{aligned}
$$

By comparing Example 1 with Example 2, we see that the procedure in Example 2 is much easier. We now use this equivalent method for division to prove that the set of nonzero rational numbers is closed under division. In order to divide any rational number (a, b) by any nonzero rational number (c, d), it is sufficient to know that (c, d) has a multiplicative inverse and that the set of rational numbers is closed under multiplication. Both of these properties were proved in Section 5.3. Therefore, division in the set of nonzero rational numbers is always possible. It should be clear to the reader that this equivalent procedure for division is the procedure normally used in division of fractions. That is, to divide one fraction by another, invert the divisor and multiply. Because of our definition of division for rational numbers, division by 0 is still impossible. However, 0 divided by any nonzero rational number is always 0.

We recall that we were motivated to develop the rational number system by the desire to find a solution for every equation of the form $a = bx$, $b \neq 0$. We observed that if a and b are integers, some equations of this form do not have a solution in the set of integers. Let us consider all equations of the form $a = bx$, where a and b are rational numbers and $b \neq 0$. This is equivalent to stating that $x = a \div b$. Because $b \neq 0$, $a \div b$ is a rational number. Hence, $x = a \div b$ is a solution of the equation $a = bx$. Consequently, all equations of the form $a = bx$, where $b \neq 0$, have the solution $x = a \div b$ in the system of rational numbers.

Example 3 Solve the equation $3x + 5 = 0$ for x.

Solution This equation can be written in the form $-5 = 3x$, and from the preceding discussion we know that $x = -\frac{5}{3}$ is a solution of the equation.

Example 4 We will now solve the equation of Example 3 by another method.

$$3x + 5 = 0,$$
$$(3x + 5) + (-5) = 0 + (-5),$$
$$3x + (5 + (-5)) = 0 + (-5),$$
$$3x + 0 = 0 + (-5),$$
$$3x = -5,$$
$$x = \frac{-5}{3},$$
$$x = -\frac{5}{3}.$$

Problems

1 Find the following quotients.

a) $(3, 8) \div (1, 2)$
b) $(0, 4) \div (3, 5)$
c) $(7, -16) \div (3, 4)$
d) $(5, 7) \div (-7, 5)$
e) $(9, 13) \div (9, 13)$
f) $(7, 16) \div (-2, 3)$

2 Use Definition 5.6 to find $(7, 8) \div (1, 2)$.

3 Use the fractional notation for rational numbers to find each quotient in Problem 1.

4 State a property of the rational numbers to justify each step in solving the equation $3x + 5 = 0$ in Example 4.

5 Find a solution for each of the following equations.

    a) $3x = 6$ b) $2x - 12 = 0$ c) $-5x + 4 = 0$ d) $3x + 8 = 5$

6 Is division on the set of rational numbers associative? Explain.

7 Is division on the set of rational numbers commutative? Explain.

8 Under what conditions on the rational numbers a and b will $a \div b = b \div a$?

5.5 THE RATIONAL NUMBERS AND ORDER

Before stating the definition for "less than" on the set of rational numbers, we will show that every rational number (a, b) can be represented by an ordered pair of integers in which the second element is greater than zero. If $b > 0$, then (a, b) is in the desired form. Now, if $b < 0$, then we use Theorem 5.1 and

$$(a, b) = (a(-1), b(-1)) = (-a, -b).$$

Since $b < 0$, $-b > 0$, and thus $(-a, -b)$ is an ordered pair of integers in which the second element is greater than zero. For example, $(2, -3)$ can be represented by $(-2, 3)$, and $(-3, -4)$ by $(3, 4)$.

Definition 5.7 If (a, b) and (c, d) are rational numbers with $b > 0$ and $d > 0$, then

$$(a, b) < (c, d) \qquad \text{if and only if} \qquad ad < bc.$$

Further,

$$(a, b) > (c, d) \qquad \text{if and only if} \qquad (c, d) < (a, b).$$

Example 1

$(2, 3) < (3, 4)$	since	$2 \cdot 4 < 3 \cdot 3.$
$(5, 2) < (11, 3)$	since	$5 \cdot 3 < 2 \cdot 11.$
$(3, 4) > (2, 3)$	since	$(2, 3) < (3, 4).$
$(3, -4) < (2, 3)$	since	$(3, -4) = (-3, 4)$ and $(-3, 4) < (2, 3).$

Theorem 5.13 If $(a, b) < (c, d)$ and $(c, d) < (e, f)$, then $(a, b) < (e, f)$.

Proof We may assume (a, b), (c, d), and (e, f) are all ordered pairs of integers with their second elements greater than zero. By the hypothesis, $(a, b) < (c, d)$ and $(c, d) < (e, f)$. Then, by Definition 5.7,

$$ad < bc \qquad \text{and} \qquad cf < de.$$

Since $b > 0$ and $f > 0$ it follows from Theorem 4.23 that

$$adf < bcf \qquad \text{and} \qquad bcf < bde.$$

Therefore $adf < bde$, and by use of the associative and commutative properties of multiplication $(af)d < (be)d$. By Theorem 4.23, $af < be$ since $d > 0$, and it follows from Definition 5.7 that $(a, b) < (e, f)$.

Theorems analogous to Theorems 4.21 — 4.25 can be proved and are left as exercises for the reader.

Problems

1 Verify each of the following.

    a) $(1, 2) < (2, 3)$ b) $(5, 7) < (8, 9)$

    c) $(-3, 8) < (1, 8)$ d) $(5, -7) < (-1, 2)$

    e) $(0, -3) > (2, -3)$ f) $(-5, -9) > (3, 8)$

2 In each of the following find all values of x in the set of integers which will make the relationship true.

    a) $(x, 3) < (20, 5)$ b) $(3, x) < (5, 20)$

    c) $(x, 4) > (2, 3)$ d) $(7, 6) > (x, 5)$

3 Suppose x and y are rational numbers with $x < y$. If $y < \frac{5}{3}$, what can be said about x?

4 We again define $a \leq b$ to mean $a < b$ or $a = b$. Further, $a \geq b$ means that $a > b$ or $a = b$. What can you say about a and b if $a \geq b$ and $b \geq a$?

5 Find a rational number z such that $\frac{1}{3} < z < \frac{1}{2}$.

6 State and prove the Trichotomy Law for the rational numbers.

7 Prove that if x and y denote rational numbers, then for every rational number z, $x < y$ if and only if $x + z < y + z$.

8 Let x and y denote rational numbers. Prove that

    a) For every rational number $z > 0$, $x < y$ if and only if $xz < yz$.

    b) For every rational number $z < 0$, $x < y$ if and only if $xz > yz$.

9 Let x, y, z, and w denote rational numbers. Prove that if $x < y$ and $z < w$, then $x + z < y + w$.

10 Let x, y, z, and w denote positive rational numbers. Prove that if $x < y$ and $z < w$, then $xz < yw$.

5.6 THE DECIMAL FORM OF A RATIONAL NUMBER

Every rational number has a decimal representation which can be obtained by long division. This fact is illustrated by the following examples.

Example 1   The decimal form of the rational number $\frac{3}{8}$ is obtained by dividing 3 by 8. Dividing, we have

$$\frac{3}{8} = .375.$$

Example 2 By long division

$$\frac{327}{500} = .654.$$

The decimals obtained in Examples 1 and 2 are often called *finite* or *terminating* decimals. The following example will deal with a different kind of decimal.

Example 3 Find the decimal form of the rational number $\frac{1}{3}$.

Solution On dividing 1 by 3 we observe that the digit 3 is repeated indefinitely in the quotient. The decimal form of $\frac{1}{3}$ is .3333 . . . .

A decimal such as .3333 . . . is called a *nonterminating repeating* decimal. Actually all the decimals we have encountered so far in our examples can be classed as nonterminating repeating decimals. For example, we can write

$$.375 = .375000 . . . \quad \text{and} \quad .654 = .654000 . . . ,$$

thus giving the decimals .375 and .654 in the form of a nonterminating repeating decimal. It will be our practice from this point forward to refer to both the finite decimals and the nonterminating repeating decimals simply as *repeating* decimals. We now continue our discussion of repeating decimals.

Example 4 Find the decimal form of the rational number $\frac{3}{7}$.

Solution By long division, we have

```
        .428571428571 . . .
    7)3.0000000
      2 8
      ‾‾‾
        20
        14
        ‾‾
         60
         56
         ‾‾
          40
          35
          ‾‾
           50
           49
           ‾‾
            10
             7
            ‾‾
            30
```

After performing six steps in the division process we obtain the remainder 3 again. If we divide 30 by 7, we repeat the factor 4 in the quotient, and subsequent divisions will add the digits 2, 8, 5, 7, 1, ... Hence, $\frac{3}{7}$ can be represented by the repeating decimal .428571428571 . . . .

In writing repeating decimals it is customary to place a bar across the block of digits to be repeated. For example, we would write

$$.3333\ldots = .\overline{3}\ldots \quad \text{and} \quad .428571428571\ldots = .\overline{428571}\ldots$$

We shall follow this practice in our work with repeating decimals.

By the division algorithm (see Section 4.15) the remainders on division by 7 must be elements of the set $\{0, 1, 2, 3, 4, 5, 6\}$. Because this set is a finite set, one of these numbers must eventually reappear as a remainder, and thus any decimal obtained by using 7 as a divisor must be a repeating decimal. Let us now consider division by a positive integer m. In dividing by m, the remainders must be elements in the set $\{0, 1, 2, \ldots, m-1\}$. Thus one of the numbers of this set must reappear as a remainder. This implies that any decimal obtained by dividing by the positive integer m must be a repeating decimal. We do not mean to imply, however, that the repeating block must contain m digits, only that it can contain no more than m digits. Because every rational number can be written in the form n/m, n and m integers with $m > 0$, we can now conclude that every rational number can be represented by a repeating decimal.

It can also be shown that every repeating decimal represents a rational number. That is, for every repeating decimal we can find a rational number with that decimal representation. Instead of presenting a detailed proof of this property, we shall be content to illustrate the property with a sequence of examples.

Example 5 Find the rational number represented by the repeating decimal .$\overline{3}$ . . . .
Solution Let A = .333 . . . . We next multiply this number by 10 and subtract A from the result. Thus

$$\begin{array}{rl} 10A = & 3.333 \ldots \\ A = & .333 \ldots \\ \hline 9A = & 3.000 \ldots \end{array}$$

By subtracting A from $10A$ we have eliminated the decimal fraction .333 . . . . We now solve the equation $9A = 3$ to obtain $A = \frac{1}{3}$. Therefore, as we knew, the rational number $\frac{1}{3}$ is represented by the decimal .$\overline{3}$ . . . .

Example 6 Find the rational number represented by the repeating decimal 2.$\overline{325}$ . . . .

Solution Let $A = 2.325325 \ldots$. We will multiply the number A by 1000 because we can eliminate the decimal fraction $.325325 \ldots$ by subtracting A from this result. Thus

$$
\begin{array}{rl}
1000A = & 2325.\overline{325} \ldots \\
A = & 2.\overline{325} \ldots \\
\hline
999A = & 2323.000 \ldots
\end{array}
$$

Solving the equation $999A = 2323$ for A, we have $A = \frac{2323}{999}$. Hence the rational number $\frac{2323}{999}$ has the decimal representation $2.\overline{325} \ldots$.

Example 7 Find the rational number represented by the repeating decimal $3.5\overline{71} \ldots$.

Solution Let $A = 3.57171 \ldots$. If A if first multiplied by 1000 and then by 10, the repeating decimal blocks will be "aligned" and the decimal fraction can be eliminated by subtracting $10A$ from $1000A$. Thus

$$
\begin{array}{rl}
1000A = & 3571.\overline{71} \ldots \\
10A = & 35.\overline{71} \ldots \\
\hline
990A = & 3536.000 \ldots
\end{array}
$$

By solving the equation $990A = 3536$ and reducing the result to lowest terms we have

$$
A = \frac{1768}{495}.
$$

As a final example, we demonstrate the superiority of logical proof over intuitive understanding in showing that $.999 \ldots = 1$.

Example 8 Prove $.999 \ldots = 1$.

Proof Let $A = .999 \ldots$. If A is multiplied by 10, we have $10A = 9.99 \ldots$. After subtracting the members of the first equation from the respective numbers of the second equation, it follows that $9A = 9$, and thus $A = 1$. Therefore $.999 \ldots = 1$.

We summarize the results of this section by noting that every rational number can be represented by a repeating decimal. Conversely, as the examples suggest, every repeating decimal is a rational number.

Problems

1 Find the decimal representation for each of the following rational numbers.

   a) $\frac{1}{5}$ b) $\frac{5}{6}$ c) $\frac{7}{8}$

d) 25

e) $\frac{1}{7}$

f) $\frac{5}{7}$

g) $\frac{2}{13}$

h) $\frac{4286}{100000}$

i) $\frac{11}{17}$

2 Since $\frac{5}{83}$ is a rational number, it can be represented by a repeating decimal. What is the maximum number of digits that the repeating block can contain? Answer the same question for the number $\frac{8}{123}$.

3 Find the rational number represented by each of the following decimals.

a) .265

b) .777 . . .

c) $1.\overline{38}$ . . .

d) $.\overline{29}$ . . .

e) $5.\overline{763}$ . . .

f) $.\overline{001}$ . . .

g) $.\overline{714285}$ . . .

h) $2.3\overline{45}$ . . .

i) $.58\overline{909}$ . . .

5.7 SUMMARY OF THE PROPERTIES OF THE RATIONAL NUMBER SYSTEM

The rational number system is an example of a mathematical system which is of particular significance. For this reason we list those properties of the rational number system which are pertinent to the structure of a mathematical system.

1) The set of rational numbers is closed under addition.

2) Addition on the set of rational numbers is associative.

3) Addition on the set of rational numbers is commutative.

4) There exists an additive identity 0 for the set of rational numbers.

5) Each rational number has an additive inverse.

6) The set of rational numbers is closed under multiplication.

7) Multiplication on the set of rational numbers is associative.

8) Multiplication on the set of rational numbers is commutative.

9) There exists a multiplicative identity 1 for the set of rational numbers and $1 \neq 0$.

10) Every rational number, except the additive identity, has a multiplicative inverse.

11) Multiplication distributes over addition on the set of rational numbers.

It has been observed that all equations of the form $a = b + x$ and $a = bx, b \neq 0$, have solutions in the rational number system, and furthermore, that the set of rational numbers is closed under subtraction and division with nonzero divisors. Even though we have not listed all the properties we proved concerning the rational number system, the above eleven properties are the ones essential to the structure of the rational number system. These properties allow us to call the rational number system a *field*. The concept of a field is discussed more fully in Chapter 8.

5.8 IRRATIONAL NUMBERS

We were motivated to develop the system of integers and the system of rational numbers by our desire to have solutions to all equations of the form $a = b + x$ and $a = bx$, $b \neq 0$, respectively. In the development of the rational number system we observed that one is always able to perform the operations of addition, subtraction, multiplication, and nonzero division. Since the set of rational numbers is closed under these four basic operations, one might suppose that there is no need for further extensions of number. However, the solution of the equation $x^2 = 2$ requires a different kind of number. That is, there is no rational number x such that $x^2 = 2$. We will use the indirect method to prove the following theorem.

Theorem 5.14 There is no rational number x such that $x^2 = 2$.

Proof (by contradiction) Assume there is a rational number x such that $x^2 = 2$. Since x is a rational number, there are integers p and q with *no common factor* such that $x = p/q$. Now,

$$\left(\frac{p}{q}\right)^2 = 2,$$

$$\frac{p^2}{q^2} = 2,$$

$$p^2 = 2q^2.$$

Thus p^2 is an even integer. Using Problem 3 in Section 1.5, we know that if p^2 is an even integer, then p is an even integer. Therefore,

$$p = 2r$$

for some integer r, and

$$p^2 = 4r^2.$$

Since $p^2 = 2q^2$ and $p^2 = 4r^2$ we have

$$2q^2 = 4r^2 \quad \text{and} \quad q^2 = 2r^2.$$

Thus q^2 is an even integer, and hence q is an even integer. We have now shown p and q to both be even and therefore to have a common factor of 2. This contradicts the assumption that p and q have no common factor. We must reject our assumption and therefore conclude that there is no rational number x such that $x^2 = 2$.

The discovery that there is no rational number x such that $x^2 = 2$ was one of the greatest achievements of the Pythagoreans, the followers of the early mathematician Pythagoras (540 B.C.). Their approach was to show that

RATIONAL, REAL, AND COMPLEX NUMBERS

no rational number corresponds to the diagonal of a square having sides of length one. New numbers had to be invented to correspond to such quantities and, since they were not rational, they came to be called *irrational numbers.* The irrational number x such that $x^2 = 2$ is denoted by $\sqrt{2}$ and is called the *square root of 2.* The development of the irrational numbers from the rational numbers is beyond the scope of this book. However, it should be noted that Georg Cantor (1845–1918) and Richard Dedekind (1831–1916) presented rigorous developments of the irrational numbers. In the next section we will show how some irrational numbers can be approximated by rational numbers.

We will not make a thorough study of the irrational number system since it is not particularly interesting as far as its structure is concerned. However, observe that the set of irrational numbers is not closed under either addition or multiplication. Consider the following:

$$\sqrt{2} + (-\sqrt{2}) = 0 \quad \text{and} \quad \sqrt{2} \cdot \sqrt{2} = 2.$$

In the first example, we have exhibited two irrational numbers whose sum is a rational number. The second example illustrates that the product of two irrational numbers can be rational. Other examples of irrational numbers are $\sqrt{3}, \sqrt{5}, \sqrt[3]{2}$, and π, the ratio of the circumference of a circle to the diameter. You will be asked in the exercises to prove that the first three of these numbers are not rational, but the proof that π is irrational is beyond the scope of this text.

Problems

1. Prove $\sqrt{3}$ is not rational. That is, show that there is no rational number x such that $x^2 = 3$.
2. Prove $\sqrt{5}$ is not rational.
3. Prove $\sqrt[3]{2}$ is not rational. That is, show that there is no rational number x such that $x^3 = 2$.
4. Prove $1 + \sqrt{2}$ is not rational. [*Hint:* Use the knowledge that -1 is rational and that the set of rational numbers is closed under addition.]
5. Prove $3\sqrt{2}$ is not rational.
6. Prove $3 + 2\sqrt{3}$ is not rational.

5.9 THE REAL NUMBER SYSTEM

In Section 5.6 it was observed that every rational number has a decimal representation which is a repeating decimal. Furthermore, every repeating decimal has a rational number representation. Recall that a repeating decimal is either a terminating decimal or a nonterminating repeating decimal. From these remarks, it is clear that no irrational number can be expressed as a repeating decimal. We shall, however, show how the irrational number $\sqrt{2}$

can be approximated by repeating decimals. In the discussion that follows, we make use of the fact that if a and b are positive numbers with $a^2 < b^2$, then $a < b$.

Since $1^2 = 1$, $2^2 = 4$, and $1 < 2 < 4$, the number x such that $x^2 = 2$ must be between 1 and 2. Thus, $1 < \sqrt{2} < 2$. By trial and error we can find a better approximation. For example, $(1.4)^2 = 1.96$ and $(1.5)^2 = 2.25$, and since $1.96 < 2 < 2.25$, then $1.4 < \sqrt{2} < 1.5$. Further investigation shows that $(1.41)^2 = 1.9881$ and $(1.42)^2 = 2.0164$, and since $1.9881 < 2 < 2.0164$, then $1.41 < \sqrt{2} < 1.42$. This procedure can be carried out until accuracy in the desired place is achieved. It should be pointed out, however, that any terminating decimal is at best an approximation of $\sqrt{2}$, since the terminating decimal would have a rational number representation and $\sqrt{2}$ is an irrational number. Thus, we may use the following sequence to obtain approximations for $\sqrt{2}$. Since

$$1^2 = 1 < 2 < 4 = 2^2,$$
$$(1.4)^2 = 1.96 < 2 < 2.25 = (1.5)^2,$$
$$(1.41)^2 = 1.9881 < 2 < 2.0164 = (1.42)^2,$$
$$(1.414)^2 = 1.999396 < 2 < 2.002225 = (1.415)^2,$$
$$(1.4142)^2 = 1.99996164 < 2 < 2.00024449 = (1.4143)^2,$$

we have

$$1 < \sqrt{2} < 2,$$
$$1.4 < \sqrt{2} < 1.5,$$
$$1.41 < \sqrt{2} < 1.42,$$
$$1.414 < \sqrt{2} < 1.415,$$
$$1.4142 < \sqrt{2} < 1.4143.$$

From this we can conclude that the decimal approximation of $\sqrt{2}$, to the nearest thousandth, is 1.414. With a little imagination one sees that this procedure could be carried on endlessly, but never reaching a point at which we have a repeating decimal actually equaling the square root of 2.

Again we state that the development of the irrational numbers from the rational numbers is beyond the scope of this text, but it can be shown that the set of all infinite decimals, repeating or not, satisfies all the requirements of a number field. Therefore, we define the set of *real numbers* to be the set of infinite decimals, and this set of numbers under the operation of addition and multiplication forms a field. We have already seen that those infinite decimals which repeat represent rational numbers and every rational number has a repeating decimal representation. Thus, by definition, those infinite decimals which do not repeat represent irrational numbers.

As to notation, we will use the symbol R to represent the set of real numbers. The symbols 0 and 1 will represent the additive and multiplicative identities, respectively. It will be assumed that $0 \neq 1$. If x is a real number, then the additive inverse of x is denoted $-x$ and the multiplicative inverse of a nonzero number x is denoted x^{-1} and, in some cases, $1/x$. At this time the reader should review the properties of a field stated in Section 5.7.

Problems

1 Is the number 5.41411411141111 . . . a rational number? Explain.

2 Is the number 37.520520052000 . . . a rational number? Explain.

3 Use the method of this section to find the decimal approximation of $\sqrt{10}$ with accuracy to the nearest thousandth.

4 Use the method of this section to find the decimal approximation of $\sqrt{3}$ with accuracy to the nearest thousandth.

5 Use the method of this section to find the decimal approximation of $\sqrt{5}$ with accuracy to the nearest ten-thousandth.

6 Use the method of this section to find the decimal approximation of $5 + \sqrt{7}$ with accuracy to the nearest thousandth.

5.10 THE REAL NUMBERS AND ORDER

To define an order relation on the set of real numbers, we will assume the existence of a subset P, whose elements are called *positive real numbers*, which has the following properties.

The Additive Property If $x \in P$ and $y \in P$, then $x + y \in P$.

The Multiplication Property If $x \in P$ and $y \in P$, then $xy \in P$.

The Trichotomy Property If x is a real number, then exactly one of the following is true:

$$x \in P, \qquad -x \in P, \qquad \text{or} \qquad x = 0.$$

Having the set P of positive real numbers, we are now able to define the "less than" relation.

Definition 5.8 If x and y denote real numbers, then $x < y$ if and only if $y - x$ is an element of the set P of positive real numbers.

By $x > y$ we again mean that $y < x$. Further, $x \leq y$ means that $x < y$ or $x = y$, and $x \geq y$ means that $x > y$ or $x = y$. Finally, $a < x < b$ means $a < x$ and $x < b$. Other combinations will be used when convenient.

By using Definition 5.8 and the properties of the set P, we can obtain all the familiar properties of the order relations. For example, if a, b, and c are real numbers such that $a < b$ and $b < c$, then $a < c$. To prove this property, we note by hypothesis that both $b - a$ and $c - b$ are elements of P. Hence,

$$(b - a) + (c - b) = c - a$$

is also an element of P because the sum of two positive real numbers is a positive real number. Knowing that $c - a$ is a positive real number, we can state by Definition 5.8 that $a < c$. This result is contained in the following theorem.

Theorem 5.15 If a, b, and c are real numbers with $a < b$ and $b < c$, then $a < c$.

Some of the other properties of the order relations are found in the following theorems.

Theorem 5.16 If a is a real number, then exactly one of the following is true:

$$a > 0, \qquad -a > 0 \qquad \text{or} \qquad a = 0.$$

We note that writing $a > 0$ is equivalent to stating that a is an element of the set P. Hence Theorem 5.16 is equivalent to the Trichotomy Property.

Theorem 5.17 If a, b, and c are real numbers with $a < b$, then $a + c < b + c$.

Theorem 5.18 Suppose a, b, and c are real numbers and $a < b$. If $c > 0$, then $ac < bc$. However, if $c < 0$, then $ac > bc$.

Proof We shall prove the first part and leave the second part for the reader. Because $a < b$, we know by Definition 5.8 that $b - a$ is a positive real number. Further, $c > 0$ also means that c is a positive real number. Hence, by the multiplication property, the product $(b - a)c = bc - ac$ is an element of P. Because $bc - ac$ is a positive real number, we conclude by Definition 5.8 that $ac < bc$.

Theorem 5.19 If a, b, c, and d are real numbers with $a < b$ and $c < d$, then

$$a + c < b + d.$$

The square of any real number is either 0 or a positive real number. That is, if x is a real number, then $x^2 \geq 0$. If $x = 0$, the result is obvious. Suppose $x > 0$. Then x^2 is the product of two positive numbers, and hence $x^2 > 0$. Suppose $-x > 0$. Then $x^2 = (-x)(-x)$ is a product of two positive numbers, and we again conclude that $x^2 > 0$. In particular, we might note that there is no real number x such that $x^2 = -1$.

RATIONAL, REAL, AND COMPLEX NUMBERS

Problems

1 Suppose $x < y$. How is $3x$ related to $3y$? How is $-2x$ related to $-2y$?

2 Suppose $x > y$. How is $x + 2$ related to $y + 2$? How is $x - 5$ related to $y - 5$?

3 How are x and y related if $x \leq y$ and $y \leq x$?

4 Suppose $x \in P$ and $-y \in P$. Is $xy \in P$? Is $-(xy) \in P$?

5 If $x < 3$ and $y < -5$, what can be said about $x + y$?

6 Find the set of real numbers x that satisfy the relation $x + 2 < -9$.

7 Show that if $a > 0$, then $a \in P$. Show also that if $a \in P$, then $a > 0$. You have now proved that writing $a > 0$ is equivalent to stating that $a \in P$.

8 On the assumption that $1 \neq 0$, prove that $1 > 0$. [*Hint:* Either $1 > 0$ or $-1 > 0$. Assume $-1 > 0$.]

9 Prove Theorem 5.17.

10 Prove the second part of Theorem 5.18.

11 Prove Theorem 5.19.

12 Is there a least real number x such that $x > 0$? Justify your answer.

5.11 THE NUMBER LINE

Every real number can be represented by a point on a line. Such a line is called a *number line*. To construct a number line we locate two points on a line L, the point on the left representing the number 0 and the point on the right representing the number 1 (see Fig. 5.1).

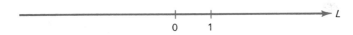

Figure 5.1

The points used to represent the numbers 0 and 1 are said to have the *coordinates* 0 and 1, respectively, and in general, if a point P represents the number a, then a is said to be the coordinate of P. To represent the other positive integers we start at the point with coordinate 1 and mark off to the right of this point equal segments, each segment having the same length as the initial segment joining the points with coordinates 0 and 1. By following a similar procedure, starting at the point representing 0 and moving to the left, we locate points to represent the negative integers (see Fig. 5.2).

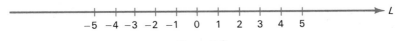

Figure 5.2

Now let us consider a positive rational number m/n. To locate the point on L corresponding to m/n we first locate the point corresponding to the rational number $1/n$. This point can be located by procedures from plane geometry. Since $m/n = m(1/n)$, we locate the point corresponding to m/n by beginning at the point corresponding to 0 and laying off, to the right along L, m consecutive segments having the same length as the segment from 0 to $1/n$. The terminal point corresponds to m/n. By laying off segments to the left of 0, we can also locate the point corresponding to the negative rational number $-(m/n)$. Thus we are able to associate with every rational number a point on line L. Figure 5.3 shows how we would locate the points corresponding to $\frac{5}{3}$ and $-\frac{4}{3}$, assuming we have found the point corresponding to $\frac{1}{3}$.

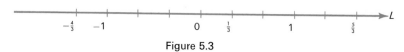

Figure 5.3

There is no single procedure that can be used to represent all the irrational numbers, and hence each case must be treated individually. We shall limit our discussion to the number $\sqrt{2}$. A method for locating the point with coordinate π will be discussed in the problems at the end of this section.

To locate the point on the line L that represents the number $\sqrt{2}$ we construct an isosceles right triangle (a triangle with two equal sides and a right angle), with one of the equal sides coinciding with the segment joining the points with coordinates 0 and 1 and with the right angle at the point with coordinate 1 (see Fig. 5.4). By the Pythagorean Theorem the hypotenuse of the triangle has length $\sqrt{2}$.

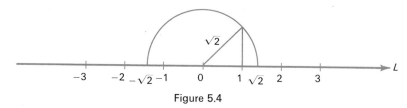

Figure 5.4

The points representing $\sqrt{2}$ and $-\sqrt{2}$ are then located by intersecting the circle with center at 0 and radius $\sqrt{2}$ with L: $\sqrt{2}$ is the point of intersection to the right of 0 and $-\sqrt{2}$ is the point of intersection to the left of 0. Both points appear in Fig. 5.4.

After a point has been located to represent each real number, the line L is called a number line. The number line establishes a one-to-one correspondence between the set of real numbers and the sets of points on line L. The choice of the points to represent the numbers 0 and 1 is quite important because each different pair of points determines a different number line. Hence the set of all number lines is an infinite set.

We observe that if $a < b$, the point on a number line with coordinate a is to the left of the point with coordinate b. As one would now expect, if $a > b$, then the point representing the number a is to the right of the point representing the number b. A number line gives us a geometric method for interpreting the relations $<$ and $>$. Furthermore, a number line provides a method of picturing subsets of the real numbers. Consider the following examples.

Example 1   On a number line darken the portion that represents the set of numbers $\{x \mid -1 \leqq x \leqq 5\}$.

Solution

The brackets are used at -1 and 5 to indicate that -1 and 5 are to be included in the representation.

Example 2   On a number line darken the portion that represents the set of numbers $\{x \mid -1 < x < 5\}$.

Solution

The parentheses are used at -1 and 5 to indicate that -1 and 5 are *not* to be included in the representation. The next example combines the use of the brackets and parenthesis.

Example 3   On a number line darken the portion that represents the set of numbers $\{x \mid -1 < x \leqq 5\}$.

Solution

The parenthesis at -1 indicates -1 is *not* to be included, whereas the bracket at 5 indicates 5 is to be included.

In each of the above examples, we darken the number line between the real numbers a and b to indicate we are considering *all* real numbers between *a* and *b*. The next example is one in which we are concerned only with the set of integers between two given real numbers.

Example 4 On a number line darken the portion that represents the set of numbers $\{x \mid x \text{ is an integer and } -1 \leq x < 5\}$.

Solution In this example we want to represent the set $\{-1, 0, 1, 2, 3, 4\}$ on a number line. The number line representation is

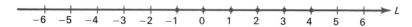

Problems

1 Draw a number line and for each of the following numbers locate a point having that number as its coordinate.

    a) 3 b) -5 c) $\frac{3}{2}$

    d) $-\frac{5}{4}$ e) $\frac{10}{3}$ f) $-\frac{3}{5}$

    g) $-\sqrt{2}$ h) $\sqrt{5}$ i) $\sqrt{13}$

2 On a number line darken the portion that represents the set of numbers $\{x \mid 1 \leq x \leq \frac{5}{2}\}$.

3 On a number line darken the portion that represents the set of numbers $\{x \mid -5 \leq x \leq -2\}$.

4 On a number line darken the portion that represents the set of numbers $\{x \mid -\frac{1}{2} < x < 3\}$.

5 On a number line darken the portion that represents the set of numbers $\{x \mid \frac{2}{3} \leq x \leq \frac{5}{2}\}$.

6 On a number line darken the portion that represents the set

$$\{x \mid x \text{ is an integer, and } -3 \leq x < 5\}.$$

7 On a number line darken the portion that represents the set

$$\{x \mid x \text{ is an integer and } -\frac{1}{2} < x \leq \frac{13}{2}\}.$$

8 If a point with coordinate x is to the left of a point with coordinate y on a number line, how is x related to y?

9 If a point with coordinate x is to the right of a point with coordinate y on a number line, how is x related to y?

10 What portion of a number line represents the set of all positive real numbers? What portion represents the set of all negative real numbers? Does the point with coordinate 0 belong to either of these sets of points?

11 If a circle with diameter 1 is placed on a number line with a point P on the circle coinciding with the point having coordinate 0, then the point

                                         RATIONAL, REAL, AND COMPLEX NUMBERS

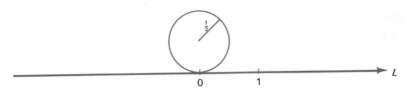

having the coordinate π can be located by "rolling" the circle to the right until the point P "touches" the number line again. In this way locate on a number line the point having coordinate π.

5.12 ABSOLUTE VALUE AND DISTANCE

To aid us in our discussion of a number line we now define the *absolute value* of a real number x.

Definition 5.9 The *absolute value* of a real number x is denoted by the symbol $|x|$ and is defined as follows:

$$1)\ |x| = x, \text{ if } x \geq 0.$$
$$2)\ |x| = -x, \text{ if } x < 0.$$

Example 1 Using the preceding definition, we have:

$|3| = 3$	because	$3 \geq 0.$
$|-5| = -(-5) = 5$	because	$-5 < 0.$
$|-\frac{3}{4}| = -(-\frac{3}{4}) = \frac{3}{4}$	because	$-\frac{3}{4} < 0.$
$|0| = 0$	because	$0 \geq 0.$
$|\pi| = \pi$	because	$\pi \geq 0.$

Definition 5.9 can be used to establish several interesting properties of absolute values. Some of these are contained in the following theorem.

Theorem 5.20 If a and b denote real numbers, then

1) $|a| \geq 0$, and furthermore, $|a| = 0$ if and only if $a = 0$.
2) $|a| = |-a|$.   3) $a \leq |a|$.
4) $|ab| = |a||b|$.   5) $|a + b| \leq |a| + |b|$.

Proof We shall prove parts (1) and (2) and leave the others for the reader. If a is a real number, then we can prove $|a| \geq 0$ by considering cases. If $a \geq 0$, then by definition $|a| = a$, and hence $|a| \geq 0$. If $a < 0$, then by definition $|a| = -a$. Since $a < 0$, $-a > 0$, and thus $|a| = -a > 0$. The other part of (1) will be listed as a problem at the end of this section.

To prove (2) we again consider cases. If $a = 0$, then $-a = 0$. Thus $|a| = |-a| = 0$ by definition. If $a > 0$, then $-a < 0$. Hence $|a| = a$ and $|-a| = -(-a) = a$. Therefore $|a| = |-a|$. If $a < 0$, then $-a > 0$, and again by definition, $|a| = -a$ and $|-a| = -a$. Therefore, once again we have $|a| = |-a|$. This proves part (2).

As a consequence of Theorem 5.20, we note that the absolute value of a number is either positive or 0. The absolute value of a number can never be negative.

We shall now discuss the problem of finding the *distance* from one point on a number line to another point. If the points have coordinates 3 and 8, then obviously we would want the distance between the points to be 5, or $8 - 3$. Likewise, if the points have coordinates $\frac{8}{3}$ and $\frac{5}{3}$, we would want the distance to be $\frac{3}{3} = 1$, or $\frac{8}{3} - \frac{5}{3}$. We might now be inclined to state that the distance from point a with coordinate a to the point with coordinate b is the difference $a - b$. However, if we are not careful, $a - b$ could be a negative number, and a negative distance is not consistent with our previous experience. For example, if in considering the distance from the point with coordinate 3 to the point with coordinate 8, we had taken the difference $3 - 8$, our result would have been -5 instead of 5. Hence the result depends on the order in which we subtract. If we choose one difference, the result is positive, whereas if we choose the other, the result is negative. This problem is easily solved, and we now use the concept of absolute value to state precisely the definition of distance from one point on a number line to another point.

Definition 5.10 Let x and y denote real numbers. The *distance* from the point with coordinate x to the point with coordinate y, denoted $d(x, y)$, is defined by the equation

$$d(x, y) = |y - x|.$$

We now illustrate Definition 5.10 with a set of examples.

Example 2

a) $d(3, 12) = |12 - 3| = |9| = 9.$

In words, we are saying that the distance from the point with coordinate 3 to the point with coordinate 12 is 9. Other examples follow.

b) $d(0, -3) = |-3 - 0| = |-3| = 3.$

c) $d(-3, -1) = |(-1) - (-3)| = |-1 + 3| = |2| = 2.$

d) $d(\frac{5}{3}, -\frac{8}{3}) = |-\frac{8}{3} - \frac{5}{3}| = |-\frac{13}{3}| = \frac{13}{3}.$

e) $d(-\frac{8}{3}, \frac{5}{3}) = |\frac{5}{3} - (-\frac{8}{3})| = |\frac{13}{3}| = \frac{13}{3}.$

f) $d(6, 6) = |6 - 6| = |0| = 0.$

An inspection of Example 2 suggests several properties of distance. First, as we expected, the distance from one point to another is either positive or 0. Parts (d) and (e) of Example 2 would suggest that perhaps $d(x, y) = d(y, x)$ for numbers x and y. These and other properties of distance are stated in the following theorem.

Theorem 5.21   If a, b and c denote real numbers, then

1) $d(a, b) = d(b, a)$.
2) $d(a, b) = 0$ if and only if $a = b$.
3) $d(a, b) \leq d(a, c) + d(c, b)$.

Proof To prove (1) we know by Definition 5.10 that $d(a, b) = |b - a|$ and $d(b, a) = |a - b|$. Thus

$$d(a, b) = |b - a|$$
$$= |-(a - b)|$$
$$= |a - b|$$
$$= d(b, a).$$

Therefore $d(a, b) = d(b, a)$.

To prove (2) we first assume that $d(a, b) = 0$.   Because $d(a, b) = |b - a|$, we must have $|b - a| = 0$.   Hence, by part (1) of Theorem 5.20, $b - a = 0$ and $a = b$.

Continuing with the proof of (2) we now assume $a = b$. Thus $b - a = 0$ and $|b - a| = 0$. Therefore $d(a, b) = 0$.

The proof of part (3) will be listed as a problem at the end of this section.

We remark that part (3) of Theorem 5.21 is often called the "triangular inequality" because of its similarity to a theorem in geometry which states that the sum of the lengths of two sides of a triangle must always exceed the length of the third side.

Problems

1 Find the value for each of the following.

    a) $|8|$ b) $|-5|$ c) $|0|$

    d) $|-\pi|$ e) $|\frac{14}{3}|$ f) $|9 - 12|$

2 Find the set of *integers* that satisfy each of the following relations.

    a) $|n| < 2$ b) $|n| \leq 5$

    c) $|m| = -1$ d) $|m - 1| < 3$

3 If $|x| = -|x|$, what is x?

4 If $x > 0$, what is the value of $|-x|$? What is the value of $|-(-x)|$?

5 Prove that $|a| = 0$ if and only if $a = 0$.

6 Prove that $|a| = |-a|$. [*Hint:* Prove the property first for $x \geq 0$ and then for $x < 0$.]

7 Find the following distances.

    a) $d(-2, 3)$ b) $d(0, -8)$ c) $d(-3, -7)$

    d) $d(-7, -3)$ e) $d(5, 5)$ f) $d(9, 2)$

8 For what values of x is $d(-3, x) = 2$?

9 For what values of x is $d(-3, x) = -2$?

10 How are a and b related if $d(a, b) = 0$?

11 Prove part (3) of Theorem 5.21.

    [*Hint:* Write $|b - a| = |(c - a) + (b - c)|$ and apply a property of absolute values.]

5.13 THE COMPLEX NUMBERS

The development of the system of integers, the system of rational numbers, and the system of real numbers was motivated by our desire to solve certain types of equations. For example, we found that some equations of the form $a = b + x$, a and b natural numbers, did not have solutions in the system of natural numbers. However, considered as equations in the system of integers, all such equations had a solution. Later, we discovered that some equations of the form $a = bx$, a and b integers with $b \neq 0$, had no solutions in the system of integers. Hence the development of the system of rational numbers. We encountered the same kind of problem in the system of rational numbers with equations such as $x^2 = 2$ and thus we constructed the system of real numbers. The problem is still with us, for we discovered in Section 5.10 that there is no real number x such that $x^2 = -1$. We now create our last number system, a system of numbers whose elements will be called *complex numbers* and a system in which equations like $x^2 = -1$ have solutions. The development is similar to that of the system of integers and the system of rational numbers, and we will depend on the reader ot supply many of the details. The concept of an ordered pair is used once again in the following definition.

Definition 5.11 If a and b denote real numbers, then the ordered pair (a, b) is called a *complex number*. The set of all complex numbers will be denoted by the symbol C, and thus

$$C = \{(a, b) \mid a \text{ and } b \text{ are real numbers}\}.$$

Example 1 Some examples of complex numbers are $(-3, \sqrt{2})$, $(0, 0)$, $(5, -\pi)$, $(16, 30)$, and $(9, -7/3)$.

Two complex numbers (a, b) and (c, d) are equal if and only if $a = c$ and $b = d$. Thus the only values of a and b for which $(a, b) = (\pi, \frac{1}{2})$ are the values $a = \pi$ and $b = \frac{1}{2}$.

Out next step in developing the system of complex numbers will be to define two operations on this set of numbers. These operations will be given the familiar names of addition and multiplication. It will be assumed throughout the following discussion that an ordered pair of numbers is always an ordered pair of real numbers and hence a complex number.

Definition 5.12 Addition of complex numbers is defined by the equation

$$(a, b) + (c, d) = (a + c, b + d).$$

Definition 5.13 Multiplication of complex numbers is defined by the equation

$$(a, b)(c, d) = (ac - bd, ad + bc).$$

These definitions are illustrated by the following example.

Example 2

a) $(2, -3) + (-4, 5) = (2 + (-4), -3 + 5) = (-2, 2).$

b) $(2, -3)(-4, 5) = (2(-4) - (-3)(5), (2)(5) + (-3)(-4))$
$$= (-8 + 15, 10 + 12) = (7, 22).$$

c) $(\sqrt{2}, 3/2) + (0, 0) = (\sqrt{2} + 0, 3/2 + 0) = (\sqrt{2}, 3/2).$

d) $(\pi, -2)(1, 0) = (\pi(1) - (-2)(0), \pi(0) + (-2)(1))$
$$= (\pi, -2).$$

Using Definition 5.12, Definition 5.13, and the properties of the system of real numbers, we can prove that the set of complex numbers is closed under the operations of addition and multiplication. Further, both addition and multiplication are associative and commutative, and multiplication distributes over addition. The proof of the associative property of addition is typical, and we shall limit our discussion to a description of that proof. If (a, b), (c, d), and (e, f) are complex numbers, then

$$\begin{aligned}((a, b) + (c, d)) + (e, f) &= (a + c, b + d) + (e, f)\\ &= ((a + c) + e, (b + d) + f)\\ &= (a + (c + e), b + (d + f))\\ &= (a, b) + (c + e, d + f)\\ &= (a, b) + ((c, d) + (e, f)).\end{aligned}$$

It can easily be verified that $(0, 0)$ is an additive identity and $(1, 0)$ is a multiplicative identity. Further, it can be proved that these identity elements are unique; they will frequently be denoted by the symbols 0 and 1, respectively. One can easily prove that $(-a, -b)$ is an additive inverse of the complex number (a, b). This element is unique, and when a single symbol such as x is used to denote a complex number, its additive inverse will be denoted as usual by $-x$. Each *nonzero* complex number has a unique multiplicative inverse (this will be discussed later in the chapter), and the multiplicative inverse of a nonzero complex number x is represented by the symbol x^{-1} or, if it is convenient, by the symbol $1/x$. We can now summarize the properties of the system of complex numbers by stating that the system is a *field* with respect to the operations of addition and multiplication. Subtraction and division will be discussed later in this section.

Once again we can identify the set of real numbers with a subset of the set of complex numbers. For example, the real number a can be identified with the complex number $(a, 0)$. The set of complex numbers

$$\{(a, 0) \mid a \text{ is a real number}\}$$

will behave exactly like the real numbers with respect to the operations of addition and multiplication, and when it is convenient, we shall use $(a, 0)$ and a interchangeably.

An order relation has been introduced in each of the number systems we have discussed thus far. Without elaboration, we now state that it will not be possible to define an order relation on the set of complex numbers.

We may recall that the development of the system of complex numbers was motivated by the desire to solve equations like $x^2 = -1$. This equation has a solution in the system of complex numbers. For instance, $(0, 1)$ is a complex number, and

$$(0, 1)^2 = (0, 1)(0, 1) = (-1, 0),$$

which we have identified with the real number -1. Thus, $x = (0, 1)$ is a solution of the equation $x^2 = -1$.

The concept of a complex number was used about the middle of the sixteenth century by the mathematician J. Cardan, who found a solution to the problem of finding two numbers whose sum is 10 and whose product is 40. However, it was not until near the close of the eighteenth century that complex numbers were freely used by mathematicians in solving equations. In Chapter 6 we shall study a variety of equations having complex solutions.

Complex numbers are often introduced as numbers of the form $a + bi$, where a and b are real numbers and i has the property that $i^2 = -1$. Using this notation, the complex number $(2, \pi)$ is written $2 + \pi i$, $(1/2, \sqrt{2})$ is written $1/2 + \sqrt{2}\, i$, $(0, 1)$ is written $0 + 1i$, etc. In computational problems this approach is perhaps more convenient because we can rely more heavily on our previous experience with real numbers and eliminate the need for memorizing a collection of formulas for performing operations on the complex numbers. If this notation is employed, then addition is defined by the equation

$$(a + bi) + (c + di) = (a + c) + (b + d)i.$$

Subtraction can be performed as follows:

$$(a + bi) - (c + di) = (a - c) + (b - d)i.$$

RATIONAL, REAL, AND COMPLEX NUMBERS

The product of two complex numbers is defined by the equation

$$(a + bi)(c + di) = (ac - bd) + (ad + bc)i.$$

The student need not memorize the latter formula because he can obtain the product by using the customary rules for multiplying two binomials, remembering that $i^2 = -1$. The following example will illustrate this procedure.

√ Example 3 Find $(2 + 3i)(-5 + 2i)$.

Solution We proceed as we would in multiplying any two binomials.

$$
\begin{aligned}
(2 + 3i)(-5 + 2i) &= -10 + 4i - 15i + 6i^2 \\
&= -10 + 4i - 15i + 6(-1) \\
&= -16 - 11i.
\end{aligned}
$$

After finding the product in the usual way, we replace i^2 by -1 and write the result in the form $a + bi$, a and b being real numbers.

If $z = a + bi$ is a complex number, then $\bar{z} = a - bi$ is called the *complex conjugate* of the number z. For example, the complex conjugate of $\pi + 3i$ is $\pi - 3i$ and the complex conjugate of $2 - \sqrt{2}\,i$ is $2 + \sqrt{2}\,i$. We observe that the conjugate of a real number $a = a + 0i$ is simply a. The use of the complex conjugate will be an aid in performing the operation of division in the set of complex numbers. A procedure for dividing two complex numbers is illustrated in the next example.

⌋ Example 4 Find the quotient

$$\frac{2 + 3i}{-5 + 2i}$$

and write the result in the form $a + bi$.

Solution The first step in finding the quotient will be to multiply the numerator and denominator of this expression by the complex conjugate of the denominator. Thus, we have

$$
\begin{aligned}
\frac{2 + 3i}{-5 + 2i} &= \frac{2 + 3i}{-5 + 2i}\,\frac{-5 - 2i}{-5 - 2i} \\
&= \frac{-10 - 4i - 15i - 6i^2}{25 + 10i - 10i - 4i^2} \\
&= \frac{-10 - 4i - 15i - 6(-1)}{25 + 10i - 10i - 4(-1)} \\
&= \frac{-4 - 19i}{29} = \frac{-4}{29} - \frac{19}{29}i.
\end{aligned}
$$

Hence
$$(2 + 3i) \div (-5 + 2i) = -\frac{4}{29} - \frac{19}{29}i.$$

Example 5 Find the multiplicative inverse for the complex number $2 + 3i$ and write the inverse in the form $a + bi$.

Solution The multiplicative inverse for $2 + 3i$ is

$$\frac{1}{2 + 3i}$$

and

$$\frac{1}{2 + 3i} = \frac{1}{2 + 3i} \cdot \frac{2 - 3i}{2 - 3i}$$

$$= \frac{2 - 3i}{4 - 9i^2}$$

$$= \frac{2 - 3i}{13}$$

$$= \frac{2}{13} - \frac{3}{13}i.$$

The inverse for any nonzero complex number $a + bi$ can be found by a method similar to that used in Example 5. This problem will be left to the reader.

Problems

1 Perform the following operations and reduce all answers to the form $a + bi$.

a) $(3 - i) + (-2 + 5i)$ b) $(-6 - 5i) - (2 - i)$

c) $(5 + 9i) + (-3 - 13i)$ d) $(-3 + i)(2 - 3i)$

e) $\dfrac{1}{i}$ f) $(1 + i)^3$ g) $\dfrac{1 + i}{1 - i}$

h) $\dfrac{2 - 3i}{3 + 4i}$ i) $\dfrac{i}{\sqrt{2} + i}$ j) i^{123}

2 Find the additive inverse for each of the following complex numbers.

a) $(2, -3)$ b) $(-\pi, 1)$ c) $(0, 0)$ d) $(8, 5/4)$

3 Find a solution for each of the following equations.

a) $x^2 = -4$ b) $x^2 = 16$

c) $2x^2 + 3 = -29$ d) $x^2 + 9 = 0$

4 Is the set $S = \{1, -1, i, -i\}$ closed with respect to addition? with respect to multiplication? Justify your answers.

RATIONAL, REAL, AND COMPLEX NUMBERS

5 Find the multiplicative inverse for each of the following complex numbers and write the result in the form $a + bi$.

a) $2i$ b) $1 + i$ c) $2 - 3i$

d) -5 e) $-4 + 5i$ f) $1 + \sqrt{2}\,i$

6 Let $a + bi$ denote a nonzero complex number. Find the multiplicative inverse for this number and write the result in the form $x + iy$.

7 In this section we proved that addition of complex numbers is associative. Justify each step of this proof.

8 Show that $(0, 0)$ is the additive identity for C. Show also that $(1, 0)$ is the multiplicative identity for C.

9 Prove that addition of complex numbers is commutative.

10 Prove that multiplication of complex numbers is commutative.

11 Let $z = a + bi$. If $\bar{z}$ denotes the conjugate of z, find $\bar{\bar{z}}$.

12 Prove that multiplication distributes over addition in the set of complex numbers.

Chapter 6

FUNCTIONS AND GRAPHS

6.1 THE CONCEPT OF A RELATION

The Cartesian product of two sets A and B was defined in Section 2.5 by the equation

$$A \times B = \{(x, y) \mid x \in A \text{ and } y \in B\}.$$

That is, the Cartesian product $A \times B$ is the collection of all ordered pairs that can be formed by choosing the first element from A and the second element from B. We continue this section with the following definition.

Definition 6.1 Let A and B denote sets. A *relation from A to B* is a subset of the set $A \times B$.

Even though a relation is a set, we will usually represent a relation by a lower-case letter of the alphabet. This is contrary to the convention followed in Chapter 2, where sets were represented by capital letters of the alphabet. If r is a relation from A to B and $(x, y) \in r$, we will sometimes write $x \, r \, y$. We note that $x \, r \, y$ does not have the same meaning as $y \, r \, x$; $x \, r \, y$ means $(x, y) \in r$, whereas $y \, r \, x$ means $(y, x) \in r$.

Definition 6.2 Let r denote a relation from A to B. The *domain* of r, denoted $D(r)$, is the set

$$D(r) = \{x \mid x \in A \text{ and } (x, y) \in r \text{ for some } y \in B\}.$$

The *range* of r, denoted $R(r)$, is the set

$$R(r) = \{y \mid y \in B \text{ and } (x, y) \in r \text{ for some } x \in A\}.$$

To rephrase Definition 6.2, the domain of a relation r is the set of all first elements of the ordered pairs which define r, and the range of r is the set of all second elements of the ordered pairs which define r. The concept of a relation will be illustrated by the following examples.

Example 1 Let $A = \{1, 2, 3\}$ and $B = \{2, 4, 6\}$. Then

$A \times B = \{(1, 2), (1, 4), (1, 6), (2, 2), (2, 4), (2, 6), (3, 2), (3, 4), (3, 6)\}$.

If

$$r = \{(1, 2), (2, 2), (3, 2)\},$$

then $r \subset A \times B$, and hence r, is a relation from A to B. The domain of r is the set $D(r) = \{1, 2, 3\}$, and the range of r is the set $R(r) = \{2\}$. Other examples of relations from A to B are the sets

$$f = \{(3, 2)\},$$
$$g = \{(2, 2), (2, 4), (2, 6)\},$$
$$h = \{(1, 2), (1, 6), (2, 4), (3, 2), (3, 6)\}.$$

To further illustrate the meaning of the terms "domain" and "range" we note that $D(h) = \{1, 2, 3\}$ and $R(h) = \{2, 4, 6\}$. Thus, for the relation h, we have $D(h) = A$ and $R(h) = B$. The sets $\emptyset$ and $A \times B$ are also examples of relations from A to B because both $\emptyset$ and $A \times B$ are subsets of $A \times B$.

Example 2 Let $A = \{1, 2, 3\}$ and $B = \{2, 3, 4\}$. If

$$r = \{(x, y) \mid x \in A, y \in B \text{ and } x < y\},$$

then r is a relation from A to B. To be more specific, we have

$$r = \{(1, 2), (1, 3), (1, 4), (2, 3), (2, 4), (3, 4)\}.$$

Thus, $D(r) = \{1, 2, 3\} = A$ and $R(r) = \{2, 3, 4\} = B$.

In dealing with relations from a set A to a set B, we find that set A is frequently equal to set B. If S denotes a set, then any subset of $S \times S$ is called a *relation on* S.

Example 3 Let $S = \{\nabla, *, \phi\}$. Then

$$f = \{(\nabla, \nabla), (\nabla, *), (*, \phi)\},$$
$$g = \{(\phi, \nabla)\}, h = \{(\nabla, \nabla), (*, *), (\phi, \phi)\}$$

and

$$s = \{(*, \phi), (*, \nabla)\}$$

are examples of relations on S because each of these sets is a subset of $S \times S$.

The concept of a relation was first discussed in Section 4.5. In that section we used phrases such as "is the same as," "is the sister of," and "is less than" to define relations. This intuitive approach to relations is equivalent to the more precise definition of this section. For example, the relation defined on the set R of real numbers by the phrase "is the same as" is the relation

$$r = \{(x, y) \mid x \in R, y \in R \text{ and } x \text{ is the same number as } y\}.$$

Thus r is the relation of equality on the set of real numbers, and it is customary to write $x = y$ if $(x, y) \in r$. The phrase "is the sister of" defines a relation s from the set of all female people to the set of all people. If F denotes the set of all female people and P denotes the set of all people, then the relation s is defined by writing

$$s = \{(x, y) \mid x \in F, y \in P \text{ and } x \text{ is a sister of } y\}.$$

The phrase "is a sister of" can be used to define a relation on an arbitrary set of people. To illustrate this with an example, let us suppose that Amanda, Shannon, David, and Matt are the children of some family. Let

$$T = \{\text{Amanda, Shannon, David, Matt}\}.$$

The relation t defined on the set T by the phrase "is the sister of" is the collection

$$t = \{(\text{Amanda, Shannon}), (\text{Amanda, David}), (\text{Amanda, Matt}),$$
$$(\text{Shannon, Amanda}), (\text{Shannon, David}), (\text{Shannon, Matt})\}.$$

Clearly, the ordered pair (David, Amanda) does not belong to the relation t because David is not a sister of Amanda. The phrase "is less than" can be used to define a relation from a set of numbers A to a set of numbers B or it can be used to define a relation on an arbitrary set of numbers. Example 2 of this section exhibits a relation from the set $\{1, 2, 3\}$ to the set $\{2, 3, 4\}$, using the phrase "is less than."

An equivalence relation on a set S was defined in Section 4.5 to be any relation on S which has the reflexive, symmetric, and transitive properties. Using the notation of this section, we can define an equivalence relation on a set S as follows:

Definition 6.3 A relation r on a set S is an *equivalence relation* on S if

1) For every $x \in S$, $(x, x) \in r$. (The reflexive property)

2) If x and y are elements of S such that $(x, y) \in r$, then $(y, x) \in r$. (The symmetric property)

3) If x, y, and z are elements of S such that $(x, y) \in r$ and $(y, z) \in r$, then $(x, z) \in r$. (The transitive property)

FUNCTIONS AND GRAPHS

Problems

1 Let $A = \{a, b, c\}$ and $B = \{2, 3\}$. Find $A \times B$. Construct five different relations from A to B. Give the domain and range for each of these relations.

2 Let $A = \{\#, *\}$ and $B = \{1, 2, 3\}$. Find $A \times B$. Construct five different relations from A to B. Give the domain and range for each of these relations. How many relations can one define from A to B?

3 Let $S = \{\#, *\}$. Find $S \times S$. Construct five different relations on S. Give the domain and range for each of these relations.

4 Let $S = \{a, b, c\}$. Find $S \times S$. Construct five different relations on S. Give the domain and range of each relation. How many relations can one define on S?

5 Let

$$A = \{\text{Little Rock, Austin, Denver, Salem}\}$$

and let

$$B = \{\text{Arkansas, Texas, Arizona, Colorado}\}.$$

Construct the relation from A to B defined by the phrase "is the capital of."

6 Let

$$A = \{\text{Popocatepetl, Mt. McKinley, Pikes Peak, Mt. Vesuvius}\}$$

and let

$$B = \{\text{The United States, Russia, Mexico, Italy}\}.$$

Construct the relation from A to B defined by the phrase "is a mountain peak in."

7 Let $A = \{2, 4, 6, 8\}$ and $B = \{1, 3, 5, 7\}$. Find the relation from A to B defined by the phrase "is greater than."

8 Let Tom, Bill, and Marie be the children of some family and let

$$S = \{\text{Tom, Bill, Marie}\}.$$

Find the relation on S defined by the phrase "is a brother of." Is this relation an equivalence relation? Explain.

9 Let A denote any set. Is $A \times A$ an equivalence relation?

10 Let $A = \{\#, \$, *\}$. Define three different equivalence relations on A.

11 Let $S = \{1, 3, 5\}$. Define a relation on S that is

a) transitive but neither reflexive nor symmetric,

b) reflexive and symmetric but not transitive,

c) symmetric but neither reflexive nor transitive,

d) not reflexive, symmetric, or transitive.

6.2 THE CONCEPT OF A FUNCTION

We begin this section with the following definition.

Definition 6.4 Let A and B denote sets. A *function from A to B* is a relation f from A to B which has the following properties:
1) The domain of f is A.
2) If $(x, y) \in f$ and $(x, z) \in f$, then $y = z$.

To recapitulate, a function f from A to B is a relation whose domain is A and which has the property that each element of A is paired with exactly one element of B. The *domain* of a function f from A to B is always A and the *range* of f is the set of elements of B which are used as second elements in the ordered pairs defining f. A function from a set S to the same set S is called a *function on S*. We will now illustrate the concept of a function with some examples.

Example 1 Let $A = \{1, 2, 3\}$ and $B = \{2, 3, 4, 5\}$. The following relations are functions from A to B.

$$f = \{(1, 2), (2, 3), (3, 4)\},$$
$$g = \{(1, 2), (2, 5), (3, 3)\},$$
$$h = \{(1, 4), (2, 4), (3, 4)\}.$$

The domain of each of these functions is the set A; $R(f) = \{2, 3, 4\}$, $R(g) = \{2, 3, 5\}$, and $R(h) = \{4\}$. Note that the function h pairs each element of A with the same element of B.

The following relations from A to B are not functions.

$$r = \{(1, 2), (3, 3)\},$$
$$s = \{(1, 2), (2, 3), (3, 4), (1, 5)\};$$

r is not a function because the domain of r does not equal $A = \{1, 2, 3\}$, and s is not a function because the number 1 is paired with two different elements of B.

Example 2 Let $S = \{\#, \$, *\}$. The following relations are functions on S.

$$f = \{(\#, \#), (\$, \$), (*, *)\},$$
$$g = \{(\#, \$), (\$, *), (*, \#)\},$$
$$h = \{(\#, \$), (\$, \$), (*, \$)\}.$$

The range of f is $\{\#, \$, *\}$, the range of g is $\{\#, \$, *\}$, and the range of h is $\{\$\}$.

The following relations on S are not functions on S.

$$r = \{(\#, \#), (\#, \$), (\#, *)\},$$
$$s = \{(\$, *)\}.$$

Let f denote a function from a set A to B. If $(x, y) \in f$, then we will often write $y = f(x)$. To illustrate this notation let us consider the function f of Example 1. We have

$$f(1) = 2 \quad \text{because} \quad (1, 2) \in f,$$
$$f(2) = 3 \quad \text{because} \quad (2, 3) \in f,$$
$$f(3) = 4 \quad \text{because} \quad (3, 4) \in f.$$

For the function h of Example 2 we have

$$h(\#) = \$ \quad \text{because} \quad (\#, \$) \in h,$$
$$h(\$) = \$ \quad \text{because} \quad (\$, \$) \in h,$$
$$h(*) = \$ \quad \text{because} \quad (*, \$) \in h.$$

If $y = f(x)$, y is sometimes called the *image* of x under the function f. It is often convenient to define a function f from a set A to a set B by specifying the image of each element of A. For example, we can define a function f from $A = \{1, 2, 3\}$ to $B = \{\$, \#, *\}$ by stating that $f(1) = \#$, $f(2) = *$, and $f(3) = *$. Using ordered pairs, we have

$$f = \{(1, \#), (2, *), (3, *)\}.$$

A function g on the set of real numbers is defined by writing

$$g(x) = 2x - 1 \quad \text{for each } x \in R.$$

To find the image of the number -3, we replace x in the expression $2x - 1$ by the number -3. Thus

$$g(-3) = 2(-3) - 1 = -6 - 1 = -7,$$

and $(-3, -7) \in g$. As another example, we note that

$$g(\tfrac{5}{2}) = 2(\tfrac{5}{2}) - 1 = 5 - 1 = 4.$$

Thus $(\tfrac{5}{2}, 4) \in g$. Other elements of the function g are $(0, -1)$, $(-1, -3)$, $(\tfrac{1}{3}, -\tfrac{1}{3})$, and $(10, 19)$. In summary,

$$g = \{(x, y) \mid x \in R \text{ and } y = 2x - 1\}.$$

Example 3 Let the function h be defined by the statement

$$h(x) = 3x^2 - 5x + 2$$

$$h(x) = 3x^2 - 5x + 2$$

for each $x \in R$. Find $h(-1)$, $h(\frac{5}{3})$, $h(0)$, and $h(10)$. Also express h as a collection of ordered pairs.

Solution

$$h(-1) = 3(-1)^2 - 5(-1) + 2$$
$$= 3 + 5 + 2$$
$$= 10;$$

$$h(\tfrac{5}{3}) = 3(\tfrac{5}{3})^2 - 5(\tfrac{5}{3}) + 2$$
$$= \tfrac{25}{3} - \tfrac{25}{3} + 2$$
$$= 2;$$

$$h(0) = 3(0)^2 - 5(0) + 2$$
$$= 2;$$

$$h(10) = 3(10)^2 - 5(10) + 2$$
$$= 300 - 50 + 2$$
$$= 252.$$

Expressing h as a collection of ordered pairs, we have

$$h = \{(x, y) \mid x \in R \text{ and } y = 3x^2 - 5x + 2\}.$$

We remark that by definition every function is a relation. However, there are many relations that are not functions.

Not all mathematicians choose to define a function as a special type of relation. Many choose to use the following definition.

Definition 6.5 (*Alternate definition of a function*) A *function f* from a set A to a set B is a rule which associates with each element of A one and only one element of B.

This definition of a function is equivalent to Definition 6.4. The only difference between the two is a difference in language and notation.

To illustrate Definition 6.5 we will use the function

$$f = \{(1, \#), (2, *), (3, *)\}$$

from the set $A = \{1, 2, 3\}$ to the set $B = \{\$, \#, *\}$. The function f is a rule which associates with each element of A one and only one element of B. To be more specific, 1 is associated with $\#$, 2 is associated with $*$, and 3 is associated with $*$. If for $a \in A$ and $b \in B$, we define $a \rightarrow b$ to mean that a is associated with b, then the function f is the function for which $1 \rightarrow \#$, $2 \rightarrow *$ and $3 \rightarrow *$.

The use of functions is not limited to mathematics. In fact we all make use of functions in our daily activities. We conclude this section with two of the more familiar examples of functions.

FUNCTIONS AND GRAPHS

Example 4 Every time we mail a letter addressed to a city in the United States we use a function to determine the postage required. If w denotes the weight of a letter in ounces, then letters for which $0 < w \leq 1$ require 6¢ postage, letters for which $1 < w \leq 2$ require 12¢ postage, letters for which $2 < w \leq 3$ require 18¢ postage, etc. We will call this function the "post office function" and we note that it is a rule which associates with every letter addressed to some point in the United States a real number. The range of this function is the set $\{6, 12, 18, 24, \ldots\}$.

Example 5 Every person working at a job covered by Old Age Security Insurance is assigned a unique number called his social security number. This pairing of people with their social security number defines a function from the set of all people covered by O.A.S.I. to the set of real numbers.

Problems

1 Let $S = \{0, 2, 4\}$. Which of the following relations on S are functions on S? For those relations which are not functions, explain why the definition of a function is not satisfied.

a) $r = \{(0, 2), (2, 2), (4, 2)\}$

b) $s = \{(0, 0), (2, 2), (4, 4)\}$

c) $t = \{(0, 2), (2, 4), (0, 4)\}$

d) $u = \{(2, 4), (4, 2)\}$

e) $v = \{(0, 2), (2, 4), (4, 0)\}$

f) $w = \{\ \}$

2 Let $A = \{\#, \$, *\}$ and $B = \{1, 3, 5, 7\}$. Construct three different functions from A to B. Give the domain and range for each function.

3 Let $A = \{2, 4, 6\}$ and $B = \{3\}$. There is only one function from A to B. What is it? $\{2,3 \ 4,3 \ 6,3\}$

4 Let $S = \{\#, \$, *\}$. Construct five different functions on S. Give the domain and range for each function.

5 Let
$$A = \{\text{Little Rock, Austin, Denver}\}$$
and let
$$B = \{\text{Arkansas, Texas, Colorado, Maine}\}.$$

Construct the relation from A to B defined by the phrase "is the capital of." Is this relation from A to B a function from A to B?

6 A function f is defined on the set of real numbers R by writing $f(x) = 3x - 4$ for each $x \in R$. Find the image of each of the following numbers under the function f.

a) 0   b) −3   c) $\frac{1}{2}$

d) 15   e) −.02   f) −10

7 A function f is defined on the set of real numbers R by writing $f(x) = 2x^2 - x - 1$ for each $x \in R$. Evaluate $f(-1)$, $f(5)$, $f(0)$, $f(-8)$, $f(\frac{1}{2})$, $f(.1)$, $f(-\frac{1}{2})$, and $f(100)$. Express the function f as a collection of ordered pairs.

8 Let a function f be defined on the set $N = \{0, 1, 2, 3, \ldots\}$ by the equation $f(x) = 2x + 1$. What is the range of f?

9 Suppose f is a function from A to B. If the elements in each pair in f are reversed in order, is the resulting set of ordered pairs always a function from B to A? Justify your answer.

10 The owner of a peach orchard has 500 trees and realizes a net profit of $20 per tree each year. Assuming the acreage remains fixed, the net profit per tree is decreased by 2¢ for each new tree planted. Knowing the number of new trees planted, define a function to give the yearly net profit for the orchard. What is the net profit if 250 new trees are planted? 600 new trees?

6.3 THE CARTESIAN COORDINATE SYSTEM

We will now consider a procedure for establishing a one-to-one correspondence between the set $R \times R$ and the set of all points in a plane. The system most often used to show this one-to-one correspondence is a *rectangular coordinate system*. It was developed by the French mathematician René Descartes and is sometimes called a *Cartesian coordinate system*.

Construct two perpendicular straight lines, one horizontal and one vertical. These two lines will be called *coordinate axes*, with the horizontal line being called the *x-axis* and the vertical line the *y-axis*. The point of intersection of the two axes will be called the *origin*, designated by the letter O. As in Section 5.11, construct a number line on each of the coordinate axes, letting O be the point representing the number zero. Further, let the point representing 1 on the *x*-axis be to the right of the point O and the point representing 1 on the *y*-axis above the point O. Even though it is not necessary, for sake of convenience let the unit length on each of the axes be the same (see Fig. 6.1).

We are now prepared to establish a one-to-one correspondence between the set of points in a plane and the set of all ordered pairs of real numbers. Let P be a point in a plane in which we have a set of coordinate axes. Construct lines through P perpendicular to each of the coordinate axes and consider the points of intersection of these lines with the coordinate axes. Call the real number associated with the point of intersection of the line with the *x*-axis the *x-coordinate*, or *abscissa*, of the point P. Call the real number associated with the point of intersection of the line with the *y*-axis the *y-coordinate*, or *ordinate*, of the point P. The *x*-coordinate and *y*-coordinate of a point taken together are called the *coordinates* of the point. In giving

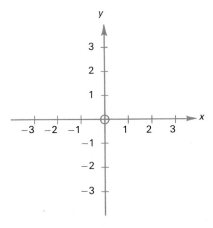

y

3

2

1

x

-3 -2 -1   1 2 3

-1

-2

-3

Figure 6.1

the coordinates of a point we will always list the x-coordinate first. Thus the coordinates of a point form an ordered pair of real numbers. It should be clear from this discussion that there is one and only one ordered pair of real numbers associated with each point in the plane. Now consider the ordered pair of real numbers (x, y). Construct the line through the point on the x-axis associated with the real number x and perpendicular to the x-axis. Further, construct the line through the point on the y-axis associated with the real number y and perpendicular to the y-axis. These two lines will intersect in one and only one point which we associate with the ordered pair (x, y). To summarize, we have established a procedure which associates with each point in a plane one and only one ordered pair of real numbers and which associates with each ordered pair of real numbers one and only one point in a plane. Therefore, we have a one-to-one correspondence between $R \times R$ and the set of all points in a plane. We indicate P and its coordinates by $P(x, y)$ (see Fig. 6.2).

In Fig. 6.2 note that the point on the x-axis associated with the real number x has y-coordinate 0 and the point on the y-axis associated with the real

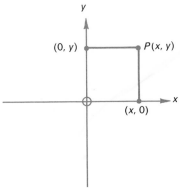

y

(0, y)   P(x, y)

x

(x, 0)

Figure 6.2

TABLE 6.1

Quadrant	Abscissa	Ordinate
I	+	+
II	−	+
III	−	−
IV	+	−

number y has x-coordinate 0. Thus the respective coordinates of these points are $(x, 0)$ and $(0, y)$. When we associate a point in a plane with an ordered pair, we say that we *plot* or *graph* the ordered pair.

In Fig. 6.3 we see that the coordinate axes divide a plane into four regions which we call *quadrants*. Table 6.1 gives the signs of the coordinates of points located in each of the quadrants.

Example 1 Graph the following points: $A(1, 3)$, $B(-\frac{1}{2}, 4)$, $C(-3, -2)$, and $D\left(\frac{\pi}{2}, -3\right)$.

Solution See Fig. 6.4.

Earlier in this chapter we noted that both relations and functions are sets of ordered pairs. By the graph of a relation or function we mean the graph of all the ordered pairs belonging to the relation or function. If a relation or function is an infinite set, all the ordered pairs belonging to the relation or

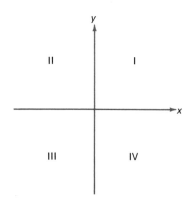

Figure 6.3

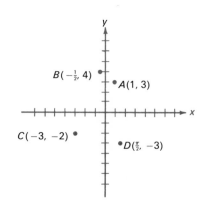

Figure 6.4

FUNCTIONS AND GRAPHS

function cannot always be graphed. However, we can approximate the graph by graphing enough pairs to achieve a pattern. The graph of the relation or function is the "smooth curve" connecting these points. It is usually convenient to make a table of values when graphing a function or relation which is defined by an equation. Observe this procedure in the following example.

Example 2 Graph the function $f(x) = 2x + 3$.

Solution We first make a table of values which gives ordered pairs to be graphed. We seek ordered pairs (x, y) such that $y = 2x + 3$.

x	1	0	−1	−2	−3
y	5	3	1	−1	−3

We now graph the ordered pairs given by our table of values and connect these points with a "smooth line" to give the graph of the function (see Fig. 6.5).

Example 3 Graph the relation

$$\{(1, 2), (1, 1), (1, 0), (0, 1), (0, 0), (0, 2), (2, 0), (2, 1)\}.$$

Solution See Fig. 6.6.

Note that the points on this graph are not connected. The reason for this is that the relation contains only those ordered pairs which are graphed.

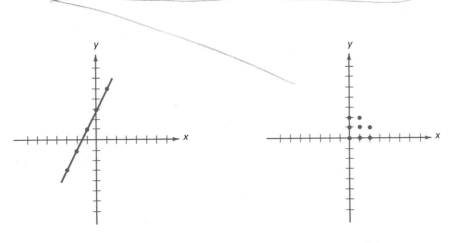

Figure 6.5   Figure 6.6

Problems

1 In each part of the following, construct a coordinate system and plot the points.

   a) (1, 2), (−3, 5), (−1, 2), (5, 3), (2, 6)

   b) $(\frac{1}{2}, 3)$, $(3, \frac{2}{3})$, $(-1, -\frac{7}{2})$, $\left(\frac{\pi}{2}, 3\right)$, (−4, 6)

   c) $(1, \frac{3}{2})$, $(-\sqrt{2}, 1)$, $(-2, -1)$, $\left(\frac{\pi}{3}, -2\right)$

2 What are the coordinates of a point which is

   a) 4 units to the left of the y-axis and 2 units above the x-axis?

   b) 5 units to the right of the y-axis and 3 units above the x-axis?

   c) $\frac{1}{2}$ unit to the left of the y-axis and 3 units below the x-axis?

   d) 4 units to the right of the y-axis and $\frac{3}{2}$ units above the x-axis?

3 a) What is the abscissa of any point on the y-axis?

   b) What is the ordinate of any point on the x-axis?

4 Without plotting tell in which quadrant each of the following points is.

   a) (3, 5)   b) $(-7, \frac{1}{2})$ c) $(-\frac{1}{2}, -\frac{3}{2})$

   d) $(-\pi, 3)$ e) $(\pi, -\frac{7}{3})$ f) (−7, 3)

   g) $(\frac{3}{4}, -\frac{3}{4})$ h) $(-\frac{3}{7}, \frac{2}{5})$ i) (7, 16)

5 Let $A = \{1, 2\}$ and $B = \{3, 4\}$. Graph each of the following relations, using a separate set of coordinate axes for each relation.

   a) $A \times B$ b) $B \times A$ c) $A \times A$ d) $B \times B$

6 Sketch the graph of the post office function mentioned in Section 6.2.

7 Sketch the graph of the relation

$$v = \{(x, y) \mid x \in A, y \in B \text{ and } x < y\},$$

where $A = \{1, 2, 3\}$ and $B = \{2, 3, 4\}$. Is v a function?

8 Sketch the graph of the relation

$$s = \{(x, y) \mid x \in A, y \in B \text{ and } x = y\},$$

where $A = \{1, 2, 3\}$ and $B = \{2, 3, 4\}$. Is s a function?

9 If the graph of a relation is intersected two or more times by any vertical line, is the relation a function? Explain.

10 The graph of the relation

$$c = \{(x, y) \mid x^2 + y^2 = 1\}$$

is a circle with center at the origin and radius 1. Is c a function? Explain.

6.4 LINEAR FUNCTIONS AND GRAPHS

In Section 6.2 we discussed the concept of a function in general. We are now prepared for a discussion of particular types of functions.

Definition 6.6 If m and b are any real numbers, the function f defined by

$$f(x) = mx + b$$

is called a *linear function*.

The linear function $f(x) = mx + b$ is the collection

$$f = \{(x, y) \mid y = mx + b\}.$$

The function f derives its name, linear function, from the fact that its graph is a straight line. Although this can be proved, we will assume it in this book. Some examples of linear functions are:

$$\begin{aligned} f(x) &= 3x + 2, \\ g(x) &= \tfrac{1}{2}x - \pi, \\ h(x) &= 5x, \\ F(x) &= -13. \end{aligned}$$

The graph of a linear function is the graph of all ordered pairs which belong to the function. Since the graph of a linear function is a straight line and since a straight line is determined by two points, it is necessary to know only two ordered pairs which belong to a linear function in order to sketch its graph. However, one can avoid some errors in graphing linear functions by graphing three or more ordered pairs belonging to the function.

Example 1 Make a table of values and graph the linear function $f(x) = x + 3$.

Solution See Fig. 6.7.

x	y
0	3
−2	1
2	5

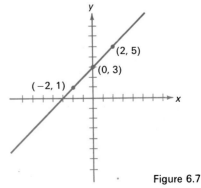

Figure 6.7

Example 2 Make a table of values and graph the linear function $f(x) = \frac{1}{3}x - 2$.

Solution See Fig. 6.8.

x	y
0	-2
6	0
-6	-4

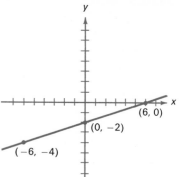

Figure 6.8

Example 3 Make a table of values and graph the linear function $f(x) = 3x$.

Solution See Fig. 6.9.

x	y
0	0
-2	-6
1	3

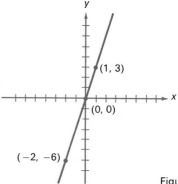

Figure 6.9

Example 4 Make a table of values and graph the linear function $f(x) = 3$.

Solution See Fig. 6.10.

x	y
0	3
4	3
-2	3

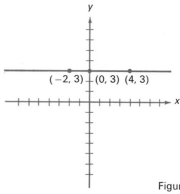

Figure 6.10

166

Examples 3 and 4 describe special types of linear functions. Let us consider a linear function $f(x) = mx + b$. If $b = 0$, then $f(x) = mx$, and the graph of such a function will always pass through the origin (see Example 3). If $m = 0$, then $f(x) = b$, and the graph is a horizontal line which passes through the point $(0, b)$ (see Example 4). A function such as $f(x) = b$ is called a *constant function*.

Since the graph of a linear function is a straight line, we might expect all straight lines to be the graph of some function. Consider the graph of the set of all ordered pairs of real numbers (x, y) such that $x = 3$. Note that no condition is placed on y, and thus we are concerned with all ordered pairs $(3, y)$, where y is a real number. It should be clear from the description of this set that it is not a function. The graph of this set is given in Fig. 6.11

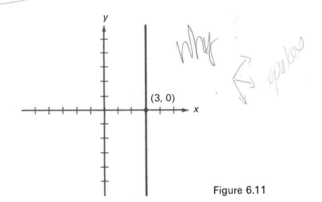

Figure 6.11

Problems

1 Given the linear function $f(x) = 3x + 2$ find:
   a) $f(1)$ b) $f(-\frac{1}{2})$ c) $f(0)$ d) $f(-16)$

2 Given the linear function $g(x) = \frac{1}{2}x - \frac{3}{4}$ find:
   a) $g(2)$ b) $g(\frac{1}{2})$ c) $g(0)$ d) $g(-3)$

3 Given the linear function $h(x) = -3x + \frac{5}{2}$ find:
   a) $h(\frac{1}{2})$ b) $h(-\frac{1}{2})$ c) $h(0)$ d) $h(1)$

4 Given the linear function $k(x) = -\frac{2}{3}x + \frac{5}{6}$ find:
   a) $k(6)$ b) $k(-3)$ c) $k(0)$ d) $k(-1)$

5 In each of the following make a table of values and sketch the graph of the given linear function.
   a) $f(x) = 3x + 2$ b) $g(x) = \frac{1}{2}x - \frac{3}{4}$
   c) $h(x) = -3x$ d) $k(x) = -\frac{2}{3}x + \frac{5}{6}$
   e) $s(x) = \frac{7}{3}$ f) $t(x) = -2.1x + .5$

6 If $f(x) = mx + b$, at what point does the graph of f intersect the y-axis? At what point does the graph of f intersect the x-axis?

7 Sketch the graph of the linear function $f(x) = x$; f is called the *identity function*.

6.5 LINEAR EQUATIONS

We recall from Section 4.5 that an *equation* is a statement that two expressions are equal. Further, any set of values for which an equation is true is called a *solution* of the equation, and the set of all solutions is called the *solution set* of the equation. A solution of an equation in one variable is often referred to as a *root* of that equation.

Associated with each linear function $f(x) = mx + b$, $m \neq 0$, there is the equation $f(x) = 0$ or $mx + b = 0$. This equation is called a *linear equation in x*. We now turn our attention to finding the solution set for such an equation, that is, finding the value or values for x such that $mx + b = 0$. If we consider the graph of f, we are seeking those values of x such that $f(x) = 0$, in other words, those points belonging to the graph of f with second coordinate zero. Since all points with second coordinate zero are on the x-axis, we seek the values of x such that $(x, 0)$ belongs to f. These values will be found where the graph of f intersects the x-axis. Since the graph of a linear function is a straight line, it can intersect the x-axis in at most one point. The only linear functions whose graphs do not intersect the x-axis are those of the form $f(x) = mx + b$ with $m = 0$, and these functions were excluded in defining a linear equation in x. To summarize, each linear equation $mx + b = 0$ has a unique solution and it can be found by graphing the linear function $f(x) = mx + b$ and reading from the graph the x-coordinate of the point of intersection of the graph of f and the x-axis. Example 1 uses this procedure to find the solution set for the linear equation $3x + 6 = 0$.

Example 1 Solve the linear equation $3x + 6 = 0$ by graphing.

Solution The first step in solving the equation $3x + 6 = 0$ by graphing is to graph the linear function $f(x) = 3x + 6$ (see Fig. 6.12). Next we approximate the x-coordinate of the point where the graph of f intersects the x-axis to be -2. That the solution set for $3x + 6 = 0$ is actually $\{-2\}$ will be shown in the next paragraph.

Note that in solving a linear equation by graphing, the solution is found by an approximation. We may check our solution x by checking to see

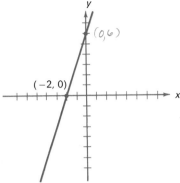

Figure 6.12

whether $f(x) = 0$. In Example 1, we have

$$f(x) = 3x + 6,$$
$$f(-2) = 3(-2) + 6$$
$$= (-6) + 6$$
$$= 0.$$

Therefore, we conclude that $x = -2$ is a solution of the equation $3x + 6 = 0$. We now turn our attention to an algebraic method for solving a linear equation. This procedure makes use of the properties of the equality relation (see Section 4.5). It avoids the necessity of an approximation, and for this reason is more desirable than the graphing method.

Let us consider the equation $mx + b = 0$, $m \neq 0$. Adding $-b$ to both members of this equation, we have.

$$(mx + b) + (-b) = 0 + (-b),$$
$$mx + (b + (-b)) = 0 + (-b),$$
$$mx + 0 = 0 + (-b),$$
$$mx = -b.$$

Since $m \neq 0$, m has a multiplicative inverse $1/m$, and multiplying both members of the equation $mx = -b$ by $1/m$, we have

$$\frac{1}{m}(mx) = \frac{1}{m}(-b),$$

$$\left(\frac{1}{m} \cdot m\right)x = \frac{1}{m}(-b),$$

$$1 \cdot x = -\frac{b}{m}, \qquad x = -\frac{b}{m}.$$

Thus $x = -b/m$ is the only possible solution to the equation $mx + b = 0$.

We verify that $x = -b/m$ is a solution by observing that

$$m\left(-\frac{b}{m}\right) + b = -b + b$$
$$= 0.$$

The procedure of this paragraph can be used to solve any linear equation.

Example 2 Solve the equation $3x + 2 = 0$.
Solution

$$3x + 2 = 0,$$
$$(3x + 2) + (-2) = 0 + (-2),$$
$$3x = -2,$$
$$\tfrac{1}{3}(3x) = \tfrac{1}{3}(-2),$$
$$x = -\tfrac{2}{3}.$$

Note: $x = -b/m$ since $b = 2$ and $m = 3$.

Some equations which do not appear in the form $mx + b = 0$ can be transformed into such an equation by using the properties of equality. For example, consider the equation $3x + 2 = x + 8$. We have

1) $$3x + 2 = x + 8,$$
$$(3x + 2) + (-8) = (x + 8) + (-8);$$
2) $$3x - 6 = x,$$
$$(3x - 6) + (-x) = x + (-x);$$
3) $$2x - 6 = 0.$$

Equations which have the same solution set are called *equivalent equations*. For example, equations (1), (2), and (3) are *equivalent equations*. We have transformed the equation $3x + 2 = x + 8$ into an equivalent equation of the form $mx + b = 0$, namely $2x + (-6) = 0$. We may use the above procedures to actually solve the equation $3x + 2 = x + 8$ without transforming the equation into the form $mx + b = 0$. For example

$$3x + 2 = x + 8,$$
$$(3x + 2) + (-2) = (x + 8) + (-2),$$
$$3x = x + 6,$$
$$3x + (-x) = (x + 6) + (-x),$$
$$2x = 6,$$
$$\tfrac{1}{2}(2x) = \tfrac{1}{2}(6),$$
$$x = 3.$$

FUNCTIONS AND GRAPHS

Operations which will transform a given equation into an equivalent equation are described below:

1) The same quantity may be added to or subtracted from both members of the given equation.

2) Both members of the given equation may be multiplied or divided by the same nonzero quantity.

Example 3 Solve the equation $5x + 3 = 2x - 1$. Check the solution.

Solution

$$5x + 3 = 2x - 1,$$
$$5x = 2x - 4,$$
$$3x = -4,$$
$$x = -\tfrac{4}{3}.$$

Check If $x = -\tfrac{4}{3}$, then

$$5x + 3 = 5(-\tfrac{4}{3}) + 3$$
$$= -\tfrac{11}{3};$$
$$2x - 1 = 2(-\tfrac{4}{3}) - 1$$
$$= -\tfrac{11}{3};$$
$$5(-\tfrac{4}{3}) + 3 = 2(-\tfrac{4}{3}) - 1,$$

and the solution checks.

Example 4 Solve the equation $\tfrac{3}{2}x - 2 = x + \tfrac{2}{3}$.

Solution

$$\tfrac{3}{2}x - 2 = x + \tfrac{2}{3},$$
$$\tfrac{3}{2}x = x + \tfrac{8}{3},$$
$$\tfrac{1}{2}x = \tfrac{8}{3},$$
$$x = \tfrac{16}{3}.$$

Example 5 Solve the equation

$$S = \frac{a - rk}{w - r}, \qquad r \neq w, \quad \text{for } k.$$

Solution

$$S = \frac{a - rk}{w - r},$$
$$S(w - r) = a - rk,$$
$$rk + S(w - r) = a,$$
$$rk = a - S(w - r),$$
$$k = \frac{a - S(w - r)}{r}, \qquad r \neq 0.$$

Note that in the statement of the equation we have the condition $r \neq w$. If this condition is not satisfied, then $(a - rk)/(w - r)$ is an undefined expression, and thus we would not have an equation. Furthermore, the multiplication by $w - r$ to obtain the second step requires $(w - r) \neq 0$ and therefore $w \neq r$. Equations of the type presented in this example are called *literal equations* in that letters are used to represent numbers.

Problems

1 Solve the following linear equations by the graphing method.

   a) $3x + 5 = 0$ b) $4x - 20 = 0$

   c) $\frac{2}{3}x + 9 = 0$ d) $\frac{1}{2}x - 6 = 0$

2 In each of the following give three equations equivalent to the given equation.

   a) $x + 3 = 0$ b) $2x - 4 = 0$

   c) $5x + \frac{1}{2} = 0$ d) $\frac{2}{3}x - 6 = 0$

Solve the following linear equations and check.

3 $3x + 9 = 0$ 4 $5x - 30 = 0$

5 $3x - 7 = 5$ 6 $7x - 1 = x$

7 $\frac{1}{2}x + 3 = x - 2$ 8 $2x + \frac{5}{2} = -3x + \frac{1}{2}$

9 $10x - 3x + \frac{2}{3} = x - 7$ 10 $\frac{1}{5}(3x - 2) = 10$

11 $\frac{2}{3}(x + 5) = -7$ 12 $\dfrac{x - 3}{2} = 14$

13 $5x - 3(x + 2) = 4$ 14 $\frac{5}{2}x = \frac{2}{3}x + 1$

15 $6x + 5 = -2x + 13$ 16 $5(x - 2) + 3 = -2(x + 2) - 5$

Solve the following literal equations for the letters indicated.

17 $d = rt$, for r 18 $i = prt$, for p

19 $s = vt + \frac{1}{2}gt^2$, for v 20 $f = a + (n - 1)d$, for n

21 $f = a + (n - 1)d$, for d 22 $S = \dfrac{a - rk}{w - r}$, for r

23 Without graphing $f(x) = 3x + 12$, give the coordinates of the point where the graph intersects the x-axis.

6.6 LINEAR EQUATIONS IN TWO VARIABLES

An equation of the form

$$ax + by + c = 0,$$

where a, b, and c are real numbers with a and b not both zero, is called a *linear equation in two variables*. By a solution of such an equation we will mean a set of two numbers x and y which will satisfy the equation. A solution of a linear equation in two variables is an ordered pair, and the set of all ordered pairs which satisfy the equation is called the solution set. Because the graph of a linear equation in two variables is a straight line and a straight line has infinitely many points, the solution set for such an equation is an infinite set. The solution set for the linear equation $ax + by + c = 0$ is the set

$$\{(x, y) \mid ax + by + c = 0\}.$$

As an illustration, let us consider the equation $2x - y + 3 = 0$. A solution of this equation can be found by giving x a value and solving the resulting equation for y. For example, if $x = 2$, we find that $y = 7$. Hence $(2, 7)$ is a solution of the given equation because $x = 2$ and $y = 7$ satisfy the equation. Other solutions are $(1, 5)$, $(0, 3)$, and $(-1, 1)$. The solution set of the equation $2x - y + 3 = 0$ is the set

$$\{(x, y) \mid 2x - y + 3 = 0\}.$$

We are frequently interested in the solution of a pair of linear equations in two variables, such as

$$a_1x + b_1y + c_1 = 0,$$
$$a_2x + b_2y + c_2 = 0.$$

By a solution of this pair of equations we mean any ordered pair (x, y) which will satisfy both equations. If A is the solution set of the first equation and B is the solution set of the second equation, then the solution set for the pair of equations is the set $A \cap B$.

If we graph a pair of linear equations in two variables, the coordinates of any point of intersection will satisfy both equations. This method for solving a pair of linear equations is called the *graphing method* and although it is perhaps the most enlightening method, it does have its disadvantages. It is often difficult to find the exact coordinates of a point of intersection of two lines, and hence an ordered pair obtained by this method is frequently just an approximation of the true solution. For this reason we should always check a solution obtained by the graphing method.

Example 1 Find the solution set for the pair of equations $x - y + 1 = 0$ and $2x + y - 7 = 0$ by the graphing method.

Solution First we graph these two equations on the same set of coordinate axes (see Fig. 6.13). From the figure it appears that these lines intersect at the point $P(2, 3)$. We can easily verify by substitution that $x = 2$ and $y = 3$ satisfy the pair of equations. Hence the solution set for this pair of equations is the set $\{(2, 3)\}$.

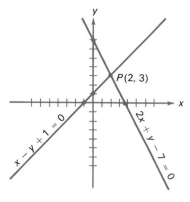

Figure 6.13

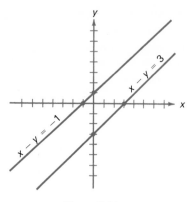

Figure 6.14

Example 2 Find the solution set for the pair of equations $x - y = -1$ and $x - y = 3$ by the graphing method.

Solution In Fig. 6.14 we have graphed both equations on the same set of axes. The two lines appear to be parallel. If this is the case, they will have no points in common and the solution set for this pair of equations will be the empty set $\varnothing$. The fact that $\varnothing$ is the solution set for this pair of equations should be apparent from an inspection of the equations. Clearly, there is no pair of numbers x and y such that the difference of the two numbers is -1 and also 3.

If a pair of equations has one and only one solution, the pair of equations is said to be *consistent*. Such a pair of equations is exhibited in Example 1. If the solution set for two equations is the empty set $\varnothing$, then the equations are said to be *inconsistent*. The equations in Example 2 are inconsistent. Were we to graph the equations $x - y = 1$ and $3x - 3y = 3$ on the same set of coordinate axes, we would discover that the lines coincided. Actually these equations are equivalent, for the second can be obtained from the first by multiplying both members of the first by 3; $\{(x, y) \mid x - y = 1\}$ is the solution set for this pair of equations. A pair of equivalent equations will have an infinite number of solutions, and two equations of this type are said to be *dependent*. Because two straight lines must intersect in a single point, be parallel, or coincide, we can summarize the remarks of this paragraph by stating that every pair of linear equations in two variables can be classified as being consistent, inconsistent, or dependent.

As we have stated previously, a solution to a pair of equations obtained by the graphing method is often only an approximation of the actual solution. An exact solution can always be found when it exists by solving the equations

FUNCTIONS AND GRAPHS

algebraically. One of the variables can always be eliminated by taking a suitable combination of the equations (or equations equivalent to the original set). The resulting equation can then be solved for the remaining variable, and the eliminated variable can be evaluated by substitution into one of the original equations. The algebraic method will be illustrated by the following examples.

Example 3 Solve the equations $x - y + 1 = 0$ and $2x + y - 7 = 0$ algebraically.

Solution The coefficients of y are numerically equal, but they have opposite signs. Hence y can be eliminated by adding the two equations.

$$
\begin{array}{r}
x - y + 1 = 0 \\
2x + y - 7 = 0 \\
\hline
3x \quad\; - 6 = 0
\end{array}
$$

Solving the equation $3x - 6 = 0$ for x, we find that $x = 2$. Substituting this value for x into the first of the two equations, we find that $y = 3$. This result agrees with the solution found by the graphing method in Example 1.

Example 4 Solve the equations $2x - y + 4 = 0$ and $3x + 2y - 1 = 0$ algebraically.

Solution If the first equation is solved for y, we find $y = 2x + 4$. Substituting this expression for y into the second equation, we obtain

$$3x + 2(2x + 4) - 1 = 0.$$

After combining like terms, we have the equation $7x + 7 = 0$, of which $x = -1$ is the solution. Hence $y = 2(-1) + 4 = 2$. The solution set for this pair of equations is the set $\{(-1, 2)\}$.

Example 5 Solve the equations $3x + 5y + 1 = 0$ and $2x + 3y + 3 = 0$ algebraically.

Solution Multiplying both members of the first equation by 2 and both members of the second equation by 3, we have

$$
\begin{array}{r}
6x + 10y + 2 = 0, \\
6x + 9y + 9 = 0.
\end{array}
$$

If the second equation is subtracted from the first, the resulting equation is $y - 7 = 0$, for which the solution is $y = 7$. Substituting $y = 7$ into one of the original equations, we find that $x = -12$. The solution set for the equation is $\{(-12, 7)\}$.

Problems

Using the graphing method, find the solution set for each of the following pairs of equations.

1 $2x - y = 1,$
$x + y = 2$

2 $3x - 5y + 15 = 0,$
$6x - 10y + 20 = 0$

3 $x + 2y - 6 = 0,$
$3x - y + 3 = 0$

4 $5x + y = 10,$
$30x + 6y = 60$

5 $2x + 5y = 4,$
$-3x + 2y = 1$

6 $x + 2y = 8,$
$2x - y = 3$

7 $x + 2y - 6 = 0,$
$x \qquad = 3$

8 $y = 2,$
$x = 1$

9 $4x + y + 1 = 0,$
$2x + 3y - 2 = 0$

Using the algebraic method, find the solution set for each of the following pairs of equations.

10 $4x + y = -1,$
$2x + 3y = 7$

11 $3x - 2y = 8,$
$2x + 3y = 1$

12 $x - 5y = 6,$
$-2x + 10y = -12$

13 $2x - y + 4 = 0,$
$3x + 6y + 1 = 0$

14 $x + 2y - 6 = 0,$
$x \qquad = 3$

15 $3x - 2y = 1,$
$3x - 2y = 5$

16 $-3x - y + 1 = 0,$
$2x + 3y - 2 = 0$

17 $2x + 5y = 2,$
$3x + 2y = 1$

18 $x - 2y = 3,$
$-3x + 6y = 6$

19 $x = 3,$
$y = -1$

20 $\frac{1}{3}x - 5y = 1,$
$2x + \frac{3}{4}y = 2$

21 $\frac{2}{3}x - y = 4,$
$4x - 6y = 24$

22 Let $A = \{(x, y) \mid 3x - 4y + 2 = 0\}$ and

$$B = \{(x, y) \mid x + 2y + 4 = 0\}.$$

Find $A \cap B$.

23 Let $A = \{(x, y) \mid 7x - 3y + 1 = 0\}$ and

$$B = \{(x, y) \mid 3x - 2y + 4 = 0\}.$$

Find $A \cap B$.

24 Let $A = \{(x, y) \mid 4x + 9y + 1 = 0\}$ and

$$B = \{(x, y) \mid 8x + 18y + 1 = 0\}.$$

Find $A \cap B$.

25 Solve the following pair of equations for x and y in terms of the co-efficients. You may assume that $a_1b_2 - a_2b_1 \neq 0$.

$$a_1x + b_1y = c_1, \qquad a_2x + b_2y = c_2.$$

In Problems 26 and 27, solve each pair of equations for x and y.

26 $\dfrac{2}{x} - \dfrac{1}{y} = 1,$

$\dfrac{3}{x} + \dfrac{2}{y} = 5$

27 $\dfrac{4}{x} + \dfrac{5}{y} = -14,$

$\dfrac{2}{x} - \dfrac{3}{y} = 26$

6.7 LINEAR EQUATIONS AND APPLICATIONS

Many practical problems can be solved by use of linear equations. In general, the procedure is to relate the known and the unknown quantities of the problem by constructing a linear equation (or pair of equations) involving the quantities. The solution to the problem is found by solving the equation (or equations) and interpreting the result. We will rely on the following examples to illustrate this procedure.

Example 1 Find three consecutive integers whose sum is 219.

Solution If we let x denote the first integer, then the next two integers are $x + 1$ and $x + 2$, respectively. Because the sum of these three integers is 219, x must satisfy the equation

$$x + (x + 1) + (x + 2) = 219.$$

Solving this equation for x, we obtain $x = 72$. The three integers are 72, 73, and 74.

Example 2 A father and son are 36 and 14 years of age, respectively. In how many years will the father's age be twice that of his son?

Solution The unknown quantity in this problem is the number of years required to make the father's age twice that of his son. Let x denote this unknown number of years. In x years the father's age will be $36 + x$. In x years the son's age will be $14 + x$. After x years the father's age is twice that of his son. Hence,

$$36 + x = 2(14 + x)$$
$$36 + x = 28 + 2x$$
$$-x = -8$$
$$x = 8.$$

In 8 years the father is 44 years of age, and his son is 22 years of age.

Example 3 Find two numbers whose sum is 115 and whose difference is 13.

Solution This problem can be solved by either of two methods. We will discuss both methods.

Method 1 Let x denote the larger of the two numbers and let y denote the other number. The sum of the two numbers $x + y$ must equal 115. Stating this condition in equation form, we have

$$x + y = 115.$$

The difference $x - y$ of the two numbers must equal 13. In equation form, we have

$$x - y = 13.$$

The two numbers can now be found by solving the equations $x + y = 115$ and $x - y = 13$ for x and y. If we add these equations, the result is

$$
\begin{array}{r}
x + y = 115 \\
x - y = 13 \\
\hline
2x = 128
\end{array}
$$

Therefore, $x = 64$. Substituting 64 for x in the first equation, we find that $y = 51$. The two numbers are 64 and 51.

Method 2 Let x denote the larger of the two numbers. Because the sum of the two numbers is 115, the other number must be $115 - x$. The difference of the numbers is 13. Thus

$$
\begin{aligned}
x - (115 - x) &= 13, \\
x - 115 + x &= 13, \\
2x &= 128, \\
x &= 64.
\end{aligned}
$$

The larger of the two numbers is 64. The other number is

$$115 - 64 = 51.$$

Example 4 The units' digit of a two-digit number is twice the tens' digit. If the digits of the number are reversed, the number is increased by 36. What is the number?

Solution If we let u denote the units' digit and let t denote the tens' digit, then $u = 2t$. Any two-digit number is equal to 10 times the tens' digit plus the units' digit. Therefore our number is

$$10t + u.$$

FUNCTIONS AND GRAPHS

If the digits are reversed, u becomes the tens' digit and t becomes the units' digit. The number obtained by reversing the digits is

$$10u + t.$$

The original number is increased by 36 when the digits are reversed. Therefore

$$(10t + u) + 36 = 10u + t,$$
$$9t - 9u + 36 = 0.$$

We now recall that $u = 2t$ and substitute this expression for u in the equation $9t - 9u + 36 = 0$. We have

$$9t - 18t + 36 = 0$$
$$-9t = -36$$
$$t = 4.$$

Therefore $u = 8$, and the number is 48.

Example 5 Mr. Jones plans a round trip to a city 210 mi away. He plans to travel 60 mi/hr going and to spend 6.5 hr for the round trip. How fast must he travel on the return trip?

Solution A problem of this type is sometimes called a motion problem. In such a problem we make use of the distance formula, which states that the distance traveled equals the rate of travel times the time traveled, or $d = rt$. As an aid in motion problems, we sometimes use a table such as that shown below in order to organize our data.

Direction	Distance	Rate	Time
Going	210	60	7/2
Returning	210	r	210/r

To complete the table we consider the trip going to the city. Since the distance to the city is 210 mi and the rate of travel is 60 mi/hr, we use the formula $d = r \cdot t$ to conclude that the time elapsed is $210/60 = 7/2$ hr. On the return trip, the distance is also 210 mi. Let r be the rate of travel on the return trip. Then the time elapsed on the return trip is $210/r$. Since the total time to be used is 6.5 hr, we have

$$\tfrac{7}{2} + 210/r = 6.5,$$
$$7r + 420 = 13r,$$
$$420 = 6r,$$
$$r = 70.$$

Therefore the return trip should be made at the rate of 70 mi/hr.

Example 6 Two cars leave the same place to travel on the same road, one at 50 mi/hr and the other at 70 mi/hr. If the second car starts 1 hr after the other, when will it overtake the first car?

Solution Let t be the number of hours the second car travels. The basic facts are summarized in the following table.

Car	Distance	Rate	Time
First	$50(t+1)$	50	$t+1$
Second	$70t$	70	t

Since the second car will overtake the first car whenever they have traveled the same distance, we equate the distances traveled by the cars.

$$70t = 50(t+1),$$
$$70t = 50t + 50,$$
$$20t = 50,$$
$$t = 2\tfrac{1}{2}.$$

Thus the second car will overtake the first $2\tfrac{1}{2}$ hr after the second car starts.

Example 7 One machine can do a piece of work in 3 hr and another in 6 hr. How long will it take them to do the work if they are operated on the same job at the same time?

Solution This type of problem is sometimes referred to as a work problem. Use is made of the fact that if it takes x units of time to complete a job, then the part of the job completed in one unit of time is $1/x$. Again it is helpful to use a table to organize the given information. Let x denote the time required for the machines working together to complete the job. Then:

Machine	Time to do complete job	Part of job completed in 1 unit of time
First	3	$1/3$
Second	6	$1/6$
Together	x	$1/x$

The part completed in one hour by the first machine added to the part completed in one hour by the second machine is the part of the job completed in one hour by the machines working together. Thus

$$1/3 + 1/6 = 1/x$$

and multiplying both sides of the equation by $6x$, we have

$$2x + x = 6,$$
$$3x = 6,$$
$$x = 2.$$

Therefore it will take 2 hr to complete the job if both machines work on the same job.

Example 8 A painter and his apprentice can paint a house in 7 days. Working alone, the painter can paint the house in 12 days. How long would it take the apprentice working by himself to paint the house?

Solution Let x be the number of days required for the apprentice to complete the job. Then:

Worker	Time to do complete job	Part of job completed in one unit of time
Painter	12	1/12
Apprentice	x	$1/x$
Together	7	1/7

From the table, we have the equation

$$1/12 + 1/x = 1/7,$$
$$7x + 84 = 12x,$$
$$5x = 84,$$
$$x = \tfrac{84}{5} = 16\tfrac{4}{5}.$$

Therefore the apprentice working alone could paint the house in $16\tfrac{4}{5}$ days.

Example 9 How many pounds of grass seed costing 90¢/lb must be mixed with 50 lb of seed costing 20¢/lb to make a mixture costing 40¢/lb?

Solution The unknown quantity is the number of pounds of the 90¢ grass seed. Let x represent this quantity. The basic facts pertaining to our problem are summarized in the following table.

Kind of seed	Pounds	Value in cents
90¢	x	$90x$
20¢	50	$50 \cdot 20$
40¢	$x + 50$	$40(x + 50)$

The value of the 90¢ seed plus the value of the 20¢ seed must equal the value of the mixture. Therefore

$$90x + 50 \cdot 20 = 40(x + 50),$$
$$90x + 1000 = 40x + 2000,$$
$$50x = 1000,$$
$$x = 20.$$

We now conclude that 20 lb of the 90¢ seed must be mixed with 50 lb of the 20¢ seed to make a mixture costing 40¢ lb.

Example 10   How much pure alcohol must be added to 5 qt of a 40% solution of alcohol and water to obtain a 90% solution?

Solution Let x represent the number of quarts of pure alcohol needed to make the 90% solution. The relevant facts are summarized in the following table.

Solution	Quantity	Amount of alcohol
Pure alcohol	x	x
40% solution	5	$(.40)(5)$
90% solution	$5 + x$	$(.90)(5 + x)$

The number of quarts of pure alcohol plus the number of quarts of alcohol in the 40% solution must equal the number of quarts of alcohol in the 90% solution. Therefore

$$x + (.40)(5) = (.90)(5 + x),$$
$$x + 2 = 4.5 + .9x,$$
$$.1x = 2.5,$$
$$x = 25.$$

Hence we should use 25 qt of pure alcohol to make the 90% mixture.

Problems

1   One number is 5 times another, and the sum of the two numbers is 156. What are the numbers?

2   One number is 6 more than twice the other, and their sum is 102. Find the numbers.

3   Find three consecutive integers whose sum is 390.

4   Find three consecutive odd integers whose sum is 69.

5   The perimeter of a rectangle is 78 ft. The length is 5 more than the width. Find the dimensions of the rectangle.

6 The perimeter of a rectangle is 880 ft. The length is 3 times the width. Find the dimensions of the rectangle.

7 In 13 yr Amanda will be 7 times as old as she was 5 years ago. How old is she now?

8 In 40 yr Matt will be 5 times as old as he was 10 yr ago. How old is he now?

9 Amanda is 5 times as old as Shannon but in 12 yr she will only be twice as old. Find the present age of each.

10 The tens' digit of a two-digit number is 3 times the units' digit. If the digits are interchanged, the number is decreased by 18. What is the number?

11 The units' digit of a two-digit number is 3 more than twice the tens' digit. If the digits of the number are reversed, the number is increased by 54. What is the number?

12 The sum of the digits of a two-digit number is 15. If the digits are interchanged, the number is decreased by 27. What is the number?

13 Eighty-five coins, consisting of dimes and quarters, amount to $13. How many coins of each kind are there?

14 A farmer sold 50 chickens, both hens and roosters, for $73. If the hens sold for $1.50 and the roosters sold for $1.00, how many of each were sold?

15 Two cars leave the same place and travel the same route, one at 50 mi/hr and the other at 65 mi/hr. If the second car starts 1.5 hr after the other, when will it overtake the first car?

16 Mr. Smith plans a round trip to a location 200 mi away. He plans to travel 60 mi/hr going and to spend 6 hr for the round trip. How fast must he travel on his return trip?

17 A man left home at 8 a.m. planning to travel 60 mi/hr. How fast must his wife travel in order to overtake him in 2 hr if she starts at 8:30 a.m.?

18 Two boys plan to row a boat upstream and return. They can row 4 mi/hr in still water, and the rate of the stream is 2 mi/hr. How far upstream can they go if the round trip is to require 3 hr?

19 Two families living 200 mi apart decided to meet.
   a) If both start at 9 a.m., when will they meet if one travels at 55 mi/hr and the other at 70 mi/hr?
   b) When will they meet if the slower starts at 8:30 a.m. and the other at 9:30 a.m.?

20 An airplane can fly 360 mi with the wind in 2 hr and back against the wind in 3 hr, with the engine speed being the same in both directions. What is the rate of the airplane in still air and what is the rate of the wind?

21 An airplane required 5 hr to fly 1200 mi with the wind. It took 6 hr to make the return trip against a wind whose velocity was 5 mi/hr less than the wind velocity on the first part of the trip. If the engine speed was the same in both directions, what was the speed of the engine? What was the velocity of the wind in each direction?

22 Mr. Smith can dig a ditch in 6 days, and his helper can dig the ditch in 8 days. How many days would it take the two working together to dig the ditch?

23 Tractor A and tractor B working together can plow a field in 5 days. Working alone, A can plow the field in 8 days. How many days would it take B working alone to plow the field?

24 Bill can do in 8 hr a job which he and Joe together can do in 3 hr. How many hours would be required for Joe to complete the job if he were working alone?

25 Working together, Tom and Sam can pick 100 boxes of strawberries in 4 hr. Tom can pick this same amount working by himself in 7 hr. How long would it take Sam working by himself to pick 50 boxes of strawberries?

26 One pipe can fill a tank in 2 hr, a second can fill it in 3 hr, and a third in 4 hr. How long will it take to fill the tank if all pipes are open?

27 A pipe can fill a swimming pool in 8 hr. The drain can empty the pool in 10 hr. If the pool is empty and the drain is left open, how long will it take the pipe to fill the pool?

28 One pipe can fill a tank in 10 hr. After the water has been running 3 hr, a second pipe is also opened and the two pipes fill the tank in $2\frac{1}{3}$ hr. In how many hours could the second pipe fill the tank?

29 How many pounds of candy worth 35¢/lb must be mixed with 15 lb of candy worth 90¢/lb to give a mixture worth 50¢/lb?

30 How many pounds each of candy worth 65¢/lb and $1.25/lb must be mixed to give a 50-lb mixture worth $1/lb?

31 How many quarts of a 75% solution of alcohol should one add to 10 qt of a 55% solution to produce a 70% solution?

32 A person has two solutions of alcohol, one 60% and the other 85%. How many gallons of each must he use to produce 20 gal of a 75% solution?

33 An automobile radiator contains 15 qt of a liquid that is 35% ethylene glycol. How many quarts must one drain off and replace by pure ethylene glycol to obtain a 55% mixture?

34 An automobile radiator contains 20 qt of a liquid that is 30% ethylene glycol. How many quarts must one drain off and replace by a solution that is 75% ethylene glycol to get a 55% solution?

FUNCTIONS AND GRAPHS

35 How much alcohol must one add to 10 qt of a solution that is 40% alcohol to obtain a 55% solution?

36 A grocer has two kinds of coffee, one worth 75¢/lb and the other worth 95¢/lb. How many pounds of the 95¢ coffee must be mixed with 50 lb of the 75¢ coffee to obtain a blend worth 80¢/lb.?

6.8 EXPONENTS AND RADICALS

In Chapter 3 we defined the nth power of a number a, where n is a positive integer, to be the product of n factors of a. Furthermore, if a is any nonzero number and n is a positive integer, we define $a^0 = 1$ and $a^{-n} = 1/a^n$. In this section we discuss the reasons for stating the latter two definitions. It should be clear that the definition for a positive integer n cannot be extended to cover these new cases. To use a, as a factor, zero or a negative number of times would make no sense. In Chapter 3 we proved that if m and n are positive integers, then

$$a^m \cdot a^n = a^{m+n} \quad \text{and} \quad (a^m)^n = a^{mn}.$$

We will now prove a theorem concerning division of like bases.

Theorem 6.1 If a is any nonzero real number and m and n are any positive integers, then

$$a^m \div a^n = \begin{cases} a^{m-n} & \text{if } m > n, \\ 1 & \text{if } m = n, \\ \dfrac{1}{a^{n-m}} & \text{if } m < n. \end{cases}$$

Proof

$$a^m \div a^n = \frac{\overbrace{a \cdot a \cdot \cdots \cdot a}^{m \text{ factors of } a}}{\underbrace{a \cdot a \cdot \cdots \cdot a}_{n \text{ factors of } a}}$$

Consider the following three cases.

1) $m > n$. Each factor of a in the denominator can be paired with a factor of a in the numerator to yield a factor of 1. After doing this, we find that $m - n$ factors of a will remain in the numerator, and thus if $m > n$, then $a^m \div a^n = a^{m-n}$.

2) $m = n$. Each factor of a in the denominator can be paired with a factor of a in the numerator to yield a factor of 1. This will reduce the expression to one involving only factors of 1, and thus the product is 1. Therefore, if $m = n$, then $a^m \div a^n = 1$.

3) $m < n$. By a procedure similar to case 1, $n - m$ factors of a will remain in the denominator. Therefore, if $m < n$, then

$$a^m \div a^n = \frac{1}{a^{n-m}}.$$

If we define $a^0 = 1$ and $a^{-n} = 1/a^n$, where a is any nonzero real number and n is a positive integer, then Theorem 6.1 can be restated to say that $a^m \div a^n = a^{m-n}$ for any integers m and n. Hence we state the following definitions.

Definition 6.7 If a is any nonzero real number, then $a^0 = 1$.

Definition 6.8 If a is any nonzero real number and n is any positive integer, then $a^{-n} = 1/a^n$.

Example 1
$$a^5 \div a^2 = a^{5-2} = a^3,$$
$$3^5 \div 3^5 = 3^{5-5} = 3^0 = 1,$$
$$7^2 \div 7^6 = 7^{2-6} = 7^{-4} = \frac{1}{7^4} = \frac{1}{2401}.$$

Theorems analogous to Theorems 3.1 and 3.2, where m and n are any integers, can also be proved.

Example 2
$$a^{-2} \cdot a^3 = a^{(-2)+3} = a^1 = a,$$
$$2^2 \cdot 2^{-5} = 2^{2+(-5)} = 2^{-3} = \frac{1}{2^3} = \frac{1}{8},$$
$$(3^{-2})^{-1} = 3^{(-2)(-1)} = 3^2 = 9.$$

The following definition is essential to a further study of exponents.

Definition 6.9 If n is any positive integer and $a^n = b$, then a is called an nth root of b.

As an example, $3^2 = 9$, and thus 3 is a second root, or square root, of 9. Likewise, -3 is a square root of 9, since $(-3)^2 = 9$. $(-2)^3 = -8$, and therefore -2 is a third root, or cube root, of -8. Often, it is convenient to refer to the *principal* nth *root* of a number b. The principal nth root of a positive number b is the positive nth root. The principal nth root of a negative number b is the negative nth root if n is odd. However, if n is even, the principal nth root is not defined. The symbol $\sqrt[n]{b}$ means the principal nth root of b and is called a *radical; n* is called the *root index*, and b is called the *radicand* of the radical. If the root index is 2, the radical usually appears as $\sqrt{b}$.

Example 3 $\qquad$ $\sqrt{9} = 3,$ $\qquad$ $\sqrt[3]{-8} = -2,$ $\qquad$ $\sqrt[4]{81} = 3.$

We are now prepared to extend our definitions concerning exponents to include the rational numbers. In making this extension, we shall take care to preserve the properties already proved for integral exponents, namely,

1) $a^m \cdot a^n = a^{m+n}$
2) $(a^m)^n = a^{mn},$
3) $a^m \div a^n = a^{m-n},$ $\qquad a \neq 0.$

If q is any positive integer and if Property 1 above is to hold, then

$$\underbrace{b^{1/q} \cdot b^{1/q} \cdot b^{1/q} \cdot \ \cdots \ \cdot b^{1/q}}_{q \text{ factors of } b^{1/q}} = b^{q/q} = b,$$

and hence we define $b^{1/q}$ as the principal qth root of b. Likewise, if p and q are positive integers with no common factors and if Property 2 is to hold, then we define $(b^{1/q})^p = b^{p/q}$. Thus $b^{1/q}$ is the principal pth root of $b^{p/q}$, and $b^{p/q}$ is the pth power of $b^{1/q}$. Using radical notation, we have $b^{p/q} = (\sqrt[q]{b})^p$. Furthermore,

$$\underbrace{b^{p/q} \cdot b^{p/q} \cdot b^{p/q} \cdot \ \cdots \ \cdot b^{p/q}}_{q \text{ factors of } b^{p/q}} = b^p,$$

and thus $b^{p/q}$ is the principal qth root of b^p. Using radical notation, we have $b^{p/q} = \sqrt[q]{b^p}$. These remarks can be summarized in the following definition.

Definition 6.10 If p and q are positive integers with no common factors, then $b^{p/q} = (\sqrt[q]{b})^p = \sqrt[q]{b^p}$.

Example 4 $\qquad$
$8^{2/3} = (\sqrt[3]{8})^2 = 2^2 = 4,$
$16^{3/2} = (16^{1/2})^3 = 4^3 = 64,$
$(-27)^{2/3} = (\sqrt[3]{-27})^2 = (-3)^2 = 9.$

It can be proved that all the theorems pertaining to integral exponents are also valid for rational exponents.

Example 5 $\qquad$
$81^{-3/4} = \dfrac{1}{81^{3/4}} = \dfrac{1}{(\sqrt[4]{81})^3} = \dfrac{1}{3^3} = \dfrac{1}{27},$

$a^{1/4} \cdot a^{1/2} = a^{1/4+1/2} = a^{3/4} = \sqrt[4]{a^3},$

$x^{1/3} \div x^{2/3} = x^{1/3-2/3} = x^{-1/3} = \dfrac{1}{x^{1/3}} = \dfrac{1}{\sqrt[3]{x}},$

$(b^{-3})^{-2} = b^{(-3)(-2)} = b^6.$

Problems

1 Evaluate the following numbers.

    a) 2^3 b) 3^{-2} c) $4^{1/2}$

    d) $(-8)^{2/3}$ e) $(16)^{-3/4}$ f) $(-27)^{-1/3}$

    g) $(32)^{4/5}$ h) $(2^{-6})^{2/3}$ i) $(2^{10})^{-3/5}$

2 Simplify each of the following and express the result in radical form.

    a) $a^{2/3} \cdot a^{1/4}$ b) $(b^{2/3})^{1/3}$ c) $x^{1/5} \div x^{1/10}$

    d) $(x^{-3/8})^8$ e) $(a^{-2/3})^{-3/4}$ f) $((-y)^{1/3})^2$

3 Simplify the following.

    a) $\dfrac{4^2 \cdot 4^3}{4^6}$ b) $(3^2)^3$ c) 3^{2^3}

    d) $(x^3y)(x^2y^3)$ e) a^3/b^0 f) $(16^9)^0$

4 Show that $(a^3)^2 = (a^2)^3$.

5 Simplify each of the following.

    a) $x^2 \cdot x^3 \cdot x$ b) $x^{1/2} \cdot x^{1/8} \cdot x^{-1/4}$

    c) $(7^2 \cdot 7)^2$ d) $3^2 \cdot (-3)^2 \cdot (-3)^3$

6 Let n be any positive integer and a and b be any real numbers. Prove $(ab)^n = a^n b^n$.

7 Let n be any positive integer and a and b be any real numbers with $b \neq 0$. Prove $(a/b)^n = a^n/b^n$.

6.9 QUADRATIC FUNCTIONS AND GRAPHS

We now turn our attention to the description of another special type of function.

Definition 6.11 If a, b, and c are real numbers with $a \neq 0$, then the function f defined by

$$f(x) = ax^2 + bx + c$$

is called a *quadratic function*.

The quadratic function f defined by the equation $f(x) = ax^2 + bx + c$ is the collection

$$f = \{(x, y) \mid y = ax^2 + bx + c\}.$$

Some examples of quadratic functions are:

1) $f(x) = 3x^2 - 5x + 4$,   2) $g(x) = -2x^2 - x + 6$,

3) $h(x) = x^2$,   4) $F(x) = 2x^2 - 3$.

The graph of a quadratic function f is the graph of the set of ordered pairs which defines f. Unlike the linear function, a quadratic function cannot usually be sketched accurately unless more than a few points are located on its graph. Consider the following examples.

Example 1 Make a table of values and graph the quadratic function $f(x)$ $= x^2 - 2x - 3$.

Solution See Fig. 6.15.

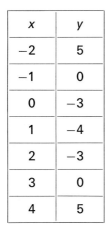

x	y
-2	5
-1	0
0	-3
1	-4
2	-3
3	0
4	5

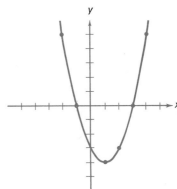

Figure 6.15

Example 2 Make a table of values and graph the quadratic function $f(x)$ $= -2x^2 + 8x - 5$.

Solution See Fig. 6.16.

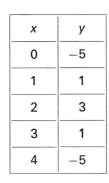

x	y
0	-5
1	1
2	3
3	1
4	-5

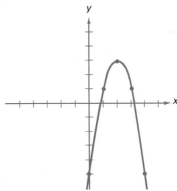

Figure 6.16

Although one opens upward and the other opens downward, the graphs in Examples 1 and 2 have the same general shape. The graph of any quadratic function is of this type and is called a *parabola*. It can be proved that the graph of the quadratic function $f(x) = ax^2 + bx + c$ opens upward if $a > 0$ and downward if $a < 0$.

From the graph in Fig. 6.16, it appears that the function

$$f(x) = -2x^2 + 8x - 5$$

of Example 2 has its maximum value at or near the point at which $x = 2$. Exactly where the maximum value of f occurs can be determined by *completing the square*, a process known to the geometer Euclid in the third century B.C. By completing the square one can express a quadratic function in terms of the square of a linear function. We will illustrate this process for the function

$$f(x) = -2x^2 + 8x - 5.$$

Our first step is to group the terms containing x^2 and x. Factoring out -2, the coefficient of x^2, we have

$$f(x) = -2(x^2 - 4x) - 5.$$

To the expression $x^2 - 4x$ inside the parentheses we add 4, the square of one-half the coefficient of x. The number 4 is to be multiplied by -2, so actually we have subtracted 8 from the function. If the function is to remain unchanged, we must also add 8 to the function. Adding and subtracting 8 in this manner, we have

$$f(x) = -2(x^2 - 4x + 4) - 5 + 8.$$

The expression $x^2 - 4x + 4$ can be written $(x - 2)^2$. Substituting $(x - 2)^2$ for $x^2 - 4x + 4$ and simplifying, we have

$$f(x) = -2(x - 2)^2 + 3.$$

We now observe that the term $-2(x - 2)^2$ is always either negative or 0, its value being 0 when $x = 2$. Since 0 is greater than any negative number, $-2(x - 2)^2$ has its maximum value when $x = 2$. Hence the maximum value of f is

$$y = f(2) = -2(2)^2 + 8(2) - 5 = 3.$$

The point $(2, 3)$ is called the *vertex* of the parabola obtained by graphing the function $-2x^2 + 8x - 5$. By graphing the vertex and a few other points, one can sketch quite accurately the graph of the parabola.

The vertex of a parabola which opens upward is the point on the parabola at which the function assumes its minimum value. Consider the following example.

Example 3 Find the vertex of the parabola obtained by graphing the function $f(x) = x^2 - 2x - 3$.

FUNCTIONS AND GRAPHS

Solution $f(x) = x^2 - 2x - 3$ is the function of Example 1 and its graph is the parabola in Fig. 6.15. Applying the process of completing the square to $f(x) = x^2 - 2x - 3$, we have

$$\begin{aligned} f(x) &= (x^2 - 2x) - 3 \\ &= (x^2 - 2x + 1) - 3 - 1 \\ &= (x - 1)^2 - 4; \end{aligned}$$

$(x - 1)^2$ is always either positive or 0, its value being 0 if $x = 1$. Hence f has its minimum value when $x = 1$, and this minimum value is

$$y = f(1) = 1^2 - 2 \cdot 1 - 3 = -4.$$

The vertex of the parabola is the point $(1, -4)$.

The process of finding the maximum or minimum of a quadratic function is often useful in solving certain types of practical problems.

Example 4 The owner of a peach orchard has 500 trees and realizes a net profit of $20 per tree each year. If the acreage remains fixed, the net profit per tree is decreased by 2¢ for each new tree planted. How many new trees should the owner plant to obtain the maximum profit?

Solution Let x denote the number of new trees the owner should plant. After planting x new trees his orchard will have $500 + x$ trees. Because the profit per tree is reduced by 2¢ for each new tree planted, the profit per tree after x new trees are planted is

$$20 - .02x,$$

and the net profit per year for the orchard is given by the function

$$f(x) = (500 + x)(20 - .02x).$$

After simplifying, we have

$$f(x) = -.02x^2 + 10x + 10,000.$$

We now seek the value of x at which this function has its maximum value. Applying the process of completing the square to the function f, we have

$$\begin{aligned} f(x) &= -.02(x^2 - 500x) + 10,000 \\ &= -.02(x^2 - 500x + (250)^2) + 10,000 + 1250 \\ &= -.02(x - 250)^2 + 11,250. \end{aligned}$$

The function f has its maximum value at $x = 250$, and the maximum value is 11,250. Therefore the owner would realize a maximum profit of $11,250 by planting 250 new trees.

Problems

In problems 1 through 10 find the maximum or minimum value of the given quadratic function. Use this information along with a suitable table of values to graph the function.

1 $x^2 + 2x - 8$ 2 $-x^2 + x - 2$
3 $x^2 + 2$ 4 $3x^2 + 12x + 7$
5 $-2x^2 + 4x + 1$ 6 $2x^2 - 8x + 5$
7 $5x^2 + 15x + 10$ 8 $-x^2 + x + 4$
9 $3x^2 - 6x$ 10 $-2x^2 + 5x + 8$

11 The sum of two numbers is 70. Select the numbers so that their product is as large as possible.

12 The sum of two times one number and three times another number is 60. Select the numbers so that their product is a maximum.

13 A man with 1200 ft of fencing desires to fence in a rectangular lot. If he wants to enclose the largest possible area, what should the dimensions of the lot be?

14 A rectangular field is to be adjacent to a river. If 600 ft of fencing are available and the side along the river requires no fencing, what are the dimensions of the field with greatest area?

6.10 QUADRATIC EQUATIONS

Associated with each quadratic function $f(x) = ax^2 + bx + c$, $a \neq 0$, we have an equation $ax^2 + bx + c = 0$ which is called a *quadratic equation in x*. One method to find the solution set of a quadratic equation is to graph the function and read the abscissa of the point or points at which the graph intersects the x-axis. These values will be the roots of the equation. The following example will illustrate this procedure.

Example 1 Solve the quadratic equation $x^2 - x - 2 = 0$ by the graphing method.

Solution Graph the fucntion $f(x) = x^2 - x - 2$ (see Fig. 6.17).

Reading the abscissa of each point of intersection of the graph of f with the x-axis, it appears that the solution set is $\{2, -1\}$. Of course, the solutions found by the graphing method are approximations and they should be checked by substitution into the equation.

Recall from the previous section that the graph of a quadratic function is always a parabola, either opening upward or downward. Considering the

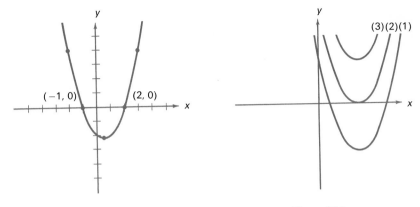

Figure 6.17   Figure 6.18

possible positions of the graph of a quadratic function relative to the x-axis is particularly enlightening when one is concerned with the roots of the associated quadratic equation. Figure 6.18 shows the three positions of the graph of a quadratic function relative to the x-axis.

In position (1), the graph of the quadratic function intersects the x-axis at two points, and thus the associated quadratic equation will have two real roots. In position (2), the graph touches the x-axis at a single point, and the associated quadratic equation has one distinct real root. Equations of this type are said to have two real roots which are equal. In position (3), the graph does not intersect or touch the x-axis, and thus there are no real solutions. We will see later in this section that such equations have two complex (but not real) roots. The solutions to such equations cannot be found by the graphing method. Because we cannot solve all quadratic equations by the graphing method and because a solution found by graphing is only an approximation, we turn to more productive and accurate methods for solving quadratic equations. We illustrate one such method, called the *factoring method*, in the following example.

Example 2 Solve the quadratic equation $x^2 - x - 2 = 0$ by factoring.
Solution Since $x^2 - x - 2 = (x - 2)(x + 1)$, we are seeking values of x such that
$$(x - 2)(x + 1) = 0.$$

The product of two real numbers can equal 0 only if one of the numbers is 0. Hence
$$x - 2 = 0 \text{ or } x + 1 = 0.$$

This is equivalent to stating that $x = 2$ or $x = -1$. Thus the solution set is $\{2, -1\}$. Note that these results agree with those in Example 1.

Example 3 Solve the quadratic equation $x^2 - 2x - 8 = 0$ by factoring.

Solution $x^2 - 2x - 8 = 0$ is equivalent to

$$(x - 4)(x + 2) = 0,$$
$$x - 4 = 0 \quad \text{or} \quad x + 2 = 0,$$
$$x = 4 \quad \text{or} \quad x = -2.$$

Thus the solution set is $\{4, -2\}$.

The quadratic expression in a quadratic equation may be difficult or even impossible to factor. The two following examples illustrate how the process of completing the square (Section 6.9) can be used in solving quadratic equations.

Example 4 Solve the quadratic equation $x^2 - x - 2 = 0$ by completing the square.

Solution By adding 2 to both members, we can write the quadratic equation $x^2 - x - 2 = 0$ as

$$x^2 - x = 2.$$

We now complete the square on the expression $x^2 - x$ by adding $\frac{1}{4}$ to both sides of the equation. Thus we have

$$x^2 - x + \tfrac{1}{4} = 2 + \tfrac{1}{4},$$
$$(x - \tfrac{1}{2})^2 = \tfrac{9}{4}.$$

Now taking the square root of both members of the last equation, we have

$$x - \tfrac{1}{2} = \pm\tfrac{3}{2},$$
$$x = \tfrac{1}{2} \pm \tfrac{3}{2}.$$

Therefore

$$x = \tfrac{1}{2} + \tfrac{3}{2} = 2 \quad \text{and} \quad x = \tfrac{1}{2} - \tfrac{3}{2} = -1$$

are solutions of the equation $x^2 - x - 2 = 0$. Again note that these results agree with those in Examples 1 and 2.

Example 5 Solve the quadratic equation $2x^2 - 3x - 1 = 0$ by completing the square.

Solution If we add 1 to both members of the equation, we have

$$2x^2 - 3x = 1.$$

We next divide both members of this equation by 2 to get

$$x^2 - \tfrac{3}{2}x = \tfrac{1}{2}.$$

FUNCTIONS AND GRAPHS

We now complete the square on the expression $x^2 - \frac{3}{2}x$ by adding $\frac{9}{16}$, the square of one-half the coefficient of x, to both sides of this equation. Thus we have

$$x^2 - \tfrac{3}{2}x + \tfrac{9}{16} = \tfrac{1}{2} + \tfrac{9}{16},$$

$$(x - \tfrac{3}{4})^2 = \tfrac{17}{16}.$$

By extracting the square root of both members of the last equation, we get

$$x - \frac{3}{4} = \frac{\pm\sqrt{17}}{4}.$$

Adding $\frac{3}{4}$ to both members, we find

$$x = \frac{3 \pm \sqrt{17}}{4}.$$

Therefore the roots of the quadratic equation are

$$x = \frac{3 + \sqrt{17}}{4} \quad \text{and} \quad x = \frac{3 - \sqrt{17}}{4}.$$

Problems

Solve the following quadratic equations by graphing.

1 $x^2 - 3x - 4 = 0$ 2 $x^2 + 4x - 12 = 0$

3 $x^2 + 2x - 15 = 0$ 4 $x^2 = -6x - 5$

Solve the following quadratic equations by factoring.

5 $x^2 + 5x - 24 = 0$ 6 $w^2 - 4w - 21 = 0$

7 $z^2 - 8z = -15$ 8 $2y^2 + 31y + 15 = 0$

Solve the following quadratic equations by completing the square.

9 $x^2 + 8x + 15 = 0$ 10 $y^2 + 2y - 3 = 0$

11 $2w^2 - w - 1 = 0$ 12 $z^2 - 2z = 35$

Solve the following quadratic equations by any method discussed in this section.

13 $x^2 - 2x - 3 = 0$ 14 $z^2 - z - 3 = 0$

15 $w^2 + 3w - 28 = 0$ 16 $y^2 - y - 3 = 0$

17 $2w^2 - w = 10$ 18 $z^2 + z + 1 = 0$

19 $2x^2 - x - 3 = 0$ 20 $x^2 - x + 1 = 0$

21   On the same coordinate axes, graph

    a) $f(x) = x^2 - 4x + 8$ b) $g(x) = x^2 - 4x + 4$

    c) $h(x) = x^2 - 4x + 1$

From observing these graphs tell the nature of the roots of the quadratic equation associated with each function.

6.11 THE QUADRATIC FORMULA

We now use the process of completing the square to derive a formula for finding the roots of the general quadratic equation

$$ax^2 + bx + c = 0, \qquad a \neq 0.$$

The first step is to add $-c$ to both sides of the equation to get

$$ax^2 + bx = -c.$$

Next we divide both members of this equation by a to obtain the equation

$$x^2 + \frac{b}{a}x = -\frac{c}{a}.$$

We now complete the square on the expression

$$x^2 + \frac{b}{a}x$$

by adding $\dfrac{b^2}{4a^2}$, the square of one-half the coefficient of x, to both sides of the equation. Thus we have

$$x^2 + \frac{b}{a}x + \frac{b^2}{4a^2} = \frac{b^2}{4a^2} - \frac{c}{a},$$

$$\left(x + \frac{b}{2a}\right)^2 = \frac{b^2 - 4ac}{4a^2}.$$

By extracting the square root of both members of the last equation, we get

$$x + \frac{b}{2a} = \frac{\pm\sqrt{b^2 - 4ac}}{2a}.$$

If we add $-\dfrac{b}{2a}$ to both members of this equation, the result is

$$x = \frac{-b \pm \sqrt{b^2 - 4ac}}{2a}.$$

Thus

$$x = \frac{-b + \sqrt{b^2 - 4ac}}{2a} \qquad \text{and} \qquad x = \frac{-b - \sqrt{b^2 - 4ac}}{2a}$$

are the only possible solutions to the equation $ax^2 + bx + c = 0$. We can show that both of these values are actually solutions by substituting them into the equation and observing that they both satisfy the equation. The equation

$$x = \frac{-b \pm \sqrt{b^2 - 4ac}}{2a}$$

is called the *quadratic formula;* it gives the solutions of the equation $ax^2 + bx + c = 0$ in terms of coefficients a, b, and c. Note that the quadratic formula gives two roots,

$$\frac{-b + \sqrt{b^2 - 4ac}}{2a} \quad \text{and} \quad \frac{-b - \sqrt{b^2 - 4ac}}{2a}.$$

Example 1 Solve the quadratic equation $x^2 - x - 2 = 0$ by using the quadratic formula.

Solution The equation $x^2 - x - 2 = 0$ is in the form $ax^2 + bx + c = 0$ with $a = 1$, $b = -1$, and $c = -2$. By the quadratic formula, we have

$$x = \frac{-(-1) \pm \sqrt{(-1)^2 - 4(1)(-2)}}{2(1)}$$

$$= \frac{1 \pm \sqrt{1 + 8}}{2}$$

$$= \frac{1 \pm 3}{2}.$$

Therefore

$$x = \frac{1 + 3}{2} = 2 \quad \text{or} \quad x = \frac{1 - 3}{2} = -1,$$

and the solution set is $\{2, -1\}$. We have now solved the equation $x^2 - x - 2 = 0$ by four methods: graphing, factoring, completing the square, and by use of the quadratic formula.

Example 2 Solve the quadratic equation $x^2 - 5x = 3$ by using the quadratic formula.

Solution Transforming the equation $x^2 - 5x = 3$ into the form $ax^2 + bx + c = 0$, we have $x^2 - 5x - 3 = 0$ with $a = 1$, $b = -5$, and $c = -3$. Therefore

$$x = \frac{-(-5) \pm \sqrt{(-5)^2 - 4(1)(-3)}}{2(1)}$$

$$= \frac{5 \pm \sqrt{25 + 12}}{2}$$

$$= \frac{5 \pm \sqrt{37}}{2}.$$

The solution set is
$$\left\{\frac{5 + \sqrt{37}}{2}, \frac{5 - \sqrt{37}}{2}\right\}.$$

Example 3 Solve the quadratic equation $4x^2 + 4x = -1$ by using the quadratic formula.

Solution The equation $4x^2 + 4x = -1$ is transformed into the desired form $4x^2 + 4x + 1 = 0$, and we have $a = 4$, $b = 4$, and $c = 1$. Then

$$x = \frac{-4 \pm \sqrt{(4)^2 - 4(4)(1)}}{2(4)}$$

$$= \frac{-4 \pm 0}{8}.$$

Thus

$$x = \frac{-4 + 0}{8} = -\frac{1}{2} \quad \text{or} \quad x = \frac{-4 - 0}{8} = -\frac{1}{2},$$

and the solution set is $\{-\frac{1}{2}\}$. The graph of the function $f(x) = 4x^2 + 4x + 1$ will touch the x-axis at the point $(-\frac{1}{2}, 0)$.

Example 4 Solve the quadratic equation $x^2 - x + 1 = 0$ by using the quadratic formula.

Solution The equation $x^2 - x + 1 = 0$ is in the required form with $a = 1$, $b = -1$, and $c = 1$. Therefore

$$x = \frac{-(-1) \pm \sqrt{(-1)^2 - 4(1)(1)}}{2(1)}$$

$$= \frac{1 \pm \sqrt{-3}}{2}$$

$$= \frac{1 \pm \sqrt{3}\,i}{2}.$$

The solution set is
$$\left\{\frac{1 + \sqrt{3}\,i}{2}, \frac{1 - \sqrt{3}\,i}{2}\right\}.$$

Note that these roots are complex numbers but not real numbers. Thus the graph of the function $f(x) = x^2 - x + 1$ will neither intersect nor touch the x-axis.

The fact that quadratic equations can be used to solve some types of practical problems will be illustrated by the following examples.

Example 5 The product of two consecutive integers is 56. What are the integers?

Solution If x denotes the first integer, then $x + 1$ is the second integer. Since the product is 56, we have the equation

$$x(x + 1) = 56,$$
$$x^2 + x = 56,$$
$$x^2 + x - 56 = 0,$$
$$(x + 8)(x - 7) = 0,$$
$$x + 8 = 0 \quad \text{or} \quad x - 7 = 0,$$
$$x = -8 \quad \text{or} \quad x = 7.$$

Thus there are two possibilities for the consecutive integers. They are -8 and -7 or 7 and 8.

Example 6 The length of a rectangle is 3 ft more than the width. The area of the rectangle is 88 sq ft. Find the dimensions of the rectangle.

Solution Let w be the width of the rectangle. Then the length of the rectangle is $w + 3$. Since the area is 88 sq ft, we have the equation

$$w(w + 3) = 88,$$
$$w^2 + 3w = 88,$$
$$w^2 + 3w - 88 = 0,$$
$$(w + 11)(w - 8) = 0,$$
$$w = -11 \quad \text{or} \quad w = 8.$$

We conclude that the width of the rectangle is 8 ft and the length is 11 ft. Note that the answer $w = -11$ is rejected since it is meaningless to have negative length.

Problems

Solve the following quadratic equations by using the quadratic formula.

1. $x^2 - 3x - 4 = 0$
2. $2y^2 + 21y + 15 = 0$
3. $z^2 - 2z - 35 = 0$
4. $2x^2 - x - 3 = 0$
5. $w^2 + w = -1$

Solve the following quadratic equations by any method.

6. $x^2 - 7x - 8 = 0$
7. $y^2 + y = 42$
8. $2w^2 - 2w - 1 = 0$
9. $z^2 + 4z + 1 = 0$
10. $y^2 - 3y - 3 = 0$
11. $2x^2 + 2x - 1 = 0$
12. $3z^2 - z = 2$
13. $4w^2 + 4w = -1$
14. $\frac{1}{6}x^2 + \frac{1}{2}x - 3 = 0$
15. $\frac{1}{3}z^2 + \frac{1}{3}z = 14$

16 By substitution show that the roots given by the quadratic formula for the equation $ax^2 + bx + c = 0$ satisfy the equation.

17 The two roots of the quadratic equation $ax^2 + bx + c = 0$ are

$$r_1 = \frac{-b + \sqrt{b^2 - 4ac}}{2a} \quad \text{and} \quad r_2 = \frac{-b - \sqrt{b^2 - 4ac}}{2a}.$$

Show that $r_1 + r_2 = -b/a$ and $r_1 \cdot r_2 = c/a$.

Using the results from Problem 17, give the sum and product of the roots of the following equations.

18 $4x^2 + 4x + 1 = 0$ 19 $x^2 - 7x - 8 = 0$

20 $\frac{1}{6}x^2 + \frac{1}{2}x - 3 = 0$

21 The product of two consecutive positive integers is 72. What are the integers?

22 The length of a rectangle is 4 in. more than the width. The area of the rectangle is 60 sq in. Find the dimensions of the rectangle.

23 A man set out 500 strawberry plants. The number of plants in each row is 5 less than the number of rows. How many plants are there in each row?

24 The sum of two numbers is 12 and the sum of their squares is 170. What are the numbers?

25 If 3 times the square of a number is decreased by 5, the result is 14 times the number. What is the number?

26 Find two consecutive integers such that their product increased by their sum is 5.

6.12 INEQUALITIES

A statement that one expression is greater than or less than another expression is called an *inequality*. Like equations, inequalities are of two main types. An inequality that is true for all permissible values of the variables involved is called an *absolute inequality*. An inequality that is true for some but not all permissible values of the variables is called a *conditional inequality*. The inequality $x^2 + 1 > 0$ is an absolute inequality, since it is true for all real values of x. Another example of an absolute inequality is $-3 < 5$. In contrast, $3x - 6 > 12$ is a conditional inequality because it is true only for values of x greater than 6. A *solution* of an inequality is a set of values for the variables for which the inequality is true. The set of all solutions is called the *solution set*. Inequalities that have the same solution set are called *equivalent inequalities*. Inequalities such as $a < b$ and $c < d$ are said to be of the *same sense*, whereas the inequalities $x < y$ and $u > v$ are said to be of *opposite sense*.

Before proceeding further with inequalities, the student should review the properties of order in Section 5.10. Theorems 6.2 through 6.4 follow directly from the properties discussed in that section.

Theorem 6.2 If the same number is added to both members of an inequality or if the same number is subtracted from both members of an inequality, the result is an inequality of the *same* sense.

Theorem 6.3 If both members of an inequality are multiplied or divided by the same *positive* number, the result is an inequality of the *same* sense.

Theorem 6.4 If both members of an inequality are multiplied or divided by the same *negative* number, the result is an inequality of *opposite* sense.

The application of Theorem 6.2, 6.3, or 6.4 to an inequality results in an equivalent inequality. Consequently, these theorems will be quite useful in solving inequalities.

Example 1 Solve the inequality $3x + 5 < 5x - 17$.

Solution If we subtract 5 from both members, we have the equivalent inequality

$$3x < 5x - 22.$$

Subtracting $5x$ from both members, we have

$$-2x < -22$$

Dividing both members by -2, we get

$$x > 11.$$

Therefore the solution set is $\{x \mid x > 11\}$.

Example 2 Find the solution set for the inequality $x^2 + 2x - 3 > 0$.

Solution We factor the left member of this inequality and consider

$$(x - 1)(x + 3) > 0.$$

The product of two numbers is positive only if both numbers are positive or if both numbers are negative. Hence we seek values of x for which

$$\left.\begin{array}{c} x - 1 > 0 \\ \text{and} \\ x + 3 > 0 \end{array}\right\} \quad \text{or} \quad \left\{\begin{array}{c} x - 1 < 0 \\ \text{and} \\ x + 3 < 0. \end{array}\right.$$

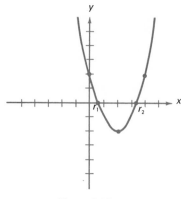

Figure 6.19

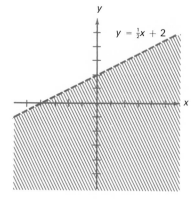

$y = \frac{1}{2}x + 2$

Figure 6.20

We find that

$$\left. \begin{array}{c} x - 1 > 0 \\ \text{and} \\ x + 3 > 0 \end{array} \right\} \quad \text{is equivalent to} \quad \left\{ \begin{array}{c} x > 1 \\ \text{and} \\ x > -3, \end{array} \right.$$

and the solution set for this pair of inequalities is $\{x \mid x > 1\}$. Similarly,

$$\left. \begin{array}{c} x - 1 < 0 \\ \text{and} \\ x + 3 < 0 \end{array} \right\} \quad \text{is equivalent to} \quad \left\{ \begin{array}{c} x < 1 \\ \text{and} \\ x < -3, \end{array} \right.$$

and the solution set for this pair of inequalities is $\{x \mid x < -3\}$. Therefore the solution set for the inequality $x^2 + 2x - 3 > 0$ is

$$\{x \mid x > 1 \text{ or } x < -3\}.$$

Example 3 Find the solution set for the inequality $x^2 - 4x + 2 < 0$.

Solution The expression $x^2 - 4x + 2$ cannot be factored, so we will use the graphing method. From the graph of the function $f(x) = x^2 - 4x + 2$ in Fig. 6.19, we see that the associated quadratic equation has two real roots which we label r_1 and r_2. For $r_1 < x < r_2$, the graph of f is below the x-axis, and consequently, $f(x) = x^2 - 4x + 2 < 0$. By using the quadratic formula, we find that $r_1 = 2 - \sqrt{2}$ and $r_2 = 2 + \sqrt{2}$. Hence the solution set for the inequality $x^2 - 4x + 2 < 0$ is

$$\{x \mid (2 - \sqrt{2}) < x < (2 + \sqrt{2})\}.$$

Example 4 Find the solution set for the inequality $x - 2y + 4 > 0$.

Solution $x - 2y + 4 > 0$ is an inequality in the two variables x and y. We will use the graphing method to find the solution set. Solving the in-

FUNCTIONS AND GRAPHS

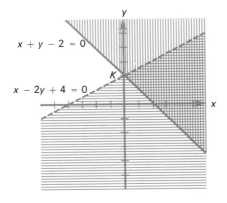

$x + y - 2 = 0$

K

$x - 2y + 4 = 0$

Figure 6.21

equality for y, we get

$$y < \tfrac{1}{2}x + 2,$$

which is called the y-form of the inequality. Thus, we are seeking those points (x, y) in the plane for which $y < \tfrac{1}{2}x + 2$. The broken line in Fig. 6.20 represents the graph of the straight line $y = \tfrac{1}{2}x + 2$. This straight line separates the plane into two regions, a region "above" the line and a region "below" the line. The coordinates of the points in the region above the line will satisfy the inequality $y > \tfrac{1}{2}x + 2$, while the coordinates of the points in the region below the line will satisfy the inequality $y < \tfrac{1}{2}x + 2$. Hence we shade the region below the line to represent the graph of the solution set for the inequality $y < \tfrac{1}{2}x + 2$ or, equivalently, $x - 2y + 4 > 0$. Note that the boundary line is broken to indicate that the points on the line do not belong to the solution set.

Example 5   Find the solution set for the pair of inequalities $x - 2y + 4 > 0$ and $x + y - 2 \geqq 0$.

Solution   If A denotes the solution set of the first inequality and B denotes the solution set of the second, then $A \cap B$ is the solution set for the pair. We will again use the graphing method. The first inequality was solved in Example 4, and its solution set is shaded horizontally in Fig. 6.21. The y-form of $x + y - 2 \geqq 0$ is

$$y \geqq -x + 2.$$

The graph of the line $y = -x + 2$ is represented by a solid line in Fig. 6.21, and the solution set for $y \geqq -x + 2$ (or $x + y - 2 \geqq 0$) consists of this line and the vertically shaded region. Hence the graph of the solution set for the pair of inequalities is the region that is shaded both vertically and horizontally. Note that the points along the lower boundary are included in the graph, but those along the upper boundary, including the point K, are not.

Problems

Find the solution set for each of the inequalities in Problems 1 through 10.

1 $7x - 5 < 4x + 10$
2 $x + 2 > 6x - 8$
3 $-2z + 1 < 3z + 18$
4 $-7x - 13 \geq -3x + 8$
5 $\frac{3}{2}w > 2w - \frac{1}{3}$
6 $x^2 - 3x - 4 > 0$
7 $2x^2 - x - 1 \leq 0$
8 $x^2 + x + 1 < 0$
9 $-2x^2 - 5x + 3 > 0$
10 $x^2 - x + 1 \geq 0$

Solve the inequalities in Problems 11 through 18 by the graphing method.

11 $3x + y - 1 < 0$
12 $2x - y + 3 > 0$
13 $-2x + 3y + 6 \geq 0$
14 $4x - 2y \leq 6$
15 $-3y > 5$
16 $3x - 2y > 1$
17 $2x < -5$
18 $-5x - 3y \leq 6$

Solve the pairs of inequalities in Problems 19 through 24 by the graphing method.

19 $x - y + 1 < 0,$
    $x + y + 1 < 0$
20 $3x + y - 6 > 0,$
    $y < 2$
21 $3x - 2y > 4,$
    $-x \leq 2$
22 $3x - 2y \geq 1,$
    $x + y < -2$
23 $2x - y + 3 > 0,$
    $2x + y + 1 \leq 0$
24 $-x + y > 2,$
    $2x + y + 1 < 0$

25 Solve the inequality $|2x - 1| > 5$ for x.

26 Solve the pair of inequalities $y > x^2$ and $x - y + 2 > 0$ by the graphing method.

27 Solve the pair of inequalities $y > x^2 - 5x + 6$ and $x + y + 1 > 0$ by the graphing method.

6.13 STATISTICAL GRAPHS

Linear functions and quadratic functions have graphs which we call *continuous-line graphs.* However, not all functions have continuous-line graphs. For example, the post office function of Section 6.2 is not a graph of this type. To conclude our discussion of functions and graphs, we will discuss some graphs of functional relationships which are not continuous-line graphs. The most commonly used graphs of this kind are bar graphs, pie charts, pictographs, and broken-line graphs. These are particularly helpful whenever one needs a visual interpretation of the functional relationships. The type of graph to use depends on the nature of the functional relationship to be emphasized.

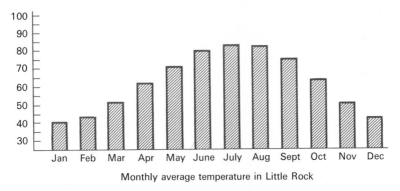

Monthly average temperature in Little Rock

Figure 6.22

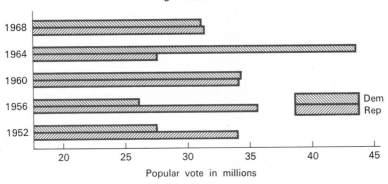

Popular vote in millions

Figure 6.23

A *bar graph* is particularly useful if we desire to compare several measures with one another. The bar graph in Fig. 6.22 shows the normal monthly average temperature at Little Rock, Arkansas. From this graph we see that the normal average temperature for the month of September is 74 degrees. Further, we see that the coldest month of the year is January. The reader will be asked to answer questions about this graph and other graphs of this section in the problems at the end of this section.

In constructing bar graphs, one uses both vertical and horizontal bars, and in both cases the length of a bar designates magnitude. The bar graph in Fig. 6.23 shows the popular vote received by each of the major-party presidential candidates in the last five elections. From this graph we see that in the 1964 election the Democratic presidential candidate received approximately 43 million popular votes. The total popular vote for the two major parties in 1968 was approximately 62 million.

A *pie chart* is particularly useful whenever we wish to compare not only a set of magnitudes with one another but also each magnitude with the total.

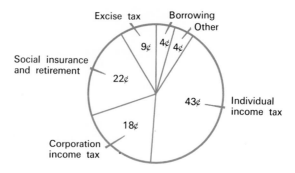

Figure 6.24

Figure 6.24 is an example of a pie chart showing the source of each dollar of federal revenue in 1969. From this pie chart we see that 43¢ of every dollar came from individual income tax. Furthermore, federal revenue from corporation income tax was twice the amount received from excise taxes.

The *pictograph* is used to illustrate the same type of functional relationship as the bar graph. There are no real advantages to a pictograph except that if it is well done, it will catch the eye. Fig. 6.25 is a pictograph showing the cattle population in the United States in four different years. From this pictograph we see that the cattle population in 1960 was approximately 95 million.

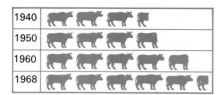

Figure 6.25. Cattle population in the United States. Each cow represents 20,000,000 head.

The *broken-line graph* is used when we wish to consider rate of change instead of comparison of magnitudes. We used the information from the bar graph in Fig. 6.22 to make a broken-line graph showing the normal monthly

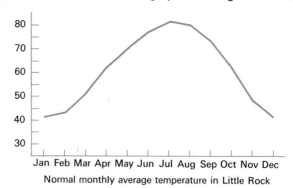

Normal monthly average temperature in Little Rock   Figure 6.26

FUNCTIONS AND GRAPHS

average temperature at Little Rock (Fig. 6.26). From this graph we see that the normal average temperature for the month of April is 62 degrees. Further, we see that there is little change in temperature from July to August ($\frac{1}{2}$ degree) and a relatively large change from March to April ($10\frac{1}{2}$ degrees).

Problems

1 Use the graph in Fig. 6.22 to answer the following questions concerning the normal average monthly temperature in Little Rock.

   a) What is the average temperature for May?

   b) What is the average temperature for October?

   c) What is the warmest month?

   d) How many months are colder than May?

   e) How many months are warmer than March?

2 Use the graph in Fig. 6.23 to answer the following questions concerning the popular vote cast for the major-party candidates in the last five elections.

   a) How many votes did the Democratic candidate receive in 1956?

   b) Which election was won by the greatest margin?

   c) How many votes did the Republican candidate receive in 1952?

   d) What was the total vote for the two major parties in 1964?

   e) Which candidate has received the most votes since 1952?

3 Use the graph in Fig. 6.24 to answer the following questions concerning the source of the federal revenue dollar in 1969.

   a) What was the major source of income for the federal government?

   b) What part of each dollar came from excise tax?

   c) What part of each dollar came from a combination of excise tax and corporation income tax?

4 Use the graph in Fig. 6.25 to answer the following questions concerning the cattle population of the United States.

   a) What was the cattle population in 1940? in 1968?

   b) Construct a bar graph using the information given.

5 Use the graph in Fig. 6.26 to answer the following questions concerning the monthly average temperature at Little Rock.

   a) The most radical change in average temperature is between which two consecutive months?

   b) The least change in average temperature is between which two consecutive months?

c) What is the average temperature for November?

d) What is the change in average temperatures from May to June?

6 The monthly normal precipitation at Little Rock is as follows: .

Month	Jan.	Feb.	Mar.	Apr.	May	June	July	Aug.	Sept.	Oct.	Nov.	Dec.
Precipitation inches	5.2	4.3	4.8	4.9	5.3	3.6	3.3	2.8	3.2	2.9	4.1	4.1

Construct a bar graph showing this information.

7 The number of immigrants admitted to the United States in the years 1960-67 is as follows:

Number of immigrants in thousands	1960	1961	1962	1963	1964	1965	1966	1967
	265	271	284	306	292	297	323	362

Construct a bar graph showing this information.

8 In 1969 the federal revenue dollar was spent as follows:

	National defense	Educational and other major social programs	Social insurance, trust funds	International	Veterans	Interest	Others
Cents	43	11	20	3	4	6	13

Make a pie chart showing this information.

9 A suggested family budget for a family of four with an annual income of $8000 (after taxes) is as follows:

	Food	Shelter	Clothing	Savings	Operating expenses	Miscellaneous
Dollars	2,000	1,500	1,000	1,400	800	1,300

Construct a pie chart showing this information.

10 The sheep population on United States farms in certain years was as follows:

	1940	1950	1960	1968
Millions	46	26	29	19

Construct a pictograph showing this information.

FUNCTIONS AND GRAPHS

11 The following table gives the average price paid to the farmer for a dozen eggs at the local market last year.

Month	Cents	Month	Cents
Jan.	35	July	27
Feb.	30	Aug.	29
Mar.	26	Sept.	34
Apr.	26	Oct.	41
May	25	Nov.	45
June	25	Dec.	46

Construct a broken-line graph to show this information.

Chapter 7

MODULAR ARITHMETIC AND APPLICATIONS

7.1 NUMBER CONGRUENCES

In this chapter we will discuss a type of mathematical system different from the number systems studied in Chapters 4 and 5. Even though the system to be studied is different from those previously examined in this book, the reader has had considerable experience with the principle on which it is based. We will introduce this new concept by considering problems one might encounter in using the ordinary clock for telling the time of day.

Let us suppose the time is 2 o'clock. What will be the time in 103 hours? We can find the answer to this question from Fig. 7.1, by imagining that we move the hour hand 103 spaces around the face of the clock. After a little effort, we find that the answer is 9 o'clock. We might be inclined to summarize our work by writing $2 + 103 = 9$. However, at this point, we must be very careful in our use of the symbols "$+$" and "$=$" because we are not dealing with an ordinary problem in addition of numbers. It is customary in a situation such as this to use the following notation:

$$2 + 103 \equiv 9 \bmod 12;$$

"mod 12" is an abbreviation of the expression "modulo 12," which means "with respect to the number 12." We are not working with the usual relation of equality, so we use the new symbol "$\equiv$." The above relation may now be read "2 plus 103 is 9 relative to the number 12." This translation will be sufficient for our present discussion. A new vocabulary will be introduced later in this section to describe relations of this kind.

Let us examine another problem of this nature. If the time is now 2 o'clock, what will be the time in 5480 hours? If we attempt to find the answer to this question by using the method of the previous problem, we are faced with the most uninteresting task of marking off 5480 spaces in Fig. 7.1. A little forethought at this point will save considerable time. We observe that each time we move the hour hand 12 spaces, we are again at 2 o'clock. If we divide 5480 by 12, we get a quotient of 456 and a remainder of 8. Thus we can solve the problem by moving the hour hand 8 spaces starting at 2 o'clock. The time in 5480 hours will be 10 o'clock, and we can summarize our work by writing

$$2 + 5480 \equiv 10 \bmod 12.$$

We now observe that the numbers $5482 = 2 + 5480$ and 10 both have the same remainder when divided by 12. Referring to the first problem of this section, we also observe that the numbers $105 = 2 + 103$ and 9 both have remainder 9 when divided by 12.

Figure 7.1

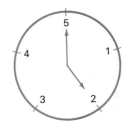

Figure 7.2

Although it is conventional for the clock to have 12 spaces, an instrument for telling time may be marked off in more or less than 12 spaces. An interesting situation develops if we consider the clock in Fig. 7.2 having 5 spaces.

If the time is initially 2 o'clock, then the time in 57 hours will be 4 o'clock. We obtain this answer either by marking off 57 spaces, starting at 2 o'clock, or by marking off 2 spaces, starting at 2 o'clock after observing that 57 has remainder 2 when divided by 5. This time we write

$$2 + 57 \equiv 4 \bmod 5.$$

The expression "mod 5" indicates that we are dealing with a clock having 5 spaces. We also observe that the numbers $59 = 2 + 57$ and 4 have the same remainder when divided by 5. As another example,

$$4 + 43 \equiv 2 \bmod 5,$$

and we again observe that the numbers $47 = 4 + 43$ and 2 have the same remainder when divided by 5.

Let M denote a positive integer. Based on the observations of this section, it would seem reasonable to assume that two numbers are related with respect to the modulus M if both numbers have the same remainder when divided by M. We state the following definition.

Definition 7.1 Let A and B be integers. If M is a positive integer, then A *is congruent to B modulo M*, written $A \equiv B$ *mod M*, if and only if A and B have the same remainder when divided by M.

We now illustrate this definition with the following examples.

Example 1 27 is congruent to 12 modulo 5 because 27 and 12 both have a remainder of 2 when divided by 5. Thus we may write

$$27 \equiv 12 \text{ mod } 5.$$

Further, we observe that 27 is congruent to each of the integers 2, 7, 17, 22, 27, 32, . . . modulo 5.

Example 2

$$33 \equiv 3 \text{ mod } 15$$

because 33 and 3 have the same remainder when divided by 15.

$$33 \equiv 18 \text{ mod } 15$$

because 33 and 18 have the same remainder when divided by 15.

$$33 \equiv 33 \text{ mod } 15$$

because 33 and 33 have the same remainder when divided by 15.

$$33 \equiv 48 \text{ mod } 15$$

because 33 and 48 have the same remainder when divided by 15.

Example 3 Find all integral values of x for which $x \equiv 51$ mod 23.

Solution If 51 is divided by 23, one obtains a quotient of 2 with a remainder of 5. We now seek integers which have a remainder of 5 when divided by 23. 5 is one such integer. Others are 28, 51, 74, 97, ... The student will observe that when one solution is found, another can be obtained by adding 23. Thus, the set of values of x for which $x \equiv 51$ mod 23 is the set

$$\{5 + 23n \mid n \text{ is an integer}\}.$$

Example 4 If -5 is divided by 7, one obtains a quotient of -1 with a remainder of 2. The student will recall that if an integer is divided by 7, the remainder is either 0 or a positive integer less than 7. Since 9 also has a remainder of 2 when divided by 7, we conclude that

$$-5 \equiv 9 \text{ mod } 7.$$

-5 is also congruent to the integers -12, -5, 2, 16, and 23 modulo 7.

For M a positive integer, a statement that one expression is congruent to another expression modulo M is called a *congruence*. The positive integer M is called the *modulus* of the congruence.

Problems

1 Consider a clock having 24 spaces. If it is initially 17 o'clock, what is the time in 543 hours? in 2134 hours?

2 Consider a clock having 6 spaces. If it is initially 3 o'clock, what is the time in 91 hours? in 5872 hours?

3 Consider a clock having 15 spaces. If it is initially 12 o'clock, what is the time in 42 hours? in 536 hours?

4 Find four integers that are congruent to the following.

a) 5 mod 8   b) 6 mod 15

c) 1 mod 3   d) −3 mod 5

Find five integers which will satisfy each of the congruences in Problems 5 through 12.

5 $x \equiv 3 \bmod 7$ 6 $x \equiv 39 \bmod 12$

7 $x \equiv 16 \bmod 35$ 8 $-17 \equiv x \bmod 10$

9 $815 \equiv x \bmod 6$ 10 $x \equiv 93 \bmod 411$

11 $x + 3 \equiv 8 \bmod 7$ 12 $2x \equiv 1 \bmod 5$

Find all integral values for x which will satisfy the congruences in Problems 13 through 18.

13 $x \equiv 7 \bmod 5$ 14 $4 \equiv x \bmod 7$

15 $x \equiv x \bmod 5$ 16 $0 \equiv 5 \bmod x$

17 $15 \equiv x \bmod 5$ 18 $7 \equiv 4 \bmod x$

7.2 PROPERTIES OF NUMBER CONGRUENCES

We recall from Section 4.16 that an integer x is said to be a *multiple* of an integer y if there exists an integer k such that $x = ky$. For example, 12 is a multiple of 4 because $12 = 3 \cdot 4$. In this example, $k = 3$. Other examples are:

> 12 is a multiple of 3 because $12 = 4 \cdot 3$.
> 34 is a multiple of 17 because $34 = 2 \cdot 17$.
> -50 is a multiple of 5 because $-50 = (-10) \cdot 5$.
> 23 is a multiple of 1 because $23 = 23 \cdot 1$.

It should be noted that every integer x is a multiple of 1 because $x = x \cdot 1$. Also an integer x is a multiple of itself since $x = 1 \cdot x$. Furthermore, 0 is a multiple of every integer x because $0 = 0 \cdot x$, regardless of the value of x.

Before investigating some of the basic properties of the congruence relation, we will show that $A \equiv B$ mod M is equivalent to the statement "$A - B$ is a multiple of M." This alternative approach will be convenient to use in proving several of the properties of number congruences.

Let us first assume that A and B are integers and M is a positive integer such that $A \equiv B$ mod M. Then A and B have the same remainder r when divided by M. If q_1 and q_2 are the respective quotients when A and B are divided by M, then

$$A = q_1 \cdot M + r \quad \text{and} \quad B = q_2 \cdot M + r.$$

It now follows from these equations that

$$r = A - q_1 \cdot M \quad \text{and also} \quad r = B - q_2 \cdot M.$$

Thus

$$A - q_1 \cdot M = B - q_2 \cdot M.$$

If we add $q_1 \cdot M - B$ to both sides of this equation, we obtain the equation

$$A - B = q_1 \cdot M - q_2 \cdot M.$$

Finally,

$$A - B = (q_1 - q_2) \cdot M.$$

Therefore we see that $A - B$ is a multiple of M by choosing $k = q_1 - q_2$.

The reader may find it interesting to prove the converse of this theorem. That is, if $A - B$ is a multiple of M, then A and B have the same remainder when divided by M. This problem will appear as an exercise at the end of this section.

We summarize the foregoing remarks in the following theorem.

Theorem 7.1 Let A and B denote integers and let M denote a positive integer. Then $A \equiv B$ mod M if and only if $A - B$ is a multiple of M.

Before proceeding we shall illustrate this new approach to number congruences by some examples.

Example 1 $23 \equiv 5$ mod 9 because $23 - 5 = 18$ and 18 is a multiple of 9.

Example 2 $7 \equiv 35$ mod 4 because $7 - 35 = -28$ and -28 is a multiple of 4. To be more specific, $-28 = (-7)4$.

Example 3 $-13 \equiv 17$ mod 10 because $-13 - 17 = -30$ and -30 is a multiple of 10.

Example 4 By using the method of this section, find three integers x such that $x \equiv 8$ mod 11.

MODULAR ARITHMETIC AND APPLICATIONS

Solution We seek values of x such that $x - 8$ is a multiple of 11. Thus we can find three solutions by solving the equations $x - 8 = 11, x - 8 = 2 \cdot 11$, and $x - 8 = 3 \cdot 11$ for x. We find that x has the values 19, 30, and 41, respectively. Other solutions can be obtained by solving equations of similar type.

The following sequence of theorems will show that the congruence relation has the same basic properties that we postulated for the relation of equality in Section 4.5. In each of these theorems we shall assume that M denotes a positive integer.

Theorem 7.2 *The reflexive property.* $A \equiv A$ mod M for every integer A.

Proof $A - A = 0$ and 0 is a multiple of every integer. Hence $A - A$ is a multiple of M, and it follows that $A \equiv A$ mod M.

Theorem 7.3 *The symmetric property.* If A and B are integers such that $A \equiv B$ mod M, then $B \equiv A$ mod M.

Proof Because $A \equiv B$ mod M, we can write $A - B = kM$ for some integer k. If we multiply both sides of this equation by -1, we obtain

$$B - A = (-k)M.$$

Thus, $B - A$ is a multiple of M, and therefore $B \equiv A$ mod M.

Theorem 7.4 *The transitive property.* If A, B, and C are integers such that $A \equiv B$ mod M and $B \equiv C$ mod M, then $A \equiv C$ mod M.

Proof Since $A \equiv B$ mod M and $B \equiv C$ mod M, both $A - B$ and $B - C$ are multiples of M. Thus there exist integers k and p such that

$$A - B = kM \qquad \text{and} \qquad B - C = pM.$$

If we add these two equations and factor out M from the two terms on the right-hand side, we have

$$A - C = (k + p)M.$$

Hence $A - C$ is a multiple of M, and we may write $A \equiv C$ mod M. The theorem is now proved.

The reader will perhaps recall the discussion of an equivalence relation from Section 4.5. Any relation that has the reflexive, symmetric, and transitive properties is called an equivalence relation. We have just proved that the congruence relation is an equivlaence relation on the set of integers.

There are two additional properties of number congruences that are essential to further work in this area.

Theorem 7.5 *The addition property.* If A, B, C, and D are integers such that $A \equiv B$ mod M and $C \equiv D$ mod M, then $A + C \equiv B + D$ mod M.

Proof The hypothesis of the theorem states that $A \equiv B$ mod M and $C \equiv D$ mod M. Thus there exist integers k and p such that

$$A - B = kM \quad \text{and} \quad C - D = pM.$$

If we add these equations and rearrange terms, we obtain

$$(A + C) - (B + D) = (k + p)M.$$

Hence $(A + C) - (B + D)$ is a multiple of M, and we have proved that $A + C \equiv B + D$ mod M.

If $C \equiv D$ mod M, then by using the definition of the congruence relation, one can show that $-C \equiv -D$ mod M. Hence, if

$$A \equiv B \text{ mod } M \quad \text{and} \quad C \equiv D \text{ mod } M,$$

it follows from Theorem 7.5 that

$$A - C \equiv B - D \text{ mod } M.$$

We conclude this section with the following theorem.

Theorem 7.6 *The multiplication property.* If A, B, C, and D are integers such that $A \equiv B$ mod M and $C \equiv D$ mod M, then

$$AC \equiv BD \text{ mod } M.$$

Problems

By using Theorem 7.1 find four integral values for x that satisfy the congruences in Problems 1 through 14.

1 $x \equiv 3$ mod 5	2 $x \equiv -6$ mod 15
3 $x \equiv 21$ mod 3	4 $x \equiv 0$ mod 11
5 $x \equiv -14$ mod 6	6 $x \equiv 43$ mod 9
7 $x \equiv -12$ mod 12	8 $x \equiv 1$ mod 5
9 $x \equiv -3$ mod 8	10 $5 \equiv x$ mod 15
11 $-31 \equiv x$ mod 7	12 $x + 3 \equiv 5$ mod 12
13 $3x \equiv 0$ mod 5	14 $2x + 5 \equiv 4$ mod 7

15   By using Theorem 7.1 find a value for x for which the following congruences are valid.

     a) $13 \equiv 2$ mod x b) $-8 \equiv 5$ mod x

16 Verify Theorem 7.5 with each of the following pairs of congruences.

    a) $71 \equiv 35$ mod 9 and $235 \equiv 199$ mod 9

    b) $-5 \equiv 8$ mod 13 and $33 \equiv 7$ mod 13

17 Verify Theorem 7.6 with each of the following pairs of congruences.

    a) $17 \equiv 2$ mod 3 and $8 \equiv 5$ mod 3

    b) $36 \equiv 6$ mod 15 and $6 \equiv -24$ mod 15

18 Prove that if $C \equiv D$ mod M, then $-C \equiv -D$ mod M.

19 Complete the proof of Theorem 7.1.

20 Prove Theorem 7.6.

7.3 ARITHMETIC MODULO 5

We will now consider an example of a mathematical system known as the system of integers modulo 5. This new system will be our first example of a finite mathematical system. The system of integers modulo 5 will be con-structed by defining two operations on the set I_5 which consists of the integers 0, 1, 2, 3, and 4. The operations called *addition modulo 5* and *multiplication modulo 5* will be denoted by the same symbols, $+$ and $\cdot$, used to denote the common operations of addition and multiplication.

To find the sum of two elements of I_5 using the operation of *addition modulo 5*, one simply takes the remainder when the ordinary sum is divided by 5. For example, using addition modulo 5, we have $0 + 3 = 3, 2 + 2 = 4$, $2 + 3 = 0$, $3 + 4 = 2$, and $4 + 4 = 3$. This method is equivalent to choosing the element of I_5 which is congruent modulo 5 to the ordinary sum. *Multiplication modulo 5* is defined in a similar manner. Thus, to find the product of two elements of I_5 using *multiplication modulo 5*, we take the remainder when the ordinary product is divided by 5. Or, equivalently, we choose the element of I_5 which is congruent modulo 5 to the ordinary product. For example, using multiplication modulo 5, we have $0 \cdot 3 = 0$, $1 \cdot 4 = 4, 2 \cdot 2 = 4, 2 \cdot 3 = 1$, and $3 \cdot 4 = 2$.

Because the system of integers modulo 5 is a finite system, we can list all sums and products of elements in this system. This is usually done by means of tables like Tables 7.1 and 7.2. In each table the symbol in the upper left-hand corner denotes the operation being tabulated. The tables are read in essentially the same way that one reads a mileage chart. For instance, to find the sum $3 + 4$, one starts with the number 3 in the first column of Table 7.1 and then moves horizontally to the square in the column headed by number 4. In this square, we find the answer, 2. As a second example, we find that the product $2 \cdot 3$ has the value 1, by starting with the number 2 in the first column of Table 7.2 and moving horizontally to the square in the column headed by the number 3. Tables 7.1 and 7.2 will be of considerable value to us in our work with arithmetic modulo 5.

TABLE 7.1. ADDITION MODULO 5

+	0	1	2	3	4
0	0	1	2	3	4
1	1	2	3	4	0
2	2	3	4	0	1
3	3	4	0	1	2
4	4	0	1	2	3

TABLE 7.2. MULTIPLICATION MODULO 5

·	0	1	2	3	4
0	0	0	0	0	0
1	0	1	2	3	4
2	0	2	4	1	3
3	0	3	1	4	2
4	0	4	3	2	1

A careful inspection of the two tables will show that I_5 is closed with respect to the operations of addition and multiplication modulo 5. That is, the sum and product modulo 5 of two elements of I_5 are again elements of I_5.

From another inspection of Tables 7.1 and 7.2 we find that 0 is the identity element for addition modulo 5 and 1 is the identity element for multiplication modulo 5. That is,

$$0 + x = x + 0 = x \quad \text{and} \quad 1 \cdot x = x \cdot 1 = x$$

for every element x in I_5. We also observe from these tables that each element of I_5 has an inverse with respect to the operation of addition. Furthermore, every element of I_5, except 0, has an inverse with respect to multiplication. Some of these inverses are exhibited in Example 1; the reader will be asked to find inverses for the other elements of I_5 in the problems at the end of this section.

Example 1   The additive inverse of 4 is 1 because

$$4 + 1 = 1 + 4 = 0.$$

0 is its own additive inverse because

$$0 + 0 = 0.$$

The multiplicative inverse of 3 is 2 because

$$3 \cdot 2 = 2 \cdot 3 = 1.$$

1 is its own multiplicative inverse because

$$1 \cdot 1 = 1.$$

Both addition and multiplication, modulo 5, are associative and commutative on I_5. Furthermore, multiplication modulo 5 distributes over addition modulo 5. The proofs of these properties will be postponed until Section 7.5.

In developing the system of integers in Chapter 4, we defined the difference $x - y$ of two integers x and y to be the integer z if and only if $x = y + z$. We then proved that this definition of subtraction is equivalent to adding the additive inverse of y to x. We shall take the latter approach in defining subtraction on the set I_5. That is, if x and y are elements of I_5, then $x - y = x + (-y)$, where $-y$ denotes the additive inverse of the element y.

Since subtraction on I_5 is defined in terms of addition, Table 7.1 can be used quite effectively in calculating differences. The following example illustrates this method.

Example 2 Using Table 7.1, we find that:

$3 - 2 = 1$ because the additive inverse of 2 is 3 and $3 + 3 = 1$.
$2 - 4 = 3$ because the additive inverse of 4 is 1 and $2 + 1 = 3$.
$0 - 1 = 4$ because the additive inverse of 1 is 4 and $0 + 4 = 4$.
$4 - 0 = 4$ because the additive inverse of 0 is 0 and $4 + 0 = 4$.

We have already stated that every element of I_5 has an additive inverse. Thus subtraction is always possible in I_5.

The definition of division on I_5 is analogous to that of subtraction. That is, if x and y are elements of I_5, then $x \div y = x \cdot y^{-1}$, where y^{-1} denotes the multiplicative inverse of the element y. Division is defined in terms of multiplication, so Table 7.2 can be used as an aid in calculating quotients.

Example 3 Using Table 7.2, we find that:

$2 \div 3 = 4$ because the multiplicative inverse of 3 is 2 and $2 \cdot 2 = 4$.
$4 \div 2 = 2$ because the multiplicative inverse of 2 is 3 and $4 \cdot 3 = 2$.
$1 \div 4 = 4$ because the multiplicative inverse of 4 is 4 and $1 \cdot 4 = 4$.

Since every element of I_5, except 0, has a multiplicative inverse, division, except by 0, is always possible in I_5.

If a and b are elements of I_5, then the equation $a + x = b$ will have a solution in I_5. The solution $x = b - a$ can be found by adding the additive inverse of a to both sides of the equation. If $a \neq 0$, the equation $ax = b$ has the solution $x = a^{-1}b$. This solution can be obtained by multiplying both sides of the equation by a^{-1}, the multiplicative inverse of a. These remarks will be illustrated by the following examples.

Example 4   Solve the equation $x + 4 = 2$ in the system of integers mod 5.

Solution   The additive inverse of 4 is 1. If 1 is added to both sides of the equation $x + 4 = 2$, we have

$$(x + 4) + 1 = 2 + 1$$
$$x + (4 + 1) = 3 \qquad \text{Associative property for addition modulo 5}$$
$$x + 0 = 3 \qquad \text{Definition of the additive inverse}$$
$$x = 3 \qquad \text{0 is the additive identity}$$

Example 5   Solve the equation $3x = 1$ in the system of integers mod 5.

Solution   The multiplicative inverse of 3 is 2. If we multiply both sides of the equation $3x = 1$ by 2, we have

$$2 \cdot (3x) = 2 \cdot 1$$
$$(2 \cdot 3) \cdot x = 2 \qquad \text{Associative property for multiplication modulo 5}$$
$$1 \cdot x = 2 \qquad \text{Definition of the multiplicative inverse}$$
$$x = 2 \qquad \text{1 is the multiplicative identity}$$

The results of Examples 4 and 5 can be obtained directly from Tables 7.1 and 7.2. However, the examples illustrate a method that can be applied to more difficult problems.

Problems

1   By using Tables 7.1 and 7.2, evaluate the following sums and products in the system of integers mod 5.

a) $1 + 3$ b) $2 \cdot 4$ c) $3 \cdot 1$

d) $2 + 4$ e) $4 \cdot 2$ f) $3 \cdot 3$

g) $4 \cdot 4$ h) $1 + 4$ i) $3 + 3$

j) $(4 + 3) + 2$ k) $2 \cdot (3 \cdot 4)$ l) $4 \cdot (4 + 2)$

2   Find the additive inverses for the elements 1, 2, and 3 in the system of integers mod 5.

3   Find the multiplicative inverses for the elements 2 and 4 in the system of integers mod 5.

4   Explain why 0 does not have a multiplicative inverse in the system of integers mod 5.

5   Use Tables 7.1 and 7.2 to evaluate the following differences and quotients in the system of integers mod 5.

a) $1 - 4$ b) $4 - 1$ c) $1 \div 2$ d) $2 - 3$

e) $3 \div 2$ f) $2 \div 4$ g) $0 \div 2$ h) $2 - 0$

i) $0 - 3$ j) $1 \div 3$ k) $3 \div 4$ l) $2 - 2$

6   Is the operation of subtraction on I_5 commutative? associative? Justify your answer.

7   Is the operation of division on I_5 commutative? associative? Justify your answer.

In Problems 8 through 16 solve the equations in the system of integers mod 5.

8 $x + 3 = 4$ 9 $4x = 2$ 10 $2x = 1$

11 $x + 1 = 4$ 12 $x + 2 = 1$ 13 $3x = 4$

14 $2x + 3 = 1$ 15 $4x + 1 = 2$ 16 $3x + 4 = 3$

7.4 ARITHMETIC MODULO 6

The system of integers modulo 5, discussed in the previous section, gave us a different and interesting example of a mathematical system. We now turn our attention to a system of similar type which we will call the system of integers modulo 6. This system, like the previous one, is a finite mathematical system. However, there are several very important differences that distinguish this new system from the system of integers modulo 5.

The system of integers modulo 6 is constructed by defining two operations on the set I_6 which consists of the integers 0, 1, 2, 3, 4, 5. As one would expect, these operations will be called *addition modulo 6* and *multiplication modulo 6* and will again be denoted by the same symbols, $+$ and $\cdot$, used to denote the ordinary operations of addition and multiplication.

The sum of two integers of I_6, using the operation of *addition modulo 6*, is the remainder which results when the ordinary sum is divided by the integer 6. For example,

$$0 + 4 = 4, \quad 2 + 3 = 5, \quad 2 + 4 = 0, \quad 3 + 5 = 2, \quad 5 + 5 = 4,$$

using addition modulo 6. This method is equivalent to choosing the element of I_6 which is congruent modulo 6 to the ordinary sum. To find the product of two elements of I_6, using *multiplication modulo 6*, one takes the remainder when the ordinary product is divided by 6. Or, equivalently, one chooses the

TABLE 7.3. ADDITION MODULO 6

+	0	1	2	3	4	5
0	0	1	2	3	4	5
1	1	2	3	4	5	0
2	2	3	4	5	0	1
3	3	4	5	0	1	2
4	4	5	0	1	2	3
5	5	0	1	2	3	4

element of I_6 which is congruent modulo 6 to the ordinary product. For example,

$$0 \cdot 2 = 0, \quad 1 \cdot 3 = 3, \quad 2 \cdot 4 = 2, \quad 3 \cdot 3 = 3, \quad 5 \cdot 4 = 2,$$

using multiplication modulo 6.

If 6 is used as the divisor in a division problem, the remainder must be one of the numbers 0, 1, 2, 3, 4, 5. Thus we see that the set I_6 is closed with respect to both addition modulo 6 and multiplication modulo 6.

Like the system of integers modulo 5, the system of integers modulo 6 is a finite system, and we can list all sums and products of elements in the system. The sums and products modulo 6 are tabulated in Tables 7.3 and 7.4, respectively. As before, the symbol in the upper left-hand corner of each table denotes the operation being tabulated. These tables are read in the same way as Tables 7.1 and 7.2. For example, to find the sum $2 + 3$, one starts with the number 2 in the first column of Table 7.3 and then moves horizontally to the square in the column headed by the number 3. In this square we find the answer 5. Tables 7.3 and 7.4 will be used extensively in this section to calculate sums, products, differences, and quotients.

From an inspection of Tables 7.3 and 7.4 we find that 0 is the identity for addition modulo 6, and 1 is the identity for multiplication modulo 6. That is,

$$0 + x = x + 0 = x \quad \text{and} \quad 1 \cdot x = x \cdot 1 = x$$

for every element x in I_6. Also each element of I_6 has an inverse with respect to the operation of addition modulo 6. For example, the inverse of 2 is 4 and the inverse of 3 is 3. The reader will find it easy to use Table 7.3 to find the additive inverse for each of the other elements of I_6. We now come to the problem of finding inverses for each of the elements of I_6 with respect to the operation of multiplication modulo 6. We are not surprised to find that the element 0 has no multiplicative inverse. However, there are other elements in I_6 which have no inverses with respect to multiplication modulo 6. For example, there is no element x of I_6 with the property that $2 \cdot x = x \cdot 2 = 1$.

TABLE 7.4. MULTIPLICATION MODULO 6

·	0	1	2	3	4	5
0	0	0	0	0	0	0
1	0	1	2	3	4	5
2	0	2	4	0	2	4
3	0	3	0	3	0	3
4	0	4	2	0	4	2
5	0	5	4	3	2	1

Thus the element 2 has no multiplicative inverse. After a closer inspection of Table 7.4 the reader will also observe that neither 3 nor 4 has an inverse with respect to multiplication modulo 6. The remaining two elements of I_6 have inverses; each of the elements 1 and 5 serves as its own inverse.

Table 7.4 reveals another unexpected property of the system of integers modulo 6. There are nonzero numbers of I_6 whose product is 0. For example, $2 \cdot 3 = 0$, but neither 2 nor 3 is 0. A nonzero number x is called a *zero divisor* if there exists another nonzero number y such that $x \cdot y = 0$. Thus both 2 and 3 are zero divisors in the system of integers mod 6. The student may find it interesting to try to find other zero divisors in this system.

This is the first time that we have encountered zero divisors in a mathematical system. The system of real numbers has no zero divisors, and the student may recall using this fact in solving quadratic equations. For instance, if $(x - 1)(x - 2) = 0$, we reason that $x - 1 = 0$ or $x - 2 = 0$ and conclude that $x = 1$ and $x = 2$ are roots of the quadratic equation $x^2 - 3x + 2 = 0$. Our work is based on the fact that the set of real numbers has no zero divisors. This method for solving quadratic equations is not valid in the system of integers mod 6 (see Problem 3 at the end of this section).

In the system of integers mod 6, as in the system of integers mod 5, both addition and multiplication are associative and commutative operations. Also, multiplication distributes over addition. The proofs of these properties will be deferred until the next section.

Subtraction on I_6 is defined by the equation $a - b = a + (-b)$, where $-b$ denotes the additive inverse of b. Every element in I_6 has an additive inverse, and therefore subtraction is always possible in I_6.

Example 1   Using Table 7.3, we find that:

$4 - 2 = 2$ because the additive inverse of 2 is 4 and $4 + 4 = 2$.
$2 - 5 = 3$ because the additive inverse of 5 is 1 and $2 + 1 = 3$.

Division on I_6 is defined by the equation $a \div b = a \cdot b^{-1}$ provided that b^{-1}, the multiplicative inverse of b, exists. 0 has no multiplicative inverse, so once again division by 0 is not defined. Furthermore, we have discovered that there are nonzero numbers in I_6 which do not have multiplicative inverses. Hence it is possible that $a \div b$ is not defined even though b is not 0.

Example 2   Using Table 7.4, we find that:

$2 \div 5 = 4$ because the multiplicative inverse of 5 is 5 and $2 \cdot 5 = 4$.
$3 \div 2$ is not defined because 2 has no multiplicative inverse in I_6.

The equation $a + x = b$ always has a solution in the system of integers mod 6, and, as in the system of integers mod 5, a solution is $x = b - a$.

Example 3   Solve the equation $2 + x = 5$ in the system of integers mod 6.

Solution   The additive inverse of 2 is 4. If 4 is added to both sides of the equation $2 + x = 5$, we have

$$4 + (2 + x) = 4 + 5$$

$$(4 + 2) + x = 3 \qquad \text{Associative property for}$$
$$\qquad\qquad\qquad\qquad \text{addition modulo 6}$$

$$0 + x = 3 \qquad \text{4 is the additive inverse}$$
$$\qquad\qquad\qquad \text{of 2}$$

$$x = 3 \qquad \text{0 is the additive identity}$$

If a^{-1} exists in the system of integers mod 6, then $x = a^{-1}b$ is a solution of the equation $ax = b$. If a^{-1} does not exist, then this equation may or may not have a solution. In fact, if a^{-1} fails to exist, the equation may have more than one solution. The following examples should help clarify these remarks.

Example 4   Solve the equation $3x = 3$ in the system of integers mod 6.

Solution   3 does not have a multiplicative inverse in I_6, so we cannot find a solution by setting x equal to $3^{-1} \cdot 3$. However, we find in Table 7.4 that $3 \cdot 1 = 3$, $3 \cdot 3 = 3$, and $3 \cdot 5 = 3$. Hence the numbers 1, 3, and 5 are solutions of the equation $3x = 3$.

Example 5   Solve the equation $2x = 3$ in the system of integers mod 6.

Solution   2 has no multiplicative inverse in I_6. Hence, we cannot find a solution by setting x equal to $2^{-1} \cdot 3$. We see from Table 7.4 that this equation has no solution, because multiplication by 2 can yield only the numbers 0, 2, and 4.

The system of integers modulo 5 and the system of integers modulo 6 are examples of mathematical systems that are similar, yet quite different. They are typical examples of modular systems. The integers 5 and 6 were chosen as the moduli because they are small and the resulting systems are fairly easy to investigate. However, any choice consisting of a prime and a nonprime positive integer would have served equally well. It can be shown that any modular system in which the modulus is a prime number has the same properties as the system of integers mod 5, and any modular system in which the modulus is nonprime has the same properties as the system of integers mod 6.

Problems

1 Using Tables 7.3 and 7.4 evaluate the following sums and products in the system of integers mod 6.

a) $1 + 4$

b) $5 + 4$

c) $5 \cdot 5$

d) $4 + 4$

e) $4 \cdot 3$

f) $5 \cdot 0$

g) $3 \cdot 5$

h) $3 + 0$

i) $3 \cdot (4 \cdot 5)$

j) $2 \cdot (3 + 2)$

k) $2 \cdot 3 + 2 \cdot 2$

l) $1 + (5 + 3)$

2 Find the additive inverses for the numbers 0, 1, 4, and 5 in the system of integers mod 6.

3 It has been established that the numbers 2 and 3 are zero divisors in the system of integers mod 6. Find all other zero divisors in this system.

4 Consider $(x - 1)(x - 2) = 0$ to be an equation in the system of integers mod 6. Clearly $x = 1$ and $x = 2$ are solutions of this equation. Find another solution of this equation in I_6.

5 Using Table 7.3, evaluate the following differences in the system of integers mod 6.

a) $1 - 4$

b) $5 - 2$

c) $0 - 1$

d) $3 - 5$

e) $0 - 3$

f) $1 - 2$

g) $4 - 0$

h) $2 - 3$

i) $2 - 4$

6 Which of the following quotients are defined in the system of integers mod 6? If the quotient is defined, use Table 7.4 to find its value.

a) $1 \div 4$

b) $5 \div 2$

c) $2 \div 5$

d) $4 \div 2$

e) $2 \div 3$

f) $4 \div 5$

g) $3 \div 1$

h) $0 \div 5$

i) $0 \div 3$

In Problems 7 through 18, which of the equations have a solution in the system of integers mod 6? Find all solutions for those which have solutions.

7 $4 + x = 5$

8 $5x = 3$

9 $x + 2 = 1$

10 $3x = 4$

11 $2x = 4$

12 $x + 5 = 4$

13 $4x = 1$

14 $5x = 1$

15 $3x + 5 = 2$

16 $5x + 2 = 3$

17 $x^2 = 1$

18 $x - 3 = 5$

7.5 THE ASSOCIATIVE, COMMUTATIVE AND DISTRIBUTIVE PROPERTIES

Let M denote a positive integer and let I_M be the set which consists of the integers 0, 1, 2, ..., M-1. To find the sum of two elements of I_M using *addition modulo M*, we take the remainder when the ordinary sum is divided by M. To find the product of two elements of I_M using *multiplication modulo M*, we take the remainder when the ordinary product is divided by M. It is our purpose in this section to prove that addition and multiplication modulo M have the associative and commutative properties. Furthermore, we shall prove that multiplication modulo M distributes over addition modulo M. In each of the following theorems, M will denote a positive integer.

Theorem 7.7   If A, B, and C are elements of I_M, then

$$(A + B) + C = A + (B + C),$$

using addition modulo M.

Proof

$$A + B = r_1,$$

using addition modulo M, if and only if $0 \leq r_1 < M$ and there exists an integer q_1 such that $A + B = q_1 M + r_1$.

$$B + C = r_2,$$

using addition modulo M, if and only if $0 \leq r_2 < M$ and there exists an integer q_2 such that $B + C = q_2 M + r_2$.

From the above equations involving r_1 and r_2, we find

$$r_1 = (A + B) - q_1 M,$$
$$r_2 = (B + C) - q_2 M.$$

Thus, using addition modulo M, we have

$$(A + B) + C = r_1 + C,$$
$$A + (B + C) = A + r_2.$$

However,

$$(r_1 + C) - (A + r_2) = [(A + B) + C - q_1 M] - [A + (B + C) - q_2 M]$$
$$= (q_2 - q_1)M.$$

Hence $r_1 + C \equiv A + r_2 \bmod M$.   Therefore $r_1 + C$ and $A + r_2$ have the same remainder when divided by M. It now follows that $(A + B) + C = A + (B + C)$, using addition modulo M.

Theorem 7.8 If A and B are elements of I_M, then $A + B = B + A$, using addition modulo M.

Proof If $+$ denotes the operation of ordinary addition and A and B are integers, we proved in Section 4.10 that $A + B = B + A$. Thus $A + B$ and $B + A$ have the same remainder when divided by M. Therefore, by Theorem 7.1, $A + B = B + A$, using addition modulo M.

The proofs of the remaining theorems of this section will be left as problems for the student.

Theorem 7.9 If A, B, and C are elements of I_M, then

$$(A \cdot B) \cdot C = A \cdot (B \cdot C)$$

using multiplication modulo M.

Theorem 7.10 If A and B are elements of I_M, then

$$A \cdot B = B \cdot A,$$

using multiplication modulo M.

Theorem 7.11 If A, B, and C are elements of I_M, then

$$A \cdot (B + C) = A \cdot B + A \cdot C,$$

using addition and multiplication modulo M.

It now follows as a special case of the theorems of this section (by choosing M equal to 5 and 6) that addition and multiplication modulo 5 and 6 are associative and commutative. Furthermore, multiplication distributes over addition.

Problems

1 Prove Theorem 7.9.

2 Prove Theorem 7.10.

3 Prove Theorem 7.11.

7.6 THE CHECK OF NINES

By using the addition and multiplication theorems for number congruences, we can prove that every positive integer is congruent modulo 9 to the sum of its digits. For example, the sum of the digits of the number 598,671 is 36, and we observe that

$$598,671 - 36 = 598,635 = (66,515)(9).$$

Therefore 598,671 is congruent modulo 9 to 36, the sum of its digits. To prove this property for any positive integer N, we recall that if

$$N = a_0 a_1 a_2 \ldots a_{n-1} a_n,$$

where each digit a_i, $i = 0, 1, 2, \ldots, n$, is one of the numbers 0, 1, 2, ..., 9 and $a_0 \neq 0$, then

$$N = a_0 10^n + a_1 10^{n-1} + \cdots + a_{n-2} 10^2 + a_{n-1} 10^1 + a_n.$$

Now observe that
$$1 \equiv 1 \text{ mod } 9,$$
$$10^1 \equiv 1 \text{ mod } 9,$$
$$10^2 \equiv 1 \text{ mod } 9,$$
$$\vdots$$
$$10^{n-1} \equiv 1 \text{ mod } 9,$$
$$10^n \equiv 1 \text{ mod } 9.$$

Furthermore, by the reflexive property of congruences,

$$a_n \equiv a_n \text{ mod } 9,$$
$$a_{n-1} \equiv a_{n-1} \text{ mod } 9,$$
$$a_{n-2} \equiv a_{n-2} \text{ mod } 9,$$
$$\vdots$$
$$a_1 \equiv a_1 \text{ mod } 9,$$
$$a_0 \equiv a_0 \text{ mod } 9.$$

By applying the multiplication property of congruences to each pair of the above sets of congruences, we have

$$a_n \equiv a_n \text{ mod } 9,$$
$$a_{n-1} 10^1 \equiv a_{n-1} \text{ mod } 9,$$
$$a_{n-2} 10^2 \equiv a_{n-2} \text{ mod } 9,$$
$$\vdots$$
$$a_1 10^{n-1} \equiv a_1 \text{ mod } 9,$$
$$a_0 10^n \equiv a_0 \text{ mod } 9.$$

Now by applying the addition property to this set of congruences, we have

$$N = a_n + a_{n-1} 10^1 + a_{n-2} 10^2 + \cdots + a_1 10^{n-1} + a_0 10^n$$
$$\equiv a_n + a_{n-1} + a_{n-2} + \cdots + a_1 + a_0 \text{ mod } 9.$$

Therefore every positive integer is congruent modulo 9 to the sum of its digits.

One of the interesting applications of the properties of number congruences is a method for checking arithmetic problems, called the *check of nines*. As one might expect from the name, we utilize the fact that every positive integer is congruent modulo 9 to the sum of its digits. We shall illustrate this procedure by a sequence of examples.

Example 1 Find the following sum and check the result by the check of nines.

$$6581$$
$$4893$$
$$2564$$
$$8933$$

Solution We first add the four numbers in the ordinary way and find that the sum is 22,971 (see Fig. 7.3). To check our answer we add the digits of each

$$6,581 \equiv 20 \equiv\ \ 2 \bmod 9$$
$$4,893 \equiv 24 \equiv\ \ 6 \bmod 9$$
$$2,564 \equiv 17 \equiv\ \ 8 \bmod 9$$
$$8,933 \equiv 23 \equiv\ \ 5 \bmod 9$$
$$\overline{22,971 \equiv\quad\ \equiv 21} \equiv 3 \bmod 9$$

$$2 + 2 + 9 + 7 + 1 \equiv 21 \equiv 3 \bmod 9 \qquad \text{Figure 7.3}$$

number, and if this sum has more than one digit, we repeat the process until a one-digit number is obtained. For example, in Fig. 7.3 the sum of the digits in 6581 is 20 and the sum of the digits of 20 is 2. The number 6581 is congruent to the number 2 mod 9. Next, we add these one-digit numbers, add the digits of that sum, and continue until the result is a one-digit number. If this one-digit number is 9, it is replaced by 0. In our example we found

$$2 + 6 + 8 + 5 = 21 \qquad \text{and finally} \qquad 2 + 1 = 3.$$

This final sum should be the same as the one-digit number obtained by applying the same process to the digits of the answer to our addition problem. If these two numbers are not the same, then we know that we must have made an error somewhere in our work.

The check of nines is not infallible. If we had obtained 79,212 or 92,712 as the sum in Example 1, then the check of nines would not have caught the error in our work. This is due to the fact that the sum of the digits of a number is not changed by a rearrangement of its digits.

Example 2 Find the following difference and check the result by the check of nines.

$$5876$$
$$-3497$$

$$5876 \equiv 26 \equiv 8 \text{ mod } 9$$
$$\underline{3497} \equiv \underline{23} \equiv \underline{5} \text{ mod } 9$$
$$2379 \qquad\ \ 3$$

$$2 + 3 + 7 + 9 \equiv 21 \equiv 3 \text{ mod } 9 \qquad \text{Figure 7.4}$$

Solution In the usual way we see that the difference of the numbers is 2379 (see Fig. 7.4). To check our answer we proceed as in Example 1 to relate the minuend and subtrahend to one-digit numbers. In our example these one-digit numbers are 8 and 5, respectively. Now instead of adding 8 and 5, we subtract 5 from 8 to get the number 3. This number is then compared wth the one-digit number obtained by adding the digits of the difference. Since both numbers are 3 in our example, we can be reasonably certain that our answer is correct.

Example 3 Find the following difference and check the result by the check of nines.

$$6798$$
$$\underline{-4793}$$

Solution The difference is found to be 2005 (see Fig. 7.5). To check this answer we proceed as in Example 2 until we relate the minuend and subtrahend to 3 and 5, respectively. In this problem the subtrahend 5 is larger than the minuend 3. We now add 9 to the minuend to obtain 12. From 12 we can subtract 5, and the result is 7. This result agrees with the number obtained by adding the digits of 2005, and hence we have a check of our work.

$$6798 \equiv 30 \equiv 3 \equiv 12 \text{ mod } 9$$
$$\underline{4793} \equiv \underline{23} \equiv \underline{5} \equiv\ \ \underline{5} \text{ mod } 9$$
$$2005 \qquad\qquad\quad 7$$

$$2 + 0 + 0 + 5 \equiv 7 \text{ mod } 9 \qquad \text{Figure 7.5}$$

Example 4 Find the following product and check the result by the check of nines.

$$278$$
$$\underline{\times 345}$$

Solution The product is found in the usual way to be 95,910 (see Fig. 7.6). We proceed as in Example 1 to relate the factors to one-digit numbers.

$$278 \equiv 17 \equiv\ \ 8 \text{ mod } 9$$
$$\underline{345} \equiv \underline{12} \equiv\ \ \underline{3} \text{ mod } 9$$
$$95910 \qquad\quad 24 \equiv 6 \text{ mod } 9$$

$$9 + 5 + 9 + 1 + 0 \equiv 24 \equiv 6 \text{ mod } 9 \qquad \text{Figure 7.6}$$

However, instead of adding these one-digit numbers, we multiply and proceed as before.

We conclude this section by showing how our work with number congruences can be used to solve a mathematical puzzle. Let us assume a friend has a number with several digits. Suppose he rearranges the digits of the number in any fashion and subtracts the smaller of these two numbers from the larger. Next, suppose he marks out all but one digit of this difference, stating that he did not leave the digit 0. If he then tells you the sum of the digits he marked out, you should be able to tell him the digit that remains. To illustrate how this problem is solved, suppose your friend has in mind the number 5812. Further, suppose he rearranges the digits to obtain the number 8521 and then subtracts 5812 from 8521 to get 2709. In this answer let us assume that he marks out 2, 0, and 9, leaving 7. From Fig. 7.7 we see that the difference, and hence the sum of its digits must be congruent to 0 modulo 9. That is, the sum of the digits of the difference must be a multiple of 9. It is now easy to see that if the sum of the digits marked out is 11, then the remaining digit must be $18 - 11 = 7$. All zero digits must be marked out to avoid ambiguity.

$$8521 \equiv 16 \equiv 7 \bmod 9$$
$$5812 \equiv 16 \equiv 7 \bmod 9$$
$$\overline{2709} \qquad \overline{0}$$

$$2 + 7 + 0 + 9 = 18 \equiv 0 \bmod 9 \qquad \text{Figure 7.7}$$

Problems

In Problems 1 through 5 add and check by the check of nines.

1	761	2	4763	3	5387	4	1375	5	6987
	592		5942		7911		4968		256
					3002		6460		23
							2109		711

In Problems 6 through 10 subtract and check by the check of nines.

6	962	7	6981	8	8763		3980	10	10,963
	−451		−4793		−3881		−1015		−8,456

In Problems 11 through 15 multiply and check by the check of nines.

11	63	12	85	13	697	14	884	15	5437
	×29		×43		×84		×596		×962

16 Choose a number with two or more digits, rearrange the digits, and subtract the smaller from the larger. What is the remainder when this result is divided by 9? Explain.

7.7 TESTS FOR DIVISIBILITY

An integer x is *divisible* by an integer y if and only if x is a multiple of y. For example, 12 is divisible by 3 because 12 is a multiple of 3. An interesting problem is that of determining when a positive integer is divisible by another positive integer without actually performing the division. The tests for divisibility discussed in this section are dependent on the fact that we can write a positive integer in expanded form (Chapter 3). The reader is surely familiar with two of the tests for divisibility which we discuss: namely, a positive integer is divisible by 2 if the last digit is 0, 2, 4, 6 or 8; and a positive integer is divisible by 5 if the last digit is 0 or 5. We now proceed to verify these and other tests for divisibility. If N is any positive integer, then N can be written in expanded form as follows:

$$N = a_0 10^n + a_1 10^{n-1} + a_2 10^{n-2} + \cdots + a_{n-1} 10^1 + a_n$$
$$= (a_0 10^{n-1} + a_1 10^{n-2} + a_2 10^{n-3} + \cdots + a_{n-1})10 + a_n.$$

We are assured that

$$(a_0 10^{n-1} + a_1 10^{n-2} + a_2 10^{n-3} + \cdots + a_{n-1})10$$

is divisible by both 2 and 5 because 10 is a multiple of 2 and 5. Therefore N is divisible by 2 if and only if the units' digit a_n is divisible by 2. Likewise, N is divisible by 5 if and only if the units' digit a_n is divisible by 5. The only digits divisible by 2 are 0, 2, 4, 6, and 8, whereas the only digits divisible by 5 are 0 and 5. Thus we have verified the two familiar tests for divisibility.

The tests for divisibility by 4 and 8 can be established by a similar procedure. The expanded form of N can be written

$$N = (a_0 10^{n-2} + a_1 10^{n-3} + a_2 10^{n-4} + \cdots + a_{n-2})100 + a_{n-1}10 + a_n.$$

Since

$$(a_0 10^{n-2} + a_1 10^{n-3} + a_2 10^{n-4} + \cdots + a_{n-2})100$$

is divisible by 4, N is divisible by 4 if and only if the number represented by the tens' and units' digits is divisible by 4. By an analogous argument we can show that a positive integer is divisible by 8 if and only if the number represented by the hundreds', tens', and units' digits is divisible by 8.

From Section 7.6 we recall that every positive integer is congruent modulo 9 to the sum of its digits. Therefore a positive integer is divisible by 9 if and only if the sum of its digits is divisible by 9. Using a procedure similar to that in Section 7.6, we can show that a positive integer is congruent modulo 3 to the sum of its digits and, therefore, divisible by 3 if and only if the sum of its digits is divisible by 3.

A positive integer is divisible by 6 if and only if it is divisible by both 2 and 3.

We have now established a test for divisibility for the positive integers 2, 3, 4, 5, 6, 8, and 9. We remark that a test for divisibility by 7 exists, but it is easier to divide by 7 than to apply the test.

Example 1 Let $N = 312,120$.

N is divisible by 2 because the units digit is 0.

N is divisible by 3 because the sum of its digits is divisible by 3.

N is divisible by 4 because 20 is divisible by 4.

N is divisible by 5 because the units digits is 0.

N is divisible by 6 because it is divisible by 2 and 3.

N is divisible by 8 because 120 is divisible by 8.

N is divisible by 9 because the sum of its digits is divisible by 9.

Example 2 Let $N = 215,115$.

N is not divisible by 2 because 5 is not divisible by 2.

N is divisible by 3 because the sum of its digits is divisible by 3.

N is not divisible by 4 because 15 is not divisible by 4.

N is divisible by 5 because the units digit is 5.

N is not divisible by 6 because it is not divisible by 2.

N is not divisible by 8 because 115 is not divisible by 8.

N is not divisible by 9 because the sum of its digits is not divisible by 9.

We will consider one more divisibility test, the test for divisibility by 11. We will use a procedure analogous to the one in Section 7.6. Recall that if $N = a_0a_1a_2 \ldots a_{n-1}a_n$, where each digit a_i, $i = 0, 1, 2, \ldots, n$, is one of the numbers $0, 1, 2, \ldots, 9$ and $a_0 \neq 0$, then

$$N = a_010^n + a_110^{n-1} + a_210^{n-2} + \cdots + a_{n-1}10 + a_n.$$

Now,

$$1 \equiv 1 \bmod 11,$$
$$10 \equiv -1 \bmod 11,$$
$$10^2 \equiv 1 \bmod 11,$$
$$10^3 \equiv -1 \bmod 11,$$
$$\vdots$$
$$10^n \equiv (-1)^n \bmod 11.$$

Furthermore,

$$a_n \equiv a_n \bmod 11,$$
$$a_{n-1} \equiv a_{n-1} \bmod 11,$$
$$a_{n-2} \equiv a_{n-2} \bmod 11,$$
$$a_{n-3} \equiv a_{n-3} \bmod 11,$$
$$\vdots$$
$$a_0 \equiv a_0 \bmod 11.$$

By applying the multiplication property of congruences to each pair of the above sets of congruences, we have

$$a_n \equiv a_n \bmod 11,$$
$$a_{n-1}10^1 \equiv (-1)a_{n-1} \bmod 11,$$
$$a_{n-2}10^2 \equiv a_{n-2} \bmod 11,$$
$$a_{n-3}10^3 \equiv (-1)a_{n-3} \bmod 11,$$
$$\vdots$$
$$a_0 10^n \equiv (-1)^n a_0 \bmod 11.$$

Next we apply the addition property of congruences to this set of congruences and have

$$N = a_n + a_{n-1}10^1 + a_{n-2}10^2 + \cdots + a_0 10^n$$
$$\equiv a_n + (-1)a_{n-1} + a_{n-2} + \cdots + (-1)^n a_0 \bmod 11.$$

This congruence states that a positive integer is congruent modulo 11 to the sum of its units' digit, hundreds' digit, ten thousands' digit, etc., minus the sum of its tens' digit, thousands' digit, hundred thousands' digit, etc. Therefore, the positive integer is divisible by 11 if and only if this difference is a multiple of 11.

Example 3   23,474 is divisible by 11 because $4 + 4 + 2 - 7 - 3 = 0$ and 0 is a multiple of 11.

Example 4   786,534 is not divisible by 11 because $4 + 5 + 8 - 3 - 6 - 7 = 1$ and 1 is not a multiple of 11.

We conclude this section by remarking that other divisibility tests could be established by procedures analogous to those in this section.

Problems

In Problems 1 through 6 use the appropriate test for divisibility to determine whether the given number is divisible by 2, 3, 4, 5, 6, 8, 9, or 11.

1 942   2 35,496   3 417,565   4 69,483

5 79,783   6 18,150   7 21,437   8 439,584

9 Find a six-digit number divisible by 5, 8, and 9.

10 Find a six-digit number divisible by 4, 5, and 11.

11 Find a six-digit number divisible by 4 and 6 but not by 8 or 9.

12 Find a six-digit number divisible by 5 and 11 but not by 2, 3, 4, 6, 8, or 9.

13 Find a six-digit number that is not divisible by 2, 3, 4, 5, 6, 8, 9, or 11.

14 Prove that every positive integer is congruent, modulo 3, to the sum of its digits.

15 Derive a test for divisibility by 13. [*Hint:* $10 \equiv (-3) \bmod 13$.]

Chapter 8

MATHEMATICAL SYSTEMS

8.1 OPERATIONS ON A SET

We have used the concept of an operation on a set quite frequently in the preceding chapters of this book. However, we have never stated precisely what is meant by this term. Since each of the mathematical systems to be discussed in this chapter involves one or more operations, it is important that we now examine this concept more closely. After a brief review of the familiar operations of addition and multiplication on the set of real numbers, it should be clear how this concept should be defined.

So that we can more carefully examine the meaning of the operation of addition on the set of real numbers, we consider the following simple examples:

$$2 + 3 = 5,$$
$$-8 + 6 = -2,$$
$$\tfrac{1}{4} + \tfrac{1}{3} = \tfrac{7}{12},$$
$$9 + 0 = 9.$$

In each of these four examples, we are associating with the pair of numbers on the left-hand side of the equation the number that is written on the right-hand side. This association could be adequately described by writing

$$(2, 3) \rightarrow 5,$$
$$(-8, 6) \rightarrow -2,$$
$$(\tfrac{1}{4}, \tfrac{1}{3}) \rightarrow \tfrac{7}{12},$$
$$(9, 0) \rightarrow 9.$$

This method of describing the addition problems suggests that we consider addition of real numbers to be a rule that associates with each ordered pair of real numbers a real number. From our previous experience with addition, we know that such a rule associates with each ordered pair of real numbers one and only one real number. Hence one can consider the operation of addition on the set of real numbers to be a function from the set $R \times R$ into the set R. The reader should review the concept of a function discussed in Section 6.2.

A similar examination of the operation of multiplication on the set of real numbers would lead us to describe this operation too as a function from $R \times R$ into the set R. This function will of course be different from the one used to define addition on the set of real numbers. For example, if A denotes the function of addition and M denotes the function of multiplication, then $A(2, 3) = 5$, $A(-5, -2) = -7$, and $A(\sqrt{3}, 2\sqrt{3}) = 3\sqrt{3}$, but $M(2, 3) = 6$, $M(-5, -2) = 10$, and $M(\sqrt{3}, 2\sqrt{3}) = 6$. The foregoing discussion would suggest that we define an operation on R to be a function from $R \times R$ into R, since each operation we considered associates with each ordered pair of real numbers a unique real number. If we were to accept this as the definition of an operation on R, we might go further and raise the following questions:

1) Can we define an operation on some set A different from R?
2) Can an operation on a set A be a function from $A \times A$ into some set B different from A?

The answers to both of these questions is yes, and in fact the sets A and B need not be sets of numbers. We now state the following definition of an operation on a set.

Definition 8.1 A *binary operation* ∗ defined on a set A is a function from $A \times A$ into a set B.

In the above definition we use the term *binary* because the operation is a function from a collection of *ordered pairs* to some set. We now illustrate this definition of a binary operation by the following examples.

Example 1   Define a binary operation ∗ on the set $A = \{1, 2\}$.

Solution   We seek a function from the set

$$A \times A = \{(1, 1), (1, 2), (2, 1), (2, 2)\}$$

to some set B.

The function ∗ defined by

$$\begin{aligned}
*(1, 1) &= 3, \\
*(1, 2) &= 4, \\
*(2, 1) &= 4, \\
*(2, 2) &= 3
\end{aligned}$$

is a function from $A \times A$ into the set $B = \{3, 4\}$. Thus, ∗ is an operation on the set A.

Operations are frequently defined by use of a table. For example, the function of Example 1 could be defined by Table 8.1. This table is read as though it were a mileage chart. For example, to find the number which ∗ associates with the ordered pair (2, 1), one starts with the number 2 in the column headed by the symbol ∗ and goes horizontally to the column headed by the number 1. Thus the operation associates with (2, 1) the number 4. The operation of Example 1 can also be described by simply writing $1 * 1 = 3$, $1 * 2 = 4$, $2 * 1 = 4$, and $2 * 2 = 3$. We are using the symbol ∗ in much the same way as we use the symbols $+$ and $\times$ for addition and multiplication.

TABLE 8.1

∗	1	2
1	3	4
2	4	3

Example 2 Define two binary operations on the set $A = \{\$, \%\}$ into the set $B = \{\cent, +, \phi\}$.

Solution We have several possibilities. Two such operations, # and △, are defined by Tables 8.2 and 8.3.

TABLE 8.2

#	$	%
$	¢	+
%	φ	¢

TABLE 8.3

△	$	%
$	+	+
%	+	+

Example 3 Define two binary operations on the set $X = \{0, 2, 4\}$ into X.

Solution Tables 8.4 and 8.5 define operations, @ and ▽, on the set $X = \{0, 2, 4\}$ into X.

TABLE 8.4

@	0	2	4
0	0	2	4
2	2	0	2
4	4	0	4

TABLE 8.5

▽	0	2	4
0	0	2	0
2	2	0	2
4	0	2	0

A set A is *closed with respect to an operation* ∗ if ∗ is a function from $A \times A$ into A. Thus the set $X = \{0, 2, 4\}$ is closed with respect to both of the operations @ and ▽ of Example 3. However, the set $A = \{1, 2\}$ is not closed with respect to the operation ∗ defined in Example 1 and, further, the set $A = \{\$, \%\}$ is not closed with respect to either of the operations # or △

defined in Example 2. The reader should be able to convince himself that the above definition of closure is equivalent to the definition of closure stated in Section 4.2.

A more detailed discussion of operations and their properties will be found in the following section.

Problems

1 Define two different binary operations on the set $A = \{0, 5, 10\}$ into the set $B = \{2, 4, 6\}$.

2 Define two different binary operations on the set $S = \{\alpha, \beta\}$ into the set $T = \{a, b\}$.

3 There is only one binary operation on the set $C = \{1, 2, 3\}$ into the set $D = \{0\}$. What is it?

4 Define two different binary operations on the set $X = \{*, \%\}$ such that X is closed with respect to each operation.

5 Define two different binary operations on the set $Y = \{0, 3, 6\}$ such that Y is closed with respect to each operation.

6 Let $E = \{0, 1\}$. E is closed with respect to which of the following operations?

a)
*	0	1
0	0	0
1	0	0

b)
#	0	1
0	0	1
1	1	0

c)
+	0	1
0	0	1
1	1	2

d)
×	0	1
0	0	0
1	0	1

e)
Δ	0	1
0	1	2
1	3	4

7 Is the set of even integers closed with respect to the operation of addition? multiplication? Justify your answers.

8 Is the set of odd integers closed with respect to the operation of addition? multiplication? Justify your answers.

9 Is the set $S = \{-1, 0, 1\}$ closed with respect to the operation of addition? multiplication? Justify your answers.

10 How many different binary operations can one define on the set $A = \{1, 2, 3\}$ into the set $B = \{5\}$?

11 How many different binary operations can one define on the set $A = \{1, 2, 3\}$ into the set $C = \{5, 10\}$?

12 How many different binary operations can one define on the set $C = \{5, 10\}$ into the set $D = \{a, b, c, d, e\}$?

13 Find a mileage chart in a world atlas or a highway atlas. Does this chart define an operation? Explain.

14 The basketball teams of Magnolia, Emerson, and Waldo play each other according to the following schedule:

	Magnolia	Emerson	Waldo
Magnolia		Dec. 14	Jan. 6
Emerson	Dec. 14		Jan. 13
Waldo	Jan. 6	Jan. 13	

Does this schedule define a binary operation on the set {Magnolia, Emerson, Waldo}? Explain.

8.2 BINARY OPERATIONS AND THEIR PROPERTIES

Let $*$ denote a binary operation on a set A. That is, let $*$ denote a function from $A \times A$ to some set B. We shall now discuss some interesting properties related to such an operation as $*$. Later in the section these properties will be illustrated by considering several different examples of binary operations. The first property on our list will be the closure property which was introduced in the preceding section.

The Closure Property The set A is *closed* with respect to a binary operation $*$ on A, if $*$ is a function from $A \times A$ into A. Or, equivalently, A is closed with respect to the binary operation $*$ if $a * b \in A$ for all elements a and b of A.

The Associative Property A binary operation $*$ on a set A is said to be *associative* if $(a * b) * c = a * (b * c)$ for all elements a, b, and c of A.

The Commutative Property A binary operation $*$ on a set A is said to be *commutative* if $a * b = b * a$ for all elements a and b of A.

The Identity Property An element e of a set A is an *identity element for a binary operation* $*$ on A if $e * a = a * e = a$ for every element a of A.

The Inverse Property Let $*$ denote a binary operation on a set A, let e denote the identity element for $*$, and let a denote an element of A. An element a^{-1} in A is called an *inverse of a with respect to* $*$ if

$$a * a^{-1} = a^{-1} * a = e.$$

The Distributive Property Let $*$ and $\#$ denote two binary operations on a set A. $*$ is *left distributive* over $\#$ in A if $a * (b \# c) = (a * b) \# (a * c)$ for all elements a, b, and c of A. $*$ is *right distributive* over $\#$ if

$$(b \# c) * a = (b * a) \# (c * a).$$

If $*$ is both left and right distributive over $\#$, we say $*$ *distributes* over $\#$.

The foregoing properties are not the only properties that binary operations can possess. They are, however, the properties of particular interest to the reader studying the structure of a mathematical system. We now consider some examples of binary operations to illustrate these properties.

Example 1   If $a * b = a + b + 6$ for all integers a and b, then $*$ is a binary operation on the set of integers.

Discussion   The set of integers is closed with respect to the operation of addition and, consequently, $a + b + 6$ is an integer for all integers a and b. It now follows that the set of integers is closed with respect to the binary operation $*$.

After observing that

$$\begin{aligned}
(a * b) * c &= (a + b + 6) * c \\
&= (a + b + 6) + c + 6 \\
&= a + b + c + 12
\end{aligned}$$

and

$$\begin{aligned}
a * (b * c) &= a * (b + c + 6) \\
&= a + (b + c + 6) + 6 \\
&= a + b + c + 12,
\end{aligned}$$

we conclude that $(a * b) * c = a * (b * c)$ for all integers a, b, and c. Hence the operation $*$ is associative on the set of integers.

We find that the commutative property for $*$ follows, by observing that

$$\begin{aligned}
a * b &= a + b + 6 \\
&= b + a + 6 \\
&= b * a
\end{aligned}$$

for all integers a and b.

An integer e is an identity for the operation $*$ if $e * a = a * e = a$ for every integer a. Since

$$e * a = a * e = a + e + 6,$$

e must satisfy the equation $a + e + 6 = a$. Hence the integer -6 is an identity for the operation $*$.

To find an inverse of an integer a with respect to the operation $*$, we seek an integer x with the property that $a * x = x * a = -6$. If $a * x = x * a = -6$, the integer x, if it exists, must satisfy the equation $x + a + 6 = -6$. By solving this equation for x, we find that $x = -a - 12$. Thus

MATHEMATICAL SYSTEMS

every integer a has an inverse, $-a - 12$, with respect to the operation $*$. For example, the inverse of 10 is -22, and the inverse of -3 is -9.

Example 2 If $a \# b = a$ for all integers a and b, then $\#$ is a binary operation on the set of integers.

Discussion Because $a \# b$ is a, an integer, for all integers a and b, the set of integers is closed with respect to the operation $\#$.

That the operation $\#$ is associative on the set of integers can be verified by observing that

$$(a \# b) \# c = a \# c$$
$$= a$$

and

$$a \# (b \# c) = a \# b$$
$$= a$$

for all integers a, b, and c.

Since $a \# b = a$ and $b \# a = b$, $a \# b \neq b \# a$ if $a \neq b$. Hence, the operation $\#$ is not commutative on the set of integers.

An integer e is an identity for $\#$ if $e \# a = a \# e = a$ for every integer a. But $e \# a$ always equals e, so there is no integer e with the property that $e \# a = a$ for every integer a. Since there is no identity element for $\#$, it is meaningless to discuss the inverse property.

Example 3 If $a \triangle b = 2a + 3b$ for all integers a and b, then $\triangle$ is a binary operation on the set of integers.

Discussion Since $2a + 3b$ is an integer for all integers a and b, the set of integers is closed with respect to the operation $\triangle$.

Using the operation $\triangle$, we have

$$(a \triangle b) \triangle c = (2a + 3b) \triangle c$$
$$= 2(2a + 3b) + 3c$$
$$= 4a + 6b + 3c$$

and

$$a \triangle (b \triangle c) = a \triangle (2b + 3c)$$
$$= 2a + 3(2b + 3c)$$
$$= 2a + 6b + 9c.$$

Since the expressions for $(a \triangle b) \triangle c$ and $a \triangle (b \triangle c)$ are not the same, we will seek a counterexample to show that $\triangle$ is not associative on the set of integers. If we let $a = 1$, $b = 2$, and $c = 3$, we find that $(a \triangle b) \triangle c = 25$ and $a \triangle (b \triangle c) = 41$. This counterexample proves that the operation $\triangle$ is not associative on the set of integers.

For integers a and b, we have

$$a \triangle b = 2a + 3b \quad \text{and} \quad b \triangle a = 2b + 3a.$$

If we let $a = 1$ and $b = 2$, then $a \triangle b = 8$ and $b \triangle a = 7$. Hence $\triangle$ is not commutative on the set of integers.

If an integer e is an identity for the operation $\triangle$, then $e \triangle a = a \triangle e = a$ for every integer a. Since $e \triangle a = 2e + 3a$, e must satisfy the equation $2e + 3a = a$ if it is to be an identity for $\triangle$. Solving this equation for e, we have $e = -a$. However, if $e = -a$, then $a \triangle e = a \triangle (-a) = 2a + 3(-a) = -a$, and $-a \neq a$ unless $a = 0$. Therefore, there is no integer e such that $e \triangle a = a \triangle e = a$ for every integer a. Since there is no identity for $\triangle$, it would be meaningless to discuss the inverse property.

Example 4 If $a\ s\ b$ equals the smaller of a and b or the common value if $a = b$, then s is a binary operation on the set $S = \{0, 1, 2, \ldots, 9, 10\}$.

Discussion If a and b are elements of S, then the smaller of a and b is also an element of S, proving that S is closed with respect to the binary operation s.

Since both $(a\ s\ b)\ s\ c$ and $a\ s\ (b\ s\ c)$ yield the smallest element of the set $\{a, b, c\}$, $(a\ s\ b)\ s\ c = a\ s\ (b\ s\ c)$ for every a, b, and c in S. Hence, s is associative on S.

Both $a\ s\ b$ and $b\ s\ a$ represent the smaller of the two numbers a and b, and we conclude that the operation s is also commutative on S.

The element $10 \in S$ is an identity for the operation s because $10\ s\ a = a\ s\ 10 = a$ for every element $a \in S$.

If $a \in S$ and $a < 10$, then $a\ s\ b \leq a < 10$, the identity, for every element $b \in S$. Hence, a has no inverse if $a < 10$. The number 10 is its own inverse because $10\ s\ 10 = 10$, the identity for the operation s.

The operation s of Example 4 is also a binary operation on the set of all integers. The set of integers is closed with respect to the operation s and s is associative and commutative on the set of integers. However, when considered as an operation on the set of integers, s has no identity element. Why?

Example 5 Table 8.6 defines a binary operation @ on the set $T = \{a, b\}$.

Discussion Table 8.6 is read in the same way as previous operations tables. For example, from Table 8.6 we see that $a @ b = b$ and $b @ b = a$. The set $T = \{a, b\}$ is closed with respect to the binary operation @. By checking all the possible cases, the reader can verify the associative and commutative properties for the operation @. The element a is the identity for @ and each element of T is its own inverse with respect to @.

TABLE 8.6

@	a	b
a	a	b
b	b	a

We will now prove that the operation $*$ of Example 1 is left distributive over the operation $\#$ of Example 2. If a, b, and c are any integers, we have

$$a * (b \# c) = a * b,$$
$$= a + b + 6,$$

and

$$(a * b) \# (a * c) = a * b,$$
$$= a + b + 6.$$

Therefore

$$a * (b \# c) = (a * b) \# (a * c)$$

for all integers a, b, and c, and we say that the operation $*$ is left distributive over the operation $\#$ in the set of integers. The reader can easily verify that $*$ is also right distributive over $\#$. Hence we say that $*$ distributes over $\#$ in the set of integers.

Problems

In each of the Problems 1 through 15 a binary operation is defined on a set of numbers. Answer the following questions about each of these operations.

a) Is the set of numbers closed with respect to the operation?

b) Is the operation associative on the set?

c) Is the operation commutative on the set?

d) Is there an identity for the operation? If so, what is the identity?

e) Which elements of the set have an inverse in the set? Give the inverse for those elements which have an inverse.

1   On the set of integers, define $\$$ by $a \$ b = a - b$.

2   On the set of integers, define $\not{c}$ by $a \not{c} b = b$.

3   On the set of integers, define $!$ by $a ! b = a + b - 1$.

4   On the set of integers, define $?$ by $a ? b = a + b + \frac{1}{2}$.

5   On the set of rational numbers, define $?$ as in Problem 4.

6   On the set of integers, define θ by $a \theta b = a + b + 10$.

7   On the set of integers, define γ by $a \gamma b = (a + b)/2$.

8   On the set of integers, define $\circ$ by $a \circ b = 2a + b$.

9   On the set of integers, define δ by $a \delta b = ab + 1$.

10   On the set $S = \{0, 1, 2, 3, 4, 5\}$, define π by $a \pi b =$ the larger of a and b or the common value if $a = b$.

11   On the set of integers, define π as in Problem 10.

12   On the set of integers, define $\propto$ by $a \propto b = a + b - ab$.

13   On the set of integers, define ϕ by $a \phi b = 3a - 2b$.

TABLE 8.7		
ω	a	b
a	a	a
b	a	b

TABLE 8.8		
β	a	b
a	b	a
b	b	a

14 On the set $S = \{a, b\}$, define ω by Table 8.7.

15 On the set $S = \{a, b\}$, define β by Table 8.8.

16 Show that the operation $*$ of Example 1 of this section is right distributive over the operation $\#$ of Example 2.

17 Is the operation θ of Problem 6 left distributive over the operation ϕ of Problem 2? Is θ right distributive over ϕ?

18 Is the operation ϕ of Problem 2 left distributive over the operation θ of Problem 6? Is ϕ right distributive over θ? Does ϕ distribute over θ?

19 Does the operation $\#$ of Example 2 of this section distribute over the operation δ of Prbolem 9? Does δ distribute over $\#$?

20 Does the operation θ of Problem 6 distribute over the operation $\circ$ of Problem 8? Does $\circ$ distribute over θ?

8.3 THE CONCEPT OF A GROUP

Let us consider an equilateral triangle such as the one in Fig. 8.1. There is a set of motions which will carry this triangle into itself. For example, if the triangle is rotated clockwise about its center through an angle of 120°, the triangle is carried into itself. The same thing is true for rotations of 240° and 360° (or, equivalently, 0°). The vertices of the triangle are labeled 1, 2, and 3 so that they can be identified in any position. We shall employ the following symbols to denote these rotations:

R_0, a clockwise rotation of 0°;
R_1, a clockwise rotation of 120°;
R_2, a clockwise rotation of 240°.

The effects of these motions are illustrated in Fig. 8.2. For greater clarity, the reader might find it helpful to cut an equilateral triangle from a piece of paper or cardboard, labeling the vertices 1, 2, and 3, and perform the motions.

Let us now consider the set $G = \{R_0, R_1, R_2\}$ consisting of these rotations. We shall define an operation $\circ$ on the set G by interpreting $A \circ B$ to be the motion resulting from first performing the motion A followed by the motion B, A and B denoting elements of G. For example, $R_1 \circ R_0$ means the

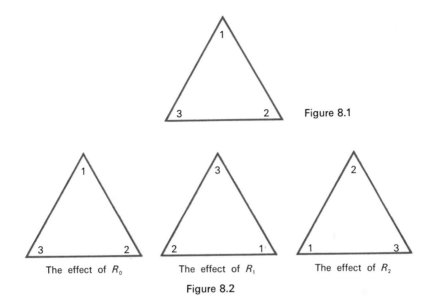

Figure 8.1

The effect of R_0 The effect of R_1 The effect of R_2

Figure 8.2

motion obtained by first rotating the triangle clockwise through an angle of 120°, followed by a clockwise rotation through an angle of 0°. The final result can be accomplished by the rotation R_1. Thus we write $R_1 \circ R_0 = R_1$. In this way we can construct Table 8.9, which provides us with an alternative method for defining the operation $\circ$.

From Table 8.9, we observe that the set G is closed with respect to the operation $\circ$. By checking all possible combinations (there are 27 of them), the reader can easily verify that the operation $\circ$ is associative. The element R_0 is an identity element for the operation $\circ$ because $R_0 \circ A = A \circ R_0 = A$ for every element A of G. Remembering that R_0 is the identity for $\circ$, we observe that $R_0 \circ R_0 = R_0$ and $R_1 \circ R_2 = R_2 \circ R_1 = R_0$. Hence, with respect to the operation $\circ$, R_0 is its own inverse, whereas R_1 and R_2 are inverses of each other. Summarizing, we observe that G is closed with respect to $\circ$, $\circ$ is associative in G, there is an identity for $\circ$, and each element of G has an inverse with respect to $\circ$. Because of these properties of the operation $\circ$,

TABLE 8.9

$\circ$	R_0	R_1	R_2
R_0	R_0	R_1	R_2
R_1	R_1	R_2	R_0
R_2	R_2	R_0	R_1

the set G with the operation $\circ$ is an example of a mathematical system called a *group*.

Definition 8.2 Let G be a set of elements and let $*$ be an operation on G. Then G with the operation $*$ is called a *group* if:

1) The set G is closed with respect to the operation $*$.
2) The operation $*$ is associative in G.
3) There exists an element e in G which is an identity element for the operation $*$.
4) Every element a in G has an inverse a^{-1} in G with respect to the operation $*$.

Suppose G with the operation $*$ is a group. G is called a *commutative* or *Abelian group* if and only if the operation $*$ is commutative in G. If one examines all cases (there are nine of them), it can be verified that the operation $\circ$ of successive rotations is commutative in the set $G = \{R_0, R_1, R_2\}$, and thus G with the operation $\circ$ is an example of a commutative, or Abelian, group.

Many examples of groups are found in Chapters 4 and 5. The set of integers with the operation of addition is a group. However, the set of integers with the operation of multiplication is not a group because 1 and -1 are the only integers having a multiplicative inverse. The set of rational numbers with addition is a group, but this same set with multiplication is not a group because the number 0 has no multiplicative inverse. Remember that *every* rational number must have an inverse for the set of rational numbers with multiplication to be a group. The set of all *nonzero* rational numbers with multiplication is a group. The reader can discover other examples of groups by studying the number system of Chapters 4 and 5. All such groups are commutative groups.

The modular systems of Chapter 7 also provide us with many interesting examples of groups. Because both addition modulo M and multiplication modulo M have the commutative property, all such groups will be commutative groups. For example, the set $\{0, 1, 2, 3, 4\}$ with addition modulo 5 is a commutative group. The same set with multiplication modulo 5 is *not* a group because the element 0 of the set has no multiplicative inverse. The set $\{1, 2, 3, 4\}$ with addition modulo 5 is *not* a group, but the same set with multiplication modulo 5 is a commutative group. The student will be asked to investigate other modular systems in the problems at the end of this section.

We shall not devote a great deal of our time here to a study of the properties of a group, but it might be interesting to prove some of the simpler ones. For example, if G with the operation $*$ is a group, we can prove that the identity e for $*$ is unique. Let us assume that e and e' are both identities for $*$. Then because e is an identity and e' is an element of G, we must have

$$e * e' = e'.$$

On the other hand, e' is an identity and e is an element of G, so we must also have

$$e * e' = e.$$

Hence we conclude that $e = e'$ or that the identity element is unique. In Problem 19 at the end of this section the reader will be asked to prove that each element of a group has a *unique* inverse with respect to the operation of the group.

Again suppose that the set G with the operation $*$ is a group. If a, b, and c are elements of G and $a * b = a * c$, then $b = c$. We prove this result by observing that $a \in G$ and hence has an inverse a^{-1} in G. Thus,

$$a^{-1} * (a * b) = a^{-1} * (a * c),$$
$$(a^{-1} * a) * b = (a^{-1} * a) * c,$$
$$e * b = e * c,$$
$$b = c.$$

Similarly, if $b * a = c * a$, then $b = c$. These properties are called the *left* and *right cancellation* properties, respectively.

The mathematicians responsible for the early work in groups did not set out to develop a revolutionary new mathematical structure. The first step toward the general theory of groups was taken by Joseph-Louis Lagrange (1736–1813) when he attempted to find a method for solving the general equation of fifth degree (the *quintic*). Although Lagrange did not explicitly recognize the existence of groups, he nevertheless discovered some of the simpler properties of groups. E. Galois (1811–1832), A. L. Cauchy (1789–1857), and A. Cayley (1821–1895) are other mathematicians prominent in the early development of groups. The word "group" was coined by Galois, and Cayley stated the earliest definition of a group. It should be noted that Galois made a highly significant and permanent contribution to mathematics even though he was killed in a pistol duel shortly before reaching his twenty-first birthday. One can only wonder about the contributions he could have made to mathematics had he lived a normal life span.

From 1870 to the 1920's, group theory dominated mathematical thought, and it is one of the major areas of mathematical activity even today.

Problems

1 Let $G = \{R_0, R_1, R_2\}$ and $\circ$ be the operation of successive rotations. Verify the associative property of $\circ$ for each of the following:

a) $(R_1 \circ R_2) \circ R_2 = R_1 \circ (R_2 \circ R_2)$

b) $(R_2 \circ R_0) \circ R_1 = R_2 \circ (R_0 \circ R_1)$

c) $(R_2 \circ R_1) \circ R_2 = R_2 \circ (R_1 \circ R_2)$

d) $(R_0 \circ R_2) \circ R_2 = R_0 \circ (R_2 \circ R_2)$

In Problems 2 through 16, use Definition 8.2 to determine whether the given set with the given operation is a group. If the structure is not a group, explain which properties do not hold.

2 $G = \{0\}$ with the operation of addition

3 $G = \{0\}$ with the operation of multiplication

4 $G = \{1\}$ with the operation of addition

5 $G = \{1\}$ with the operation of multiplication

6 $G = \{0, 1\}$ with the operation of addition

7 $G = \{0, 1\}$ with the operation of multiplication

8 The set of multiples of 5 with the operation of addition

9 The set $\{0, 1, 2, 3\}$ with addition mod 4

10 The set $\{0, 1, 2, 3\}$ with multiplication mod 4

11 The set $\{1, 2, 3\}$ with addition mod 4

12 The set $\{1, 2, 3\}$ with multiplication mod 4

13 The set $\{0, 2\}$ with addition mod 4

14 The set $\{0, 2\}$ with multiplication mod 4

15 The set $\{1, 3\}$ with addition mod 4

16 The set $\{1, 3\}$ with multiplication mod 4

17 In this section we proved that if a, b, and c are elements of a group G and $a * b = a * c$, $*$ denoting the operation in G, then $b = c$. Justify each step of this proof.

18 Let G with the operation $*$ be a group. Prove that if a, b, and c are elements of G and $b * a = c * a$, then $b = c$.

19 Let G with the operation $*$ be a group. Prove that each element of G has a *unique* inverse with respect to $*$.

20 What is the least number of elements a group can have?

21 Let G with the operation $*$ be a group. Prove each of the following properties.

a) $(a^{-1})^{-1} = a$ for every $a \in G$

b) $(a * b)^{-1} = b^{-1} * a^{-1}$ for every a, b, in G.

8.4 FURTHER EXAMPLES OF GROUPS

If a group has a finite number of elements, it is called a *finite group*. If the number of elements in a group is infinite, it is called an *infinite group*. The group of rotations of an equilateral triangle discussed in the previous section is an example of a finite group, whereas the set of integers with addition and the set of nonzero rational numbers with multiplication are examples of infinite groups. In this section we shall examine several other examples of groups, both finite and infinite.

The set of integers mod 5 and the set of integers mod 6 with the respective operations of addition mod 5 and addition mod 6 (see Sections 7.3 and 7.4) provide us with examples of finite groups. Furthermore, the nonzero elements of I_5 under the operation of multiplication mod 5 are an example of a finite group. Since some nonzero elements of I_6 fail to have inverses with respect to the operation of multiplication mod 6, the nonzero elements of I_6 with the operation of multiplication mod 6 are *not* a group. In general, the set $I_M = \{0, 1, 2, 3, \ldots, M\text{-}1\}$ with the operation of addition mod M is an example of a finite group. If M is a prime number, the nonzero elements of I_M with the operation of multiplication mod M are a commutative group, whereas if M is not a prime number, the nonzero elements of I_M with multiplication mod M are *not* a group.

As another example of a finite group, consider the set $G = \{2, 4, 6, 8\}$ with the operation of multiplication mod 10. Table 8.10 gives all possible multiplications. From Table 8.10 it is clear that the set G is closed with respect to multiplication mod 10. In Section 7.5 it was shown that multiplication in any modular system is an associative operation, and thus multiplication mod 10 is associative on G. From Table 8.10 we see that 6 is the identity element, since $x \cdot 6 = 6 \cdot x = x$ for every x in G. Furthermore, each element in G has an inverse, since the inverse of 6 is 6, the inverse of 4 is 4, and 2 and 8 are inverses of each other. Therefore, the four properties defining a group are satisfied, and G with the operation of multiplication mod 10 is a group. Since multiplication mod 10 is a commutative operation (Section 7.5), this is an example of a commutative group.

As a final example of a finite group, consider the set $U = \{1, -1, i, -i\}$ with the operation of ordinary multiplication of complex numbers, i being the number such that $i^2 = -1$. Table 8.11 gives all possible multiplications in U. From Table 8.11 we see that U is closed under multiplication, 1 is the identity, and each element has an inverse. Since multiplication of complex numbers is associative, U with the operation of multiplication of complex numbers is a group. Since the operation is also commutative, this is an example of a

TABLE 8.10

·	2	4	6	8
2	4	8	2	6
4	8	6	4	2
6	2	4	6	8
8	6	2	8	4

TABLE 8.11

·	1	−1	i	−i
1	1	−1	i	−i
−1	−1	1	−i	i
i	i	−i	−1	1
−i	−i	i	1	−1

commutative group. The elements of U are called the fourth roots of unity, since $1^4 = (-1)^4 = (i)^4 = (-i)^4 = 1$.

As another example of an infinite group, consider the set of even integers with the ordinary operation of addition. For a finite group, we can construct an operation table. For an infinite group, we cannot do this. We will, however, use some of the properties already known about the set of integers to prove that the set of even integers with addition is a group. Since the sum of two even integers is even, the set of even integers is closed under addition. Addition on the set of integers is associative, and thus addition on the set of even integers is associative. The identity element is 0, and each even integer a has as its inverse the even integer $-a$. Therefore the set of even integers with addition is a group. Since addition on the set of integers is commutative, addition on the set of even integers is commutative, and thus this is an example of a commutative group.

Another example of an infinite group is the set of positive rational numbers with the operation of multiplication. Since the product of two positive rational numbers is a positive rational number, the set is closed under multiplication. Multiplication on the set of rational numbers is associative, and thus multiplication on the set of positive rational numbers is associative. The identity for the set is the positive rational number 1, and each positive rational number a has as its inverse the positive rational number $1/a$. Thus the set of positive rational numbers with multiplication of rational numbers is a group. Furthermore, since multiplication of rational numbers is commutative, the group is a commutative group. Each of the statements used in showing that the set of positive rational numbers with multiplication is a commutative group is verified in Chapter 5.

In Section 8.3 the set of motions on an equilateral triangle consisting of R_0, R_1, and R_2 with the operation $\circ$ defined on this set of motions was shown to be a group. To review the meaning of the operation $\circ$, we recall that $R_1 \circ R_2$ is to be interpreted to be the motion which will place the triangle in the same position as a clockwise rotation of $120°$ followed by a clockwise rotation of $240°$. These two rotations, performed successively, are equivalent to a rotation of $360°$, or in fact $0°$. Therefore, $R_1 \circ R_2 = R_0$. We presently define three new motions on a equilateral triangle called *reflections*. The set of reflections we consider are those about the lines D_1, D_2, and D_3 which are illustrated in Fig. 8.3. These reflections will be referred to as D_1, D_2, and D_3, respectively. If we consider the triangle in Fig. 8.3 to be in a given position, then Fig. 8.4 shows the position of the vertices after the triangle has been subjected to each of the reflections D_1, D_2, and D_3. Table 8.12 is the table for the operation $\circ$ on the set $M = \{R_0, R_1, R_2, D_1, D_2, D_3\}$. As an example, $R_2 \circ D_1$ is the motion obtained by first rotating the triangle clockwise through an angle of $240°$ followed by a reflection in the line D_1. Part (a) of Fig. 8.5 shows the triangle in the original position, part (b) shows the triangle after it has been subjected to R_2, and part (c) shows the position of the vertices

MATHEMATICAL SYSTEMS

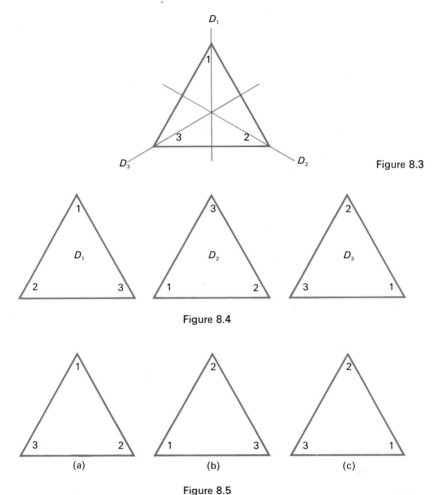

Figure 8.3

Figure 8.4

Figure 8.5

(a) (b) (c)

of the triangle after the triangle in part (b) has been subjected to D_1. Note that we can obtain this result by subjecting the triangle in the original position to the reflection D_3. Therefore $R_2 \circ D_1 = D_3$. The other entries in Table 8.12 are obtained in a similar fashion. As in Section 8.3, the reader may find it helpful to use a paper or cardboard triangle as an aid in visualizing the results in Table 8.12.

From Table 8.12, it is clear that M is closed with respect to the operation $\circ$. To verify the associative law, one would need to check all possible cases (there are 216 cases). The reader should examine several of these. For example,

$$(R_1 \circ D_1) \circ D_3 = D_2 \circ D_3 = R_2 \quad \text{and} \quad R_1 \circ (D_1 \circ D_3) = R_1 \circ R_1 = R_2.$$

TABLE 8.12

○	R_0	R_1	R_2	D_1	D_2	D_3
R_0	R_0	R_1	R_2	D_1	D_2	D_3
R_1	R_1	R_2	R_0	D_2	D_3	D_1
R_2	R_2	R_0	R_1	D_3	D_1	D_2
D_1	D_1	D_3	D_2	R_0	R_2	R_1
D_2	D_2	D_1	D_3	R_1	R_0	R_2
D_3	D_3	D_2	D_1	R_2	R_1	R_0

Therefore,

$$(R_1 \circ D_1) \circ D_3 = R_1 \circ (D_1 \circ D_3).$$

It is clear that R_0 is the identity, R_0, D_1, D_2, D_3 are their own inverses, while R_1 and R_2 are inverses of each other. Thus M with the operation $\circ$ defined by Table 8.12 is a group. Since $D_2 \circ R_2 = D_3$ and $R_2 \circ D_2 = D_1$, M is *not* a commutative group.

Problems

1 Prove that the set $I_3 = \{0, 1, 2\}$ with addition mod 3 is a group.
2 Prove that the set $I_7 = \{0, 1, 2, 3, 4, 5, 6\}$ with addition mod 7 is a group.
3 Prove that the set $B = \{1, 2, 3, 4\}$ with multiplication mod 5 is a group.
4 Prove that the set $X = \{1, 2\}$ with multiplication mod 3 is a group.
5 Prove that the set $Y = \{1, 2, 3, 4, 5, 6\}$ with multiplication mod 7 is a group.
6 Prove that the set $Z = \{1, 2, 3, 4, 5\}$ with multiplication mod 6 is not a group.
7 Prove or disprove that the set of odd integers with addition is a group.
8 Prove or disprove that the set of odd integers with multiplication is a group.
9 Prove or disprove that the set of multiples of 3 with addition is a group.
10 Prove or disprove the $\{1, -1\}$ with multiplication is a group.
11 Use Table 8.12 to verify the following:
    a) $(R_1 \circ D_2) \circ R_1 = R_1 \circ (D_2 \circ R_1)$
    b) $(D_1 \circ D_3) \circ R_2 = D_1 \circ (D_3 \circ R_2)$
    c) $(R_1 \circ D_1) \circ D_3 = R_1 \circ (D_1 \circ D_3)$

12 Use Table 8.12 to list three cases for which the commutative property does not hold.

13 Prove or disprove that the set of integers with the operation $*$ defined by $a * b = a + b - 5$ is a group.

14 Prove or disprove that the set of integers with the operation $\cent$ defined by $a \cent b = b$ is a group.

15 Prove or disprove that the set of integers with the operation $\#$ defined by $a \# b = a + b - ab$ is a group.

8.5 PERMUTATION GROUPS

Consider the set $S = \{1, 2, 3\}$ and the set of all one-to-one correspondences from S to S. There are six such one-to-one correspondences:

1) $1 \leftrightarrow 1,$
    $2 \leftrightarrow 2,$
    $3 \leftrightarrow 3.$

2) $1 \leftrightarrow 1,$
    $2 \leftrightarrow 3,$
    $3 \leftrightarrow 2.$

3) $1 \leftrightarrow 2,$
    $2 \leftrightarrow 1,$
    $3 \leftrightarrow 3.$

4) $1 \leftrightarrow 2,$
    $2 \leftrightarrow 3,$
    $3 \leftrightarrow 1.$

5) $1 \leftrightarrow 3,$
    $2 \leftrightarrow 1,$
    $3 \leftrightarrow 2.$

6) $1 \leftrightarrow 3,$
    $2 \leftrightarrow 2,$
    $3 \leftrightarrow 1.$

Each of these one-to-one correspondences is actually a function from S into S whose range is the set S. Such a function is said to be a *one-to-one function from S onto S*.

Definition 8.3 A *permutation of n symbols* is a one-to-one function from a set S with n elements onto itself.

In view of Definition 8.3, each of the six one-to-one correspondences listed above is an example of a permutation of three symbols. As a matter of convenience we introduce a notation for representing a permutation. For example, the permutation

$$\begin{matrix} 1 \leftrightarrow 1 \\ 2 \leftrightarrow 2 \\ 3 \leftrightarrow 3 \end{matrix} \quad \text{will be denoted by} \quad \begin{bmatrix} 1 & 2 & 3 \\ 1 & 2 & 3 \end{bmatrix}$$

and the permutation

$$\begin{matrix} 1 \leftrightarrow 3 \\ 2 \leftrightarrow 1 \\ 3 \leftrightarrow 2 \end{matrix} \quad \text{will be denoted by} \quad \begin{bmatrix} 1 & 2 & 3 \\ 3 & 1 & 2 \end{bmatrix}.$$

Using this notation, we find that the image of any element in the first row is the element directly below that element. For example, the permutation

$$\begin{bmatrix} 1 & 2 & 3 \\ 3 & 2 & 1 \end{bmatrix}$$

is the function from $\{1, 2, 3\}$ onto $\{1, 2, 3\}$ such that 3 is the image of 1, 2 is the image of 2, and 1 is the image of 3. If we call this permutation α, then $\alpha(1) = 3$, $\alpha(2) = 2$, and $\alpha(3) = 1$. Corresponding to the six one-to-one correspondences from the set $S = \{1, 2, 3\}$ onto intself we have the following six permutations:

$$\alpha = \begin{bmatrix} 1 & 2 & 3 \\ 1 & 2 & 3 \end{bmatrix}, \qquad \beta = \begin{bmatrix} 1 & 2 & 3 \\ 1 & 3 & 2 \end{bmatrix},$$

$$\gamma = \begin{bmatrix} 1 & 2 & 3 \\ 2 & 1 & 3 \end{bmatrix}, \qquad \epsilon = \begin{bmatrix} 1 & 2 & 3 \\ 2 & 3 & 1 \end{bmatrix},$$

$$\delta = \begin{bmatrix} 1 & 2 & 3 \\ 3 & 1 & 2 \end{bmatrix}, \qquad \rho = \begin{bmatrix} 1 & 2 & 3 \\ 3 & 2 & 1 \end{bmatrix}.$$

The set of all permutations on the set

$$\{S = 1, 2, 3, \ldots, n\}$$

is denoted by S_n. Thus

$$S_3 = \{\alpha, \beta, \gamma, \epsilon, \delta, \rho\}.$$

We now define an operation $\circ$ on S_n which we will call *multiplication of permutations*. If F and G are elements of S_n,

$$(F \circ G)(i) = G(F(i))$$

for each $i = 1, 2, \ldots, n$. We illustrate this definition by considering two examples of products in S_3. For example, $(\beta \circ \gamma)(i) = \gamma(\beta(i))$, $i = 1, 2, 3$. Now

$$(\beta \circ \gamma)(1) = \gamma(\beta(1)) = \gamma(1) = 2,$$
$$(\beta \circ \gamma)(2) = \gamma(\beta(2)) = \gamma(3) = 3,$$
$$(\beta \circ \gamma)(3) = \gamma(\beta(3)) = \gamma(2) = 1.$$

Therefore

$$\beta \circ \gamma = \begin{bmatrix} 1 & 2 & 3 \\ 2 & 3 & 1 \end{bmatrix} = \epsilon.$$

Also, $(\delta \circ \rho)(i) = \rho(\delta(i))$, $i = 1, 2, 3$. Thus

$$(\delta \circ \rho)(1) = \rho(\delta(1)) = \rho(3) = 1,$$
$$(\delta \circ \rho)(2) = \rho(\delta(2)) = \rho(1) = 3,$$
$$(\delta \circ \rho)(3) = \rho(\delta(3)) = \rho(2) = 2.$$

TABLE 8.13

○	α	ε	δ	β	ρ	γ
α	α	ε	δ	β	ρ	γ
ε	ε	δ	α	ρ	γ	β
δ	δ	α	ε	γ	β	ρ
β	β	γ	ρ	α	δ	ε
ρ	ρ	β	γ	ε	α	δ
γ	γ	ρ	β	δ	ε	α

Therefore

$$\delta \circ \rho = \begin{bmatrix} 1 & 2 & 3 \\ 1 & 3 & 2 \end{bmatrix} = \beta.$$

Table 8.13 gives all possible multiplications in S_3. It is clear from the table that S_3 is closed under multiplication of permutations and that α is an identity. Furthermore, each element of S_3 has an inverse with respect to multiplication of permutations. By checking all cases, it can be verified that multiplication of permutations is associative on S_3 (it can be shown that multiplication of permutations is associative on S_n for any positive integer n). It should now be clear that S_3 with multiplication of permutations is a group. Since

$$\rho \circ \beta = \epsilon \qquad \text{and} \qquad \beta \circ \rho = \delta,$$

S_3 is not a commutative group. It can be proved that the set S_n (n any positive integer) with the operation of multiplication of permutations is a group. In general, the operation of multiplication of permutations is *not* commutative.

Permutations provide a convenient way of describing the set of rotations and reflections of an equilateral triangle discussed in the previous section. For example, R_0 leaves each vertex fixed and thus can be represented by the permutation α of S_3. D_2 moves the vertex in position 1 to position 3, the vertex in position 2 to position 2, and the vertex in position 3 to position 1. Therefore, D_2 can be represented by ρ. In a similar manner, R_1 can be represented by ϵ, R_2 by δ, D_1 by β, and D_3 by γ. If these representations are used, then Table 8.13 will be identical with Table 8.12.

As a second example of a permutation group, we consider a set of rotations and reflections of a square. The set of rotations we consider are: R_0, a clockwise rotation of $0°$; R_1, a clockwise rotation of $90°$; R_2, a clockwise rotation of $180°$; and R_3, a clockwise rotation of $270°$. The set of reflections we consider are those about the lines X, Y, D_1, and D_2 which are

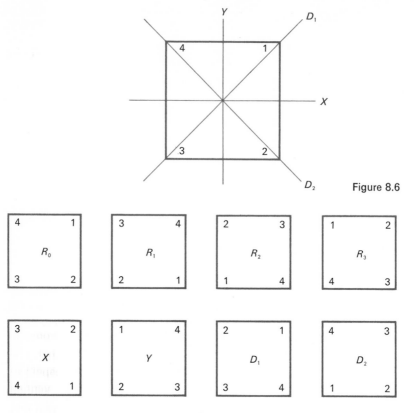

Figure 8.7

illustrated in Fig. 8.6. If we consider the square in this figure to be in a given position, then Fig. 8.7 shows the position of the vertices after each of the rotations R_0, R_1, R_2, R_3 and each of the reflections X, Y, D_1, D_2.

Using permutations, we have

$$R_0 = \begin{bmatrix} 1 & 2 & 3 & 4 \\ 1 & 2 & 3 & 4 \end{bmatrix}, \quad R_1 = \begin{bmatrix} 1 & 2 & 3 & 4 \\ 2 & 3 & 4 & 1 \end{bmatrix},$$

$$R_2 = \begin{bmatrix} 1 & 2 & 3 & 4 \\ 3 & 4 & 1 & 2 \end{bmatrix}, \quad R_3 = \begin{bmatrix} 1 & 2 & 3 & 4 \\ 4 & 1 & 2 & 3 \end{bmatrix},$$

$$X = \begin{bmatrix} 1 & 2 & 3 & 4 \\ 2 & 1 & 4 & 3 \end{bmatrix}, \quad Y = \begin{bmatrix} 1 & 2 & 3 & 4 \\ 4 & 3 & 2 & 1 \end{bmatrix},$$

$$D_1 = \begin{bmatrix} 1 & 2 & 3 & 4 \\ 1 & 4 & 3 & 2 \end{bmatrix}, \quad D_2 = \begin{bmatrix} 1 & 2 & 3 & 4 \\ 3 & 2 & 1 & 4 \end{bmatrix}.$$

Table 8.14 gives all possible multiplications on the set of permutations $S = \{R_0, R_1, R_2, R_3, X, Y, D_1, D_2\}$.

MATHEMATICAL SYSTEMS

TABLE 8.14

○	R_0	R_1	R_2	R_3	X	Y	D_1	D_2
R_0	R_0	R_1	R_2	R_3	X	Y	D_1	D_2
R_1	R_1	R_2	R_3	R_0	D_1	D_2	Y	X
R_2	R_2	R_3	R_0	R_1	Y	X	D_2	D_1
R_3	R_3	R_0	R_1	R_2	D_2	D_1	X	Y
X	X	D_2	Y	D_1	R_0	R_2	R_3	R_1
Y	Y	D_1	X	D_2	R_2	R_0	R_1	R_3
D_1	D_1	X	D_2	Y	R_1	R_3	R_0	R_2
D_2	D_2	Y	D_1	X	R_3	R_1	R_2	R_0

From Table 8.14, it is clear that S is closed under multiplication, R_0 is the identity, and each element of S has an inverse. Furthermore, Table 8.14 can be used to show that the operation of multiplication is associative on S. From these remarks, we conclude that S with multiplication of permutations is a group. However, $D_1 \circ Y = R_3$ and $Y \circ D_1 = R_1$, and therefore multiplication is not commutative on S. Hence S is not a commutative group.

If we consider S_n, the identity permutation is the permutation

$$\begin{bmatrix} 1 & 2 & 3 & \dots & n \\ 1 & 2 & 3 & \dots & n \end{bmatrix}.$$

Furthermore, we can find the inverse of a permutation by reading the array from bottom to top. For example, if

$$\alpha = \begin{bmatrix} 1 & 2 & 3 & 4 & 5 & 6 \\ 3 & 4 & 6 & 1 & 5 & 2 \end{bmatrix},$$

then

$$\alpha^{-1} = \begin{bmatrix} 1 & 2 & 3 & 4 & 5 & 6 \\ 4 & 6 & 1 & 2 & 5 & 3 \end{bmatrix}.$$

Problems

1   Let α, β, and γ be the following permutations:

$$\alpha = \begin{bmatrix} 1 & 2 & 3 & 4 & 5 \\ 2 & 3 & 5 & 4 & 1 \end{bmatrix}, \qquad \beta = \begin{bmatrix} 1 & 2 & 3 & 4 & 5 \\ 3 & 5 & 4 & 1 & 2 \end{bmatrix},$$

$$\gamma = \begin{bmatrix} 1 & 2 & 3 & 4 & 5 \\ 2 & 1 & 3 & 5 & 4 \end{bmatrix}.$$

Find the products in (a) through (i).

a) $\alpha \circ \beta$　　　　　　b) $\beta \circ \gamma$　　　　　　c) $\gamma \circ \beta$

d) $(\alpha \circ \gamma) \circ \beta$　　　　e) β^{-1}　　　　　　f) α^{-1}

g) $\alpha \circ \beta^{-1}$　　　　h) $(\beta \circ \gamma) \circ \alpha$　　i) $(\gamma \circ \alpha^{-1})^{-1}$

2　Use Table 8.13 to show that the set of permutations $B = \{\alpha, \gamma\}$ with multiplication of permutations is a group.

3　Use Table 8.13 to show that the set of permutations $A = \{\alpha, \epsilon, \delta\}$ with multiplication of permutations is a group.

4　Use Table 8.14 to find the inverse of each element of the set

$$S = \{R_0, R_1, R_2, R_3, X, Y, D_1, D_2\}.$$

5　Use Table 8.14 to show that the set of permutations $D = \{R_0, X\}$ with multiplication of permutations is a group.

6　Use Table 8.14 to show that the set of permutations $C = \{R_0, R_1, R_2, R_3\}$ with multiplication of permutations is a group.

7　Consider the set of rotations of a regular pentagon consisting of:

R_0, a rotation of $0°$,　　　　　　R_3, a clockwise rotation of $216°$,

R_1, a clockwise rotation of $72°$,　　R_4, a clockwise rotation of $288°$.

R_2, a clockwise rotation of $144°$,

Label the vertices of a regular pentagon and denote each of the above rotations as a permutation. Prove that this set of permutations with multiplication of permutations is a group.

8.6 SUBGROUPS

In the previous section it was shown that the set of permutations

$$S = \{R_0, R_1, R_2, R_3, X, Y, D_1, D_2\}$$

with the operation $\circ$ of multiplication of permutations is a group. Let $T = \{R_0, R_1, R_2, R_3\}$ and consider the operation of multiplication of permutations on T (see Table 8.15). It is clear from the table that T is closed with respect to the operation of multiplication of permutations, R_0 is the

TABLE 8.15

$\circ$	R_0	R_1	R_2	R_3
R_0	R_0	R_1	R_2	R_3
R_1	R_1	R_2	R_3	R_0
R_2	R_2	R_3	R_0	R_1
R_3	R_3	R_0	R_1	R_2

identity element, and each element of T has an inverse. Furthermore, since multiplication of permutations is an associative operation, the set T with the operation of multiplication of permutations is a group. This example motivates the following definition.

Definition 8.4 Let G with the operation $*$ be a group. A set H is a *subgroup of G* if and only if:

1) H is a subset of G,   2) H with the operation $*$ is a group.

It is clear from the above paragraph and Definition 8.4 that T is a subgroup of S. Another example of a subgroup of S is the set $V = \{R_0, X\}$. It will be left as an exercise for the reader to show that V is a subgroup of S. There are several other subgroups of S. It can be shown, although it is beyond the scope of this text, that the number of elements in a subgroup of a finite group must divide the number of elements in the group. This result was obtained by the French mathematician Joseph Louis Lagrange (1736–1813), who was perhaps the greatest mathematician of the eighteenth century. As an example of Lagrange's result, S has 8 elements, and thus, if a subset of S is to be a subgroup of S, the number of elements in the subset must divide 8. Thus a subgroup of S must have 1, 2, 4, or 8 elements. However, it is important to note that the above remarks do not imply that any subset of S with 1, 2, 4, or 8 elements will be a subgroup of S. Another interesting result is that the identity element of a group G is also the identity element of any subgroup of G. These results can be very helpful in eliminating some subsets of a group from the list of possible subgroups. Any subset of the above set S with 3, 5, 6, or 7 elements cannot be a subgroup of S, since none of these numbers divide 8. Furthermore, any subset not containing R_0 cannot be a subgroup of S, since R_0 is the identity element of S.

If the set G with some operation is a group, it is clear that G is a subgroup of itself since $G \subset G$ and G is a group. Furthermore, the set $H = \{e\}$, where e is the identity element of G, is also a subgroup of G. This is relatively easy to verify and is left as an exercise for the reader. The two subgroups mentioned in this paragraph are often referred to as the *trivial subgroups* of the group G. Any subgroup of the group G which is not a trivial subgroup is called a *proper subgroup*.

The set $T = \{R_0, R_1, R_2, R_3\}$ with the operation $\circ$ of multiplication of permutations presents us with an example of a special type of group. To discuss this special type of group we need to define the concept of exponents for elements of a group.

Definition 8.5 If a is an element of the group G with operation $*$, then

1) $a^0 = e$, where e is the identity of G,

2) $a^1 = a$, and $a^n = a^{n-1} * a$ for every positive interger n,

3) $a^{-n} = (a^{-1})^n$ for every positive integer n.

To illustrate Definition 8.5, we now return to the group T with the operation $\circ$. We have

$$R_1^0 = R_0,$$
$$R_1^1 = R_1,$$
$$R_1^2 = R_1 \circ R_1 = R_2,$$
$$R_1^3 = R_1^2 \circ R_1 = R_2 \circ R_1 = R_3,$$
$$R_1^4 = R_1^3 \circ R_1 = R_3 \circ R_1 = R_0,$$
$$R_1^{-1} = (R_1^{-1})^1 = (R_3)^1 = R_3,$$
$$R_1^{-2} = (R_1^{-1})^2 = (R_3)^2 = R_3 \circ R_3 = R_2.$$

If we consider the set of all integral powers of R_1, we obtain the four distinct elements R_0, R_1, R_2, and R_3. Thus each element of T can be represented as an integral power of R_1. For this reason, $T = \{R_0, R_1, R_2, R_3\}$ with the operation $\circ$ is called a *cyclic group*, and R_1 is called a *generator* of the group. The reader should verify that both R_2 and R_3 will also generate the group T.

Recall that the set $U = \{1, -1, i, -i\}$ with multiplication of complex numbers is a group (see Table 8.11). The question now arises as to whether or not U is a cyclic group. To answer this question, we examine the powers of each of the elements of U. Clearly, all the powers of an identity element are the identity element itself. Thus 1 generates the set $\{1\}$, which is a subgroup of U. However, 1 does not generate U. If we consider the powers of -1, we find that -1 generates the set $\{1, -1\}$, which can also be shown to be a subgroup of U. The powers of i are $i^1 = i$, $i^2 = -1$, $i^3 = -i$, and $i^4 = 1$. Therefore i is a generator of U, and thus U is a cyclic group. The element $-i$ also generates U as $(-i)^1 = -i$, $(-i)^2 = -1$, $(-i)^3 = i$, and $(-i)^4 = 1$. An interesting result in the study of groups is that given a finite group G, any element a of G will generate a subgroup of G. The proof of this is beyond the scope of this text, but in the above example we observed that each element of the set $U = \{1, -1, i, -i\}$ generates a subgroup of U.

Each example considered in this section has concerned a finite group. We now turn our attention to the infinite group consisting of the set of integers with the operation of addition. If we consider all the powers of the integer 1 we see that 1 generates the set. We must remember here that the operation is addition, and thus a power of an element implies a repeated addition. For example,

$$1^0 = 0,$$
$$1^1 = 1,$$
$$1^2 = 1 + 1 = 2,$$
$$1^3 = 1^2 + 1 = 2 + 1 = 3.$$

The successive positive powers of 1 will generate the set of positive integers.

MATHEMATICAL SYSTEMS

Further,

$$1^{-1} = -1,$$
$$1^{-2} = (1^{-1})^2 = (-1) + (-1) = -2,$$
$$1^{-3} = (1^{-1})^3 = (1^{-1})^2 + (1^{-1})$$
$$= (-2) + (-1) = -3.$$

The successive negative powers of 1 will generate the negative integers. Therefore the set of integers with addition is a cyclic group, and the integer 1 is a generator of this group. The reader should verify that -1 will also generate the group of integers.

An an example of a subgroup of the set of integers under addition, consider the set of even integers. This subgroup is an example of a cyclic subgroup with generators 2 and -2.

Problems

1 Show that the set $V = \{R_0, X\}$ is a subgroup of the group of permutations

$$S = \{R_0, R_1, R_2, R_3, X, Y, D_1, D_2\}.$$

2 Find four subgroups, each with two elements, of the group of permutations

$$S = \{R_0, R_1, R_2, R_3, X, Y, D_1, D_2\}.$$

3 Show that the set of multiples of 5 with addition is a subgroup of the group of integers with addition.

4 If a group G has 10 elements, can there be a subgroup of G with 6 elements? Explain.

5 If a group G has 24 elements, what is the possible number of elements in a subgroup of G?

6 Assuming that e is the identity element of a group G, show that $\{e\}$ is a subgroup of G.

7 The set $G = \{2, 4, 6, 8\}$ with the operation of multiplication mod 10 is a group. Show that the set $H = \{4, 6\}$ is a subgroup of G.

8 The group G of Problem 7 is a cyclic group. List all generators of the group G.

9 It can be shown that any subgroup of a cyclic group is cyclic. Therefore the subgroup H in Problem 7 is cyclic. What is a generator of H?

10 The set $I_4 = \{0, 1, 2, 3\}$ with addition mod 4 is a group. Find all the proper subgroups of I_4.

11 The set $I_5 = \{0, 1, 2, 3, 4\}$ with addition mod 5 is a group. Are there any proper subgroups of I_5? Explain.

12 The set of multiples of 3 with addition is a cyclic group. Find a generator of the group.

8.7 FIELDS

To have a group one must have a set G on which there is defined a single binary operation. However, we know from experience that many sets have two or more binary operations defined on them. We have seen that it is possible to define many operations on the set of real numbers; notable among these operations are addition and multiplication. We shall now define a mathematical system that consists of a set and two binary operations defined on the set.

Definition 8.6 Let F be a set and let $\#$ and $*$ denote two binary operations defined on F. Then the set F with the operations $\#$ and $*$ is called a *field* if:

1) F with the operation $\#$ is a commutative group;

2) the elements of F, excluding the identity element for the operation $\#$, is a commutative group with respect to the operation $*$;

3) $*$ distributes over $\#$ in F.

We have at our disposal many interesting examples of fields. The set of rational numbers is a field with respect to the operations of addition and multiplication. Both the set of real numbers and the set of complex numbers are fields with respect to addition and multiplication. However, the set of integers with addition and multiplication is not a field because *not* every nonzero integer has a multiplicative inverse. The set $I_5 = \{0, 1, 2, 3, 4\}$ with addition and multiplication mod 5 is another example of a field. The set $I_6 = \{0, 1, 2, 3, 4, 5\}$ is not a field with respect to addition and multiplication mod 6 because the nonzero elements 2, 3, and 4 have no inverses with respect to the operation of multiplication mod 6. In general, we can say that the set $I_M = \{0, 1, 2, \ldots, M\text{-}1\}$ with the operations of addition and multiplication mod M is a field if and only if M is a prime number. The student can easily construct other examples of fields.

If F with operations $\#$ and $*$ is a field, then F is called a *finite field* whenever F is a finite set. If F is an infinite set, then F is called an *infinite field*. For example, the set of rational numbers, the set of real numbers, and the set of complex numbers are infinite fields. The set I_5 with addition and multiplication mod 5 is an example of a finite field.

Let F be a field with respect to the operations $\#$ and $*$. From Definition 8.6 we know that there must exist in F an identity element for each of these operations. Actually we proved in Section 8.3 that the identity element of a group is unique, and thus the identity elements for the two operations of a field F must also be unique. For convenience, we shall agree to use the symbols u and e to denote the identities for the operations $\#$ and $*$, respectively. If a is an element in a field F with operations $\#$ and $*$, we shall agree to use the symbols $\bar{a}$ and a^{-1} to denote the inverses of a with regard to $\#$ and $*$, respectively. It will also be understood throughout this section that when we refer to a field F with operations $\#$ and $*$, $\#$ denotes the operation with respect to which *each* element of F has an inverse.

Definition 8.6 further requires that each element of F have an inverse in F with respect to the operation $\#$ and that, except for u, each element of F have an inverse in F with respect to the operation $*$. Let us prove that an arbitrary element a of F has a unique inverse in F with respect to the operation $\#$. We will do this by assuming that $\bar{a}$ and a' are both inverses of a and show that $\bar{a} = a'$. Remembering that u denotes the identity for the operation $\#$, we have

$$\begin{aligned}
\bar{a} &= u \# \bar{a} && \text{Definition of } u \\
&= (a' \# a) \# \bar{a} && \text{Definition of } a' \\
&= a' \# (a \# \bar{a}) && \text{The associative property of } \# \\
&= a' \# u && \text{Definition of } \bar{a} \\
&= a' && \text{Definition of } u
\end{aligned}$$

Hence, $\bar{a} = a'$, and the element a has a unique inverse with respect to the operation $\#$. To prove that, except for u, every element of F has a unique inverse with respect to the operation $*$, one would proceed in a similar fashion.

If $a \# b = a \# c$ for some a, b, and c in a field F, then $b = c$. Furthermore, if $a * b = a * c$ for some a, b, and c in F with $a \neq u$, then $b = c$. In Section 8.3 we proved this property to be valid in an arbitrary group, and consequently $\#$ and $*$ must have this property in F. We will refer to these properties as the *left cancellation properties* of a field. Because both $\#$ and $*$ are commutative, *right cancellation properties* can easily be derived from the left cancellation properties.

If a and b are elements of a field F with operations $\#$ and $*$, then every equation of the form $a \# x = b$ has a solution in F. To find a solution, we recall that each element a has an inverse with respect to $\#$ in F and proceed as follows:

$$\begin{aligned}
a \# x &= b, \\
\bar{a} \# (a \# x) &= \bar{a} \# b, \\
(\bar{a} \# a) \# x &= \bar{a} \# b, \\
u \# x &= \bar{a} \# b, \\
x &= \bar{a} \# b.
\end{aligned}$$

Hence $x = \bar{a} \# b$ is a solution of the equation $a \# x = b$. By following a similar procedure, we can also prove that every equation of the form $a * x = b$, where a and b are elements of F with $a \neq u$, has a solution in F.

A very useful property in a field F with operations $\#$ and $*$ is that

$$u * a = a * u = u$$

for every element a in F. Because $u * a = a * u$ for every a in F, it will be sufficient to prove that $a * u = u$. We first observe that

$$a * u = a * (u \# u) \qquad \text{Definition of } u$$
$$= (a * u) \# (a * u) \qquad * \text{ is left distributive over } \#$$

Using this result, we have

$$a * u = (a * u) \# (a * u)$$
$$(a * u) \# u = (a * u) \# (a * u) \qquad \text{Definition of } u$$
$$u = a * u \qquad \qquad \text{Left cancellation}$$
$$\qquad \qquad \qquad \qquad \qquad \text{property for } \#$$
$$a * u = u. \qquad \qquad \text{Reflexive property of}$$
$$\qquad \qquad \qquad \qquad \text{the equality relation}$$

We have now proved that $a * u = u * a = u$ for every element a in F.

If a and b are elements of a field F with operations $\#$ and $*$ and $a * b = u$, then $a = u$ or $b = u$. This property is easily proved by assuming that one of the elements a or b is not equal to u and then showing that the other element must equal u. Let us suppose that $a \neq u$. Then by Definition 8.6, a has an inverse a^{-1} with respect to the operation $*$. It now follows that if $a * b = u$, then

$$a^{-1} * (a * b) = a^{-1} * u$$
$$a^{-1} * (a * b) = u \qquad \qquad \text{Property of } u \text{ with}$$
$$\qquad \qquad \qquad \qquad \text{respect to } *$$
$$(a^{-1} * a) * b = u \qquad \qquad \text{Associative property}$$
$$\qquad \qquad \qquad \qquad \text{for } *$$
$$e * b = u \qquad \qquad \text{Definition of } a^{-1}$$
$$b = u. \qquad \qquad \text{Definition of } e$$

Thus, if $a * b = u$ and $a \neq u$, then $b = u$. That is, if $a * b = u$, then $a = u$ or $b = u$.

In proving the properties of this section we have used only the properties of an arbitrary field. Hence all these properties will be true in any field, whether the field be a subset of the real numbers, a modular system, or a field entirely different from those with which we are familiar. One of the significant advantages of this abstract approach is that it often saves us considerable time by allowing us to avoid unnecessary duplication of effort.

Galois and Niels Abel (1802–1829) were the first mathematicians who did significant work in fields, with the concept of a field originally arising in their work on the solution of equations by radicals. These two mathematicians are responsible, perhaps more than any others, for the abstract approach to mathematics which distinguishes today's mathematics from that of earlier times. Abel, like Galois, died long before realizing his full potential. He died a pauper at the age of twenty-seven from tuberculosis.

Problems

In Problems 1 through 9, use Definition 8.6 to determine whether the given set with the given operations is a field. If the structure is not a field, explain which properties do not hold.

1   $F = \{0, 1\}$ with the operations of addition and multiplication

2   $F = \{-1, 0, 1\}$ with the operations of addition and multiplication

3   $F = \{0, 1, 2\}$ with the operations of addition and multiplication mod 3

4   $F = \{0, 1, 2, 3\}$ with the operations of addition and multiplication mod 4

5   $F = \{0, 1, 2, 3, 4, 5, 6\}$ with the operations of addition and multiplication mod 7

6   $F = \{0, 2, 4, 6\}$ with the operations of addition and multiplication mod 7

7   $F = \{a + b\sqrt{2} \mid a$ and b are rational numbers$\}$ with the operations of addition and multiplication

8   $F = \{a + b\sqrt{3} \mid a$ and b are rational numbers$\}$ with the operations of addition and multiplication

9   R is the set of real numbers with operations $\#$ and $*$ defined by the equations $a \# b = a + b - 1$ and $a * b = a + b - ab$ for all real numbers a and b.

In Problems 10 through 14 prove the indicated property in a field F with operations $\#$ and $*$. As usual, we shall agree that u denotes the identity for $\#$ and that e denotes the identity for $*$. F is a commutative group with respect to $\#$, and F (excluding u) is a commutative group with respect to $*$

10   If $a * b = c * b$ for elements a, b, and c in F with $b \neq u$, then $a = c$.

11   If $a * b * c = u$ for some elements a, b, and c in F, then at least one of the elements a, b, or c is u.

12   An element $a \neq u$ in F is called a *zero divisor* if there exists another element $b \neq u$ in F such that $a * b = u$. Prove that F has no zero divisors.

13   $a * \bar{b} = \overline{a * b}$ for all elements a and b in F.

14   $\bar{a} * b = \overline{a * b}$ for all elements a and b in F.

15   What is the least number of elements a field can have?

Chapter 9

GEOMETRY

9.1 INTRODUCTION

For as many as 4000 years man has studied that branch of mathematics referred to as *geometry*. Geometry deals with the measurement, properties, and relationships of points, lines, angles, surfaces, and solids. It has its roots in man's experience with physical objects. Primitive man's first experience with geometry was in observation of certain shapes and forms as they occurred in nature. The Babylonians of 2000 to 1600 B.C. were concerned primarily with areas and volumes. Studying the remnants of their civilization makes it apparent that they must have been familiar with the procedures for finding the area of a rectangle, the area of certain triangles and trapezoids, as well as the volume of certain solids.

Perhaps the greatest contributions to geometry were made by the Greeks. They were the first to introduce logic and formal reasoning into geometry and to present geometry as an abstract mathematical system. The most famous of the Greek mathematicians was Euclid. Very little is known about his life except that he probably was a professor of mathematics at the University of Alexandria. Even though exact dates are unknown, historians believe that he lived during the third century B.C. His great reputation is due primarily to his authorship of the *Elements*. However, not all of the work appearing in the *Elements* can be attributed to Euclid. It is generally accepted that the work on proportions (Book V) and a number of other propositions contained in the *Elements* are not Euclid's original contribution. Instead the *Elements* is a consolidation of Euclid's work and the work of his predecessors into a logical sequence. The *Elements* is one of the greatest mathematical expositions of all times. Much of the material contained in it is found in high school geometry texts even today. As a matter of interest we list the ten assumptions Euclid made in order to prove the 465 propositions contained in his *Elements*. The first five listed were referred to as "common notions", whereas the second five were referred to as "postulates." The distinction between postulates and common notions is that postulates were more mathematical in nature.

Common Notions

1) Things which are equal to the same thing are also equal to one another.

2) If equals be added to equals, the wholes are equals.

3) If equals be subtracted from equals, the remainders are equal.

4) Things which coincide with one another are equal to one another.

5) The whole is greater than the part.

Postulates

Let the following be postulated:

1) To draw a straight line from any point to any point.

2) To produce a finite straight line continuously in a straight line.

3) To describe a circle with any center and distance.

4) That all right angles are equal to one another.

5) That, if a straight line falling on two straight lines make the interior angles on the same side less than two right angles, the two straight lines, if produced indefinitely, meet on that side on which are the angles less than the two right angles.

The fifth postulate, called the *parallel postulate*, perhaps has gained more attention than any other statement made in mathematical history. For years mathematicians have tried to prove that this is not a postulate but a theorem and, upon failure to do so, have substituted new postulates. These new sets of postulates have given rise to new kinds of geometry referred to as *non-Euclidean geometries*.

No effort will be made in this text to develop formally Euclidean geometry. We will be concerned primarily with fundamental concepts concerning points, lines, and space. We choose an informal approach and rely heavily on the intuition of the reader.

9.2 POINTS, LINES, PLANES, AND SPACE

We recall from Chapter 1 that some terms are left undefined in the study of a mathematical system. Among the undefined terms used in geometry are *point*, *line*, *plane*, *space*, and *betweenness*. Each person has some notion of what is meant by each of these terms. However, any attempt to define them formally is likely to be more confusing than useful. One of the criticisms of Euclid's *Elements* is that Euclid made an attempt to define, or explain, all of his important terms. Among these attempted definitions are:

A *point* is that which has no part.

A *line* is breadthless length.

A *straight line* is a line which lies evenly with the points on itself.

A *surface* is that which has length and breadth only.

A *plane surface* is a surface which lies evenly with straight lines in itself.

Each of the terms in the above definitions is so inherent in a discussion of geometry that formally defining it is confusing.

We picture a point by making a dot on a piece of paper. Since a point has *no* dimensions, the size of the dot is completely immaterial. However, the smaller the dot, the better our idea of the meaning of a point. The use of a dot to represent a point is analogous to using a numeral to represent a number. Thus a dot is the physical representation of the idea of a point. When we say "draw a particular set of points," we mean "make marks which represent those points." We use a capital letter located near the point to name the point. We shall think of three-dimensional space as being the set of all points, and this space shall be the universal set for our discussion of geometry.

A line (we shall use line and straight line synonymously) is a particular subset of space. A line has no thickness; however, it does extend indefinitely in two directions. We name a line by naming any two points belonging to the line and placing a double arrow over the names of the points placed in juxtaposition. As an example of this procedure, the line in Fig. 9.1 can be named $\overleftrightarrow{PQ}$, $\overleftrightarrow{PR}$, $\overleftrightarrow{QR}$, $\overleftrightarrow{QP}$, $\overleftrightarrow{RQ}$, or $\overleftrightarrow{RP}$ by using the points P, Q, and R in pairs.

Figure 9.1

Since P, Q, and R belong to the same line, they are called *collinear* points. A line continues indefinitely in two directions. We indicate this in Fig. 9.1 by using arrow heads at each end of the representation of the line. Another procedure for naming a line is the use of a small letter as in Fig. 9.2.

Figure 9.2

Two interesting questions arise concerning points and lines. The first question is: "Given a single point P in space, how many lines contain P?" It is simple to visualize that infinitely many lines can contain P. The second question is: "Given two distinct points P and Q in space, how many lines contain both P and Q?" As in answering the first question, we rely on our intuition to answer that the two points uniquely determine a line. That is, there is one and only one line which contains both P and Q. A result of this observation is that two distinct straight lines can intersect in at most one point. Suppose two distinct lines m and n intersect in the distinct points P and Q. Then P and Q would determine *two* distinct lines, namely, m and n. This contradicts the statement that two distinct points determine a unique line. Therefore two straight lines can intersect in at most one point (their intersection could be the empty set). A point P on a line m separates m into two *half-lines*. P is called the *endpoint* of the half-lines. If a half-line contains its endpoint, it is said to be *closed*. If it does not contain its endpoint it is said to be *open*. We are now prepared to state a definition.

Definition 9.1   A *ray* is a closed half-line.

Figure 9.3

In Fig. 9.3, the point P separates the line m into two half-lines. It should be clear that P determines two rays. One would be the ray containing P and all points of m to the right of P. The other contains P and all points of m to the left of P. We name a ray by using the names of the endpoint and some other point on the ray. For example, in Fig. 9.4 the ray having endpoint A and extending to the right is named $\overrightarrow{AB}$. The ray having endpoint A and extending to the left is named $\overrightarrow{AC}$.

Figure 9.4

The use of set notation (Chapter 2) is very helpful in a study of geometry since we are concerned with sets of points. As an example, from Fig. 9.4, we have

$$\overrightarrow{AB} \cap \overrightarrow{AC} = \{A\}, \qquad \overrightarrow{AB} \cup \overrightarrow{AC} = \overleftrightarrow{AB},$$
$$\overrightarrow{CA} \cap \overrightarrow{AB} = \overrightarrow{AB}, \qquad \overrightarrow{CA} \cup \overrightarrow{AB} = \overrightarrow{CA}.$$

We remark that $\overrightarrow{CA}$ and $\overrightarrow{CB}$ denote the same ray. In Fig. 9.4, A separates $\overleftrightarrow{AB}$ into the rays $\overrightarrow{AB}$ and $\overrightarrow{AC}$ which are called *opposite rays*.

Definition 9.2   A subset of a line containing two points and all the points between them is called a *line segment*.

It is clear from Definition 9.2 that two points determine a line segment. In Fig. 9.4 the points A and B determine a line segment. We denote the line segment determined by A and B by $\overline{AB}$ or $\overline{BA}$. Thus $\overline{AB}$ is the set of points consisting of A, B, and all the points between A and B. A and B are called endpoints of the line segment. We recall that the term "between" is an undefined term. Two line segments are equal if and only if they have identical endpoints. Thus, if $\overline{AB} = \overline{CD}$, then A is the same as C and B is the same as D, or A is the same as D and B is the same as C. If line segments $\overline{AB}$ and $\overline{CD}$ can be placed upon each other so that they coincide, they are said to be *congruent*. If $\overline{AB}$ is congruent to $\overline{CD}$, we write $\overline{AB} \cong \overline{CD}$.

Example 1 We observe the following from Fig. 9.5.

a) $\overrightarrow{SP} \cap \overrightarrow{QR} = \overrightarrow{QR}$

b) $\overrightarrow{SP} \cup \overline{PQ} = \overrightarrow{SQ}$

c) $\overrightarrow{SP} \cap \overrightarrow{QR} = \varnothing$

d) $\overline{PQ} \cap \overrightarrow{QR} = \{Q\}$

e) $\overrightarrow{SP} \cap \overrightarrow{QS} = \overrightarrow{SQ}$

f) $\overline{PQ} \subset \overline{SR}$

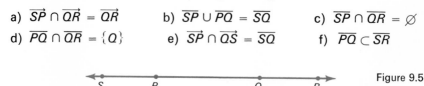

Figure 9.5

We have discussed the point, which can be considered as zero-dimensional, and the line, which can be considered one-dimensional. Now let us discuss the plane. A plane can be thought of as a subset of space lying on a flat surface. A plane has no thickness but it extends indefinitely in all other directions. It can be thought of as having infinite length and infinite width and therefore as two-dimensional. We shall use Greek letters to denote planes.

If A and B are distinct points, they determine a unique line $\overleftrightarrow{AB}$. How many planes contain $\overleftrightarrow{AB}$ as a subset? The reader should be able to visualize that the answer to this question is "infinitely many." Thus two distinct points do not determine a unique plane. To answer the question as to how many points are required to determine a unique plane, consider the following experiment. Suppose we have a four-legged table in which the legs are not all of the same length. How many legs will contact the floor? The answer is three and this suggests that three distinct noncollinear points determine a unique plane. Points belonging to the same plane are said to be *coplanar*.

If two distinct planes intersect, their intersection is a line. Again we rely on intuition and let one plane be represented by a wall in a room and the other by the ceiling. The intersection of the wall and the ceiling is clearly a line. If we consider the ceiling and floor as representing two distinct planes, they never intersect, and thus their intersection is the empty set. If the intersection of two distinct planes is the empty set, they are said to be *parallel*. Similarly, if m and n are lines in the same plane and $m \cap n = \varnothing$, then m and n are *parallel*. If lines m and n are parallel, we write $m \parallel n$. If p and q are lines in different planes and $p \cap q = \varnothing$, then p and q are called *skew lines*. In Fig. 9.6, m is parallel to n, and p and q are skew lines. If the intersection of a line and a plane is $\varnothing$, the line is said to be parallel to the plane.

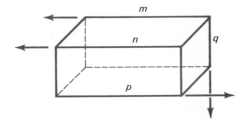

Figure 9.6

Let α be a plane and m a line. We summarize the properties of intersection of m and α with the following statements.

1) If $m \subset \alpha$, then $m \cap \alpha = m$.

2) If m is parallel to α, then $m \cap \alpha = \varnothing$.

3) If $m \not\subset \alpha$ and $m \cap \alpha \neq \varnothing$, then $m \cap \alpha$ is exactly one point.

We summarize other properties of intersection discussed in this section in the following statements.

1) If m is a line and $A \in m$, then $m \cap \{A\} = \{A\}$.

2) If m and n are two distinct lines, they intersect in at most one point. If $m \parallel n$ or if m and n are skew lines, then $m \cap n = \varnothing$.

3) If α and β are two nonparallel planes, their intersection is a line. If α and β are parallel, then $\alpha \cap \beta = \varnothing$.

We conclude this section with three observations concerning separation.

1) A point P on a line m separates m into three disjoint sets, the point itself and two open half-lines.

2) A line m on a plane α separates α into three disjoint sets, the line m itself and two open *half-planes*.

3) A plane α separates space into three disjoint sets, the plane α itself and two open *half-spaces*.

The meanings of half-plane and half-space are analogous to the meaning of half-line mentioned previously in this chapter.

Problems

1 Consider the following line with the designated points.

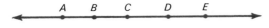

Find the following.

a) $\overrightarrow{BC} \cap \overrightarrow{DE}$

b) $\overline{BD} \cup \overline{CD}$

c) $\overline{AD} \cap \overline{BE}$

d) $\overline{AD} \cap \overrightarrow{BE}$

e) $\overline{BC} \cup \overrightarrow{CD}$ f) $\overrightarrow{DE} \cap \overrightarrow{CB}$

g) $\overleftrightarrow{AC} \cap \overline{BD}$ h) $\overrightarrow{AC} \cap \overrightarrow{BA}$

i) $\overrightarrow{DA} \cup \overrightarrow{BE}$ j) $\overrightarrow{BC} \cup \{B\}$

2 Consider the given figure and find:

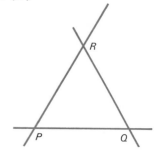

a) $\overrightarrow{PQ} \cap \overrightarrow{QR}$

b) $\overrightarrow{PQ} \cap \overrightarrow{QP}$

c) $\overrightarrow{PQ} \cap (\overrightarrow{PR} \cap \overrightarrow{QR})$

d) $\overrightarrow{RP} \cap (\overrightarrow{PQ} \cup \overrightarrow{QR})$

3 Consider the given figure and find:

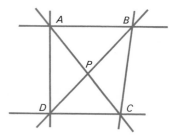

a) $\overline{BD} \cap \overline{AC}$

b) $\overrightarrow{AB} \cap \overline{CB}$

c) $\overrightarrow{PB} \cup \overrightarrow{PD}$

d) $(\overline{DC} \cup \overline{CB}) \cap \overline{BD}$

e) $\overline{AB} \cap \overline{CD}$

f) $\overrightarrow{PA} \cap \overrightarrow{DB}$

g) $(\overline{DA} \cup \overline{AB} \cup \overline{BC}) \cap \overline{AC}$

4 Let A, B, and C be noncollinear points. Indicate which of the following are true and which are false.

a) $\overleftrightarrow{AB} = \overleftrightarrow{BC}$ b) $\overline{AB} = \overline{BA}$ c) $\overline{AB} = \overline{AC}$

d) $\overrightarrow{AB} \cap \overrightarrow{AC} = \emptyset$ e) $\overrightarrow{AB} \cap \{C\} = \emptyset$ f) $\overrightarrow{CB} \cap \overrightarrow{AB} = \{B\}$

5 If A, B, and C are collinear with B between A and C, which of the following are true and which are false?

a) $\overrightarrow{AB} \cap \overrightarrow{BC} = \overrightarrow{BC}$ b) $\overrightarrow{BC} \cup \overrightarrow{BA} = \overleftrightarrow{CA}$

c) $\overrightarrow{AB} \subset \overrightarrow{BC}$ d) $\overrightarrow{BA} \subset \overleftrightarrow{AC}$

e) $\overrightarrow{BC} \cap \overrightarrow{BA} = \{C\}$ f) $\overrightarrow{BA} \cap \overrightarrow{BC} = \{B\}$

g) $\overrightarrow{BC} \cup \overrightarrow{BA} = \overleftrightarrow{AB}$ h) $\overrightarrow{BC} \subset \overrightarrow{BA}$

6 What is the greatest number of lines determined by three noncollinear points?

7 Suppose A, B, C, and D are coplanar points no three of which are collinear. How many lines do they determine?

8 Suppose A, B, C, and D are noncoplanar points no three of which are collinear. How many lines do they determine?

9 A line m on a plane α separates the plane into three disjoint sets, the line itself and two half-planes. Does a line segment $\overline{AB}$ which is a subset of α separate α into three disjoint sets?

9.3 ANGLES

More people are more familiar with the idea of an *angle* than with the concepts of points, lines, planes, and space. We shall now formally define this term.

Definition 9.3 An *angle* is the union of two rays having a common endpoint. The rays are called the *sides* of the angle, and the common endpoint is called the *vertex*.

Figure 9.7 is a representation of the angle which is the union of rays $\overrightarrow{PQ}$ and $\overrightarrow{PR}$. The sides of the angle in the figure are the rays $\overrightarrow{PQ}$ and $\overrightarrow{PR}$, and the vertex of the angle is P. There are three ways commonly used to name an angle such as the one in Fig. 9.7. They are:

1) Use the symbol $\angle$ with the vertex P, that is, $\angle P$.

2) Use the symbol $\angle$ with the points P, Q, and R, that is, $\angle QPR$ or $\angle RPQ$. Whenever this procedure is used the vertex is *always* the second point named.

3) Use a small letter placed as the Greek letter θ is placed in Fig. 9.7.

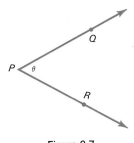

Figure 9.7

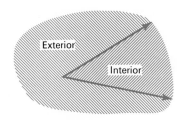

Figure 9.8

According to Definition 9.3, the set of points belonging to an angle are those belonging to the two rays which form the angle. If we consider an angle as a subset of a plane, then the angle separates the plane into three disjoint sets:

1) The set of points belonging to the angle.

2) The set of points called the *interior* of the angle.

3) The set of points called the *exterior* of the angle.

These three sets are represented in Fig. 9.8.

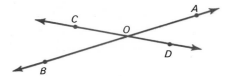

Figure 9.9

Figure 9.9 shows the intersection of the two lines $\overleftrightarrow{AB}$ and $\overleftrightarrow{CD}$. We name the point of intersection O. Observe that $\angle AOC$ and $\angle COB$ have the same vertex O and a common ray $\overrightarrow{OC}$. Two angles with a common vertex and a common side are called *adjacent angles*. Thus, $\angle AOC$ and $\angle COB$ are adjacent angles. Another pair of adjacent angles is $\angle BOD$ and $\angle DOA$. Can you find another pair of adjacent angles in this figure? The angles $\angle AOD$ and $\angle COB$ are nonadjacent angles since they do not have a common ray. Two angles, such as $\angle AOD$ and $\angle COB$, which are nonadjacent angles formed by the intersection of two lines, are called *vertical angles*. Find another pair of vertical angles in Fig. 9.9. In the figure, angles $\angle AOC$ and $\angle COB$ are adjacent angles with their noncommon rays on the same straight line. Thus their union is the union of a line and a ray with endpoint on that line. Two such angles are said to be *supplementary angles*. $\angle BOD$ and $\angle DOA$ are also supplementary angles. Can you find another pair of supplementary angles in Fig. 9.9?

If angles $\angle ABC$ and $\angle DEF$ can be placed on each other so that they coincide, they are said to be *congruent*. If $\angle ABC$ is congruent to $\angle DEF$, we write $\angle ABC \cong \angle DEF$.

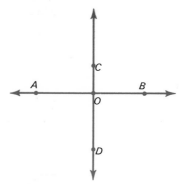

Figure 9.10

In Fig. 9.10, $\overleftrightarrow{AB}$ intersects $\overleftrightarrow{CD}$ in the point O. If $\angle AOC \cong \angle COB$, we say $\overleftrightarrow{AB}$ is perpendicular to $\overleftrightarrow{CD}$, and write $\overleftrightarrow{AB} \perp \overleftrightarrow{CD}$. Furthermore, $\angle AOC$ and $\angle COB$ are called *right angles*.

Problems

For Problems 1 through 3 use the figure at the top of page 275.

1 Tell which of the marked angles are adjacent angles.

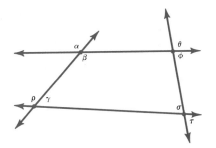

2 Tell which of the marked angles are vertical angles.

3 Tell which of the marked angles are supplementary angles.

4 Consider the figure below.

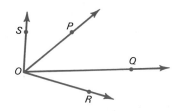

a) Are $\angle POQ$ and $\angle QOR$ adjacent angles? Explain.

b) Are $\angle POR$ and $\angle POQ$ adjacent angles? Explain.

5 From the given figure find the following:

a) $\angle ABC \cap \overline{BC}$ b) $\angle ABC \cap \overline{AC}$

c) $\angle BCA \cap \overrightarrow{AB}$ d) $\angle ABC \cap \angle ACB$

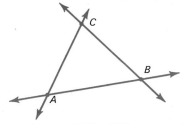

6 In the figure in Problem 5, is $\overrightarrow{AB} \cup \overline{BC}$ an angle? Explain.

7 In the figure in Problem 5, is $\overrightarrow{AB} \cup \overrightarrow{BC}$ an angle? Explain.

8 In the figure in Problem 5, is $\overrightarrow{AB} \cup \overrightarrow{AC}$ an angle? Explain.

9 Draw a figure of two adjacent angles. Is the union of these two angles an angle? Explain.

10 Draw a figure so that the intersection of an angle and a line is:

a) the empty set   b) a single point

c) exactly two points   d) a ray

11 Draw a figure so that the intersection of two angles is:

a) the empty set

b) a single point

c) exactly two points

d) exactly three points

e) exactly four points

f) a ray

g) a line segment

9.4 CURVES

Suppose a pencil is used to make a mark on a surface. A set of points which one can represent by a mark made without lifting the pencil is called a *curve*. In our treatment of curves we will assume that they are *plane curves*, that is, curves lying in a plane. Some examples of curves are given in Fig. 9.11. From these examples it is clear that a curve may pass through a point more than once [part (c)]. A *simple curve* passes through no point more than once. In Fig. 9.11, (a), (b), and (d) are simple curves but (c) is not. Parts (c) and (d) are drawn so that the drawing starts and stops at the same point. Such curves are called *closed curves*. Curves such as those in (a) and (b) are called *open curves*. Lines, line segments, and angles are all examples of simple curves which are open. Simple curves which are closed are referred to as *simple closed curves*. One could think, intuitively, of a simple closed curve as one which can be deformed, by stretching or contracting without tearing, into a circle. In Fig. 9.11, (d) is the only example of a

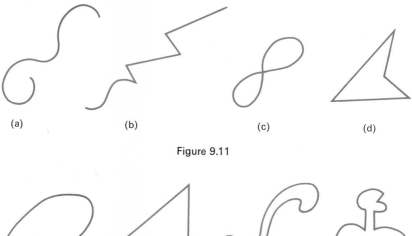

| (a) | (b) | (c) | (d) |

Figure 9.11

| (a) | (b) | (c) | (d) |

Figure 9.12

GEOMETRY

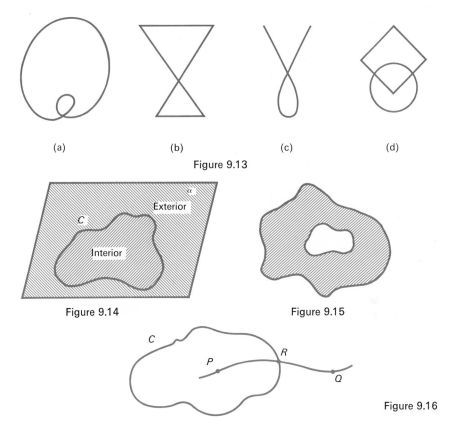

(a)   (b)   (c)   (d)

Figure 9.13

Exterior

C

Interior

α

Figure 9.14

Figure 9.15

C

P

R

Q

Figure 9.16

simple closed curve. Figure 9.12 gives some more examples of simple closed curves. None of the curves in Fig. 9.13 is a simple closed curve.

Any simple closed curve separates the plane which contains it into three disjoint sets, namely, the curve itself, the *interior* of the curve, and the *exterior* of the curve. This result is actually a theorem known as the Jordan Curve Theorem. We will illustrate these remarks in Fig. 9.14 with the simple closed curve C which is a subset of the plane ∝. The curve itself is disjoint with the interior and disjoint with the exterior. Therefore, the plane is the union of C, the interior of C, and the exterior of C. The union of the interior of a simple closed curve and the curve itself is called a *region*. The curve is called the *boundary* of the region. The set of points on and between the two simple closed curves in Fig. 9.15 (shaded portion) is also referred to as a region. The curves are the boundaries of the region.

If P is a point in the interior of a simple closed curve C and Q any point in the exterior of C, then the intersection of C with any curve containing P and Q contains at least one point of C. Conversely, if every curve containing P and Q contains a point of the curve C, then P is in the interior of C and Q is in the exterior of C, or vice versa. In Fig. 9.16 the intersection is the point R.

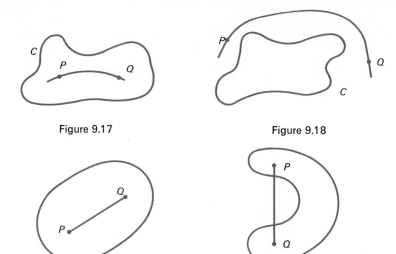

Figure 9.17

Figure 9.18

Figure 9.19

Figure 9.20

If and *P Q* are both interior or both exterior, then there is a curve containing *P* and *Q* which has no points in common with *C* (see Figs. 9.17 and 9.18).

A closed curve is *convex* if and only if the line segment joining any two points of its interior is itself a subset of the interior. The closed curve in Fig. 9.19 is convex, but the closed curve in Fig. 9.20 is *not* convex.

Problems

1 Classify the given curves as open or closed.

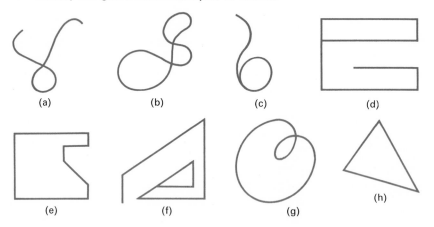

(a)   (b)   (c)   (d)

(e)   (f)   (g)   (h)

2 Classify the curves in Problem 1 as simple or not simple.

3 Which curves in Problem 1 are simple closed curves?

4 Which curves in Problem 1 are convex?

5 Draw two simple closed curves which intersect in exactly one point. Classify the union of these curves as simple or not simple, as open or closed.

6 Draw a straight line and a simple closed curve which intersect in exactly two points; in exactly three points.

7 In the given figure classify the named points as on the curve, interior to the curve, or exterior to the curve. Is the curve convex?

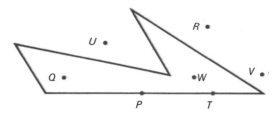

8 Draw a simple curve which is open.

9 Draw a closed curve which is not simple.

10 Draw a curve which is convex.

11 Draw a simple closed curve which is not convex.

12 The given figure is a closed curve. See whether you can begin at some point and trace the complete curve without lifting your pencil.

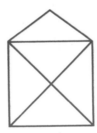

9.5 POLYGONS

A set of simple closed curves of particular interest and importance is the set of *polygons*.

Definition 9.4 A *polygon* is a simple closed curve which is the union of line segments.

The line segments forming the polygon in Definition 9.4 are called the *sides* of the polygon. If the intersection of two sides is not empty, the intersection is called a *vertex* and these two sides are said to be *adjacent sides*.

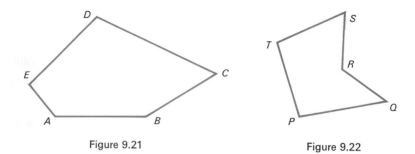

| Figure 9.21 | Figure 9.22 |

The endpoints of any side are called *adjacent vertices*. A line segment joining any two nonadjacent vertices is called a *diagonal* of the polygon. We name a polygon by using the names of the vertices. As an example, the polygon in Fig. 9.21 is named *ABCDE*. The sides of polygon *ABCDE* are $\overline{AB}, \overline{BC}, \overline{CD}, \overline{DE},$ and $\overline{EA}$. The vertices are *A, B, C, D,* and *E*. Polygon *ABCDE* is an example of a *convex polygon* whereas polygon *PQRST* in Fig. 9.22 is not convex. The union of a polygon and its interior is called a *polygonal region*.

It is often convenient to use the phrase *angle of a polygon*. In Fig. 9.23, $\angle ABC$ is formed by rays $\overrightarrow{BA}$ and $\overrightarrow{BC}$ which contain sides $\overline{BA}$ and $\overline{BC}$ of the polygon *ABCD*. $\angle ABC$ is an angle of polygon *ABCD*. In general, an *angle of a polygon* is an angle formed by two rays which contain any two adjacent sides of the polygon. The other angles of polygon *ABCD* in Fig. 9.23 are $\angle BCD, \angle CDA,$ and $\angle DAB$. While the vertices and sides of a polygon are subsets of the polygon, the angles of the polygon are not.

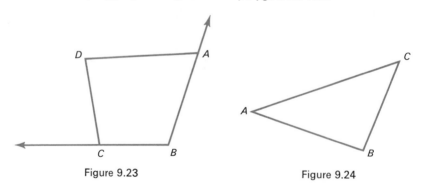

| Figure 9.23 | Figure 9.24 |

A *triangle* is a three-sided polygon. If we let *A, B,* and *C* be three non-collinear points and draw $\overline{AB}, \overline{AC},$ and $\overline{BC}$, then the polygon *ABC* is a triangle and we denote it by $\triangle ABC$ (see Fig. 9.24). Thus, $\triangle ABC = \overline{AB} \cup \overline{AC} \cup \overline{BC}$. The term "triangle" signifies three angles. Our choice of the definition for polygon suggests that perhaps we should use the term "trilateral" to signify

GEOMETRY

three sides. The region determined by a triangle is referred to as a *triangular region*.

A *quadrilateral* is a four-sided polygon. In Fig. 9.23, quadrilateral $ABCD = \overline{AB} \cup \overline{BC} \cup \overline{CD} \cup \overline{AD}$.

A polygon in which all the sides are congruent is called a *regular polygon*. We consider two polygons to be congruent if they can be made to coincide.

We conclude this section by mentioning some particular types of triangles and quadrilaterals.

1) A triangle with all sides congruent is called an *equilateral* triangle.

2) A triangle with all angles congruent is called an *equiangular* triangle.

3) A triangle with two sides congruent is called an *isosceles* triangle.

4) If an angle of a triangle is a right angle, the triangle is called a *right* triangle.

5) A quadrilateral whose opposite sides lie on parallel lines is called a *parallelogram*.

6) A quadrilateral with one pair of opposite sides lying on parallel lines is called a *trapezoid*.

7) A parallelogram with all angles congruent is called a *rectangle*.

8) A rectangle with all sides congruent is called a *square*.

9) A parallelogram with all sides congruent is called a *rhombus*.

Problems

1 Classify the following curves as polygon or not polygon.

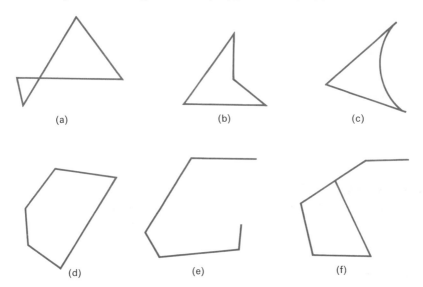

(a)   (b)   (c)

(d)   (e)   (f)

2 Which polygons in Problem 1 are convex?

3 Which curves in Problem 1 are triangles?

4 Which curves in Problem 1 are quadrilaterals?

5 Triangle ABC is drawn below. Describe the following.

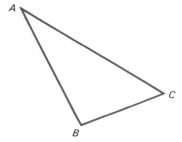

a) $\overline{AB} \cap \overline{BC}$

b) $\overrightarrow{AB} \cap \triangle ABC$

c) $(\overrightarrow{AB} \cup \overrightarrow{BC}) \cap \overline{AC}$

d) $\overleftrightarrow{AC} \cap \triangle ABC$

e) $\overleftrightarrow{AC} \cap \angle ABC$

f) $\overleftrightarrow{BC} \cap \angle ACB$

g) $(\overleftrightarrow{AB} \cap \overleftrightarrow{BC}) \cap \overleftrightarrow{AC}$

h) $\angle BAC \cap \angle CBA$

6 How many diagonals does a triangle have? Explain.

7 Draw a triangle ABC and a quadrilateral $PQRS$ such that the intersection of the two is exactly one point; exactly two points; exactly three points; exactly four points.

8 Draw two triangles which intersect in exactly one point; exactly two points; exactly three points.

9 How many diagonals does a quadrilateral have?

10 Draw a five-sided polygon (pentagon) $ABCDE$ such that the intersection of diagonals $\overline{BE}$ and side $\overline{DE}$ is $\overline{DE}$.

11 Draw a six-sided polygon (hexagon) $ABCDEF$ such that the intersection of diagonal $\overline{DF}$ with the interior of $ABCDEF$ is the empty set.

12 Draw an eight-sided polygon (octagon) which is convex.

9.6 CIRCLES

Polygons provide us with many examples of simple closed curves with which we are familiar. Another familiar class of simple closed curves is the set of *circles*.

Definition 9.5 A *circle* is a simple closed curve having a point, O, in its interior, such that if P and Q are any two points belonging to the curve, $\overline{OP} \cong \overline{OQ}$.

In Definition 9.5, the point O is called the *center* of the circle. The center, belonging to the interior of the circle, is not a point of the circle. Any line segment with one endpoint at the center and the other on the circle is called

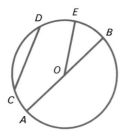

Figure 9.25

a *radius* of the circle. By the very definition of a circle, all radii of a given circle are congruent.

A line segment with endpoints on a circle is called a *chord* of the circle. If a chord passes through the center of a circle, the chord is called a *diameter* of the circle. We illustrate all the terms described thus far by observing the circle in Fig. 9.25. The point O is the center of the circle. $\overline{OE}$, $\overline{OB}$, and $\overline{OA}$ are all radii of the circle. $\overline{CD}$ and $\overline{AB}$ are chords of the circle, and $\overline{AB}$ is a diameter of the circle.

Any two points on a circle, along with the points on the circle between the two points, are called an *arc* of the circle. For example, the points B and D in Fig. 9.25 determine two arcs, the arc containing E and the arc containing C (it also contains A). These arcs are denoted $\overparen{BED}$ and $\overparen{DCB}$, respectively. $\overparen{DCB}$ could also be denoted $\overparen{DAB}$. Note that the circle is the set

$$\overparen{BED} \cup \overparen{DCB}.$$

Circles with the same center are called *concentric circles*. In Fig. 9.26, the four circles are concentric.

Figure 9.26

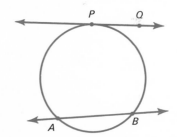

Figure 9.27

The intersection of a circle and a line may be the empty set, a single point, or two points. If the intersection is a single point, the line is called a *tangent line*, and the point is called a *point of tangency*. If the intersection of a line and a circle is two points, the line is called a *secant*. In Fig. 9.27, $\overleftrightarrow{PQ}$ is a tangent line, P is a point of tangency, and $\overleftrightarrow{AB}$ is a secant.

The union of a circle and its interior is called a *circular region*.

Problems

1 In the given figure, give the name of:

a) the center   b) a radius

c) a chord   d) a diameter

e) a tangent line   f) a point of tangency

g) a secant   h) a point of the interior

i) a point of the exterior   j) an arc.

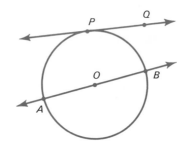

2 Given any circle, what is the intersection of all the diameters of the circle?

3 Draw two circles whose intersection is exactly one point; exactly two points.

4 Draw three circles whose intersection is exactly one point; exactly two points.

5 If the center of a circle is O and $\overline{OB}$ is a radius of the circle, what is the intersection of the circle and $\overline{OB}$?

6 If the center of a circle is O and $\overline{AB}$ is a diameter of the circle, what is the intersection of $\overline{AB}$ and the circle? of $\overline{AB}$ and the interior of the circle? of $\overline{AB}$ and exterior of the circle?

7 If $\overleftrightarrow{PQ}$ is a tangent line of a circle and P is a point of tangency, what is the intersection of $\overleftrightarrow{PQ}$ and the circle? of $\overleftrightarrow{PQ}$ and the interior of the circle? of $\overleftrightarrow{PQ}$ and the exterior of the circle?

8 If $\overleftrightarrow{AB}$ is a secant of a circle and A and B belong to the circle, what is $\overleftrightarrow{AB}$ intersection the circle? What is $\overleftrightarrow{AB}$ intersection the interior of the circle? What is $\overleftrightarrow{AB}$ intersection the exterior of the circle?

9 Would a ring or a coin be better to illustrate the concept of a circle? Explain.

9.7 SIMPLE CLOSED SURFACES

Our discussion of sets of points belonging to space has thus far been concentrated on sets of points in which all the points lie in a single plane. We now consider certain sets of points in which the points do not all lie in the same plane.

Consider a box with rectangular sides or a ball in space. The surfaces of these objects (if we consider them to have no thickness) separate space into three disjoint sets. In the case of the box we have points outside the box, points on the surface of the box, and points inside the box. Similar statements can be made about the ball. Any set of points which separates space into three disjoint sets, points on a surface, points interior to the surface, and points exterior to the surface, is called a *simple closed surface*. The union of a simple closed surface and its interior is called a *solid*. Our discussion of simple closed surfaces will be limited to a few particular types, most of which are probably familiar to the reader. We shall rely heavily on pictures for our discussion.

Any simple closed curve bounded by polygons and polygonal regions is called a *polyhedron*. Again consider the rectangular box in space, the sides of which have no thickness. The sides of this box are rectangles and thus the box is a polyhedron. Note that the ball is not a polyhedron. The box belongs to a subset of the set of polyhedrons called *prisms*. In general, a *prism* is a simple closed surface formed by two polygonal regions of the same kind contained in parallel planes along with quadrilateral regions joining the two polygonal regions. Figure 9.28 illustrates three types of prisms.

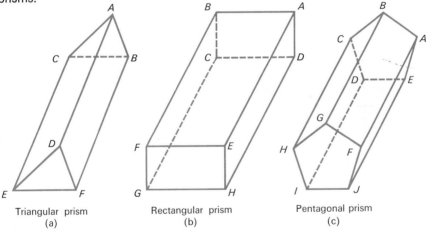

Triangular prism (a) Rectangular prism (b) Pentagonal prism (c)

Figure 9.28

In Fig. 9.28(a), △ABC and △DEF are congruent and lie in parallel planes. The triangular regions ABC and DEF are called *bases* of the prism. The rectangular regions ABED, ACFD, and BCFE are called *lateral faces* of the prisms. The *sides* of a prism are the bases and lateral faces. The line segments in which the sides intersect are called *edges*, and the intersections

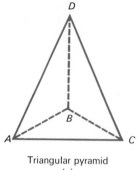

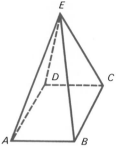

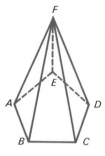

Triangular pyramid (a)   Rectangular pyramid (b)   Pentagonal pyramid (c)

Figure 9.29

of edges and bases are *vertices* of the prism. Thus, in Fig. 9.28(a), the vertices are *A, B, C, D, E,* and *F*; the edges are $\overline{AB}, \overline{AC}, \overline{BC}, \overline{DE}, \overline{DF}, \overline{EF}, \overline{BE},$ $\overline{AD}$, and $\overline{CF}$. The prisms in Fig. 9.28 have their edges perpendicular to their bases and are called *right prisms*.

The Swiss mathematician Euler (1707–1783) gave a formula relating the number of vertices, sides, and edges of a polyhedron. If *V* is the number of vertices, *S* the number of sides, and *E* the number of edges, then

$$V + S - E = 2.$$

We note that the triangular prism in Fig. 9.28 has six vertices, five sides, and nine edges, and these values satisfy Euler's formula.

Figure 9.29 illustrates another type of polyhedron called a *pyramid*. In general, a *pyramid* is a simple closed surface formed by a polygonal region, a point not in the plane containing the region, and triangular regions joining the point and the sides of the polygonal region. In Fig. 9.29(a), the vertices of the pyramid are *A, B, C,* and *D*. The edges are $\overline{AB}, \overline{BC}, \overline{AC}, \overline{AD}, \overline{BD}$, and $\overline{DC}$. The triangular region *ABC* is the base and the triangular regions *ADC*, *BCD*, and *ABC* are the lateral faces. Note that $4 + 4 - 6 = 2$, and Euler's formula is satisfied.

Figure 9.30 illustrates three types of simple closed surfaces which are not polyhedrons. The surface in Fig. 9.30(a) has the property that if *P* and *Q* are any points on the surface, $\overline{OP} \cong \overline{OQ}$. It is called a *sphere*. The point *O* is called the *center* of the sphere. Any line segment with one endpoint at the center and the other on the surface is called a *radius* of the sphere. Thus $\overline{OP}$ is a radius of the sphere in Fig. 9.30(a). Any line segment with endpoints on the surface is called a *chord* of the sphere, and any chord passing through the center of the sphere is called a *diameter* of the sphere. In Fig. 9.30(a), $\overline{PQ}$ is a chord.

GEOMETRY

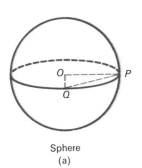

Sphere
(a)

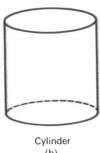

Cylinder
(b)

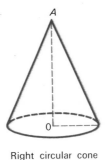

Right circular cone
(c)

Figure 9.30

The surface in Fig. 9.30(b) is called a *cylinder*, more specifically a *right circular cylinder*, since the bases are circles and the sides are perpendicular to the bases.

The surface in Fig. 9.30(c) is called *circular cone*. The base is a circle. More specifically, it is called a *right circular cone* in that the line $\overleftrightarrow{AO}$ through the center of the base is perpendicular to the plane containing the base.

We again remark that we are relying heavily on the intuition of the reader in this chapter, and especially so in this section. Even though we have chosen this informal approach, we feel that the reader should at least be familiar with geometric figures.

Problems

In Problems 1 through 4 list all vertices, sides, and edges and verify Euler's formula for the given polyhedron.

1 The rectangular prism in Fig. 9.28.

2 The pentagonal prism in Fig. 9.28.

3 The rectangular pyramid in Fig. 9.29.

4 The pentagonal pyramid in Fig. 9.29.

5 Let β be a plane parallel to the base of a triangular pyramid. If the intersection of β and the pyramid contains more than one point, what kind of curve is the intersection?

6 Repeat Problem 5, using a pentagonal pyramid.

7 Repeat Problem 5, using a right circular cylinder.

8 Repeat Problem 5, using a right circular cone.

9 If a plane β intersects a sphere in more than one point, what kind of curve is the intersection?

10 A heptagon is a seven-sided polygon. Assuming that the bases of a right prism are heptagons, give the number of vertices, edges, and sides and verify Euler's formula.

11 Repeat Problem 10, using a decagon, a ten-sided polygon.

9.8 MEASUREMENT

To measure a set, we associate with the set a nonnegative real number. We have already established a procedure for measuring sets like "the set of all states in the United States." An appropriate measure of such a set is its cardinal number. Another set for which the cardinal number is an appropriate measure is the set of all stars in the Andromeda Nebula. These above sets are examples of *discrete sets*, and the measure of a discrete set is its cardinal number. The cardinal number of a discrete set may be quite large, and in fact a discrete set may be infinite. The set of all points on a number line corresponding to the set of natural numbers is an example of a discrete set whose measure is infinite.

In this section we will establish procedures for measuring a different kind of set. Instead of answering the question "How many?" we will be interested in the questions "How long?" or "How much?" These are questions that pertain to what is called a *continuous set*. Some examples of continuous sets are line segments, regions of a plane, and solids. The distance from one city to another, the area of a state in square miles, and the volume of water falling over Niagara Falls in a given period of time are all examples of measurements associated with continuous sets.

In our work on measurement we will often use the concept of congruent geometric figures. Congruent geometric figures have the same size and shape, and each is an exact copy of the other. Some pairs of congruent geometric figures are pictured in Fig. 9.31.

Figure 9.31

To measure a continuous set, we associate with the set a nonnegative real number, the number being determined by a comparison of the set with another set of the same kind. For example, to measure a line segment we compare it with a segment called a *unit segment*. A region is measured by comparing it with a *unit region*, and a solid is measured by comparing it with a *unit solid*. The symbol $m(S)$ is often used to represent the measure of a set S.

We shall illustrate the remarks of the preceding paragraph by considering the measurement of line segments, or *linear measure*. Linear measure is often referred to as *length*. If we measure the edge of a desk with a ruler and find it to have length 54 inches, then we are comparing the edge of the desk, considered as a line segment, with a unit segment called an "inch." Using the inch as the unit of measure, the desk has length 54 or measure 54. If one reads from a mileage chart that the distance from Chicago to San Francisco is 2233 miles, this can be interpreted to mean that the length of the line segment joining the two cities is the same as the length of 2233 one-mile segments. In this case, the unit of measure is the "mile," and the measure of the line segment from Chicago to San Francisco is 2233. To illustrate the use of an arbitrary line segment as a unit of measure, let us refer to Fig. 9.32, in which we choose the segment $\overline{PQ}$ as our unit segment. If the edge of a sheet of paper is placed next to the unit segment $\overline{PQ}$ and points corresponding to P and Q are marked on the edge, the sheet of paper can be used as a ruler to approximate the length of the line segment $\overline{AE}$. Using a sheet of paper marked in this manner, we find that each of the segments $\overline{AB}$, $\overline{BC}$, $\overline{CD}$, and $\overline{DE}$ has the same length as the unit segment $\overline{PQ}$. Hence the length of the segment $\overline{AE}$ is four times the length of the unit segment $\overline{PQ}$. That is, with respect to the unit segment $\overline{PQ}$, the length of $\overline{AE}$ is 4.

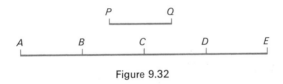

Figure 9.32

Trade and commerce within a region often necessitate the acceptance of a unit of measure by a large number of people. Such a unit of measure is then referred to as a *standard unit of measure*. The standard units of measure in the United States are established by the United States Congress, and copies of these standards are housed at the National Bureau of Standards in Washington, D.C. The standard units of measure commonly used in the United States are those of the English system of measures.

Unlike the measurement of a discrete set, the measurement of a continuous set is never exact. We do not mean to imply by this statement that the length of a line segment can never be exactly one foot. We mean simply that it is impossible to verify that the length is exactly one foot. In the first place, we can never be certain that a measuring device is an exact duplicate of the standard unit of measure. The approximate nature of measurement is also affected by the fact that the end result depends on the judgement of the person doing the measuring.

Problems

1 Using the segment $\overline{AB}$ as the unit segment, find the measure of $\overline{CD}$ for each case in the figure below.

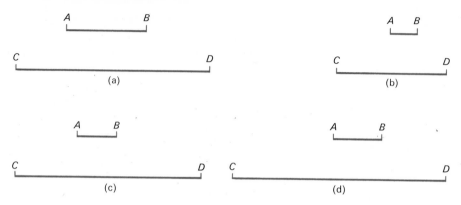

(a)   (b)   (c)   (d)

2 Use a ruler to find the length of your room in inches. Ask a friend to perform the same measurement. Do the two results agree?

9.9 THE METRIC SYSTEM

Toward the end of the eighteenth century a group of French scientists called a meeting of scientists from many countries in an effort to establish a set of standard units of measures which could be used internationally. As a consequence of that meeting, we have the *metric system* of measures which we shall discuss in detail in this section.

The standard unit of linear measure in the metric system is the *meter*. Originally, the meter was to be one ten-millionth of the distance measured along a meridian from the equator to the north pole. This length was agreed on after a geodetic survey. Actually, the meter was defined to be the distance between two finely engraved lines on the International Meter Bar stored near Paris. Copies of the International Meter Bar are distributed throughout the world. The United States copy is housed at the National Bureau of Standards in Washington, D.C. In 1960 the General Conference of Weights and Measures defined the meter to be 1,650,763.73 wavelengths of the orange-red radiation of the isotope krypton-86. It has been shown experimentally that this new definition does not vary significantly from the original. An advantage of this new definition is that the exact meter can be reproduced in a well-equipped laboratory, and therefore the copies of the International Meter Bar need not be returned to Paris for rechecking.

The developers of the metric system had hoped that in time the system would be used universally. Their hope has been almost fulfilled in that nearly all the civilized world has adopted the metric system. In 1965 the British government announced that it was encouraging the adoption of the metric system, and by 1975 the greater part of British industry should have effected the change. In 1968 the Congress of the United States passed legislation providing for a three-year study of the feasibility of adopting the metric system. This was its first legislation concerning the metric system since 1866 when Congress adopted the metric system as an optional system of measures. The standard units in the English system are now defined in terms of the standard units of the metric system. For example, the yard is now defined to be .9144 meter.

The subdivisions of the meter (the basic standard unit of linear measure) are the decimeter ($\frac{1}{10}$ meter), centimeter ($\frac{1}{100}$ meter), and millimeter ($\frac{1}{1000}$ meter). Multiples of the meter are the dekameter (10 meters), hectometer (100 meters) and kilometer (1000 meters). Table 9.1 lists the relationship of these units of linear measure.

The basic standard unit of capacity measure is the liter (approximately 1.06 U.S. liquid quarts), and the basic standard unit of weight measure is the gram (a pound is approximately 453.5934 grams). The same prefixes are used with these units as are used with the meter. Table 9.2 lists the relationships of the units used in measuring capacity and weight.

TABLE 9.1

Linear measure
1000 millimeters
= 100 centimeters
= 10 decimeters
= 1 meter
= 0.1 dekameter
= 0.01 hectometer
= 0.001 kilometer

TABLE 9.2

Capacity measure	Weight measure
1000 milliliters	1000 milligrams
= 100 centiliters	= 100 centigrams
= 10 deciliters	= 10 decigrams
= 1 liter	= 1 gram
= 0.1 dekaliter	= 0.1 dekagram
= 0.01 hectoliter	= 0.01 hectogram
= 0.001 kiloliter	= 0.001 kilogram

There are two tremendous advantages to the metric system. It is decimal in nature and thus fitted to our numeration system. Furthermore, the systems of linear, capacity, and weight measure are related as follows. One liter of pure water weighs one kilogram and occupies 1000 cubic centimeters under a pressure of 76 centimeters of mercury at 4 degrees centigrade. Thus one cubic centimeter of pure water weighs one gram.

TABLE 9.3

1 inch = 2.54 centimeters	1 centimeter = 0.4 inch
1 yard = 0.914 meter	1 meter = 1.1 yards
1 mile = 1.6 kilometers	1 kilometer = .62 mile
1 liquid quart = 0.95 liter	1 liter = 1.05 liquid quarts
1 dry quart = 1.1 liters	1 liter = .91 dry quart
1 pound = 0.45 kilogram	1 kilogram = 2.2 pounds

For reference purposes, some of the units of the English and metric systems are compared in Table 9.3. These equivalents are all approximate.

We conclude this section with some examples illustrating the use of the metric system and the procedure of changing from the English system to the metric system, and vice versa.

Example 1   Convert 15 meters to centimeters.

Solution   From Table 9.1, we know that 1 meter is 100 centimeters, and therefore 15 meters is 1500 centimeters.

Example 2   Convert 3 hectoliters to deciliters.

Solution   From Table 9.2, we know that .01 hectoliter equals 10 deciliters. Multiplying by 100, we see that 1 hectoliter is equal to 1000 deciliters. Therefore 3 hectoliters is 3000 deciliters.

Example 3   Convert 17 centigrams to kilograms.

Solution   From Table 9.2, 100 centigrams is equal to 0.001 kilogram. Dividing by 100, we find that 1 centigram is equal to 0.00001 kilogram. Therefore 17 centigrams is 0.00017 kilogram.

Example 4   Convert 350 miles to kilometers.

Solution   From Table 9.3, 1 mile is approximately 1.6 kilometers. Therefore 350 miles is approximately 350 × 1.6 = 560.0 kilometers.

Example 5   Convert 300 grams to pounds.

Solution   Since 1 gram equals 0.001 kilogram, 300 grams equals 0.3 kilogram. From Table 9.3, 1 kilogram is approximately 2.2 pounds. Therefore 0.3 kilogram is 0.3 × 2.2 = 0.66 pounds, and 300 grams is approximately 0.66 pound.

Problems

1 Make the following conversions.

a) 5 meters to kilometers
b) 15 kilometers to centimeters
c) 3 dekaliters to liters
d) 14 centiliters to milliliters
e) 300 grams to hectograms
f) 150 hectograms to decigrams
g) 1750 milliliters to kiloliters
h) 3475 centimeters to hectometers
i) 615 kilograms to milligrams
j) 327 decimeters to dekameters

2 Make the following conversions.

a) 15 meters to yards
b) 20 centimeters to inches
c) 14 liters to liquid quarts
d) 5 kilograms to pounds
e) 17 inches to centimeters
f) 5 yards to meters
g) 7 miles to kilometers
h) 13 pounds to kilograms
i) 8 miles to meters
j) 19 kilograms to ounces

3 What is the weight of 15 centiliters of pure water?

4 What is the weight in pounds of 10 liters of pure water?

5 Express in liters the amount of pure water which weighs 300 hectograms.

6 Express in liquid quarts the amount of pure water which weighs 3 kilograms.

7 Express in liquid pints the amount of pure water which weighs 350 dekagrams.

8 Which is better time, 100 yards in 9.2 seconds or 100 meters in 10 seconds?

9 If milk costs $1.15 per gallon, how much should a liter cost?

10 If bacon is 75¢ per pound, how much should a kilogram cost?

11 Which is a faster rate of travel, 65 miles per hour or 90 kilometers per hour?

12 A six-foot two-inch man weighs 215 pounds. Express his height in centimeters and his weight in kilograms.

9.10 MEASUREMENT OF POLYGONS AND POLYGONAL REGIONS

A measure of a polygon, called its *perimeter*, is defined to be the sum of the lengths of the sides of the polygon. For example, if the lengths of the sides of a quadrilateral are 5, 3, 9, and 8, the perimeter of the quadrilateral is $5 + 3 + 9 + 8 = 25$. If the lengths of the sides are expressed in inches, the perimeter is 25 inches; if the lengths of the sides are expressed in meters, the perimeter is 25 meters.

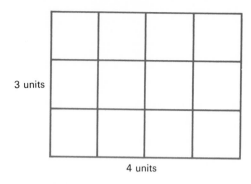

3 units

4 units

Figure 9.33

A measure of a polygonal region is called its *area*. Although any region could be used as a unit of area measure, it is convenient to choose a square region that measures one unit on a side as the unit for determining area. This unit of area measure is referred to as a *unit square*. Consider the rectangular region in Fig. 9.33, two adjacent sides of which have measure 4 units and 3 units. This rectangular region can be covered by 12 nonoverlapping unit squares, and hence we say that the area of the region is 12 square units. If the unit of length is the inch, the area is 12 square inches; if the unit of length is the kilometer, the area is 12 square kilometers. The reader is undoubtedly familiar with the formula

area of a rectangular region = length times width

or

$$A = lw$$

for determining the area of a rectangular region. The "length" and "width" represent the measures of two adjacent sides of the rectangle. Clearly this formula is correct if the length and width are integers, as in Fig. 9.33. Actually the formula is correct if the length and width are expressed as any real numbers. We shall accept this formula for the area of a rectangular region to derive area formulas for other polygonal regions.

We recall from Section 9.5 that a parallelogram is a quadrilateral whose opposite sides lie on parallel lines. It can be shown that the opposite sides of a parallelogram are both parallel and equal. Consider the parallelogram $ABCD$ in Fig. 9.34. We shall refer to the side $\overline{DC}$ as the *base* of the parallelogram. The line segment $\overline{AE}$ through the vertex A and perpendicular to the

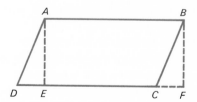

Figure 9.34

GEOMETRY

base $\overline{DC}$ is called an *altitude* to the base $\overline{DC}$. Since it can be shown that $\triangle AED \cong \triangle BFC$, the area of the region bounded by parallelogram $ABCD$ is equal to the area of the region bounded by the rectangle $ABFE$. Hence, if b denotes the length of the base and a denotes the length of an altitude to that base, then we have the formula

$$\text{area of a region bounded by a parallelogram} = ba$$

or

$$A = ba.$$

Example 1 Find the area of the region bounded by the parallelogram in Fig. 9.35.

Solution The area is $12 \cdot 7 = 84$ square units.

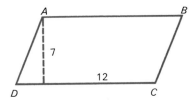 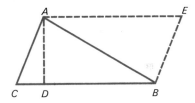

Figure 9.35   Figure 9.36

Using the formula for the area of a region bounded by a parallelogram, we can develop a formula for the area of a triangular region. Consider the triangle ABC in Fig. 9.36 with base $\overline{CB}$ and altitude $\overline{AD}$. If we construct through A a line parallel to $\overleftrightarrow{CB}$ and through B a line parallel to $\overleftrightarrow{CA}$, then it can be shown that $\triangle ABC \cong \triangle AEB$. Hence the area of the region bounded by $\triangle ABC$ is one-half the area of the region bounded by the parallelogram $AEBC$. If we let b denote the length of the base and a denote the length of the altitude to that base, we have the formula

$$\text{area of a triangular region} = \tfrac{1}{2} ba$$

or

$$A = \tfrac{1}{2} ba.$$

Example 2 Find the area of the region bounded by $\triangle ABC$ in Fig. 9.37.

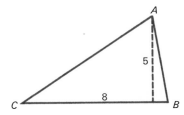

Figure 9.37

Solution From Fig. 9.37 we see that b = 8 and a = 5. Hence

$$A = \tfrac{1}{2} (8) (5) = 20 \text{ square units.}$$

We are now ready to discuss a method for finding the area of an arbitrary polygonal region. Consider the five-sided polygon *ABCDE* in Fig. 9.38.

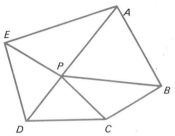

Figure 9.38

If we locate a point *P* in the interior of the polygonal region and construct line segments joining *P* to each of the vertices of the polygon *ABCDE*, the polygonal region is subdivided into the five triangular regions bounded by △*ABP*, △*BCP*, △*CDP*, △*DEP*, and △*EAP*. The area of the region bounded by the polygon *ABCDE* is then found by taking the sum of the areas of the triangular regions. The area of an *n*-sided polygon can be found in a similar manner. It is interesting to note that this method for finding the area of a polygonal region is independent of how the point *P* is chosen in the interior of the region. This fact is proved in more advanced treatments of geometry.

Problems

1 If the area of a triangular region is 48 square meters and one side has length 8 meters, what is the length of the altitude to this side?

2 If the area of a triangular region is 72 square centimeters and the length of an altitude is 7 centimeters, what is the length of the side to which the altitude is drawn?

3 If the lengths of two consecutive sides of a parallelogram are 5 feet and 8 feet and the length of an altitude joining the two 5-foot sides is 4 feet, what is the length of an altitude joining the 8-foot sides?

4 A rectangle is 8 inches long and 6 inches wide. If another rectangle, three times as long, bounds a region with the same area, how wide is the rectangle?

5 Draw a rectangular region whose area is the same as the region bounded by the parallelogram below.

GEOMETRY

6 Find the areas bounded by each of the polygons below.

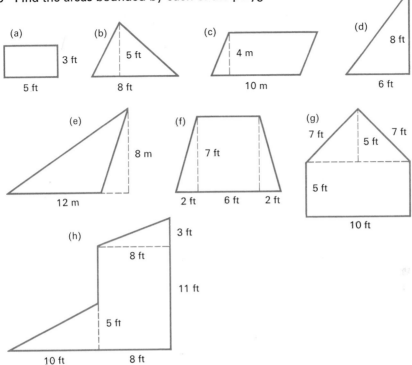

(a)

3 ft

5 ft

(b)

5 ft

8 ft

(c)

4 m

10 m

(d)

8 ft

6 ft

(e)

8 m

12 m

(f)

7 ft

2 ft   6 ft   2 ft

(g)

7 ft   5 ft   7 ft

5 ft

10 ft

(h)

3 ft

8 ft

11 ft

5 ft

10 ft   8 ft

7 Estimate the area of each of the triangles below by estimating the number of squares enclosed.

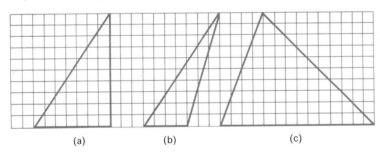

(a)   (b)   (c)

9.11 MEASUREMENT OF CIRCLES AND CIRCULAR REGIONS

Associated with a circle is a measure, called its *circumference*, which is analogous to the perimeter measure of a polygon. Early Egyptian and Babylonian mathematicians recognized that the ratio of the circumference of a circle to the measure of a diameter of the circle is a constant. This constant is denoted by the Greek letter π. From the above observation we have the formula $\pi = c/d$ or $c = \pi d$, where c is the circumference of the circle and d the measure of a diameter. Even though the ratio c/d was known to be constant, the exact value of π was not known. The Babylonians (2000–1600 B.C.) used the value $\pi = 3$. From the Rhind papyrus (about 1650 B.C.) it appears that the Egyptians approximated

$$\pi = (\tfrac{4}{3})^4 = \tfrac{256}{81} = 3.1604 \cdots .$$

In the fifth century B.C., the Greeks proved that the ratio of the circumference of a circle to the measure of a diameter of the circle is constant. The proof appeared in the writings of Hippocrates of Chios (not the great physician Hippocrates). His proof did not give an actual numerical value for π. In the third century B.C., the Greek mathematician Archimedes established that π is between $\tfrac{223}{71}$ and $\tfrac{22}{7}$ or that, to two decimal places, π is 3.14. In this text we shall use as approximations of π either $\tfrac{22}{7}$ or 3.14.

We now turn our attention to a measure of a circular region called its *area*. To define the area of a circular region we shall rely on a procedure similar to the one used by Archimedes to give an approximation of the number π.

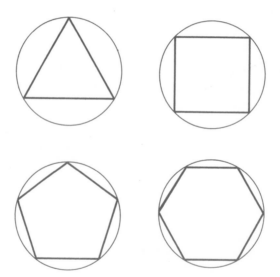

Figure 9.39

In Fig. 9.39 an equilateral triangle, a square, a regular pentagon, and a regular hexagon are inscribed in a given circle. The areas of these polygonal regions provide us with approximations to the area of the circular region. Furthermore, the more sides the regular polygon has, the closer the area of the polygonal region approximates the area of the circular region. Using this approximating method, it can be shown that the area A of a circular region is given by

$$A = \tfrac{1}{2}rc,$$

where r is the measure of a radius of the circle and c is the measure of the circumference. Since $c = \pi d$ and $d = 2r$, we have

$$A = \pi r^2.$$

Problems

In Problems 1 through 6, find the circumference of the circle with radius having the given measure. In each case find the area of the circular region determined by the circle.

1 14 inches	2 35 centimeters	3 3 meters
4 5.6 feet	5 6 yards	6 2.5 millimeters

7 If the measure of a radius of a circle is twice that of another circle, how do the circumferences of the two circles compare?

8 If the measure of a radius of a circle is twice that of another circle, how do the areas of the circular regions determined by the two circles compare?

9 The measure of the radius of the earth is approximately 4000 miles. Find the distance around the earth at the equator.

10 Suppose we have a circle with circumference of 44 units, and a square with perimeter 44 units. Which region, the circular region or the square region, has the largest area?

11 Suppose r is the radius measure of a circle. How much increase in circumference will result by increasing the radius measure by 1 unit?

12 If the measure of the radius of the earth were increased by 1 foot, how much increase in circumference at the equator would result? If the measure of the radius of a basketball were increased by 1 foot, how much increase in circumference would result? If the measure of the radius of base of a Coke bottle were increased by 1 foot, how much increase in the circumference of the base would result? Explain these results. [*Hint*: See Problem 11.]

9.12 MEASUREMENT OF SURFACES AND SOLIDS

One measure associated with a simple closed surface is its *surface area*. Our discussion of surface area will be restricted to right prisms, pyramids, right circular cylinders, right circular cones, and spheres.

In the case of a right prism or a pyramid, the surface area is the sum of the areas of its sides. In Fig. 9.40 the surface area of the rectangular prism is the sum of the areas of the rectangular regions *ABCD*, *EFGH*, *ADHE*, *BCGF*, *ABFE*, and *CDHG*. Since the opposite sides of the prism have equal

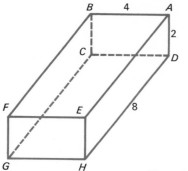
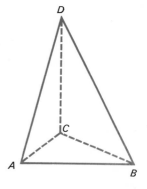

Figure 9.40

area, the surface area is twice the sum of the areas of the rectangular regions *ABCD*, *ADEH*, and *ABFE*. Using the dimensions given, the surface area is

$$A = 2(2 \cdot 4 + 2 \cdot 8 + 4 \cdot 8)$$
$$= 2(8 + 16 + 32)$$
$$= 2(56)$$
$$= 112 \text{ square units.}$$

The surface area of the triangular pyramid in Fig. 9.40 is the sum of the areas of the triangular regions *ABC*, *ADC*, *ADB*, and *BCD*.

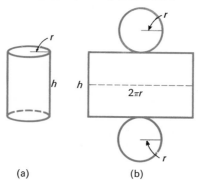

(a)   (b)   Figure 9.41

The surface area of the right circular cylinder in Fig. 9.41 (a) is the sum of the areas of the bases and the lateral surface. Since each base of the cylinder is a circular region with radius of measure r, it has area πr^2. There are two bases, and thus the surface area of the bases is $2\pi r^2$. To find the area of the lateral surface, imagine the cylinder to be cut and unfolded as in Fig. 9.41 (b). The lateral surface becomes a rectangular region with width h and length $2\pi r$ (the circumference of the base). Thus the lateral surface has area $2\pi rh$. Therefore the surface area of the cylinder is

$$A = 2\pi r^2 + 2\pi rh.$$

GEOMETRY

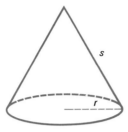

Figure 9.42

The surface area of the right circular cone in Fig. 9.42 is the sum of the areas of the base and the lateral surface. The base is a circular region with radius of measure r and thus has area πr^2.

The area of the lateral surface can be determined by a procedure much like that used in finding the area of a circular region. We will not discuss this process, but simply state that the area is πrs, where r is the measure of the radius of the base and s is the measure of the slant height (as labeled in Fig. 9.42). Thus the surface area of a right circular cone is

$$A = \pi r^2 + \pi rs.$$

We conclude our discussion of surface area by stating that the surface area of a sphere, with radius of measure r, is

$$A = 4\pi r^2.$$

A derivation of this formula requires a knowledge of calculus. As a matter of interest, the reader should note that the surface area of the sphere is four times the area of the circular region formed by passing a plane through the center of the sphere.

Another measure associated with a simple closed surface is a measure of the solid bounded by the surface and is called the *volume* of the solid. Any number of solids could be used as a unit of volume measure, but it is convenient to choose the solid bounded by a right rectangular prism with all edges having unit length. Any right rectangular prism with all edges congruent is called a *cube*. Thus the unit of volume measure is the solid bounded by a cube with edges of unit length and is called the *unit cube*. Consider the solid bounded by the right rectangular prism in Fig. 9.43 with dimensions as shown. To find the volume of this solid, we must determine how many units cubes can be fitted into it. Figure 9.43 demonstrates that 2 unit cubes can be placed on one edge, 3 unit cubes on a second, and 4 on the third edge. Thus, there are two layers, each having 12 unit cubes fitted into the solid, and its volume is 24 unit cubes. To generalize, the volume of a solid bounded by a right rectangular prism is the number of unit cubes that can be placed on one edge, called the *length*, times the number of unit cubes that can be placed along a

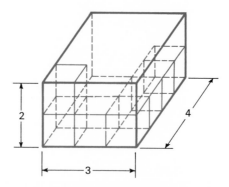

Figure 9.43

second edge, called the *width*, times the number of unit cubes that can be placed along the third edge, called the *height*. If the measure of the edges of the solid are integers, it is easy to see that the formula $V = lwh$, where l, w, and h refer to the measures of the length, width, and height of the solid, gives the number of unit cubes which can be fitted into the solid. This formula holds if l, w, and h are any positive real numbers. In Fig. 9.43 the length of the solid is 4, the width is 3, and the height is 2.

Note that the formula $V = lwh$ can be stated as $V = Bh$, where B is the area of the base of the solid and h the height. This formula can be used to find the volume of any solid bounded by a right prism. That is, the volume of the solid is given by $V = Bh$, where B is the area of the base of the right prism bounding the solid and h the height. To illustrate the use of this formula, consider the solid bounded by the right triangular prism in Fig. 9.44. The base is a triangle with area of $\frac{1}{2}(4)(3) = 6$ square units, and the height of the prism is 8 units. Therefore the volume of the solid is 48 cubic units.

8

3

4

Figure 9.44

One can show that the volume of the solid bounded by a pyramid is given by $V = \frac{1}{3}Bh$, where B is the area of the base and h the height of the pyramid. Using this result, we can show that the volume of the solid bounded by a cone is

$$V = \frac{1}{3}\pi r^2 h.$$

GEOMETRY

The volume of a solid bounded by a right circular cylinder is given by the formula

$$V = \pi r^2 h.$$

Further, the volume of the solid bounded by a sphere can be shown to be

$$V = \tfrac{4}{3}\pi r^3.$$

Problems

1 Find the surface area of the given right rectangular prism. The dimensions are given in meters. Express your answer in square meters; in square centimeters.

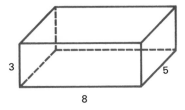

2 Find the volume of the solid bounded by the prism in Problem 1. Express your answer in cubic meters; in cubic centimeters.

3 Find the surface area of the given right circular cylinder. The dimensions are given in inches. Express your answer in square inches; in square feet.

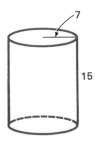

4 Find the volume of the solid bounded by the cylinder in Problem 3. Express your answer in cubic inches; in cubic feet.

5 Find the surface area of a sphere of radius 14 centimeters. Find the volume of the solid determined by this sphere.

6 A rose garden is rectangular in shape and has dimensions of 8 feet by 15 feet. A 3-foot walk is to be built around the garden. If the walk is 4 inches thick, how many cubic feet of concrete will be required to build it?

7 How many square inches of metal are required to make a cylindrical tin can 10 inches tall and 7 inches in diameter? Disregard waste material.

8 A silo is built in the shape of a right circular cylinder with a cone on top, as shown below. All dimensions are given in feet. Find the volume of the silo.

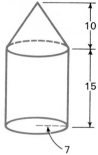

9 A cylindrical can has diameter equal to its height. A spherical ball just fits into the can. Show that the surface area of the ball is equal to the lateral surface area of the can.

Chapter 10

PROBABILITY
AND STATISTICS

10.1 COUNTING PROBLEMS

The solution to many problems depends on a listing of all possible ways a particular event can happen. The simple process of counting is often the most efficient method to use in obtaining such a listing. To illustrate, let us consider the set

$$A = \{\text{Matt, David, John, Amanda, Marie}\},$$

and determine the number of ways a committee, consisting of one boy and one girl, can be chosen from the set A. One way of enumerating all the possibilities is by use of a *tree diagram*, such as the one drawn in Fig. 10.1.

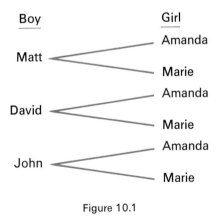

Figure 10.1

From this diagram one can see that for each way of choosing a boy for the committee, there are two ways of choosing a girl. Since a boy can be chosen in three different ways, six different committees can be formed. These are

Matt – Amanda,   Matt – Marie,
David – Amanda,   David – Marie,
John – Amanda,   John – Marie.

In forming the committee it makes no difference whether we choose a boy or a girl first. Hence the tree diagram in Fig. 10.2 could also be used to list all possible committees. From this diagram we see that for each way of choosing a girl, there are three ways of choosing a boy. A girl can be chosen in two different ways, so it again follows that the committee can be selected in six different ways. Using the diagram in Fig. 10.2, we would obtain the same six committees as before.

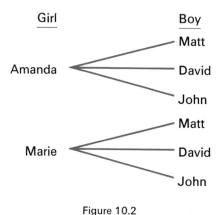

Figure 10.2

Example 1 A man can travel between City A and City B by car, bus, plane, or boat. In how many ways can he travel from City A to City B and return if he desires to use a different means of transportation for each trip?

Solution To list all the possibilities we shall use the tree diagram in Fig. 10.3. The man can travel from City A to City B by four different means, and for each of these four means he can return to City A by three different means. Hence he can travel from City A to City B and return by 12 different means, using a different means of transportation for each trip.

In solving the two preceding problems we have used the *Fundamental Counting Principle* which states that if one event can happen in N_1 ways, and for each way this first event can happen, a second event can happen in N_2 ways, then the two events can happen in $N_1 \cdot N_2$ different ways. In general, the Fundamental Counting Principle states that if for each way the first two events can happen a third event can occur in N_3 ways, and so on for k events, N_k denoting the number of ways the kth event can happen for

From City A to City B	From City B to City A

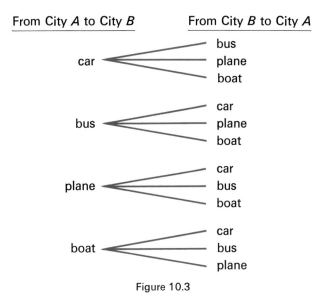

Figure 10.3

each combination of the first $k - 1$ events, then the k events can happen in

$$N_1 \cdot N_2 \cdot N_3 \cdot \ \cdots \ \cdot N_k$$

different ways. This principle will be used frequently in the sections that follow.

Example 2 As in Example 1, let us suppose that a man can travel from City A to City B by car, bus, plane, or boat. In how many ways can he travel from City A to City B and return if he can use the same means of transportation for each trip?

Solution The man can travel from City A to City B by four different means, and for each of these he can return to City A by four different means. Therefore, the Fundamental Counting Principle states that he can travel from City A to City B and return by $4 \cdot 4 = 16$ different means.

Example 3 Three coins are tossed. If we assume that each comes up heads or tails, in how many ways can the three coins fall?

Solution The first coin can fall in two different ways, heads or tails. For each way the first coin falls, the second coin can fall in two ways, and for each way the first two coins can fall, the third coin can fall heads or tails. Therefore the three coins can fall in $2 \cdot 2 \cdot 2 = 8$ different ways. The tree diagram in Fig. 10.4 can be useful in listing the possible outcomes. They are *HHH, HHT, HTH, HTT, THH, THT, TTH,* and *TTT,* where *HHH* means that all three coins fall heads, *HHT* means that the first and second coins fall heads and the third coin falls tails, etc.

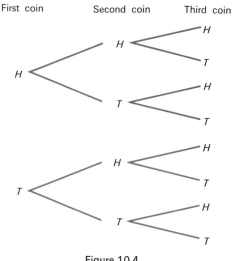

First coin   Second coin   Third coin

Figure 10.4

Problems

1 Let $B = \{$Mary, Jill, Larry, Bill, John, Tom$\}$. How many different committees consisting of a boy and a girl can be formed from this set? Draw a tree diagram and list all the possible committees.

2 How many different committees consisting of a boy and a girl can be selected from a group consisting of five boys and eight girls?

3 How many different committees consisting of a boy and two girls can be selected from a group consisting of five boys and eight girls?

4 How many three-digit numerals can be formed by using elements of the set $\{1, 2, 3, 4, 5\}$, with the restriction that no digit can be repeated?

5 Solve Problem 4 without the restriction that no digit can be repeated.

6 How many even three-digit numerals can be formed by using elements of the set $\{1, 2, 3, 4, 5\}$ if repetitions are allowed?

7 How many odd three-digit numerals can be formed by using elements of the set $\{1, 2, 3, 4, 5\}$ if repetitions are allowed?

8 A man has five coats, three shirts, and 13 ties. Assuming that any combination of these is acceptable, in how many ways can the man choose a coat, a shirt, and a tie?

9 Four coins are tossed. If we assume that no coin lands on its edge, in how many ways can the four coins fall? Draw a tree diagram and list these outcomes in the form *HHHH, HHHT*, etc.

10 A room has five doors. In how many ways can a person enter by one door and leave by a different door? Draw a tree diagram and list these

possibilities in the form D_1D_2, D_3D_5, etc. D_i represents the ith door for $i = 1, 2, 3, 4, 5$.

11 The inscription on a license plate in the state of Arkansas consists of three letters followed by a three-digit numeral. Duplications of letters and digits are permitted. For example, AAA 000 is a legitimate number. How many different plates can be made using this design?

12 In how many ways can five people sit in a row of five chairs?

13 In how many ways can eight people sit in a row of eight chairs?

10.2 PERMUTATIONS

A *permutation of a set of n elements* is any *ordered arrangement* of the set of elements. To illustrate, suppose $S = \{A, B, C\}$ and consider the problem of listing all the permutations of the set S. In any arrangement of the set S, a letter for the first position can be chosen in three ways from S. After a letter has been chosen for the first position, a letter for the second position can be chosen in two ways, and after letters have been chosen for the first two positions, we can choose a letter for the third position in only one way. Hence the Fundamental Counting Principle states that there are six permutations of the set S. A tree diagram is helpful in listing these permutations. The permutations are

$$\text{ABC, ACB, BAC, BCA, CAB, and CBA.}$$

The symbol $P(n, n)$ will denote the number of permutations of a set of n elements. For each arrangement of a set with n elements, there are n choices for the first position, $n - 1$ choices for the second position, $n - 2$ choices for the third position, and so forth, until we come to the last position where we have only one choice (see Table 10.1). Hence, by the Fundamental Counting Principle,

$$P(n, n) = n \cdot (n - 1) \cdot (n - 2) \cdot \,\cdots\, \cdot (2) \cdot (1).$$

TABLE 10.1

Position	1st	2nd	3rd	4th	$\cdots$	nth
Number of choices	n	$n - 1$	$n - 2$	$n - 3$	$\cdots$	1

This formula for $P(n, n)$ can be written in a more compact form if we use the factorial notation introduced in Section 4.16. The symbol $n!$ is read "*n factorial*" and is defined by the equation

$$n! = n \cdot (n - 1) \cdot (n - 2) \cdot \,\cdots\, \cdot (2) \cdot (1).$$

For example,

$$1! = 1,$$
$$2! = 2 \cdot 1 = 2,$$
$$3! = 3 \cdot 2 \cdot 1 = 6,$$
$$4! = 4 \cdot 3 \cdot 2 \cdot 1 = 24,$$
$$5! = 5 \cdot 4 \cdot 3 \cdot 2 \cdot 1 = 120.$$

Using this new notation we can write

$$P(n, n) = n!.$$

Example 1 The number of permutations of a set with four elements is $4! = 24$. The number of permutations of a set with five elements is $5! = 120$.

The reader may recall having seen the expression "permutation of a set of n elements" defined in Section 8.5. The reader who has studied Section 8.5 should be able to convince himself that, except for terminology, the definition of that section is equivalent to the definition of this section. Hence the word "permutation" is not being used to refer to two entirely different concepts.

If r elements are chosen from a set having n elements, then any permutation of these r elements is called a *permutation of the n elements taken r at a time*. $P(n, r)$ will represent the number of permutations of a set of n objects taken r at a time. For each arrangement of n elements taken r at a time, there are n choices for the first position, $n - 1$ choices for the second position, $n - 2$ choices for the third position, and so forth, until we come to the rth position where we have

$$n - (r - 1) = n - r + 1$$

choices (see Table 10.2). Hence, by the Fundamental Counting Principle, we have

$$P(n, r) = n \cdot (n - 1) \cdot (n - 2) \cdot \cdots \cdot (n - r + 1).$$

However,

$$P(n, r) = n \cdot (n - 1) \cdot (n - 2) \cdot \cdots \cdot (n - r + 1)$$
$$= \frac{n \cdot (n - 1) \cdot (n - 2) \cdot \cdots \cdot (n - r + 1)}{1}$$
$$\cdot \frac{(n - r) \cdot (n - r - 1) \cdot \cdots \cdot (2) \cdot (1)}{(n - r) \cdot (n - r - 1) \cdot \cdots \cdot (2) \cdot (1)}$$
$$= \frac{n!}{(n - r)!}.$$

TABLE 10.2

Position	1st	2nd	3rd	4th	$\cdots$	rth
Number of choices	n	$n-1$	$n-2$	$n-3$	$\cdots$	$n-r+1$

Therefore, using factorial notation, we have

$$P(n, r) = \frac{n!}{(n-r)!}.$$

If we choose $r = n$ in this formula, we would like the result to be the same as $P(n, n)$, which has the value $n!$. If we define $0! = 1$, then we have

$$P(n, n) = \frac{n!}{(n-n)!} = \frac{n!}{0!} = \frac{n!}{1} = n!.$$

This agrees with the previous formula for $P(n, n)$.

Example 1 of the previous section could have been solved by finding the number of permutations of four things taken two at a time:

$$P(4, 2) = \frac{4!}{(4-2)!} = \frac{4!}{2!} = 4 \cdot 3 = 12,$$

and this agrees with the result we obtained by use of a tree diagram. We will now consider a sequence of examples to further illustrate the use of permutations.

Example 2 Find $P(11, 4)$.

Solution

$$
\begin{aligned}
P(11, 4) &= \frac{11!}{(11-4)!} \\
&= \frac{11!}{7!} \\
&= \frac{11 \cdot 10 \cdot 9 \cdot 8 \cdot (7!)}{7!} \\
&= 11 \cdot 10 \cdot 9 \cdot 8 \\
&= 7920.
\end{aligned}
$$

Example 3 How many two-digit numerals can be formed by using digits of the set $\{1, 2, 3, 4, 5, 6\}$ if each digit can be used at most once?

Solution We seek the number of permutations of six elements taken two at a time:

$$P(6, 2) = \frac{6!}{(6-2)!} = \frac{6!}{4!} = 6 \cdot 5 = 30.$$

Therefore 30 two-digit numerals can be formed by using digits of the set {1, 2, 3, 4, 5, 6} if each digit is used at most once. A tree diagram could be used to list these numerals.

Example 4 Five people enter a room containing nine chairs. In how many different ways can these five people be seated?

Solution We want to know the number of ways in which nine chairs can be occupied five at a time. Hence the number of different seating arrangements is the number of permutations of nine objects taken five at a time:

$$\begin{aligned} P(9, 5) &= \frac{9!}{(9-5)!} \\ &= \frac{9!}{4!} \\ &= 9 \cdot 8 \cdot 7 \cdot 6 \cdot 5 \\ &= 15{,}120. \end{aligned}$$

Therefore the five people can seat themselves in 15,120 different ways.

Although the number of permutations of the letters of the word "number" is clearly 6!, the number of permutations of the six letters of the word "freeze" will be fewer than 6!, because the letter "e" appears three times in the word. Consider the following example.

Example 5 Find the number of permutations of the six letters of the word "freeze."

Solution Three letters of the word "freeze" are alike and three are different. We can obtain all the permutations of the letters of the word "freeze" by distributing the letters f, r, and z in the six positions in all possible ways and then by filling in the vacant positions with the three e's. This is equivalent to finding $P(6, 3)$, the number of permutations of six things taken three at a time. Since $P(6, 3) = 120$, the six letters of the word "freeze" can be arranged in 120 different ways.

Using the method of Example 5, we can obtain a more general result. If a set S consists of n elements, P_1 of one kind, P_2 of another kind, P_3 of a third kind, . . . , P_r of an rth kind, then it can be shown that the number of permutations of the set S is given by

$$\frac{n!}{P_1! \cdot P_2! \cdot P_3! \cdot \cdots \cdot P_r!}.$$

Example 6   Find the number of permutations of the nine letters of the word "Tennessee."

Solution   In the word "Tennessee", there are four e's, two n's, and two s's. Therefore, the number of permutations is

$$\frac{9!}{4!\,2!\,2!} = 3780.$$

Problems

1   Evaluate each of the following numbers.

    a) 6!   b) 7!   c) 8!

    d) 9!   e) 10!

In each of the Problems 2 through 6, state the meaning of the given symbol and then find its value.

2   $P(6, 2)$

3   $P(10, 5)$

4   $P(13, 3)$

5   $P(8, 1)$

6   $P(15, 6)$

7   How many permutations of six letters each can be formed from the letters of the word "number"?

8   How many permutations of eight letters each can be formed from the letters of the word "problems"?

9   How many permutations of three letters each can be formed from the letters of the word "number"? from "Republican"?

10   How many four-digit numerals can be formed by using digits of the set $\{1, 2, 3, 4, 5, 6, 7\}$ if each digit can be used at most once?

11   In how many different ways can four students be seated in a row consisting of eleven chairs?

12   How many batting orders are possible after a baseball coach selects his nine players?

13   In how many ways can a group consisting of four boys and three girls be seated on a bench if a boy must be seated at each end of the bench?

14   In how many ways can five mathematics books and three history books be arranged on a shelf so that all the books on a subject are together?

15 Find the number of permutations of the eight letters in the word "Arkansas."

16 Find the number of permutations of the ten letters of the word "googol-plex."

17 Find the number of permutations of the eleven letters of the word "Mississippi."

18 Prove that $P(n, n - 1) = P(n, n)$.

19 Prove the $(P(n, n - r)) \cdot (P(r, r - 1)) = P(n, n)$.

10.3 COMBINATIONS

Let S denote a set with n elements. A *combination of the n elements of S taken r at a time* is any subset of S which contains r elements. In permutations, the order of the elements is important. However, in combinations, the order of the elements is unimportant. For example, the six permutations of the set $S = \{A, B, C\}$ of three elements taken two at a time are AB, AC, BA, BC, CA, and CB, whereas $\{A, B\}$, $\{A, C\}$, and $\{B, C\}$ are the only combinations of the three elements of S taken two at a time.

Example 1 Let $S = \{A, B, C, D\}$. Find all combinations of the elements of S taken three at a time.

Solution We are seeking the subsets of S which contain three elements. They are $\{A, B, C\}$, $\{A, B, D\}$, $\{A, C, D\}$, and $\{B, C, D\}$.

The number of combinations of n elements taken r at a time will be denoted by the symbol $C(n, r)$. One can easily see that $C(n, n) = 1$, since a set S with n elements has only one subset with n elements. For every combination of n elements taken r at a time, there will be $r!$ permutations of these r elements. Hence we have the relationship

$$P(n, r) = r! \, C(n, r).$$

If this equation is solved for $C(n, r)$, then we have

$$C(n, r) = \frac{P(n, r)}{r!}.$$

However, recalling that $P(n, r) = n!/(n - r)!$, making this substitution in the above equation, and simplifying, we have

$$C(n, r) = \frac{n!}{r! \, (n - r)!}.$$

Example 2   Find $C(12, 3)$.

Solution

$$C(12, 3) = \frac{12!}{3!(12 - 3)!}$$

$$= \frac{12!}{3! \, 9!}$$

$$= \frac{12 \cdot 11 \cdot 10 \cdot 9!}{3 \cdot 2 \cdot 1 \cdot 9!}$$

$$= \frac{12 \cdot 11 \cdot 10}{3 \cdot 2 \cdot 1}$$

$$= 2 \cdot 11 \cdot 10$$

$$= 220.$$

Example 3   The PTA of Sally Cone Elementary School has 38 members. How many committees of five people can be formed from this group?

Solution   The number of committees is equal to the number of combinations of 38 objects taken five at a time:

$$C(38, 5) = \frac{38!}{5! \, (38 - 5)!}$$

$$= \frac{38!}{5! \, 33!}$$

$$= \frac{38 \cdot 37 \cdot 36 \cdot 35 \cdot 34}{5 \cdot 4 \cdot 3 \cdot 2 \cdot 1}$$

$$= 501,942.$$

Therefore 501,942 committees consisting of five members each can be formed from the membership of the Sally Cone PTA.

Example 4   A sack contains six red balls and five green balls. In how many ways can five balls be withdrawn if three of the five balls are red and the remaining two are green?

Solution   Three red balls can be chosen from six red balls in $C(6, 3) = 20$ different ways. After three red balls are chosen from the sack, two green balls can be chosen in $C(5, 2) = 10$ different ways.   Using the Fundamental Counting Principle, we conclude that three red balls and two green balls can be drawn from the sack in $10 \cdot 20 = 200$ different ways.

Example 5   How many groups of two or more persons can be chosen from five people?

Solution A group consisting of two people can be chosen from five people in $C(5, 2) = 10$ different ways, a group of three people can be chosen in $C(5, 3) = 10$ ways, a group of four people can be chosen in $C(5, 4) = 5$ ways, and a group consisting of five people can be chosen in $C(5, 5) = 1$ way. Therefore a group consisting of two or more persons can be chosen from a group of five people in

$$C(5, 2) + C(5, 3) + C(5, 4) + C(5, 5) = 10 + 10 + 5 + 1 = 26$$

different ways.

Problems

In each of Problems 1 through 6, state the meaning of the given symbol and then find its value.

1 $C(5, 3)$ 2 $C(11, 4)$

3 $C(10, 8)$ 4 $C(43, 4)$

5 $C(8, 8)$ 6 $C(5, 0)$

7 In how many ways can one choose five books to read from a collection of 18 books?

8 In how many ways can a group of 12 ladies be divided into subgroups of four each to play bridge?

9 In how many ways can a set of 13 cards be drawn from a set of 52 playing cards?

10 In how many ways can a person choose three coins from a collection consisting of a penny, a nickel, a dime, and a quarter?

11 In how many ways can one choose a committee consisting of two men and three women from a group containing eight men and eleven women?

12 A group consisting of seven people is to travel to a convention in two cars. If three people ride in one car and four people ride in the other, in how many ways can the group be divided for the trip?

13 A sack contains seven red marbles, five white marbles, and 12 blue marbles. In how many ways can nine marbles be drawn from the sack if two of the marbles are red, three are white, and four are blue?

14 How many groups of two or more people can be chosen from a group of eight people?

15 How many different sums of money can be formed using any combination (one or more) of the following six coins: a penny, a nickel, a dime, a quarter, a half-dollar, and a dollar?

16 Prove that $C(n, r) = C(n, n - r)$.

17 Prove that $C(k, i) + C(k, i - 1) = C(k + 1, i)$ if $1 \leq i \leq k$.

10.4 INTRODUCTION TO PROBABILITY

Probability deals with the likelihood that a particular event will occur. The founding of mathematical probability is attributed to the mathematicians Pierre de Fermat (1601–1665) and Blaise Pascal (1623–1662). In 1654 a gaming problem was proposed to Pascal by a gambler, Chevalier de Méré. Pascal communicated the problem to Fermat, and in solving the problem, the two men established the fundamental principles of probability. Since its inception, the study of probability has attracted the attention of some of history's great mathematicians. James Bernoulli (1654–1705), A. de Moivre (1667–1754), and P. S. Laplace (1749–1827) are among those who made significant contributions to this field. Laplace's *Théorie Analytique des Probabilités*, 1812, is considered by many to be the greatest contribution by one person to the theory of probability.

In recent years, probability and the related field of statistics have been used extensively in such diverse areas as biology, economics, genetics, physics, and sociology. A knowledge of probability is essential to the study of quantum theory, a theory which revolutionized the field of physics in the 1920's.

10.5 SAMPLE SPACES AND EVENTS

Let us suppose that a coin is tossed. Assuming that it does not land on its edge, we know that it must fall either heads or tails. If we consider the tossing of a coin to be an *experiment*, then the outcome of the experiment must be an element of the set $\{H, T\}$, H denoting heads and T denoting tails. The set $\{H, T\}$ is called a *sample space* for the experiment, and the elements of the set are *sample points*. If three coins are tossed and we are interested in the way each coin falls, we can use the tree-diagram in Fig. 10.4 to obtain all the possible outcomes. A sample space for this experiment is the set

$$\{HHH, HHT, HTH, HTT, THH, THT, TTH, TTT\}.$$

The reader is reminded that *HHH* denotes the outcome in which all three coins fall heads, *HHT* denotes the outcome in which the first two coins fall heads and the third coin falls tails, etc. The sample space for an experiment often depends on a person's point of view. For example, if in tossing three coins one is interested only in recording the number of heads and the number of tails that appear, then the elements of the sample space could be ordered pairs of numbers, the first number representing the number of heads and the second number representing the number of tails. If this attitude is taken, then the set

$$\{(3, 0), (2, 1), (1, 2), (0, 3)\}$$

is a sample space for the experiment of tossing three coins. In general, we state the following definition.

Definition 10.1 A *sample space* S for an experiment is any set having the property that any performance of the experiment results in *one and only one* element of S. The elements of a sample space are called *sample points*.

Example 1 What is a sample space for tossing a pair of dice?

Solution Usually in tossing a pair of dice we do not distinguish one die from the other; we are interested only in the total number of dots that appear. If this attitude is taken, the sample space for tossing a pair of dice is the set

$$\{2, 3, 4, 5, 6, 7, 8, 9, 10, 11, 12\}.$$

If it is possible to distinguish between the dice (perhaps one is red and the other is blue), a person might wish to record the number of dots that appear on each die of the pair. This information could be recorded by listing ordered pairs such as (5, 2) or (3, 1), the first number being the number of dots on the red die and the second number being the number of dots on the blue die. The sample space for this experiment is then a collection of ordered pairs, namely, the set of ordered pairs pictured in Fig. 10.5.

(1, 1)	(1, 2)	(1, 3)	(1, 4)	(1, 5)	(1, 6)
(2, 1)	(2, 2)	(2, 3)	(2, 4)	(2, 5)	(2, 6)
(3, 1)	(3, 2)	(3, 3)	(3, 4)	(3, 5)	(3, 6)
(4, 1)	(4, 2)	(4, 3)	(4, 4)	(4, 5)	(4, 6)
(5, 1)	(5, 2)	(5, 3)	(5, 4)	(5, 5)	(5, 6)
(6, 1)	(6, 2)	(6, 3)	(6, 4)	(6, 5)	(6, 6)

Figure 10.5

Example 2 Let us suppose that in tossing a pair of dice, a person is interested only in the total number of dots that appear on the two dice. The set

$$S_1 = \{2, 3, 4, 5, 6, 7, 8, 9, 10, 11, 12, 100\}$$

is an acceptable sample space for the experiment even though the outcome 100 is impossible (we will later define its probability to be zero). However, the set

$$S_2 = \{2, 3, 4, 5, 6, 7, 8, 9, 10, 11, 12, \text{an odd number}\}$$

is not a sample space for the experiment because a performance of the experiment could result in more than one element of S_2. For example, if 5 dots appear, the experiment results in two elements of S_2, namely, 5 and "an

PROBABILITY AND STATISTICS

odd number." The set

$$S_3 = \{2, 3, 4, 5, 6, 7, 8, 9, 10, 11\}$$

is also not a sample space for the experiment because the outcome 12 is not an element of S_3.

    A sample space for an experiment may be *finite* or it may be *infinite*. In this text we will consider only finite sample spaces. Infinite sample spaces are considered in more advanced discussions on probability.

    If S denotes a sample space for an experiment, then any subset E of the sample space is called an *event*. An event E is said to *occur* if the outcome of the experiment is any element of E. For example, if

$$S = \{HHH, HHT, HTH, HTT, THH, THT, TTH, TTT\}$$

is chosen as the sample space for the experiment of tossing three coins, then the sets

$$S_1 = \varnothing, \qquad S_2 = \{HHH\},$$
$$S_3 = \{HHH, HHT, HTH, THH\},$$

and

$$S_4 = \{HTT, THT, TTH\}$$

are four of the 256 possible events. The event S_4, that of getting exactly two tails, is said to occur if the outcome of the experiment is HTT, THT, or TTH. We note that the sample space for any experiment is a subset of itself and hence is an event.

    Since an event is a set, new events can be formed by using the operations on sets. For example, if A and B denote events, then

1) $A \cup B$ is the event that occurs if A occurs *or* B occurs (or both A and B occur);

2) $A \cap B$ is the event that occurs if A occurs *and* B occurs;

3) A', the complement of A, is the event that occurs if A does not occur.

If $A \cap B = \varnothing$, then the events A and B are said to be *mutually exclusive*. In other words, two events are mutually exclusive if they cannot occur simultaneously.

Example 3 Let us take the set $S = \{1, 2, 3, 4, 5, 6\}$ to be the sample space for tossing a single die. Let A be the event that an even number appears, B the event that an odd number appears, and C the event that a number greater than 3 appears. That is,

$$A = \{2, 4, 6\}, \qquad B = \{1, 3, 5\}, \qquad C = \{4, 5, 6\}.$$

Then

A ∪ B = {1, 2, 3, 4, 5, 6}, the sample space S;

B ∪ C = {1, 3, 4, 5, 6}, an event in which 2 does not occur;

B ∩ C = {5}, the event that 5 occurs;

C′ = {1, 2, 3}, the event that a number less than 4 occurs.

Since A ∩ B = ∅, the events A and B are mutually exclusive. That is, an even number and an odd number cannot occur simultaneously.

Problems

1 Consider the experiment of tossing two coins. Give two sample spaces for this experiment.

2 Three coins are tossed and the number of heads is recorded. Which of the following sets are sample spaces for this experiment? Why do the others fail to qualify as sample spaces?

a) {1, 2, 3}   b) {0, 1, 2, 3}

c) {0, 1, 2, 3, 4, 5}   d) {0, 2, odd}

e) {0, 1, odd}   f) {less than 2, 1 or more}

3 A die is rolled once. Which of the following sets are sample spaces for this experiment? Why do the others fail to qualify as sample spaces?

a) {odd, even}   b) {2, 4, 5}   c) {1, 2, 3, odd}

d) {less than 5, greater than or equal to 5}

e) {1, 2, 3, 4, 5, 6, 7, 8, 9, 10}   f) {1, 3, 5, 7, 8, even}

4 A card is drawn at random from an ordinary deck of playing cards. Give three possible sample spaces for this experiment.

5 A coin and a die are tossed. Construct a sample space S for this experiment. If E is the event that the coin falls tails, express the event E as a subset of S.

6 Take the collection of ordered pairs in Fig. 10.5 as the sample space S for tossing a pair of dice. If E_1 is the event that a 7 is rolled, express the event E_1 as a subset of S. Do the same thing for E_2 if E_2 is the event that either a 7 or an 11 is rolled.

7 Let S = {R, B, Y, G} be a sample space for a certain experiment. List all the possible events of this sample space.

8 Let S = {1, 2, 3, 4, 5, 6} be the sample space for tossing a single die. E_1 is the event of obtaining a number greater than 3, E_2 is the event of obtaining a number less than or equal to 5, and E_3 is the event of obtaining a prime number. Express the events E_1, E_2, and E_3 as subsets of the sample space S and then find each of the following events.

a) $E_1 \cup E_2$ b) $E_1 \cap E_2$ c) E_1'

d) $E_1 \cap E_3$ e) $E_1 \cup E_3$ f) $E_2 \cap E_3'$

9 Let $S = \{1, 2, 3, 4, 5, 6\}$ be the sample space for tossing a single die and let $E = \{2, 3, 5, 6\}$. Find an event $E_1 \neq \emptyset$ such that E and E_1 are mutually exclusive.

10 Let three coins be tossed and the number of heads be observed. The set $S = \{0, 1, 2, 3\}$ is the sample space for this experiment. Let E_1 be the event of obtaining no heads, E_2 be the event of obtaining at least 2 heads, and E_3 be the event of obtaining either no heads or 3 heads. Express the events E_1, E_2, and E_3 as subsets of the sample space S and then find each of the following events.

a) $E_1 \cup E_2$ b) $E_2 \cap E_3$ c) E_2'

d) $E_3 \cap E_1$ e) $E_1' \cup E_3$ f) $(E_2 \cup E_3)'$

11 Let S be a sample space and let E denote an event of S. What conditions must be imposed on E to ensure that the events E and $\emptyset$ are mutually exclusive?

10.6 PROBABILITY MEASURES

Let $S = \{e_1, e_2, \ldots, e_n\}$ be a finite sample space with the n sample points $e_1, e_2, \ldots, e_n$. We now turn our attention to the problem of introducing a numerical measure of the likelihood that an element of S will occur.

Definition 10.2 A *probability measure* on a sample space

$$S = \{e_1, e_2, \ldots, e_n\}$$

is any function, denoted Pr, from the set S into the set of real numbers which has the following properties:

1) $\Pr(e_i) \geq 0$ for $i = 1, 2, 3, \ldots, n$,
2) $\Pr(e_1) + \Pr(e_2) + \cdots + \Pr(e_n) = 1$.

$\Pr(e_i)$ is called the *probability* that e_i will occur.

The range of a probability measure Pr on a sample space S is a subset of the set $\{x \mid 0 \leq x \leq 1\}$. It is customary to agree that $\Pr(e_i) = 0$ if and only if the outcome e_i is impossible. For example, if a marble is drawn from a sack of red marbles, the probability that a white marble is drawn is 0. We shall further agree that $\Pr(e_i) = 1$ if and only if the outcome e_i is certain to happen. Hence, if a marble is drawn from a sack of red marbles, then the probability that a red marble is drawn is 1.

We will now illustrate the meaning of a probability measure on a sample space by considering some examples. These examples were carefully chosen, and finding a probability measure will pose no great problem. However, finding a probability measure in a real life situation is frequently a difficult task, and it is often necessary to conduct an extensive study to obtain an accurate probability measure on a sample space.

Example 1 In tossing a true coin, one is interested in whether the coin falls heads or tails. Define a probability measure for the sample space related to this experiment.

Solution The sample space for this experiment is the set $S = \{H, T\}$. Since the coin is a true coin, these outcomes are equally likely to occur. The sum of the probabilities must equal 1, so we define $\Pr(H) = \frac{1}{2}$ and $\Pr(T) = \frac{1}{2}$. The function Pr is a probability measure on the set $S = \{H, T\}$.

Example 2 A marble is drawn at random from a sack containing two red marbles and one blue marble. If no distinction is made between the two red marbles, define a probability measure on the sample space related to this experiment.

Solution There are two possible outcomes to this experiment, a red marble (R) is drawn or a blue marble (B) is drawn. Hence the sample space is the set $S = \{R, B\}$. The probability of drawing a red marble should be twice that of drawing a blue marble. If x denotes the probability of drawing a blue marble, then $2x$ is the probability of drawing a red marble. Since the sum of the probabilities must equal 1, we have $x + 2x = 1$. Solving this equation for x, we get $x = \frac{1}{3}$. We now define $\Pr(R) = \frac{2}{3}$ and $\Pr(B) = \frac{1}{3}$ to obtain a probability measure on the sample space $S = \{R, B\}$.

Example 3 A marble is drawn at random from a sack containing two red marbles, three white marbles, and one blue marble. If $S = \{R, W, B, Y\}$ with R, W, B denoting the obvious outcomes and Y denoting the outcome in which a yellow marble is drawn, define a probability measure Pr on S.

Solution Since Y is an impossible event, we will define $\Pr(Y) = 0$. The event R is twice as likely to occur as B, and the event W is three times as likely to occur as B. Hence, if x denotes the probability of B, then $\Pr(R) = 2x$ and $\Pr(W) = 3x$. The sum of the probabilities of the events R, W, B, and Y must equal 1. This leads to the equation

$$2x + 3x + x + 0 = 1,$$

for which the solution is $x = \frac{1}{6}$. If we define $\Pr(R) = \frac{2}{6} = \frac{1}{3}$, $\Pr(W) = \frac{3}{6} = \frac{1}{2}$, $\Pr(B) = \frac{1}{6}$, and $\Pr(Y) = 0$, Pr is a probability measure on the sample space $S = \{R, W, B, Y\}$.

PROBABILITY AND STATISTICS

Let $S = \{e_1, e_2, \ldots, e_n\}$ be a sample space for a given experiment and let Pr denote a probability measure on S. Further, let E denote an event of S. Recalling that an event E is simply a subset of the sample space S, $E = \varnothing$ or

$$E = \{f_1, f_2, \ldots, f_k\}, \qquad 1 \leq k \leq n,$$

where $f_1, f_2, \ldots, f_k$ are elements of S. We will prove later in this section that $\Pr(\varnothing)$ is always 0. If $E \neq \varnothing$, then the *probability of the event E* is defined by

$$\Pr(E) = \Pr(f_1) + \Pr(f_2) + \cdots + \Pr(f_k).$$

This definition will be used in the following examples.

Example 4 A marble is drawn at random from a sack which contains a red marble (R), a white marble (W), and a blue marble (B). What is the probability that the marble is either red or white?

Solution The sample space for the experiment is the set $S = \{R, W, B\}$ and the event whose probability is desired is the subset $E = \{R, W\}$. Since the outcomes R, W, and B are equally likely to occur, we define

$$\Pr(R) = \Pr(W) = \Pr(B) = \tfrac{1}{3}.$$

Hence

$$\Pr(E) = \Pr(R) + \Pr(W) = \tfrac{1}{3} + \tfrac{1}{3} = \tfrac{2}{3}.$$

Example 5 In Example 3, what is the probability that a red, white, or yellow marble is drawn?

Solution The event whose probability is desired is the event $E = \{R, W, Y\}$. Hence

$$\Pr(E) = \Pr(R) + \Pr(W) + \Pr(Y) = \tfrac{1}{3} + \tfrac{1}{2} + 0 = \tfrac{5}{6}.$$

We will now discuss a few of the basic properties of a probability measure. Let Pr be a probability measure on a sample space

$$S = \{e_1, e_2, \ldots, e_n\}.$$

Considered as an event, the probability of the sample space S is given by

$$\Pr(S) = \Pr(e_1) + \Pr(e_2) + \cdots + \Pr(e_n).$$

Since Pr is a probability measure on S,

$$\Pr(e_1) + \Pr(e_2) + \cdots + \Pr(e_n) = 1.$$

Hence $\Pr(S) = 1$, and we now state this result as a theorem.

Theorem 10.1 If Pr is a probability measure on a sample space S, then $Pr(S) = 1$.

The reader can easily prove the following theorem.

Theorem 10.2 Let Pr denote a probability measure on a sample space S. If E is an event of S, then $0 \leq Pr(E) \leq 1$.

Let A and B be mutually exclusive events of a sample space

$$S = \{e_1, e_2, \ldots, e_n\}.$$

Then we have

$$A = \{f_1, f_2, \ldots, f_r\} \quad \text{and} \quad B = \{g_1, g_2, \ldots, g_s\},$$

where f_i $(1 \leq i \leq r)$ and g_i $(1 \leq i \leq s)$ are all elements of S. Further, $A \cap B = \varnothing$. Thus,

$$A \cup B = \{f_1, f_2, \ldots, f_r, g_1, g_2, \ldots, g_s\},$$

and

$$
\begin{aligned}
Pr(A \cup B) &= Pr(f_1) + \cdots + Pr(f_r) + Pr(g_1) + \cdots + Pr(g_s) \\
&= (Pr(f_1) + \cdots + Pr(f_r)) + (Pr(g_1) + \cdots + Pr(g_s)) \\
&= Pr(A) + Pr(B).
\end{aligned}
$$

This result is stated in the following theorem.

Theorem 10.3 Let S be a sample space with probability measure Pr. If A and B are mutually exclusive events of S, then

$$Pr(A \cup B) = Pr(A) + Pr(B).$$

Theorem 10.3 can be extended by mathematical induction to cover any number of pairwise mutually exclusive events.

If Pr is a probability measure on a sample space S, then we can use Theorem 10.3 to prove that $Pr(\varnothing) = 0$. If A is any event of S, then we can write $A = A \cup \varnothing$. A and $\varnothing$ are mutually exclusive, so by Theorem 10.3 we have

$$Pr(A) = Pr(A) + Pr(\varnothing).$$

Solving this equation for $Pr(\varnothing)$, we find $Pr(\varnothing) = 0$.

By using Theorem 10.3, one can also prove that $Pr(A') = 1 - Pr(A)$. The proof will be left as an exercise for the reader.

Problems

1 Let $S = \{A, B, C, D\}$ and define a probability measure Pr on S by taking $Pr(A) = \frac{1}{3}$, $Pr(B) = \frac{1}{4}$, $Pr(C) = \frac{1}{4}$, and $Pr(D) = \frac{1}{6}$. What is the probability of the event $E_1 = \{A, D\}$? of $E_2 = \{B, C, D\}$?

2 A coin is drawn at random from a sack that contains a penny, a nickel, and a dime. Define the appropriate probability measure on the sample space $S = \{P, N, D\}$. What is the probability of the event $E = \{P, D\}$?

3 A marble is drawn at random from a sack containing three red marbles and one blue marble. Define the appropriate probability measure on the sample space $S = \{R, B\}$.

4 A single die is tossed. Assuming the die is fair, define the appropriate probability measure on the sample space $S = \{1, 2, 3, 4, 5, 6\}$. What is the probability that the outcome is an odd number? What is the probability that the outcome is an odd number less than 5?

5 A single die is tossed. Assuming the die is fair, define the appropriate probability measure on the sample space $S = \{1, 2, 3, 4, 5, 6, 7, 8\}$.

6 A single die is tossed. Assuming the die is fair, define the appropriate probability measure on the sample space $S = \{1, 2 \text{ or } 3, 4 \text{ or more}\}$. What is the probability of the event $E = \{1, 4 \text{ or more}\}$? What is the probability of the event $E_2 = \{2 \text{ or } 3, 4 \text{ or more}\}$?

7 A coin is drawn at random from a purse containing three pennies, one nickel, and two quarters. Define the appropriate probability measure on the sample space $S = \{P, N, Q\}$. What is the probability of the event $E_1 = \{P, Q\}$? of the event $E_2 = \{N, Q\}$?

8 A marble is drawn at random from a sack containing three red marbles, three white marbles, and 12 blue marbles. Define the appropriate probability measure on the sample space $S = \{R, W, B\}$. What is the probability of drawing either a red marble or a blue marble?

9 A card is drawn at random from an ordinary deck of 52 playing cards. Define an appropriate probability measure and find the probability that the card is black. What is the probability that the card is a heart? What is the probability that the card is a heart, a spade, or a diamond?

10 Let Pr be a probability measure defined on a sample space S and let E be an event of S. Prove that $0 \leq \Pr(E) \leq 1$.

11 Let Pr be a probability measure defined on a sample space S and let A denote an event of S. Prove that $\Pr(A') = 1 - \Pr(A)$.

10.7 THE EQUIPROBABLE MEASURE

If the outcomes of a sample space S are equally likely to occur and $n(S)$ denotes the number of outcomes in S, then each outcome should be assigned the probability $1/n(S)$. This probability measure is called the *equiprobable measure on S*. For example, if a true coin is tossed, the outcomes of the sample space $\{H, T\}$ are both equally likely to occur, and the equiprobable measure is appropriate for the space. It is the measure Pr for which $\Pr(H) = \Pr(T) = \frac{1}{2}$. If a fair die is rolled, the outcomes 1, 2, 3, 4, 5, and 6 are all equally likely to occur, and hence the equiprobable measure is appropriate for the sample space $\{1, 2, 3, 4, 5, 6\}$. Using the equiprobable measure, each element of the space has probability $\frac{1}{6}$.

Let S be a sample space for which the equiprobable measure is the appropriate measure, and let E denote an event of S. Since each element of E has probability $1/n(S)$ and $n(E)$ denotes the number of elements in E, we have

$$\Pr(E) = \underbrace{\frac{1}{n(S)} + \frac{1}{n(S)} + \cdots + \frac{1}{n(S)}}_{n(E) \text{ times}} = \frac{n(E)}{n(S)}.$$

We now state this result as a theorem, and illustrate it with some examples.

Theorem 10.4 Let S denote a sample space for which the equiprobable measure is the appropriate measure. If E is any event of S, then

$$\Pr(E) = \frac{n(E)}{n(S)},$$

where $n(E)$ and $n(S)$ denote the number of elements in E and S, respectively.

Example 1   If three true coins are tossed, what is the probability of getting exactly two heads?

Solution   The set

$$S = \{HHH, HHT, HTH, HTT, THH, THT, TTH, TTT\}$$

is a sample space for this experiment. All the outcomes of S are equally likely to occur, so the equiprobable measure is the appropriate measure. The event whose probability we seek is the event

$$E = \{HHT, HTH, THH\}.$$

Since E has three elements and S has eight elements, we conclude by Theorem 10.4 that $\Pr(E) = \frac{3}{8}$. That is, if three true coins are tossed, the probability of getting exactly two heads is $\frac{3}{8}$.

Example 2   In rolling a pair of fair dice, what is the probability that either a seven or an eleven is rolled?

Solution   A sample space for this experiment, having 36 elements, is pictured in Fig. 10.5. The outcomes of this sample space are equally likely to occur, so the equiprobable measure is the appropriate measure. The event of rolling either a 7 or an 11 is the event

$$E = \{(1, 6), (2, 5), (3, 4), (4, 3), (5, 2), (6, 1), (5, 6), (6, 5)\},$$

and it has eight elements. Therefore, by Theorem 10.4,

$$\Pr(E) = \tfrac{8}{36} = \tfrac{2}{9}.$$

That is, the probability of rolling either a 7 or an 11 with a pair of fair dice is $\tfrac{2}{9}$.

Example 3 Let a card be chosen at random from an ordinary deck of 52 playing cards. Let A denote the event of picking a heart and let B denote the event of picking a face card. Find

$$\Pr(A), \qquad \Pr(B), \qquad \text{and} \qquad \Pr(A \cap B).$$

Solution A sample space S is the set of 52 cards in the deck. Since all the cards of the deck are equally likely to be chosen, the equiprobable measure is the appropriate measure. There are 13 hearts and 12 face cards (i.e. jack, queen, or king) in a deck of cards. Hence A has 13 elements and B has 12 elements. By Theorem 10.4,

$$\Pr(A) = \tfrac{13}{52} = \tfrac{1}{4} \qquad \text{and} \qquad \Pr(B) = \tfrac{12}{52} = \tfrac{3}{13}.$$

The event $A \cap B$ is the event whose elements are heart face cards. Thus

$$A \cap B = \{\text{jack of hearts, queen of hearts, king of hearts}\}.$$

Since $A \cap B$ has three elements, $P(A \cap B) = \tfrac{3}{52}$.

Example 4 A sack contains six red marbles and nine blue marbles. Two marbles are chosen at random from the sack. What is the probability that both marbles are red?

Solution Let the sample space S for this experiment be the set of all pairs of marbles that can be chosen from the sack. Since a pair of marbles is chosen at random, one pair is just as likely to be chosen as another pair. Thus all the sample points of S are equally likely to occur, and the equiprobable measure is the appropriate measure. The event E is the set of all pairs of red marbles that can be chosen from the sack. The number of elements in S is the number of combinations of 15 things taken two at a time, and the number of elements in E is the number of combinations of six things taken two at a time. To be more explicit,

$$n(S) = C(15, 2) = \frac{15!}{13!\, 2!} = 105,$$

and

$$n(E) = C(6, 2) = \frac{6!}{4!\, 2!} = 15.$$

Therefore, by Theorem 10.4,

$$\Pr(E) = \tfrac{15}{105} = \tfrac{1}{7}.$$

Problems

1 A box contains five nickels, three dimes, and four quarters. If a coin is drawn at random from the box, what is the probability that it is a dime?

2 If three true coins are tossed, what is the probability that one will fall heads and two will fall tails? all three will fall tails?

3 What is the probability of rolling a five in a toss of a pair of fair dice?

4 What is the probability of rolling an even number in a toss of a pair of fair dice?

5 What is the probability of rolling either a three or an eight in a toss of a pair of fair dice?

6 A card is chosen at random from an ordinary deck of 52 playing cards. What is the probability that the card is a face card (i.e. jack, queen, or king)?

7 A sack contains eight red marbles, eleven blue marbles, and three white marbles. If a marble is chosen at random from the sack, what is the probability that it is a white marble? What is the probability that it is either red or blue?

8 Four fair coins are tossed. What is the probability that all four will land heads? that two coins will fall heads and two will fall tails?

9 Three fair coins are tossed. What is the probability of obtaining more heads than tails?

10 Two marbles are chosen at random from a sack that contains seven red marbles and eleven blue marbles. What is the probability that both marbles will be red? that both marbles are the same color?

11 Two marbles are chosen at random from a sack that contains five red marbles and twelve blue marbles. What is the probability that both marbles are the same color? that one is red and one is blue?

12 Two cards are chosen at random from an ordinary deck of 52 cards. What is the probability that both are clubs? that one is a club and one is a heart?

13 Three apples are chosen from a box of 20 apples, six of which are green. What is the probability that none of the three is green? that exactly one is green? that at least one is green?

14 Four married couples are present at a party. If two people are chosen at random, what is the probability that they are married? that one is a female and the other is a male?

15 Three cards are chosen at random from an ordinary deck of 52 cards. What is the probability that all three are hearts? That one is a club, one is a heart, and one is a spade?

10.8 CONDITIONAL PROBABILITY

Let A and B denote two events with the same sample space. The probability that A occurs, given that B occurs, is called the *conditional probability of A, given B*, and is denoted by the symbol $\Pr(A \mid B)$. From the Venn diagram in Fig. 10.6, we see that in a sense $\Pr(A \mid B)$ measures the probability of A with respect to the reduced space B. The only way that A can occur, given that B has occurred, is for an outcome of $A \cap B$ to occur. Thus $\Pr(A \mid B)$ should be the ratio of the probability of $A \cap B$ to the probability of B. This leads us to state the following definition.

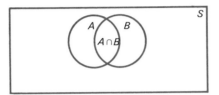

Figure 10.6

Definition 10.3 If A and B denote two events with the same sample space and $P(B) > 0$, then

$$\Pr(A \mid B) = \frac{\Pr(A \cap B)}{\Pr(B)} .$$

We will now illustrate the use of this definition with several examples.

Example 1 A sack contains three black marbles and two red marbles. A marble is chosen at random from the sack, and without replacing the first marble, we choose a second marble at random from the sack. Letting B denote the event in which the first marble chosen is black and R denote the event in which the second marble chosen is red, find $\Pr(R \mid B)$.

Solution We will use the symbols B_1, B_2, and B_3 to represent the black marbles and R_1 and R_2 to represent the two red marbles. The sample space for this experiment consists of 20 elements, each of which is placed in the appropriate region of the Venn diagram in Fig. 10.7. The symbols used to

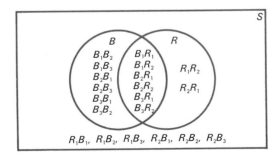

Figure 10.7

represent the outcomes of the sample space have the obvious meaning. For example, the symbol B_1R_1 means that a black marble is drawn first and a red marble is drawn second. All the outcomes of the sample space S are equally likely to occur, so it will be appropriate to use the equiprobable measure. To use Definition 10.3 to find $Pr(R \mid B)$, we must know $Pr(R \cap B)$ and $Pr(B)$. From Fig. 10.7 we see that $n(R \cap B) = 6$ and $n(B) = 12$. Since $n(S) = 20$, we have

$$Pr(R \cap B) = \tfrac{6}{20} = \tfrac{3}{10} \qquad \text{and} \qquad Pr(B) = \tfrac{12}{20} = \tfrac{3}{5},$$

and, by Definition 10.3, we have

$$Pr(R \mid B) = \frac{\tfrac{3}{10}}{\tfrac{3}{5}} = \tfrac{15}{30} = \tfrac{1}{2}.$$

Therefore, since we know that the first marble was black, the probability is $\tfrac{1}{2}$ that the second marble chosen is red.

Example 2   Suppose three true coins are tossed and we record the way each coin falls. Let A denote the event in which the first coin is a head, and let B denote the event in which at least one tail appears. Find $Pr(A \mid B)$.

Solution   The sample space for this experiment is the set

$$S = \{HHH, HHT, HTH, HTT, THH, THT, TTH, TTT\}.$$

All the elements of S are equally likely to occur, so the equiprobable measure will be used. The events A and B are the sets

$$A = \{HHH, HHT, HTH, HTT\}, \quad B = \{HHT, HTH, HTT, THH, THT, TTH, TTT\}.$$

From the sets A and B we find that

$$Pr(A \cap B) = \frac{n(A \cap B)}{n(S)} = \tfrac{3}{8}, \qquad Pr(B) = \frac{n(B)}{n(S)} = \tfrac{7}{8}.$$

Hence, by Definition 10.3,

$$Pr(A \mid B) = \frac{\tfrac{3}{8}}{\tfrac{7}{8}} = \tfrac{3}{7}.$$

That is, since we know that at least one tail appears, the probability is $\tfrac{3}{7}$ that the first coin falls heads.

Definition 10.3 is often useful in the form

$$Pr(A \cap B) = Pr(A \mid B)\, Pr(B).$$

Consider the following example.

Example 3 A sack contains five red marbles and seven black marbles. A marble is chosen at random from the sack, and without replacing the first marble, we choose a second marble at random from the sack. If B denotes the event in which the first marble chosen is black, and R denotes the event in which the second marble is red, find $Pr(B \cap R)$.

Solution The sample space for this experiment consists of $P(12, 2) = 132$ outcomes, so it will be impractical to picture the sample space as we did in Example 1. However, all the outcomes of the sample space are equally likely to occur, so the equiprobable measure will be used. Since

$$Pr(B \cap R) = Pr(R \mid B)\ Pr(B),$$

we can solve our problem by finding $Pr(R \mid B)$ and $Pr(B)$. The event B contains seven elements in a sample space with twelve outcomes. The equiprobable measure is being used, so

$$Pr(B) = \tfrac{7}{12}.$$

We recall that $Pr(R \mid B)$ is the probability of choosing a red marble on the second draw, knowing that a black marble was chosen on the first draw. If a black marble is chosen on the first draw, then the sack contains five red marbles and six black marbles for a total of eleven. Relative to this new sample space with eleven elements, the event of choosing a red marble contains five elements. Since the equiprobable measure is being used, we have

$$Pr(R \mid B) = \tfrac{5}{11}.$$

Therefore

$$Pr(B \cap R) = \tfrac{5}{11} \cdot \tfrac{7}{12} = \tfrac{35}{132}.$$

That is, the probability of choosing a black marble on the first draw and a red marble on the second draw is $\tfrac{35}{132}$.

The reader should observe that in Example 3 we introduced a method for finding conditional probability that does not require the use of the formula in Definition 10.3. This method should be used whenever it is convenient. We should also note that there is another way of finding $Pr(B \cap R)$ in Example 3. We observe that there are seven ways of drawing a black marble from a sack containing seven black marbles and five red marbles, and after a black marble has been chosen, there are five ways of choosing a red marble from those that remain. Consequently, by the Fundamental Counting Principle, there are $7 \cdot 5 = 35$ ways of getting a black marble on the first draw and a red marble on the second draw. Two marbles can be chosen from the sack in 132 different ways, so we have $Pr(B \cap R) = \tfrac{35}{132}$. In working problems pertaining to probability, the reader will find that the "common sense" approach is often the best.

It sometimes happens that $\Pr(A \mid B) = \Pr(A)$. This equation states that the probability of A is not affected by the occurrence of B. When this is the case, we say that A *is independent of B*. Using the formula in Definition 10.3, we see that $\Pr(A \mid B) = \Pr(A)$ if and only if

$$\Pr(A \cap B) = \Pr(A)\,\Pr(B).$$

From this last equation we see that the event A is independent of the event B if and only if B is independent of A. That is, if B does not affect the probability of A, then A does not affect the probability of B. We will now state a definition and consider some examples.

Definition 10.4 Let A and B be two events with the same sample space. The events A and B are *independent* if and only if

$$\Pr(A \cap B) = \Pr(A)\,\Pr(B).$$

Example 4 Two true coins are tossed. What is the probability that both will fall heads?

Solution Since we are interested in whether the coins fall heads or tails, $S = \{H, T\}$ is an appropriate sample space. The equiprobable measure will be used. If we let A denote the event in which the first coin falls heads and B denote the event in which the second coin falls heads, then we have $\Pr(A) = \frac{1}{2}$ and $\Pr(B) = \frac{1}{2}$. How the first coin falls has no effect whatever on how the second coin will fall, so that events A and B are independent. Therefore,

$$\Pr(A \cap B) = \tfrac{1}{2} \cdot \tfrac{1}{2} = \tfrac{1}{4}.$$

That is, the probability that both coins will fall heads is $\frac{1}{4}$.

Example 5 For the events A and B of Example 2, we have

$$\Pr(A) = \tfrac{1}{2}, \qquad \Pr(B) = \tfrac{7}{8}, \qquad \text{and} \qquad \Pr(A \cap B) = \tfrac{3}{8}.$$

Since

$$\Pr(A) \cdot \Pr(B) = \tfrac{1}{2} \cdot \tfrac{7}{8} = \tfrac{7}{16},$$

it follows that

$$\Pr(A \cap B) \neq \Pr(A) \cdot \Pr(B).$$

Therefore the events of Example 2 are not independent.

Example 6 If a true coin is tossed and a fair die is rolled, what is the probability that the coin will fall heads and that a four will show on the die?

Solution We shall take the set

$$S = \{H1, H2, H3, H4, H5, H6, T1, T2, T3, T4, T5, T6\}$$

as our sample space (the elements of S have the obvious meaning), and choose the equiprobable measure on S. If A denotes the event in which the coin falls heads and B denotes the event in which a four shows on the die, then clearly A and B are independent events. Since, $\Pr(A) = \frac{1}{2}$ and $\Pr(B) = \frac{1}{6}$, we have

$$\Pr(A \cap B) = \Pr(A) \Pr(B) = \frac{1}{2} \cdot \frac{1}{6} = \frac{1}{12}.$$

This result can easily be verified by observing that

$$A = \{H1, H2, H3, H4, H5, H6\} \quad \text{and} \quad B = \{H4, T4\}.$$

It then follows that $A \cap B = \{H4\}$ and $\Pr(A \cap B) = \frac{1}{12}$.

In general, the probability that each of a set of independent events will occur is the product of the separate probabilities of the events. This fact will be useful in some of the problems that follow.

Problems

1 A fair die is rolled. Given that an even number is rolled, what is the probability that the number is two or greater?

2 Two true coins are tossed. Given that at least one coin falls heads, what is the probability that both fall heads?

3 One hundred true coins are tossed. Given that 99 of these coins fall heads, what is the probability that the 100th coin also falls heads?

4 A sack contains eight white marbles and five blue marbles. A marble is chosen at random from the sack, and without replacing the first marble, we choose a second marble at random from the sack. If the first marble is white, what is the probability that the second marble is also white? If the first marble is red, what is the probability that the second marble is white?

5 A sack contains 11 white marbles and four blue marbles. A marble is chosen at random from the sack, and without replacing the first marble, we choose a second marble at random from the sack. What is the probability that the first marble is white and the second marble is blue? that both marbles are blue?

6 Three true coins are tossed and the way each falls is noted. If the first coin falls heads, what is the probability that at least one tail will appear? that no tail will appear?

7 A pair of fair dice is rolled. If a five shows on one die, what is the probability that the number of dots showing on the pair is nine?

8 A card is drawn at random from an ordinary deck of 52 playing cards, and without replacing the first card, we choose a second card at random

from the deck. If the first card is an ace, what is the probability that the second card is also an ace ? If the first card is a five, what is the probability that the second card is an ace ?

9 Four cards are drawn at random from an ordinary deck of 52 playing cards. Without replacing these four cards, we choose a fifth card at random from the deck. If the four cards consist of three aces and a two, what is the probability that the fifth card is also an ace ? If the four cards consist of two aces and two kings, what is the probability that the fifth card is either an ace or a king ?

10 Each of three sacks contain one red marble, one white marble, and one blue marble. One marble is chosen at random from each of the three sacks. Given that two of the marbles are blue, what is the probability that the third is also blue ? Given that two of the marbles are blue, what is the probability that the third is white ?

11 Two true coins are tossed. What is the probability that the first falls heads and the second tails ?

12 If a true coin is tossed and a fair die is rolled, what is the probability that the coin will fall tails and that a number greater than two will show on the die ?

13 If a true coin is tossed and a fair die is rolled, what is the probability that the coin will fall tails and that an odd number will show on the die ?

14 One sack contains three red marbles and five blue marbles, and a second sack contains eight red marbles and seven blue marbles. If a marble is chosen at random from each sack what is the probability that both will be red ? that both will be blue ? that both will be the same color ?

15 A sack contains eight red marbles and five blue marbles. A marble is chosen at random from the sack. The first marble is replaced and a second marble is chosen at random. What is the probability that both marbles are red ? that one marble is red and the other is blue ?

16 Four true coins are tossed. What is the probability that all four land heads ?

17 A card is drawn at random from an ordinary deck of 52 playing cards, a true coin is tossed, and a pair of fair dice is rolled. What is the probability that the card is a face card (i.e. jack, queen or king), the coin lands tails, and the pair of dice shows eight dots ?

10.9 EMPIRICAL PROBABILITY

If an event occurs f times in n performances of an experiment, the *relative frequency* of the event for the n performances is f/n. To illustrate, let us suppose the experiment is that of tossing two coins and the event is that of obtaining two heads. This experiment was performed 1000 times, and the relative frequency of the event was calculated after each set of 100 performances. The results are recorded in Table 10.3, where n denotes the number of performances and f denotes the number of times the event of obtaining two heads occurred. If we assume that the coins being used in the experiment are true coins and apply the equiprobable measure to the sample space $\{HH, HT, TH, TT\}$, we find that the probability of the event of obtaining two heads is .250. From Table 10.3, we observe that the relative frequency of this event is reasonably close to the probability .250 when the number n is large.

TABLE 10.3

n	f	Relative frequency
100	21	.210
200	43	.215
300	79	.263
400	100	.250
500	122	.244
600	148	.247
700	176	.251
800	203	.254
900	221	.246
1000	251	.251

Further experimentation would show that the larger n becomes, the more nearly the relative frequency approaches the probability .250. Experience has also shown this to be true of other types of experiments, and this fact suggests that when n is large we define a probability measure on a sample space by defining the probability of an event to be the relative frequency of that event. Such a measure is called an *empirical measure* on the sample space. The empirical measure of an event will depend on the values of n and f and will likely change as n changes. Usually, however, the change is quite small when n is significantly large. We now illustrate this type of measure by some examples.

Example 1 Of 1000 bolts taken from an assembly line, 23 were found to be defective. What is the probability that another bolt taken from the line is defective?

Solution Using an empirical probability measure, the probability that a given bolt is defective is $\frac{23}{1000} = .023$.

Example 2 A loaded die is rolled 5000 times and six dots appear on 543 of these rolls. What is the probability that six dots will appear on a given roll of the die?

Solution Using an empirical probability measure, the probability of obtaining a six on a given roll is $\frac{543}{5000} = .109$.

Empirical probability applied to information given in a *mortality table* is used by insurance companies to set their rates. The American Experience Table of Mortality (see Table I in the Appendix) is such a table, and its use will be illustrated by the following examples.

Example 3 What is the probability that a person 20 years old will live to be 30?

Solution From Table 1 we find that of 100,000 people alive at age 10, 92,637 will live to age 20, while 85,441 will live to age 30. Therefore, the ratio

$$\frac{85,441}{92,637} = .922$$

gives the empirical probability that a person of 20 will live to age 30.

Example 4 What is the probability that a person 35 years old will live to be 65?

Solution From Table 1 we find that of 100,000 people alive at age 10, 81,882 will live to age 35, and 49,341 will live to age 65. Therefore, the ratio

$$\frac{49,341}{81,882} = .603$$

gives the empirical probability that a person of age 35 will live to the age of 65.

Problems

1 A grocer finds that seven apples in a box of 84 are spoiled. What is the empirical probability that an apple picked at random is spoiled?

2 In recent years a community of 340,000 population has had an average of 15,380 college graduates at any one time. What is the empirical probability that a person picked at random from the community is a college graduate?

3 In 50,000 miles of highway travel, a person witnessed six serious accidents. What is the probability that he will witness a serious accident in his next mile of highway travel?

4 In a college of 5000 students there are 2150 commuters. What is the probability that a student picked at random will be a commuter?

PROBABILITY AND STATISTICS

5 Of the 110,000 books in a library, 2500 are mathematics books. If a book is chosen at random from the library, what is the probability that it will be a mathematics book?

6 What is the probability that a person 10 years old will live to be 65?

7 What is the probability that a person 21 years old will live to be 70?

8 What is the probability that a person 35 years old will live to be 40?

9 What is the probability that a person 80 years old will live to be 82?

10 What is the probability that a person 50 years old will live to be 55? that a person 20 years old will live to be 55?

10.10 ODDS AND MATHEMATICAL EXPECTATION

One often hears statements like "The odds in favor of the Red Sox winning the pennant are 3 to 1" or "The odds against Elderberry Queen winning the fifth race at Churchill Downs are 1 to 6." The following definition will help to explain the meaning of such statements.

Definition 10.5 The *odds in favor* of the occurrence of an event are the ratio of the probability that the event will occur to the probability that the event will not occur. The *odds against* the occurrence of an event are the reciprocal of the odds in favor of the occurrence of the event.

Example 1   A card is chosen at random from an ordinary deck of 52 playing cards. What are the odds in favor of the card being an ace?

Solution   The probability that an ace is chosen at random from the deck is $\frac{4}{52} = \frac{1}{13}$, and the probability that an ace is not chosen is $\frac{12}{13}$. Hence, by Definition 10.5, the odds in favor of drawing an ace are

$$\frac{\frac{1}{13}}{\frac{12}{13}} = \frac{1}{12}, \qquad \text{or} \qquad 1 \text{ to } 12.$$

Example 2   What are the odds in favor of throwing a seven or an eleven on one roll of a pair of fair dice? What are the odds against the occurrence of this event?

Solution   The probability of rolling either a seven or an eleven is $\frac{2}{9}$ and the probability of not rolling a seven or eleven is $\frac{7}{9}$. Hence the odds in favor of rolling a seven or an eleven are

$$\frac{\frac{2}{9}}{\frac{7}{9}} = \frac{2}{7}.$$

That is, the odds in favor of rolling a seven or an eleven are 2 to 7. The odds against rolling a seven or an eleven are

$$\frac{\frac{1}{2}}{\frac{7}{7}}, \quad \text{or} \quad 7 \text{ to } 2.$$

Frequently there is a payoff for the occurrence of a given event. For example, if a gambler rolls either a seven or an eleven on the first roll of a pair of dice, he will win a certain amount of money. The *mathematical expectation* of an event is the product of the probability that the event will occur and the amount of money received for the occurrence of the event. For example, if a person receives $3.00 every time a two appears on one roll of a fair die, his mathematical expectation for the event is $(\frac{1}{6})$ (3.00) $= \$.50$. Thus one should expect to pay $.50 for each roll of the die for the game to be a fair one. Mathematically speaking, the person should eventually break even. With a "bit of luck" he could come out the winner.

If an event has n outcomes with probabilities $p_1, p_2, \ldots, p_n$, with respective payoffs of $m_1, m_2, \ldots, m_n$, then the mathematical expectation E of the event is defined by the equation

$$E = p_1 m_1 + p_2 m_2 + \cdots + p_n m_n.$$

Example 3 Suppose a die is loaded in such a way that on a single roll the probability for a one, two, three, four, or five is $\frac{1}{10}$, and the probability for a six is $\frac{1}{2}$. If a person receives 10 cents for a one, 20 cents for a two, 30 cents for a three, 40 cents for a four or five, and nothing for a six, what is his mathematical expectation in this game?

Solution The expected value in cents is

$$(\tfrac{1}{10}) \ (10) + (\tfrac{1}{10}) \ (20) + (\tfrac{1}{10}) \ (30) + (\tfrac{1}{10}) \ (40) + (\tfrac{1}{10}) \ (40) + (\tfrac{1}{2}) \ (0) = 14.$$

This result can be interpreted to mean that 14 cents would be a fair price for playing the game. A higher price would give the operator the advantage.

Problems

1 A card is chosen at random from an ordinary deck of 52 playing cards. What are the odds in favor of the card being a face card (i.e. jack, queen, or king)? What are the odds against the card being a face card?

2 Three true coins are tossed. What are the odds in favor of obtaining two heads? no heads? What are the odds against the occurrence of these two events?

3 A marble is drawn at random from a sack containing five red marbles, three white marbles, and eight blue marbles. What are the odds in favor of the marble being red? What are the odds against a white marble being drawn?

4 What are the odds in favor of rolling an eight on a roll of a pair of fair dice? What are the odds against this event happening?

5 One hundred tickets are sold for a raffle for which the grand prize is $500. If a person buys eight tickets, what is his mathematical expectation? What is a fair price for a single ticket?

6 If a person rolls a five on a single roll of a pair of fair dice, he is paid $12. What is his mathematical expectation?

7 A person tosses two true coins and receives $10 if both fall heads. What is his mathematical expectation?

8 A man chooses a marble at random from a box that contains two red marbles, three white marbles, and five blue marbles. If he is paid 10 cents for a red marble, 20 cents for a white marble, and 30 cents for a blue marble, what is his mathematical expectation? What is a fair price to pay for playing this game?

9 A man holds three identical envelopes. One is empty, one contains a five-dollar bill, and the third contains a ten-dollar bill. A person selects an envelope and keeps its contents. What is his expectation?

10.11 INTRODUCTION TO STATISTICS

The science of collecting, organizing, analyzing, and interpreting data so as to make certain inferences is called *statistics*. The question now arises as to the role of mathematics in statistics. Clearly, the collection and organization of data require little or no mathematical knowledge. However, the analysis and interpretation given to the data collected require, to some degree, a working knowledge of mathematics. The degree of knowledge which is required depends on what type of inferences are to be made from the analysis of the collected data. Little more than a knowledge of arithmetic will be necessary for the topics of statistical methods covered in this text. In view of the foregoing statements it should be clear to the reader that statistics, as far as mathematics is concerned, is applied mathematics.

In collecting data concerning characteristics of a set of objects, it is often impossible or inconvenient to observe the entire set of objects since the set may contain a large number of elements or even be infinite. Instead of observing the entire set of objects, called the *population*, one observes a subset of the population, called a *sample*. As an example, one may be doing a study concerning the television viewing habits of the American adult. Instead of questioning the entire American adult population, one could question a sample of only 10,000, 1000, or even 100 adults. If a sample is fairly representative of a population, conclusions about the population can be inferred after an analysis of the sample. Making inferences in this manner is referred to as *inductive statistics*. Note that inductive reasoning is used in this instance. Because inferences made through inductive statistics are uncertain, the language of probability is often employed to state conclusions.

Perhaps the most familiar examples of the use of inductive statistics are public opinion polls. For example, prior to a presidential election, pollsters interview a small sample of voters as to how they plan to vote. Based on an analysis of the replies from the sample, the pollsters then make inferences as to the results of the forthcoming election. Of course, these inferences may turn out to be incorrect. If a sample is selected from the population in such a way that every member of the population has an equal chance of being selected, the sample is called a *random sample*. A *selected sample* is a sample in which individual differences in the members of a population are represented proportionately. The poll mentioned above as an example would be based on a random sample if the names of the voters to be polled were taken from a registration roll. For a selected sample, one might consider such things as age, sex, education, geographical location, socio-economic status, etc.

The aspect of statistics in which one simply collects, organizes, and analyzes a set of data without making any inferences is called *descriptive* or *deductive statistics*. The process of recording a student's grades throughout the semester and then finding the average of these grades is an example of descriptive statistics. In the following sections of this chapter we shall compute such descriptive measures as the mean and standard deviation which are needed in inductive statistics.

In conclusion we see that statistics is concerned not only with the collection, organization, and analysis of data but also with the inferences which can be made after the analysis is completed. It would be a mistake to assume that all problems can be solved through a use of statistics. However, the students in the natural sciences, business, and social sciences feel an ever increasing need for an understanding of statistical methods.

10.12 MEASURES OF CENTRAL TENDENCY

In this section we shall consider three descriptive measures which are sometimes used to make inferences about a population or a sample. These measures are the *arithmetic mean*, the *median*, and the *mode*. All three of these measures are averages, and each has its merits and its limitations. Since each of these measures, at least from some point of view, is most representative of the elements in a population or sample, they are called *measures of central tendency*. We shall not only describe how to determine these measures, but also discuss the relative merits and limitations of each. The values of individual measures in a set of measures are called *variates*.

The *arithmetic mean* of a set of N variates, $X_1, X_2, X_3, \ldots, X_N$ is denoted by $\overline{X}$ and defined by

$$\overline{X} = \frac{X_1 + X_2 + X_3 + \cdots + X_N}{N}.$$

The arithmetic mean is often referred to simply as the mean. This measure of central tendency is perhaps the descriptive measure with which the reader is most familiar. Let us consider the following example.

Example 1 Throughout the semester, David made the following grades in his history class: 83, 95, 90, 87, 75, 93, 94, 88, 96, and 90. What is the arithmetic mean of these grades?

Solution

$$\overline{X} = \frac{83 + 95 + 90 + 87 + 75 + 93 + 94 + 88 + 96 + 90}{10}$$

$$= \frac{891}{10}$$

$$= 89.1$$

In mathematics we often use the symbol

$$\sum_{i=1}^{N} X_i$$

to denote the sum of all the X_i's for $i = 1, 2, 3, \ldots, N$. With this notation, called *sigma notation* or *summation notation*, the arithmetic mean of the N variates $X_1, X_2, X_3, \ldots, X_N$ is given by

$$\overline{X} = \frac{\sum_{i=1}^{N} X_i}{N}.$$

This notation makes the representation of many statements less burdensome. The following examples illustrate the use of the sigma notation.

Example 2

a)
$$\sum_{i=1}^{N} a_i = a_1 + a_2 + a_3 + \cdots + a_N.$$

b)
$$\sum_{i=1}^{5} i = 1 + 2 + 3 + 4 + 5 = 15.$$

c) $$\sum_{i=1}^{6} 2i = 2(1) + 2(2) + 2(3) + 2(4) + 2(5) + 2(6)$$
$$= 2 + 4 + 6 + 8 + 10 + 12$$
$$= 42.$$

d) $$\sum_{i=2}^{5} (i + 1) = (2 + 1) + (3 + 1) + (4 + 1) + (5 + 1)$$
$$= 3 + 4 + 5 + 6$$
$$= 18.$$

e) $$\sum_{i=1}^{7} 1 \text{ means } 1 + 1 + 1 + 1 + 1 + 1 + 1 = 7.$$

f) $$\sum_{i=3}^{6} i^2 = 3^2 + 4^2 + 5^2 + 6^2$$
$$= 9 + 16 + 25 + 36$$
$$= 86.$$

Sometimes we associate with each of the variates in a set of data a weighting factor which depends on the importance of the variate. Suppose the N variates $X_1, X_2, X_3, \ldots, X_N$ have the respective weighting factors $w_1, w_2, w_3, \ldots, w_N$. Then the *weighted arithmetic mean* is given by

$$\bar{X} = \frac{w_1 X_1 + w_2 X_2 + w_3 X_3 + \cdots + w_N X_N}{w_1 + w_2 + w_3 + \cdots + w_N} = \frac{\sum_{i=1}^{N} w_i X_i}{\sum_{i=1}^{N} w_i}.$$

Consider the following example in which we make use of the weighted mean.

Example 3 Matt made scores of 96, 88, and 86 on three math exams during the semester. On the final exam he made 92. If the final exam is weighted three times as much as a regular exam, find the mean of his grades.

Solution Since the final exam is to be weighted three times that of a regular exam, we assign the weight of 1 to each of the regular exams and the weight of 3 to the final exam. Thus,

$$\bar{X} = \frac{1(96) + 1(88) + 1(86) + 3(92)}{1 + 1 + 1 + 3}$$
$$= \frac{96 + 88 + 86 + 276}{6}$$
$$= \frac{546}{6}$$
$$= 91.0.$$

The second measure of central tendency we consider is called the *median*. The median of a set of variates, arranged according to magnitude, is the middle variate if there is an odd number of variates or it is the mean of the two middle variates if there is an even number of variates. In a set of variates, just as many variates will occur which are greater than the median as will occur which are less than the median.

Example 4 The weights of the individual players on a football team are: 203, 174, 196, 183, 215, 135, 162, 198, 211, 178, and 197 pounds. What is the median weight?

Solution Arranging the weights in order of magnitude, we have:

$$215, 211, 203, 198, 197, 196, 183, 178, 174, 162, 135.$$

Since there are eleven variates, the middle variate is the sixth one. Therefore, the median weight is 196 pounds.

Note that in the solution to Example 4 we listed the heaviest weight first. We could have just as well listed the lightest weight first, as long as the variates occur in order according to magnitude. We use this latter approach in finding the median for the set of tests scores given in Example 1 of this section. The scores in ascending order are 75, 83, 87, 88, 90, 90, 93, 94, 95, and 96. Since there are 10 variates, the median is the arithmetic mean of the fifth and sixth scores. The fifth and sixth scores are both 90, and therefore the median score is 90.

The third measure of central tendency we consider is the *mode*. The mode of a set of variates is the variate which occurs most frequently, or the most common variate. Given a set of variates, the mode may not even exist, and even if it does exist, it may not be unique. The set of scores in Example 1 of this section, 83, 95, 90, 87, 75, 93, 94, 88, 96, and 90 has the mode 90, since the variate 90 occurs twice and each other variate only once. The set of weights in Example 4 of this section has *no* mode since no variate occurs more than once. As an example of a set of variates in which the mode is not unique, consider the numbers 30, 37, 42, 35, 28, 37, 44 and 35. Here we see that the variates 35 and 37 each occur twice, whereas each of the other variates occurs only once. Thus we have two modes, 35 and 37. Such a set as this, a set with two modes, is said to be *bimodal*.

The question now arises as to why we need the three different averages: mean, median, and mode. Each of these measures characterizes the total set of variates in a different way. The mean is a magnitude average, the median a positional average, and the mode a frequency average. In general, the mean best characterizes the entire set of variates since it is influenced by each and every variate. However, the mean can be misleading, especially if one or two of the variates differ radically from the rest. As an example, suppose

Shannon made grades of 93, 94, 87, and 50 on four English tests. The mean of these scores is 81. In this case, the mean is certainly not representative of the variates. A better average to use in this case would be the median, which is 90. Remember that an average is supposed to be representative of the entire set of variates. As another example in which the arithmetic mean is an inappropriate measure, consider the problem of a shoe store manager replenishing his stock. He is certainly not concerned with the mean shoe size of shoes sold in his store. The mean would probably turn out to be some size not even manufactured. The median size shoe sold is also an inappropriate average for his purpose. Since the manager is more concerned with how many pairs of each size shoe to order, the best average for his problem is the mode. The average to be used in a given situation depends on the information one desires to describe. For many sets of variates, the mean, median, and mode are almost the same. One should be cautious as to which average is used whenever someone says, "That is average."

Problems

In Problems 1 through 6, find the value of the given sums.

1 $\sum_{i=1}^{7} i$

2 $\sum_{i=2}^{6} 3i$

3 $\sum_{i=4}^{8} (i + 3)$

4 $\sum_{i=1}^{7} (i^2 + 1)$

5 $\sum_{i=3}^{6} (3i^2 + 1)$

6 $\sum_{i=1}^{5} (2i^2 + i - 1)$

In Problems 7 through 10 for the given set of measures, find the mean, median, and mode.

7 13, 17, 21, 22, 17, 15, 28, 21, 17, 13, 15

8 3.5, 4.6, 5.7, 3.9, 4.6, 5.3, 4.2

9 246, 257, 362, 158, 312, 286, 310

10 43.1, 43.5, 42.9, 43.2, 43.6, 42.8, 43.1, 43.4

11 Amanda made the following scores on exams: 90, 83, 95, 87, and 91. What was the mean score? the median score?

12 The heights of the members of a basketball team are as follows: 5'10", 6'1", 5'6", 6'5", and 6'4". What is the mean height? the median height?

13 A student's grades on four projects are 93, 85, 88, and 90. These grades have the weights of 2, 3, 2, and 4, respectively. Find the weighted mean of these grades.

14 A company has 100 employees. Seventy employees earn $2.50 per hour, 20 employees earn $3.25 per hour, and 10 employees earn $4.00 per hour. What is the mean wage per hour for the 100 employees? the median? the mode? Does the mean or median better represent the average wage?

15 A football team made scores of 14, 27, 13, 7, 20, 37, 18, and 21 in playing eight games. What was the mean score? the median score?

16 If the mean annual income of professional workers is $15,000 and of nonprofessional workers is $5000, can we conclude that the mean annual income of both sets together is $10,000? Explain.

17 In Problem 16, suppose the ratio of nonprofessional workers to professional workers is 7 to 1. Find the mean annual income of both sets together.

18 A student's grades on homework, hour exams, and the final exam in a math course are 85, 96, and 84, respectively. If the weights assigned to these grades are 1, 4, and 2, respectively, what is the mean grade? If equal weights are used, what is the mean grade?

19 If the manager of a hat shop says that the average hat sold in his shop is size $6\frac{7}{8}$, which average is he most likely referring to: mean, median, or mode?

10.13 FREQUENCY DISTRIBUTIONS

Recall from the previous section that to compute the arithmetic mean of a set of measures, no particular arrangement of the variates is required. However, to compute the median, it is essential to arrange the variates according to magnitude, and finding the mode is also easier if the variates are arranged in some order. Often the set of variates under consideration is much larger than any encountered in the previous section, and some order in the set considerably facilitates the computation of the mean, median, and mode. Furthermore, computation of some of the other descriptive measures used in statistics makes it almost imperative that the variates be organized. In this section, we will therefore consider some of the procedures used in organizing raw data.

When we organize a large collection of raw data, it is often useful to distribute the data into classes and determine the number of variates belonging to each class, called the *class frequency*. A table used for the arrangement of data by classes, together with the respective class frequencies, is called a *frequency distribution*. Table 10.4 is a frequency distribution of I.Q. scores of the 535 freshmen at Zilch College.

An inspection of Table 10.4 reveals that the first class consists of I.Q.'s from 140.5 to 145.5 and the number of freshmen in this class is three. Thus the class frequency of this class is three. The symbol 140.5 – 145.5 used to denote this class is called a *class interval*. The numbers 140.5 and 145.5 are called *class limits*, 140.5 being the *lower limit* and 145.5 the *upper limit*. The difference between the lower limit and the upper limit of a class interval is called the *class size*. The arithmetic mean of the upper and lower limits is called the *class mark*, Thus, in this example, the class size in each case is five.

TABLE 10.4

I.Q.	Number of freshmen
140.5 – 145.5	3
135.5 – 140.5	15
130.5 – 135.5	20
125.5 – 130.5	25
120.5 – 125.5	47
115.5 – 120.5	73
110.5 – 115.5	96
105.5 – 110.5	115
100.5 – 105.5	87
95.5 – 100.5	40
90.5 – 95.5	14

As a further example, the class interval 115.5 – 120.5 has class frequency 73, and the class mark for this class interval is 118. Data organized as in Table 10.4 are called *grouped data*.

The grouping of data, as in constructing a frequency distribution, generally destroys much of the original detail of the data. For example, in considering the class interval 125.5 – 130.5, we know only that 25 freshmen belong to this class. We do *not* know whether 1, 5, 15, or, as a matter of fact, whether any of the freshmen have I.Q.'s of 128. However, even though many details of the raw data are destroyed, it often proves profitable to construct a frequency distribution in order to analyze a set of measures.

Having observed an example of a frequency distribution (Table 10.4), we are now prepared to discuss the construction of such a table. For this discussion, we will rely upon a specific set of raw data. Table 10.5 gives the weights of the 50-member football squad at Zilch College. The first step in the process of constructing a frequency distribution is to find the difference in the largest and smallest measures. This difference is called the *range* of the variates. In our example, the largest weight is 229 and the smallest is 136, and therefore the range is 93. We now divide the range into a convenient number of class intervals, usually between 5 and 20. The number of class intervals is arbitrary. They need not be of the same size, but we shall follow that practice in this text. In forming the class intervals care is taken to make

TABLE 10.5

151	216	147	189	192	136	165	169	209	201
185	197	147	152	167	175	181	149	183	159
190	201	209	179	199	168	190	200	153	176
156	139	187	215	147	137	177	229	144	191
201	197	178	193	167	225	185	189	217	180

sure that none of the variates occur as class interval limits. We will construct a frequency distribution using 10 class intervals, and thus the class size will need to be 10, since the range, 93, divided by the number of class intervals, 10, is 9.3, and we need every variate to be within a class interval. Table 10.6 gives a frequency distribution using 10 class intervals of the data given in Table 10.5. Table 10.6 was also used as a tally sheet to determine the number of variates in each class interval. Other frequency distributions could be constructed for this set of data.

TABLE 10.6

Class interval	Tally	Frequency
222.5 – 232.5	II	2
212.5 – 222.5	III	3
202.5 – 212.5	II	2
192.5 – 202.5	HHT III	8
182.5 – 192.5	HHT HHT	10
172.5 – 182.5	HHT II	7
162.5 – 172.5	HHT	5
152.5 – 162.5	IIII	4
142.5 – 152.5	HHT I	6
132.5 – 142.5	III	3

Frequently, we use the class mark of a class interval as a measure that is representative of each variate in the class interval. We can use the class marks and the weighted mean to compute the arithmetic mean for the set of data. The weight assigned each class mark is the class frequency. This work is summarized in Table 10.7. Thus we have

$$\bar{X} = \frac{8985}{50} = 179.7 \text{ pounds.}$$

TABLE 10.7

Class mark (X)	Class frequency (f)	$f \cdot X$
227.5	2	455.0
217.5	3	652.5
207.5	2	415.0
197.5	8	1580.0
187.5	10	1875.0
177.5	7	1242.5
167.5	5	837.5
157.5	4	630.0
147.5	6	885.0
137.5	3	412.5
Sums	50	8985.0

Of course this is *not* the exact mean, since the computation of the mean by this procedure assumes that the class mark in each case is the mean of the variates in the class interval. However, it is usually a very good approximation of the mean. The mean in this case is 179.78.

We now turn our attention to two graphical representations of frequency distributions called the *histogram* and *frequency polygon*. A *histogram* is a set of rectangles having bases on a horizontal axis with centers at the class marks and lengths equal to the class interval sizes. In this case in which the class intervals are all of the same length, the height of each rectangle is

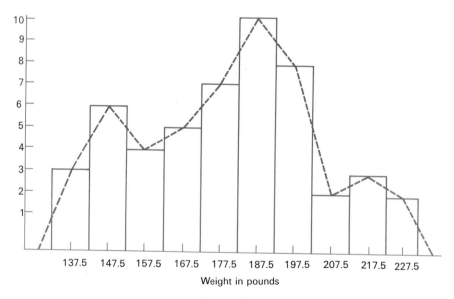

Weight in pounds

Figure 10.8

equal to the class frequency. In general, the areas of the rectangles are pro-
portional to the class frequencies. A *frequency polygon* is a broken line graph
of class frequency plotted against class mark. It can be obtained by connecting the midpoints of the tops of the rectangles in the histogram. Figure
10.8 is the histogram and accompanying frequency polygon for the frequency
distribution in Table 10.6. These two procedures are used to give a pictorial
presentation of a frequency distribution. The reader may notice the similarity
of a histogram and a bar graph (see Section 6.13).

Problems

1　Construct a frequency distribution having seven class intervals for the
weights given in Table 10.5.

2　Repeat Problem 1, using 15 class intervals.

3　Construct a histogram and frequency polygon for the frequency distribution given in Table 10.4.

4　Use the class marks and the weighted mean to find the mean of the I.Q.'s
for which Table 10.4 is the frequency distribution.

5　A class of 30 math students had the following semester averages.

96	52	81	60	70
85	83	80	74	59
71	93	77	65	76
96	73	85	68	79
61	73	82	70	69
78	79	87	63	55

a)　What is the range of the variates ?

b)　Construct a frequency distribution with five class intervals.

c)　Construct the histogram and frequency polygon for the frequency
distribution in part (b).

d)　Use class marks to compute the mean and compare this to the
actual mean.

e)　What are the median and the mode for this set of variates ?

6　Construct a frequency distribution having eight class intervals for the data
given in Problem 5. Construct the corresponding histogram and frequency
polygon.

7　The scores made by 40 freshman male students on an entrance exam
were as follows.

29	30	28	37	34	24	18	29	24	28
27	22	33	19	36	37	39	24	30	23
35	33	19	22	35	29	29	31	29	34
17	23	23	28	27	34	27	37	32	29

a) What is the range of the variates?

b) Construct a frequency distribution with five class intervals.

c) Construct the histogram and frequency polygon for the frequency distribution in part (b).

d) Use class marks to compute the mean and compare this to the actual mean.

8 Construct a frequency distribution having seven class intervals for the data given in Problem 7. Construct the corresponding histogram and frequency polygon.

10.14 MEASURES OF DISPERSION

In this section we shall discuss some descriptive measures which describe the degree to which a set of data tends to spread out about an average. These measures are called *measures of dispersion*. We have already encountered one such measure, the *range*. The range is very easy to calculate but it is not generally looked upon as a very useful measure of dispersion. Since it is based only on the two extreme variates, it does not tell anything about the dispersion of the variates which fall in between. Each of the following three sets of data

a)   16, 32, 32, 32, 32;

b)   16, 16, 16, 32;

c)   16, 20, 24, 28, 32;

has range $32 - 16 = 16$, but the dispersions differ radically.

A second measure used in considering the dispersion of a set of variates is the *mean deviation*. The mean deviation of a set of N variates $X_1, X_2, X_3, \ldots, X_N$ is defined by

$$\text{Mean Deviation} = \text{MD} = \frac{\sum_{i=1}^{N} |X_i - \overline{X}|}{N}$$

The mean deviation tells us how much on the average (mean) the individual variates differ from the arithmetic mean of the variates. In general, the larger the mean deviation, the larger the dispersion of the variates. It should be noted that in the formula for mean deviation, use is made of the absolute value of the deviation of each variate from the arithmetic mean. The reason for this is that if we consider deviations from the mean to be positive or negative, the sum of all deviations from the mean will be zero. This will be illustrated in the following example.

Example 1   Find the mean deviation for the numbers 5, 7, 11, 13, 17, 19.

Solution We organize our work in Table 10.8, from which it is clear that the sum of the deviations from the mean is zero.

TABLE 10.8

X	$X - \overline{X}$	$|X - \overline{X}|$
5	−7	7
7	−5	5
11	−1	1
13	1	1
17	5	5
19	7	7
72	0	26

Using Table 10.8, we have

$$\overline{X} = \frac{5 + 7 + 11 + 13 + 17 + 19}{6} = 12$$

and

$$MD = \frac{7 + 5 + 1 + 1 + 5 + 7}{6} = \frac{26}{6} = 4\tfrac{1}{3}.$$

This result is interpreted to mean that the average deviation from the mean is $4\tfrac{1}{3}$.

If the variates $X_1, X_2, \ldots, X_M$ occur with frequencies $f_1, f_2, \ldots, f_M$, respectively, then

$$MD = \frac{\sum_{i=1}^{M} f_i \cdot |X_i - \overline{X}|}{N}, \qquad \text{where} \qquad N = \sum_{i=1}^{M} f_i.$$

This form is useful when we consider grouped data where the X_i's represent class marks and the f_i's the corresponding class frequencies.

The most widely used measure of dispersion is the *standard deviation*. The standard deviation of the set of N variates $X_1, X_2, \ldots, X_N$ is defined by

$$\text{Standard Deviation} = \sigma = \sqrt{\frac{\sum_{i=1}^{N} (X_i - \overline{X})^2}{N}}.$$

This formula may seem unwieldy and, indeed, even impossible. However, if we organize our data, the computational work is not as difficult as it might seem at first glance.

Example 2   Find the standard deviation for the set of numbers 5, 7, 11, 13, 17, 19.

Solution   We organize our work in Table 10.9.

TABLE 10.9

X	$X - \bar{X}$	$(X - \bar{X})^2$
5	−7	49
7	−5	25
11	−1	1
13	1	1
17	5	25
19	7	49
72	0	150

$$\bar{X} = \tfrac{72}{6} = 12$$

$$\sigma = \sqrt{\tfrac{150}{6}} = \sqrt{25} = 5$$

If the set variates $X_1, X_2, \ldots, X_M$ occur with respective frequencies $f_1, f_2, \ldots, f_M$, then

$$\sigma = \sqrt{\frac{\sum_{i=1}^{M} f_i \cdot (X_i - \bar{X})^2}{N}}, \qquad \text{where} \qquad N = \sum_{i=1}^{M} f_i.$$

This formula for σ is particularly useful whenever we consider grouped data by letting the X_i's be the class marks and the f_i's the respective class frequencies. We use this formula in the solution of the following example.

Example 3   Find the standard deviation of the set of weights in Table 10.5.

Solution   We make use of the frequency distribution in Table 10.6 and the fact that $\bar{X} = 179.78$, which we round off to 179.8. From Table 10.10, we have

$$\sigma = \sqrt{\frac{27858.47}{50}} = \sqrt{557.17} = 23.6.$$

Each of the measures of dispersion discussed is a descriptive measure. However, we can use the standard deviation to make inferences. In *most* cases met in statistical practice, about 68% of the data will be between $\bar{X} - \sigma$ and $\bar{X} + \sigma$. Furthermore, about 95% of the data will lie between

PROBABILITY AND STATISTICS

TABLE 10.10

Weight	Class mark	$X - \bar{X}$	$(X - \bar{X})^2$	f	$f(X - \bar{X})^2$
222.5 – 232.5	227.5	47.7	2275.29	2	4550.58
212.5 – 222.5	217.5	37.7	1421.29	3	4263.87
202.5 – 212.5	207.5	27.7	767.29	2	1534.58
192.5 – 202.5	197.5	17.7	313.29	8	2506.32
182.5 – 192.5	187.5	7.7	59.29	10	592.90
172.5 – 182.5	177.5	− 2.3	5.29	7	37.03
162.5 – 172.5	167.5	−12.3	151.29	5	756.45
152.5 – 162.5	157.5	−22.3	497.29	4	1989.16
142.5 – 152.5	147.5	−32.3	1043.29	6	6259.74
132.5 – 142.5	137.5	−42.3	1789.29	3	5367.84
				50	27858.47

TABLE 10.11

		Number of variates	Percent of variates
$\bar{X} - \sigma$	156.2	31	62%
$\bar{X} + \sigma$	203.4		
$\bar{X} - 2\sigma$	132.6	50	100%
$\bar{X} + 2\sigma$	227.0		
$\bar{X} - 3\sigma$	109.0	50	100%
$\bar{X} + 3\sigma$	250.6		

$\bar{X} - 2\sigma$ and $\bar{X} + 2\sigma$, and about 99% will lie between $\bar{X} - 3\sigma$ and $\bar{X} + 3\sigma$. Table 10.11 shows the dispersion of the weights in Table 10.5.

The fact that Table 10.11 doesn't entirely agree with the inferences made concerning the dispersion of the variates from the mean isn't completely unexpected. In order for these inferences to be entirely correct, the variates must satisfy a normal distribution, a concept to be discussed in a later section of this chapter. As always in using inductive reasoning, we can only infer or predict results, *not* guarantee them.

Problems

In Problems 1 through 3 find the range, mean deviation, and standard deviation for the given set of numbers.

1 2, 6, 11, 1, 9.

2 3, 5, 6, 1, 1, 7, 3, 2, 8, 9.

3 12, 7, 3, 6, 18, 5, 10.

4 Find the standard deviation for the data given in Table 10.4 (Section 10.13). Assume $\overline{X} = 112.5$. How many variates would you expect to be between $112.5 - \sigma$ and $112.5 + \sigma$? What is the actual number of variates in this range?

5 Find the standard deviation for the data given in Problem 5 of Section 10.13.

6 Find the standard deviation for the data given in Problem 7 of Section 10.13.

7 Table 10.12 gives the weights of 480 fourth-, fifth- and sixth-grade children by class marks.

TABLE 10.12

Class Mark	72	76	80	84	88	92	96	100	104	108	112	116	120	124	128
Frequency	4	8	17	27	46	65	86	71	55	37	28	17	12	4	3

a) Find the weighted mean.

b) Use the weighted mean to find the mean deviation.

c) Use the weighted mean to find the standard deviation.

d) Assuming normal distribution, how many variates would you expect to find between $\overline{X} - \sigma$ and $\overline{X} + \sigma$?

10.15 THE BINOMIAL THEOREM

The following equations can be verified by direct multiplications.

$$(a + b)^1 = a + b,$$
$$(a + b)^2 = a^2 + 2ab + b^2,$$
$$(a + b)^3 = a^3 + 3a^2b + 3ab^2 + b^3,$$
$$(a + b)^4 = a^4 + 4a^3b + 6a^2b^2 + 4ab^3 + b^4,$$
$$(a + b)^5 = a^5 + 5a^4b + 10a^3b^2 + 10a^2b^3 + 5ab^4 + b^5.$$

In observing these powers of $a + b$ we notice the following patterns:

1) The number of terms in each expansion is one more than the power of $(a + b)$.

2) The exponent of a in the first term is the power of $(a + b)$ and in each succeeding term it decreases by 1.

3) The exponent of b in the first term is zero and in each succeeding term it increases by 1.

4) In each term the sum of the exponents of a and b is the power of $(a + b)$.

5) The coefficients of the terms are arranged symmetrically.

6) The coefficients of the first and last terms are 1.

7) The coefficients of the second term and the next-to-last term are the power of $(a + b)$.

8) Each coefficient after the first one may be determined from the previous term as follows: the coefficient in any term times the exponent of a in that term divided by the number of the term in the expansion gives the coefficient of the next term.

If we can assume that the above patterns will hold for any positive integer n, then we will have

$$(a + b)^n = a^n b^0 + \frac{n}{1} a^{n-1}b + \frac{n(n - 1)}{1 \cdot 2} a^{n-2}b^2$$

$$+ \frac{n(n - 1)(n - 2)}{1 \cdot 2 \cdot 3} a^{n-3}b^3 + \cdots$$

$$+ \frac{n(n - 1)(n - 2) \cdots (n - r + 2)}{1 \cdot 2 \cdot 3 \cdot \cdots \cdot (r - 1)} a^{n-r+1}b^{r-1} + \cdots$$

$$+ \frac{n(n - 1)(n - 2) \cdots (1)}{1 \cdot 2 \cdot 3 \cdot \cdots \cdot n} a^0 b^n.$$

Recalling the discussion on combinations from Section 10.3, we have

$$C(n, 0) = \frac{n!}{0! \, (n - 0)!} = 1,$$

$$C(n, 1) = \frac{n!}{1! \, (n - 1)!} = \frac{n}{1},$$

$$C(n, 2) = \frac{n!}{2! \, (n - 2)!} = \frac{n(n - 1)}{1 \cdot 2},$$

$$C(n, 3) = \frac{n!}{3! \, (n - 3)!} = \frac{n(n - 1)(n - 2)}{1 \cdot 2 \cdot 3},$$

$$\vdots$$

$$C(n, r - 1) = \frac{n!}{(r - 1)! \, (n - r + 1)!} = \frac{n(n - 1)(n - 2) \cdots (n - r + 2)}{1 \cdot 2 \cdot 3 \cdot \cdots \cdot n},$$

$$\vdots$$

$$C(n, n) = \frac{n!}{n! \, (n - n)!} = 1,$$

and therefore

$$(a + b)^n = C(n, 0)a^n b^0 + C(n, 1)a^{n-1}b + C(n, 2)a^{n-2}b^2$$
$$+ C(n, 3)a^{n-3}b^3 + \cdots + C(n, r - 1)a^{n-r+1}b^{r-1} + \cdots$$
$$+ C(n, n)a^0 b^n.$$

Using the summation notation of Section 10.12, we can write

$$(a + b)^n = \sum_{i=0}^{n} C(n, i)a^{n-i}b^i.$$

Before formally stating and proving this as a theorem, we prove a result concerning combinations. This result is stated in Problem 17 of Section 10.3.

Theorem 10.5 If $1 \leq i \leq k$, then $C(k, i) + C(k, i - 1) = C(k + 1, i)$.

Proof

$$C(k, i) + C(k, i - 1) = \frac{k!}{i! \, (k - i)!} + \frac{k!}{(i - 1)! \, (k - i + 1)!}$$

$$= \frac{k! \, (k - i + 1) + k! \, i}{i! \, (k - i + 1)!}$$

$$= \frac{k! \, (k - i + 1 + i)}{i! \, (k - i + 1)!}$$

$$= \frac{k! \, (k + 1)}{i! \, (k - i + 1)!}$$

$$= \frac{(k + 1)!}{i! \, (k + 1 - i)!}$$

$$= C(k + 1, i).$$

We are now prepared to prove the following theorem, called the *binomial theorem*.

Theorem 10.6 The Binomial Theorem. For every positive integer n,

$$(a + b)^n = \sum_{i=0}^{n} C(n, i)a^{n-i}b^i.$$

Proof Since this is a proposition to be proved true for *every* positive integer, it suggests a proof by mathematical induction. If $n = 1$, we have

$$(a + b)^1 = a + b,$$

and

$$\sum_{i=0}^{1} C(1, i)a^{1-i}b^i = C(1, 0)a^1 b^0 + C(1, 1)a^0 b^1 = a + b.$$

Therefore the proposition holds for the positive integer 1. We now assume that it holds for the positive integer k. That is,

$$(a + b)^k = \sum_{i=0}^{k} C(k, i)a^{k-i}b^i.$$

Based on this assumption we wish to show that the proposition is true for the positive integer $k + 1$. That is, we wish to show that

$$(a + b)^{k+1} = \sum_{i=0}^{k+1} C(k + 1, i)a^{(k+1)-i}b^i.$$

Now,

$$
\begin{aligned}
(a + b)^{k+1} &= (a + b)(a + b)^k \\
&= (a + b)\left(\sum_{i=0}^{k} C(k, i)a^{k-i}b^i\right) \\
&= a\left(\sum_{i=0}^{k} C(k, i)a^{k-i}b^i\right) + b\left(\sum_{i=0}^{k} C(k, i)a^{k-i}b^i\right) \\
&= \sum_{i=0}^{k} C(k, i)a^{k-i+1}b^i + \sum_{i=0}^{k} C(k, i)a^{k-i}b^{i+1} \\
&= C(k, 0)a^{k+1}b^0 + \sum_{i=1}^{k} C(k, i)a^{k-i+1}b^i \\
&\quad + \sum_{i=0}^{k-1} C(k, i)a^{k-i}b^{i+1} + C(k, k)a^0 b^{k+1} \\
&= C(k + 1, 0)a^{k+1}b^0 + \sum_{i=1}^{k} C(k, i)a^{k-i+1}b^i \\
&\quad + \sum_{i=1}^{k} C(k, i - 1)a^{k-i+1}b^i + C(k + 1, k + 1)a^0 b^{k+1} \\
&= C(k + 1, 0)a^{k+1}b^0 + \sum_{i=1}^{k} [C(k, i) + C(k, i - 1)]a^{k-i+1}b^i \\
&\quad + C(k + 1, k + 1)a^0 b^{k+1} \\
&= \sum_{i=0}^{k+1} C(k + 1, i)a^{(k+1)-i}b^i.
\end{aligned}
$$

Thus, by mathematical induction, the theorem is established. Note that in the proof we made use of Theorem 10.5. We also used the fact that $C(k, 0) = C(k + 1, 0)$ and $C(k, k) = C(k + 1, k + 1)$.

Because the numbers $C(n, 0), C(n, 1), \ldots, C(n, n)$ are the coefficients in the expansion of $(a + b)^n$, they are called *binomial coefficients*. If we write the coefficients of the expansion of $(a + b)^n$, where n is a nonnegative

integer, in a triangular array, we have

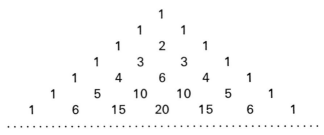

which is known as *Pascal's Triangle*. The first row lists the coefficients in the expansion of $(a + b)^0$; the second row, the coefficients in the expansion of $(a + b)^1$; the third row, the coefficients in the expansion of $(a + b)^2$, and in general the $(n + 1)$-row lists the coefficients in the expansion of $(a + b)^n$. It is easy to continue Pascal's Triangle to any number of rows as each entry in the triangle, except the 1 at the top, is the sum of the numbers appearing immediately above to the right and to the left. The fact that the triangle can be continued in this way is actually established in Theorem 10.5, which is called Pascal's Rule.

Problems

1 Expand $(a + b)^7$.

2 Expand $(a + b)^9$.

3 Expand $(2 + 3)^5$ by the binomial theorem and then evaluate.

4 Expand $(3 + 7)^3$ by the binomial theorem and then evaluate.

5 Expand $(a - b)^7$. [*Hint:* Write $a - b = a + (-b)$.]

6 Find 101^4 by expanding $(100 + 1)^4$.

7 Find 99^3 by expanding $(100 - 1)^3$.

8 Find the eighth, ninth, and tenth rows of Pascal's Triangle.

10.16 BINOMIAL AND NORMAL DISTRIBUTIONS

There are many interesting applications based on the binomial theorem and the binomial coefficients. Among these are the concepts of *binomial distribution* and *normal distribution*. It is our purpose in this section to discuss some of the aspects of these concepts.

If we toss three coins simultaneously, all three may fall heads, two may fall heads and one may fall tails, one may fall heads and two come up tails, or all three may come up tails. The tree diagram used to determine the sample space for this experiment is given in Fig. 10.4. In observing the sample space, we see that three heads occur 1 time, two heads 3 times, one head

PROBABILITY AND STATISTICS

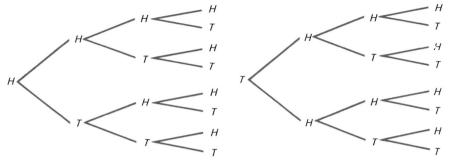

Figure 10.9

3 times, and zero heads 1 time. These frequencies 1, 3, 3, 1 are the coefficients in the expansion of $(a + b)^3$, and the sum of the frequencies is $2^3 = 8$. In summary, if this experiment is conducted eight times with true coins, the most likely frequencies would be three heads 1 time, two heads 3 times, one head 3 times, and zero heads 1 time.

If we toss four coins simultaneously, a sample space for this experiment can be obtained from Fig. 10.9. We see that four heads occur 1 time, three heads 4 times, two heads 6 times, one head 4 times, and zero heads 1 time. These frequencies 1, 4, 6, 4, 1 are the coefficients in the expansion of $(a + b)^4$, and the sum of the frequencies is $2^4 = 16$. If this experiment is conducted 16 times with true coins, the most likely frequencies would be four heads 1 time, three heads 4 times, two heads 6 times, one head 4 times, and zero heads 1 time.

We can generalize the foregoing remarks for any positive integer n. If n true coins are tossed simultaneously 2^n times, the most likely frequencies of $n, n - 1, n - 2, \ldots, 2, 1, 0$ heads, respectively, are the coefficients in the expansion of $(a + b)^n$, and the sum of these frequencies is 2^n. This generalization can be proved, but we shall not do so in this text.

If we toss five true coins $2^5 = 32$ times, the expected frequencies would be five heads 1 time, four heads 5 times, three heads 10 times, two heads 10 times, one head 5 times, and zero heads 1 time. Since these are true coins, the equiprobable measure is appropriate, and the respective probabilities of 5, 4, 3, 2, 1, and 0 heads are $\frac{1}{32}, \frac{5}{32}, \frac{10}{32}, \frac{10}{32}, \frac{5}{32}$, and $\frac{1}{32}$. Such a probability distribution is often called the *binomial distribution*.

If we toss six true coins $2^6 = 64$ times, the respective probabilities of 6, 5, 4, 3, 2, 1, and 0 heads are $\frac{1}{64}, \frac{6}{64}, \frac{15}{64}, \frac{20}{64}, \frac{15}{64}, \frac{6}{64}$, and $\frac{1}{64}$. Figure 10.10 is a histogram of the expected distribution of the number of heads when six coins are tossed simultaneously. The width of each rectangle is 1, and the height is the corresponding probability. Since the sum of the probabilities is 1, the sum of the areas of the rectangles is 1. If we construct the corre-

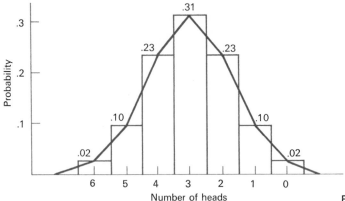

Figure 10.10

sponding frequency polygon (see Fig. 10.10), the area under this curve will also be 1.

Regardless of the value of n, the sum of the probabilities of n, $n - 1$, $n - 2$, $\cdots$, 2, 1, 0 heads will be 1. If we let n increase without bound, the frequency polygon constructed as above will approach a smooth curve which is called the *normal curve*. The distribution represented by this curve is referred to as *normal distribution*. Notice that the curve will resemble a bell which explains the often used term, "bell curve."

Problems

1 If seven coins are tossed simultaneously $2^7 = 128$ times, what is the expected distribution of heads?

2 If eight coins are tossed simultaneously $2^8 = 256$ times, what is the expected distribution of heads?

3 If seven coins are tossed simultaneously, what is the probability of obtaining exactly 7 heads? exactly 5 heads? exactly 3 heads? exactly 4 tails?

4 If eight coins are tossed simultaneously, what are the respective probabilities of obtaining exactly 8, 7, 6, 5, 4, 3, 2, 1, and 0 heads? Construct a histogram and frequency polygon showing these results.

5 Toss five coins simultaneously 32 times and record the numbers of heads on each toss. Compare your results with the expected results. To improve the chances of obtaining the expected results, have a number of friends perform the same experiment and combine your results. To obtain the distributions, divide the combined frequencies by the number of persons involved.

6 If four coins are tossed simultaneously, what is the probability that 2 or more heads will occur? 3 or more? 4 or more?

PROBABILITY AND STATISTICS

7 If five coins are tossed simultaneously, what is the probability that 3 or more heads will occur? 4 or more tails will occur? exactly 2 tails will occur?

10.17 CORRELATION

To date our discussion of statistical measures has been concerned with an analysis of a single group of variates. *Correlation* is a term applied to the relationship between two variates. We will consider the simplest of relationships between two variates, the *linear relationship*.

Table 10.13 gives data concerning 15 students at Zilch College. The second column shows the scores made by the students on an entrance examination; the third column shows their four-year grade point averages; the fourth column shows their grade point averages in math; the fifth column shows their grade point average in English.

The purpose in giving the entrance exam to a student is to help predict the grade point averages he will achieve in the various fields which he may choose. Such predictions can be very helpful in career counseling. Many interesting questions arise about such predictions. For example, if a student makes 19 on the entrance exam, what overall grade point average can he

TABLE 10.13

Student	Entrance exam (X)	Grade point average (Y)	Math grade point average (Z)	English grade point average (W)
A	28	3.9	3.7	3.8
B	27	3.3	3.4	3.0
C	26	3.5	3.5	3.5
D	23	3.1	3.2	2.9
E	23	3.5	3.5	2.7
F	22	3.0	2.9	3.8
G	21	3.1	2.9	3.4
H	20	3.0	2.6	2.4
I	20	2.7	2.8	2.5
J	20	2.6	2.4	2.5
K	18	3.0	2.7	2.9
L	18	2.5	2.5	1.9
M	16	2.1	1.9	2.3
N	16	2.3	2.0	2.6
O	14	1.9	1.9	1.8
Total	312	43.5	42.0	42.0
Mean	20.8	2.9	2.8	2.8

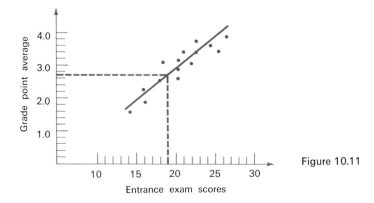

Figure 10.11

expect? What math grade point average can he expect? What English grade point average can he expect? Should he choose a mathematically oriented career or should he avoid such fields? In using the data in Table 10.13, we are concerned with the relatedness or correlation between a students performance on the entrance exam and the students overall grade point average, math grade point average and English grade point average.

Figure 10.11 is a *scatter diagram* with the overall grade point averages plotted against the corresponding entrance exam scores. The straight line through the scattered points is drawn to represent the trend as accurately as possible. We can now use this straight line to predict the overall grade point of an entering student. In this situation, we say that the relationship between the variates is linear. As an example, if a student makes 19 on the entrance exam, we find on the straight line (see Fig. 10.11) the overall grade point average associated with that score. Therefore we would predict that the student would make an overall grade point of 2.7.

If, in a scatter diagram, the points lie relatively close to a straight line, then we say that there is a high correlation between the two variables. If the points are widely scattered, then the correlation is small. Figure 10.12 illustrates these statements.

We now turn our attention to a descriptive measure, called the *coefficient of correlation*, which is a measure of relatedness between two variables when

High correlation   Low correlation

Figure 10.12

PROBABILITY AND STATISTICS

TABLE 10.14

Entrance exam score (X)	Overall grade point average (Y)	$X-\bar{X}$	$(X-\bar{X})^2$	$(Y-\bar{Y})$	$(Y-\bar{Y})^2$	$(X-\bar{X})(Y-\bar{Y})$
28	3.9	7.2	51.84	1.0	1.00	7.20
27	3.3	6.2	38.44	.4	.16	2.48
26	3.5	5.2	27.04	.6	.36	3.12
23	3.1	2.2	4.84	.2	.04	.44
23	3.5	2.2	4.84	.6	.36	1.32
22	3.0	1.2	1.44	.1	.01	.12
21	3.1	.2	.04	.2	.04	.04
20	3.0	− .8	.64	.1	.01	− .08
20	2.7	− .8	.64	− .2	.04	.16
20	2.6	− .8	.64	− .3	.09	.24
18	3.0	−2.8	7.84	.1	.01	− .28
18	2.5	−2.8	7.84	− .4	.16	1.12
16	2.1	−4.8	23.04	− .8	.64	3.84
16	2.3	−4.8	23.04	− .6	.36	2.88
14	1.9	−6.8	46.24	−1.0	1.00	6.80
Total 312	43.5	0	238.40	0	4.28	29.40
Mean 20.8	2.9	0	15.89	0	.29	1.96

their relationship is approximately linear. If X and Y are linearly related variables with σ_X and σ_Y their respective standard deviations, then the coefficient of correlation is given by the formula

$$\text{Coefficient of Correlation} = r = \frac{\overline{(X - \bar{X})(Y - \bar{Y})}}{\sigma_X \sigma_Y}.$$

In order to compute the coefficient of correlation it is convenient to organize the work by means of a table. Table 10.14 is the organization of the data used to compute the coefficient of correlation between the entrance exam scores and the overall grade point averages given in Table 10.13.

From Table 10.14 we now have

$$\overline{(X - \bar{X})(Y - \bar{Y})} = 1.96,$$
$$\sigma_X = \sqrt{15.89} = 3.99,$$
$$\sigma_Y = \sqrt{.29} = .53,$$
$$\sigma_X \sigma_Y = 2.11,$$

and thus

$$r = \frac{1.96}{2.11} = .93.$$

The coefficient of correlation obtained as in the above example must have a value between -1 and 1. This measure can be used to make inferences about the relatedness of two variables in the following ways:

1) If $r = 0$, then there is *no* relatedness between the two variables.

2) If $r = 1$, a change in one variable brings about an exactly predictable change in the other. Furthermore, a positive change in one variable brings about a positive change in the other.

3) If $r = -1$, a change in one variable brings about an exactly predictable change in the other. In this case, a positive change in one variable brings about a negative change in the other.

4) Intermediate values indicate varying degrees of relatedness between the two variables.

In our example, we found the coefficient of correlation between the entrance exam score and the overall grade point average to be .93. This indicates that the overall grade point average is highly related to the entrance exam score. If, from Table 10.13, we compute the coefficient of correlation between the entrance exam score and the English grade point average, we find that it is .75. This indicates that the two are related but not nearly so strongly as the entrance exam score and the overall grade point average.

Problems

1 Use the scatter diagram in Fig. 10.11 to predict the overall grade point average of a student who makes 25 on the entrance exam; a student who makes 16; a student who makes 21.

2 Use the data in Table 10.13 to construct a scatter diagram plotting the math grade point average against the entrance exam score. Use this diagram to predict the math grade point average of a student who makes 25 on the entrance exam; a student who makes 16; a student who makes 21.

3 Repeat Problem 2, plotting the English grade point average against the entrance exam score.

4 Use the data in Table 10.13 to construct a scatter diagram, plotting the math grade point average against the English grade point average.

5 In each of the following use the data in Table 10.13 to compute the required coefficient of correlation.

a) Between the entrance exam score and the math grade point average

b) Between the entrance exam score and the English grade point average

c) Between the math grade point average and the English grade point average

Chapter 11

INTEREST AND ANNUITIES

11.1 SIMPLE INTEREST

Interest is money paid for the use of money. Since nearly everyone borrows or invests money at some time or other, a basic knowledge of interest and how it is computed is essential to modern living.

Interest is computed on the basis of the money invested, the rate of interest, and the time for which the money is invested. The money invested is called the *principal*. The *rate of interest* is a percentage to be applied to the principal, and normally is stated as a percentage per year. The *time* involved in a transaction is measured in years (or fractions of a year) to agree with the time element of the rate. The *amount* or *accumulated value of the principal* is the sum of the principal and the interest. It is customary to adopt the following notations:

P = principal (in dollars and cents),
r = rate of interest (a percentage per year),
t = time (in years),
I = the interest earned,
S = the amount or accumulated value of the principal.

When only the principal earns interest for the duration of the transaction, the interest earned during this time is called *simple interest*. The simple interest earned by investing a principal P for t years at a rate r (converted to a decimal or fraction equivalent) is computed by the formula

$$I = Prt.$$

The amount S is computed by the formula

$$S = P + I.$$

However, recalling that $I = Prt$, we have

$$S = P + Prt = P(1 + rt).$$

The foregoing remarks are illustrated by the following examples.

Example 1 Compute the simple interest earned by $1000 invested at 6% for 5 years. What is the accumulated value of the principal?

Solution We have $P = \$1000$, $r = .06 = \frac{6}{100}$, and $t = 5$. Hence

$$I = Prt = (\$1000)(\tfrac{6}{100})(5) = \$300$$

and

$$S = P + I = \$1000 + \$300 = \$1300.$$

Example 2 Compute the amount to which $2000 accumulates if invested at 5% for $2\frac{1}{2}$ years.

Solution We have $P = \$2000$, $r = .05 = \frac{5}{100}$, and $t = \frac{5}{2}$. Hence

$$S = P(1 + rt) = \$2000(1 + .125) = \$2250.$$

If the time element t in a simple interest problem is stated in months, the time t may be converted to years by dividing by 12. However, if the time t is stated as a certain number of days, there are two ways to proceed. One is to represent a year by 365 days (or 366 in the event of a leap year). Interest computed on this basis is called *exact interest*. A second method is to represent a year by 360 days. The use of a 360-day year simplifies the arithmetic involved and, because of a smaller denominator in the time factor, it also increases the interest collected by the lender. Interest computed on the basis of a 360-day year is called *ordinary interest*, and it is the method most commonly used by banks. If the type of interest is not specified in this book, it will be assumed that it is ordinary interest.

Example 3 Find the ordinary simple interest earned by an investment of $500 if invested at 8% for 135 days.

Solution We have $P = \$500$, $r = \frac{8}{100}$, and $t = \frac{135}{360} = \frac{3}{8}$. Therefore

$$I = (\$500)(\tfrac{8}{100})(\tfrac{3}{8}) = \$15.$$

Example 4 Find the exact simple interest earned by an investment of $500 if invested at 8% for 135 days (you may assume that a leap year is not involved). Find the amount to which the principal accumulates.

Solution We have $P = \$500$, $r = \frac{8}{100}$, and $t = \frac{135}{365} = \frac{27}{73}$. Hence

$$I = (\$500)(\tfrac{8}{100})(\tfrac{27}{73}) = \$14.80,$$
$$S = P + I = \$500 + \$14.80 = \$514.80.$$

Sometimes the time element is expressed as the time between two dates. When the time element is given in this form, we will always find the actual number of days between the two dates; an approximate number of days will never be used in this book. Table II in the Appendix provides us with a convenient method for finding the actual number of days between two dates, and we will illustrate its use by the following examples.

Example 5 Find the actual number of days between June 10 and September 27.

Solution From Table II we see that September 27 is the 270th day of the year and June 10 is the 161st day of the year. Hence, the actual number of days between June 10 and September 27 is 270 − 161 = 109.

Example 6 Find the actual number of days between April 13, 1957, and March 8, 1958.

Solution From Table II we see that April 13 is the 103rd day of the year, so the number of days in 1957 is found to be 262 by subtracting 103 from 365. March 8 is the 67th day of 1958, so the actual number of days between April 13, 1957, and March 8, 1958, is 262 + 67 = 329.

If February 29 is included in the time period in question, we always add one day to the result obtained by use of Table II. However, if February 29 is not included in the time period, we do not change the value obtained from the table, even though a leap year may be involved. Another example on computing simple interest follows.

Example 7 Find the ordinary simple interest earned by an investment of $2000 if invested at 6% from April 19 to December 2.

Solution From Table II we find the actual number of days between April 19 and December 2 to be 227. Hence

$$I = (\$2000)\left(\tfrac{6}{100}\right)\left(\tfrac{227}{360}\right) = \$75.67.$$

The formulas $I = Prt$, $S = P + I$, and $S = P(1 + rt)$ are algebraic equations, and each can be solved for any one of the quantities it contains if the values of the others are known. Consider the following examples.

Example 8 A loan company lends an individual $1000 under the conditions that the debt be repaid by twelve monthly payments of $112.50 each, the first payment due one month after the loan is transacted. What interest rate is the loan company charging?

Solution The individual pays the loan company (12)($112.50) = $1350, the accumulated value of the loan. Solving the equation $S = P + I$ for I, we get $I = S - P$. Substituting S = $1350 and P = $1000, we find

$$I = S - P = \$1350 - \$1000 = \$350.$$

From $I = Prt$, we have $r = I/Pt$. Therefore

$$r = \frac{\$350}{\$1000(1)} = \frac{35}{100} = 35\%.$$

Example 9 What principal must be invested at a simple interest rate of 5% to amount to $3000 after two years?

Solution From the equation $S = P(1 + rt)$ we have

$$P = \frac{S}{1 + rt}.$$

Substituting S = $3000, $r = \frac{5}{100}$, and $t = 2$, we have

$$P = \frac{\$3000}{1 + \frac{1}{10}} = \frac{\$3000}{\frac{11}{10}} = \frac{\$30,000}{11} = \$2727.27.$$

Therefore $2727.27 invested at 5% will amount to $3000 after two years.

Problems

1 Compute the simple interest earned by $5000 invested at 10% for 3 years. What is the accumulated value of the principal?

2 Compute the simple interest earned by $3000 invested at $4\frac{1}{2}$% for 8 months. What is the accumulated value of the principal?

3 Find the ordinary simple interest earned by $1000 invested at 7% for 235 days. What is the accumulated value of the principal?

4 Find the exact simple interest earned by $1000 invested at 7% for 235 days. What is the accumulated value of the principal?

5 Find the ordinary simple interest earned by $500 invested at 5% for the period between May 19 and August 23.

6 Find the exact simple interest earned by $200 invested at 4% for the period between July 14 and December 5.

7 Find the ordinary simple interest earned by $1500 invested at $7\frac{1}{2}$% for the period between September 8, 1966, and June 3, 1967.

8 Find the exact simple interest earned by $750 invested at 6% for the period between August 22, 1967 and May 14, 1968.

9 At what simple interest rate will $975 amount to $1000 after 120 days?

10 An investment of $100 amounts to $125 after two years. What is the simple interest rate used?

11 A person pays $125 per month for 12 months to borrow $1000. What simple interest rate is he being charged?

12 Determine how long it will take a principal of $1000 to amount to $1125 at 5% simple interest.

13 What principal must be invested at a simple interest rate of 6% to amount to $5000 after 10 years?

14 What principal must be invested at a simple interest rate of 4% to amount to $1000 after 5 years?

15 What principal must be invested at a simple interest rate of 7% to amount to $750 after 6 years?

16 At what simple interest rate will an investment double itself in 20 years?

11.2 COMPOUND INTEREST

In many business transactions the interest due at the end of a given period of time is added to the original principal. This new principal earns interest during a second period of time, equal in duration to the first, and this interest is added to the second principal to form a third principal. This process of periodically adding interest to the principal is then continued throughout the term of the investment. When interest is computed and added to the principal, it is said to be *compounded* or *converted* into principal. The period of time between two successive conversions is called the *conversion period*. The sum due at the end of the transaction is called the *sum* or *compound amount*, and the difference in the compound amount and the original principal is called *compound interest*. An example is appropriate at this point in our discussion.

Example 1 Find the compound interest earned by a principal of $1000 if this principal is invested for two years at a rate of 6% with interest compounded semiannually (i.e. twice per year).

Solution At the end of the first half-year, the interest earned by the investment is

$$(\$1000)(.06)(\tfrac{1}{2}) = (\$1000)(.03) = \$30.$$

This interest is converted into principal, and $1030 becomes the principal for the second half-year. At the end of the second half-year, interest is computed on $1030 at 6% for one-half year. This interest is

$$(\$1030)(.06)(\tfrac{1}{2}) = (\$1030)(.03) = \$30.90,$$

and it is added to $1030 to obtain a new principal of $1060.90. Interest earned by this new principal for the next half-year is

$$(\$1060.90)(.06)(\tfrac{1}{2}) = (\$1060.90)(.03) = \$31.83.$$

This interest is converted into principal, and the principal for the final half-year of the period of investment is $1092.73. The interest earned during the final half-year is

$$(\$1092.73)(.06)(\tfrac{1}{2}) = (\$1092.73)(.03) = \$32.78.$$

Adding $32.78 to $1092.73 we obtain $1125.51, the sum or compound amount due at the end of the two-year period. The compound interest, the difference between the compound amount and the original principal, is $125.51. For comparison, the simple interest earned by $1000 invested at 6% for two years is $120.

A compound interest rate is always stated as a rate per year. For convenience, we shall assume that an interest rate is a compound interest rate unless it is specifically stated to be a simple interest rate. We shall also agree that a rate of interest, either stated or assumed to be a compound interest rate, is compounded annually (once per year) unless otherwise stated.

We now turn our attention to the development of a formula for computing compound interest. We shall let the symbol i represent the interest rate per conversion period. That is,

$$i = \frac{\text{stated annual rate}}{\text{the number of times per year interest is compounded}}.$$

The symbol n will be used to represent the total number of times interest is compounded during a given transaction. That is,

$n =$ (number of times interest is converted per year) · (number of years covered by the transaction).

Let us now assume that a principal P is invested for n conversion periods at the rate i per conversion period. Using the simple interest formula $S = P(1 + rt)$, where rt is i for one conversion period, we find that the compound amount at the end of the first conversion period is $P(1 + i)$. Repeating this process for the second conversion period, using $P(1 + i)$ as the new principal, we find that $P(1 + i)^2$ is the compound amount at the end of the second period. At the end of the third period, the compound amount is $P(1 + i)^3$, and so forth, to the end of the transaction. If S denotes the compound amount at the end of n conversion periods, then we have

$$S = P(1 + i)^n.$$

This result should be proved by use of the Principle of Mathematical Induction. The proof will be listed as a problem at the end of this section.

To be able to use the formula we have just developed for finding the compound amount, it will be necessary to have some method for evaluating the factor $(1 + i)^n$. Although this can be done by other methods, we will use Table III in the Appendix, which gives values of $(1 + i)^n$ for certain common interest rates and a limited range of values of n (more complete tables are available elsewhere). The value of a table such as Table III in computing compound interest should be clear from the following examples.

Example 2 Find the compound amount of $1000 invested for 10 years at 8% compounded quarterly. What is the compound interest?

Solution We have $P = \$1000$, $i = 8\% \div 4 = 2\%$, and $n = (4)(10) = 40$. Thus

$$S = (\$1000)(1 + 2\%)^{40}.$$

Ordinarily $(1 + 2\%)^{40}$ would be somewhat difficult to calculate. However, from Table III we find that $(1 + 2\%)^{40} = 2.208039$. Therefore, to the nearest cent, $S = \$2208.04$. The compound interest is

$$\$2208.04 - \$1000 = \$1208.04.$$

Example 3 Find the compound amount of $300 invested for four years at 6% compounded monthly. What is the compound interest?

Solution We have $P = \$300$, $i = 6\% \div 12 = \frac{1}{2}\%$, and $n = (12)(4) = 48$. Thus

$$S = (\$300)(1 + \tfrac{1}{2}\%)^{48}.$$

From Table III we find that $(1 + \tfrac{1}{2}\%)^{48} = 1.270489$. Therefore, to the nearest cent, $S = \$381.15$. The compound interest is $81.15.

One is often concerned with the problem of finding the principal that must be invested on some given date to amount to a certain sum at the end of a specified period of time. If a principal invested on some given date amounts to a certain sum on some future date, then this principal is called the *present value* of the sum which is due later. A formula for finding the present value P of a sum S can be obtained by solving the equation $S = P(1 + i)^n$ for P. Multiplying both members of this equation by $(1 + i)^{-n}$, we get

$$P = S(1 + i)^{-n}.$$

To use this formula we must have some method for finding the factor $(1 + i)^{-n}$. Table IV in the Appendix gives the values of this factor for certain values of i and for a limited range of values of n (more complete tables are available elsewhere). Consider the following examples.

Example 4 How much money must one invest on some given date at 5% compounded quarterly to have $1000 five years later?

Solution We seek the present value of $1000 due in five years. We have $S = \$1000$, $i = 5\% \div 4 = 1\frac{1}{4}\%$, and $n = 20$. Hence

$$P = (\$1000)(1 + 1\tfrac{1}{4}\%)^{-20}.$$

From Table IV we find that

$$(1 + 1\tfrac{1}{4}\%)^{-20} = .780008.$$

Therefore, to the nearest cent, $P = \$780.01$. That is, $780.01 invested for five years at 5% compounded quarterly will amount to $1000.

Example 5 Find the present value of $5000 due in 20 years if money can be invested at the rate of 7% compounded semi-annually.

Solution We have $S = \$5000$, $i = 7\% \div 2 = 3\frac{1}{2}\%$, and $n = (2)(20) = 40$. Hence

$$P = (\$5000)(1 + 3\tfrac{1}{2}\%)^{-40}.$$

From Table IV we find that $(1 + 3\tfrac{1}{2}\%)^{-40} = .252572$. Therefore $P = \$1262.86$ to the nearest cent. In other words, $1262.86 invested at the rate of 7% compounded semiannually will amount to $5000 in 20 years.

Problems

1 Find the compound amount of $500 invested for 15 years at 6% compounded semiannually. What is the compound interest? Compare this with the interest earned by $500 invested at 6% simple interest for 15 years.

2 Find the compound amount of $100 invested for 25 years at 5% compounded annually. What is the compound interest? Compare this with the interest earned by $100 invested at 5% simple interest for 25 years.

3 If $2000 is put in a savings account that pays 5% compounded semi-annually, how much will be in the account after 15 years?

4 Find the compound amount of $800 after 10 years if invested at (a) 5% compounded annually, (b) 5% compounded semiannually. What is your conclusion?

5 Find the compound interest earned by $1000 if invested at 8% compounded quarterly for 8 years and 9 months.

6 Find the compound amount of $500 after three years if invested at (a) 4% compounded semiannually, (b) 4% compounded monthly. What is your conclusion?

7 A property of exponents can be used to help calculate the value of $(1 + 5\%)^{120}$ from Table III. Use this value to find the compound amount of $100 invested at 5% for 120 years.

8 Find the present value of $1000 due in 12 years if money can be invested at the rate of 8% compounded quarterly.

9 Find the present value of $3000 due in 4 years if money can be invested at the rate of 6% compounded monthly.

10 How much must one invest on some given date at 5% compounded quarterly to have $2000 after 10 years?

11 How much must one invest on some given date at 5% compounded yearly to have $10,000 after 30 years?

12 Use a property of exponents to calculate $(1 + 5\%)^{-60}$ from Table IV. Use this value to find the present value of $1000 due in 60 years at 5%.

13 Let S denote the compound amount of a principal P invested for n conversion periods at a rate i per conversion period. Prove by mathematical induction that

$$S = P(1 + i)^n$$

for every positive integer n.

11.3 ARITHMETIC PROGRESSIONS

An *infinite sequence* is a function from the set of positive integers into the set of real numbers. Such a sequence can be specified by writing

$$a_1, a_2, a_3, \ldots, a_n, \ldots,$$

where a_n is the real number which corresponds to the positive integer n. This concept will be illustrated by the following examples.

Example 1   An example of an infinite sequence is

$$1, \frac{1}{2}, \frac{1}{3}, \frac{1}{4}, \frac{1}{5}, \ldots, \frac{1}{n}, \ldots$$

For this sequence

$$a_1 = 1, a_2 = \frac{1}{2}, a_3 = \frac{1}{3}, \ldots, a_n = \frac{1}{n}, \ldots$$

Example 2   A second example of an infinite sequence is

$$1, -1, 1, -1, 1, -1, \ldots, (-1)^{n+1}, \ldots$$

For this sequence

$$a_1 = 1, a_2 = -1, a_3 = 1, \ldots, a_n = (-1)^{n+1}, \ldots$$

Example 3 As a third example, consider the infinite sequence

$$\frac{1}{2}, \frac{2}{3}, \frac{3}{4}, \frac{4}{5}, \frac{5}{6}, \ldots, \frac{n}{n+1}, \ldots$$

For this sequence

$$a_1 = \frac{1}{2}, a_2 = \frac{2}{3}, a_3 = \frac{3}{4}, \ldots, a_n = \frac{n}{n+1}, \ldots$$

An *arithmetic progression* is a sequence in which each term after the first is obtained by adding the same number, called the *common difference*, to the preceding term. It is clear from the definition that the common difference can be found by taking any term, except the first, and subtracting the preceding term.

Example 4 The sequence 3, 5, 7, 9, ... is an arithmetic progression in which the common difference is 2.

Example 5 The sequence 10, 5, 0, −5, −10, ... is an arithmetic progression in which the common difference is −5.

We shall adopt the following notation in referring to arithmetic progressions:

a_1, the first term,
d, the common difference,
a_n, the nth term,
S_n, the sum of the first n terms.

Using this notation, we can represent the first n terms of an arithmetic progression by

$$a_1, a_1 + d, a_1 + 2d, a_1 + 3d, \ldots, a_1 + (n-1)d.$$

From this representation we see that the nth term of an arithmetic progression can be expressed in terms of the first term and the common difference by the equation

$$a_n = a_1 + (n-1)d.$$

Example 6 Find the 20th term of the arithmetic progression 3, 5, 7, 9, ...

Solution In the given arithmetic progression, $a_1 = 3$ and $d = 2$. Thus

$$a_{20} = 3 + (20-1)2 = 3 + (19)(2) = 41.$$

Example 7 Find the first seven terms of the arithmetic progression in which the first term is 7 and the seventh term is 22.

Solution For the given progression, $a_1 = 7$ and $a_7 = 22$. Since

$$a_7 = a_1 + 6d,$$

we have

$$22 = 7 + 6d,$$
$$15 = 6d,$$
$$2\tfrac{1}{2} = d.$$

Thus the first seven terms of the progression are

$$7,\ 9\tfrac{1}{2},\ 12,\ 14\tfrac{1}{2},\ 17,\ 19\tfrac{1}{2},\ 22.$$

Example 8 Find the first five terms of the arithmetic progression in which the third term is 7 and the seventh term is -13.

Solution For the given progression, $a_3 = 7$ and $a_7 = -13$. Thus

$$a_3 = 7 = a_1 + 2d \qquad \text{and} \qquad a_7 = -13 = a_1 + 6d.$$

Subtracting the respective members of the first equation from those of the second, we have

$$-20 = 4d \qquad \text{or} \qquad d = -5.$$

Substituting this value into the equation $7 = a_1 + 2d$, we find $a_1 = 17$. Therefore the first five terms of the progression are

$$17,\ 12,\ 7,\ 2,\ -3.$$

To find the sum of the first n terms of an arithmetic progression, we have

$$S_n = a_1 + (a_1 + d) + \cdots + [a_1 + (n-2)d] + [a_1 + (n-1)d].$$

If the terms in the right-hand member of this equation are written in reverse order, the equation becomes

$$S_n = [a_1 + (n-1)d] + [a_1 + (n-2)d] + \cdots + (a_1 + d) + a_1.$$

If we add the respective members of these two equations, we have

$$2S_n = [2a_1 + (n-1)d] + [2a_1 + (n-1)d] + \cdots$$
$$+ [2a_1 + (n-1)d] + [2a_1 + (n-1)d].$$

Since there are n terms $2a_1 + (n-1)d$ in the right-hand member of this equation, we have

$$2S_n = n[2a_1 + (n-1)d],$$

$$S_n = \frac{n}{2}[2a_1 + (n-1)d].$$

This equation can be used to find the sum of the first n terms of an arithmetic progression whenever a_1, n, and d are known. This equation can be written

$$S_n = \frac{n}{2}[a_1 + (a_1 + (n - 1)d)].$$

Recalling $a_n = a_1 + (n - 1)d$, we can then express the equation in the form

$$S_n = \frac{n}{2}(a_1 + a_n).$$

This equation gives the sum of the first n terms of an arithmetic progression in terms of n, a_1, and a_n. Both equations for the sum of the first n terms of an arithmetic progression can be established by mathematical induction.

Example 9   Find the sum of the first 25 terms of the arithmetic progression 3, 8, 13, ...

Solution   For the given progression, $a_1 = 3$ and $d = 5$. Using the equation

$$S_n = \frac{n}{2}[2a_1 + (n - 1)d],$$

we have

$$S_{25} = \frac{25}{2}[2(3) + (25 - 1)5]$$

$$= \frac{25}{2}(6 + 120)$$

$$= 1575.$$

Example 10   The sum of the first 25 terms of an arithmetic progression is 525. The 25th term is 39. Find the first term and the common difference.

Solution   Substituting into the equation

$$S_n = \frac{n}{2}(a_1 + a_n),$$

we have

$$S_{25} = 525 = \frac{25}{2}(a_1 + 39).$$

Solving this equation for a_1, we find $a_1 = 3$. Since $a_{25} = a_1 + 24d$,

$$39 = 3 + 24d,$$

and thus

$$d = \frac{3}{2}.$$

Problems

In Problems 1 through 6 write the next three terms in the given arithmetic progression and find S_n for the given value of n.

1. $3, 7, 11, \ldots,$ $n = 7$
2. $15, 13, 11, \ldots, n = 15$
3. $\frac{1}{2}, 1, \frac{3}{2}, \ldots,$ $n = 18$
4. $38, 31, 24, \ldots, n = 8$
5. $-10, -7, -4, \ldots, n = 9$
6. $\frac{5}{3}, 1, \frac{1}{3}, \ldots,$ $n = 5$

In Problems 7 through 12, three of the elements $a_1, a_n, d, n,$ and S_n of an arithmetic progression are given. Find the missing elements.

7. $a_1 = 3, d = 6, n = 15$
8. $a_1 = -2, n = 8, S_n = 70$
9. $d = \frac{2}{3}, n = 7, S_n = 21$
10. $a_1 = 17, n = 9, a_n = -39$
11. $d = 3, n = 15, a_n = 31$
12. $a_1 = 4, d = 5, S_n = 104$

12. The 3rd and 20th terms of an arithmetic progression are 15 and 117, respectively. Find the first term.

14. The 15th and 40th terms of an arithmetic progression are 37 and 112, respectively. Find the 25th term.

15. Find the sum of the first 50 positive integers.

16. Find the sum of the first 50 even positive integers.

17. Find the sum of the first 50 odd positive integers.

18. Prove by mathematical induction the relation $a_n = a_1 + (n - 1)d$ for the nth term of an arithmetic progression.

19. Prove by mathematical induction the relation

$$S_n = \frac{n}{2}[2a_1 + (n - 1)d]$$

for the sum of the first n terms of an arithmetic progression.

11.4 GEOMETRIC PROGRESSIONS

A *geometric progression* is a sequence in which each term after the first is obtained by multiplying the preceding term by the same number, called the *common ratio*. It is clear from the definition that the common ratio (if it is not zero) can be found by taking any term, except the first, and dividing it by the preceding term.

Example 1   The sequence $3, 6, 12, \ldots$ is a geometric progression in which the common ratio is 2.

Example 2   The sequence $2, 1, \frac{1}{2}, \frac{1}{4}, \ldots$ is a geometric progression in which the common ratio is $\frac{1}{2}$.

Example 3 The sequence $1, -2, 4, -8, \ldots$ is a geometric progression in which the common ratio is -2.

We shall adopt the following notation in referring to geometric progressions:

a_1, the first term,
r, the common ratio,
a_n, the nth term,
S_n, the sum of the first n terms.

Using this notation, we can represent the first n terms of a geometric progression by

$$a_1, a_1 r, a_1 r^2, a_1 r^3, \ldots, a_1 r^{n-1}.$$

From this representation we see that the nth term of a geometric progression can be expressed in terms of the first term and the common ratio by the equation

$$a_n = a_1 r^{n-1}.$$

Example 4 Find the seventh term of the geometric progression $2, 1, \frac{1}{2}, \frac{1}{4}, \ldots$

Solution In the given progression, $a_1 = 2$ and $r = \frac{1}{2}$. Thus

$$a_7 = 2\left(\tfrac{1}{2}\right)^6 = 2\left(\tfrac{1}{64}\right) = \tfrac{1}{32}.$$

Example 5 Find the first three terms of the geometric progression in which the fourth term is 1 and the eighth term is $\frac{1}{81}$.

Solution For the given progression, $a_4 = 1$ and $a_8 = \frac{1}{81}$. Thus

$$a_4 = 1 = a_1 r^3 \qquad \text{and} \qquad a_8 = \tfrac{1}{81} = a_1 r^7.$$

If we divide the members of the second equation by the respective members of the first, we have

$$\frac{1}{81} = \frac{1}{r^4}, \qquad \text{or} \qquad r = \frac{1}{3}.$$

Since

$$a_1 = \frac{1}{r^3} = \frac{1}{\left(\tfrac{1}{3}\right)^3} = \frac{1}{\tfrac{1}{27}} = 27,$$

the first three terms of the progression are

$$27, 9, 3.$$

To find the sum of the first n terms of a geometric progression, we have

$$S_n = a_1 + a_1 r + a_1 r^2 + a_1 r^3 + \cdots + a_1 r^{n-1}.$$

Multiplying both members of this equation by r, we have

$$rS_n = a_1r + a_1r^2 + a_1r^3 + \cdots + a_1r^{n-1} + a_1r^n.$$

Subtracting the members of this equation from the respective members of the previous equation, we have

$$S_n - rS_n = a_1 - a_1r^n,$$
$$(1 - r)S_n = a_1(1 - r^n).$$

Solving for S_n, we obtain

$$S_n = \frac{a_1(1 - r^n)}{1 - r}, \qquad r \neq 1.$$

This equation can be used to find the sum of the first n terms of a geometric progression whenever a_1, n, and r are known. This equation can be written

$$S_n = \frac{a_1 - a_1r^n}{1 - r}, \qquad r \neq 1.$$

Since $a_n = a_1r^{n-1}$, we have $ra_n = a_1r^n$, and substituting into the latter equation for S_n, we obtain

$$S_n = \frac{a_1 - ra_n}{1 - r}, \qquad r \neq 1.$$

Both equations for the sum of the first n terms of a geometric progression can be established by mathematical induction.

Example 6 Find the sum of the first six terms of the geometric progression 3, 6, 12, . . .

Solution For the given progression, $a_1 = 3$ and $r = 2$. Using the equation

$$S_n = \frac{a_1 - a_1r^n}{1 - r},$$

we have

$$S_6 = \frac{3 - 3(2)^6}{1 - 2}$$

$$= \frac{3 - 3(64)}{-1}$$

$$= 189.$$

In our discussion of progressions so far, we have considered only the sum of a finite number of terms. In the case of arithmetic progressions it is clear that one could never sum infinitely many terms of a progression. The same is true of a geometric progression if $|r| > 1$. However, the sum S of infinitely many terms of a geometric progression exists if $|r| < 1$ and

$$S = \frac{a_1}{1 - r}.$$

Whenever S exists, we shall refer to it as the *sum* of the geometric progression.

Example 7 Find the sum of the geometric progression $2, 1, \frac{1}{2}, \ldots$

Solution For the given progression, $a_1 = 2$ and $r = \frac{1}{2}$. Therefore

$$S = \frac{2}{1 - \frac{1}{2}} = \frac{2}{\frac{1}{2}} = 4.$$

Example 8 Find the sum of the geometric progression $\frac{2}{3}, -\frac{2}{9}, \frac{2}{27}, \ldots$

Solution For the given progression, $a_1 = \frac{2}{3}$ and $r = -\frac{1}{3}$. Therefore

$$S = \frac{\frac{2}{3}}{1 - (-\frac{1}{3})} = \frac{\frac{2}{3}}{1 + \frac{1}{3}} = \frac{\frac{2}{3}}{\frac{4}{3}} = \frac{1}{2}.$$

Problems

In Problems 1 through 6 write the next three terms in the given geometric progression and find S_n for the given value of n.

1 $2, 6, 18, \ldots,$ $n = 7$ 2 $-3, 1, -\frac{1}{3}, \frac{1}{9}, \ldots, n = 5$

3 $\frac{1}{4}, \frac{1}{2}, 1, \ldots,$ $n = 6$ 4 $\frac{3}{4}, \frac{1}{2}, \frac{1}{3}, \ldots,$ $n = 5$

5 $1, -1, 1, -1, \ldots, n = 8$ 6 $\frac{2}{3}, -\frac{4}{9}, \frac{8}{27}, \ldots,$ $n = 4$

In Problems 7 through 12, three of the elements, $a_1, a_n, r, n,$ and S_n of a geometric progression are given. Find the missing elements.

7 $a_1 = 2, r = 2, n = 6$ 8 $a_1 = 9, n = 5, S_n = \frac{121}{9}$

9 $r = -\frac{1}{2}, n = 3, a_n = \frac{1}{4}$ 10 $a_1 = 27, n = 4, a_n = 1$

11 $r = -5, n = 3, a_n = \frac{1}{5}$ 12 $a_1 = \frac{2}{3}, r = -\frac{2}{3}, S_n = \frac{14}{27}$

In Problems 13 through 16 find the sum of the given geometric progression.

13 $2, \frac{2}{3}, \frac{2}{9}, \cdots$ 14 $-\frac{1}{3}, \frac{1}{6}, -\frac{1}{12}, \cdots$

15 $96, 64, 42\frac{2}{3}, \cdots$ 16 $-\frac{3}{8}, \frac{1}{16}, -\frac{1}{96}, \cdots$

17 The second and fifth terms of a geometric progression are 27 and 1, respectively. Find the seventh term.

18 The third and sixth terms of a geometric progression are $-\frac{1}{3}$ and $\frac{1}{81}$, respectively. Find the first term.

19 The sum of a geometric progression is 6 and the first term is 3. Find the common ratio.

20 The sum of a geometric progression is $\frac{2}{3}$ and the common ratio is $-\frac{1}{2}$. Find the first term.

21 Prove by mathematical induction the relation $a_n = a_1 r^{n-1}$ for the nth term of a geometric progression.

22 Prove by mathematical induction the relation

$$S_n = \frac{a_1(1 - r^n)}{1 - r}, \qquad r \neq 1,$$

for the sum of the first n terms of a geometric progression.

23 What can be said about any geometric progression with $r = 1$? What about the sum S_n?

11.5 ORDINARY ANNUITIES

An *annuity* is a series of equal payments made at equal intervals of time. Payments on a home loan and monthly payments to a retirement fund are examples of annuities that are familiar to most people.

The time between two successive payments of an annuity is called its *payment period*, and the time from the beginning of the first payment period to the end of the last payment period is called the *term of the annuity*. In this text we shall consider only annuities in which the payment period is the same as the conversion period of the interest rate. The symbol R will be used to denote the periodic payment of an annuity and the letter n to represent the total number of payment periods in the term of the annuity. Since we are considering only annuities in which the payment periods and the interest conversion periods coincide, n also represents the number of interest conversions in the term of the annuity.

An *ordinary annuity* is an annuity in which the payments are made at the ends of the payment periods. Note that for ordinary annuities the term begins one payment period before the first payment and ends with the last payment. We shall restrict our attention here to ordinary annuities.

The *amount S of an annuity* is the sum of the accumulated values of all the payments of the annuity, each accumulated to the end of the term of the annuity. The *present value A of an annuity* is the sum of the present values of all the payments of the annuity at the beginning of the term of the annuity. The following example should illustrate these concepts.

Example 1 Find the amount S and the present value A of an ordinary annuity of $1000 to be paid every six months for two years if money is worth 10% compounded semiannually.

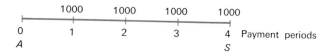

Figure 11.1

Solution A line diagram of this annuity is shown in Fig. 11.1. Since the first payment earns interest for three interest periods, the second payment for two periods, the third for one period, and the fourth for zero periods, we have

$$S = 1000(1 + 5\%)^3 + 1000(1 + 5\%)^2 + 1000(1 + 5\%)^1 + 1000.$$

Using Table III in the Appendix gives

$$\begin{aligned} S &= 1000(1.157625) + 1000(1.102500) + 1000(1.05) + 1000 \\ &= 1157.63 + 1102.50 + 1050.00 + 1000 \\ &= \$4310.13. \end{aligned}$$

The present value of the annuity is the sum of the present values of the four payments of the annuity at the beginning of the term of the annuity. Hence

$$\begin{aligned} A = {}&1000(1 + 5\%)^{-1} + 1000(1 + 5\%)^{-2} \\ &+ 1000(1 + 5\%)^{-3} + 1000(1 + 5\%)^{-4}. \end{aligned}$$

Using Table IV in the Appendix gives

$$\begin{aligned} A &= 1000(.952380) + 1000(.907029) + 1000(.863837) + 1000(.822702) \\ &= 952.38 + 907.03 + 863.84 + 822.70 \\ &= \$3545.95. \end{aligned}$$

Let us now consider an ordinary annuity with periodic payment R which has n payment periods in its term. A line diagram for such an annuity is shown in Fig. 11.2.

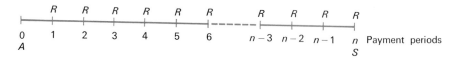

Figure 11.2

If i denotes the interest rate per conversion period, then

$$S = R(1 + i)^{n-1} + R(1 + i)^{n-2} + \cdots + R(1 + i)^2 + R(1 + i)^1 + R.$$

If we reverse the order of the terms in the preceding equation, we have

$$S = R + R(1 + i)^1 + R(1 + i)^2 + \cdots + R(1 + i)^{n-2} + R(1 + i)^{n-1},$$

and we recognize S as being the sum of the first n terms of a geometric progression with common ratio $(1 + i)$. Hence, using the formula for the sum of the first n terms of a geometric progression gives

$$S = \frac{R(1 - (1 + i)^n)}{1 - (1 + i)}$$

$$= R\frac{(1 + i)^n - 1}{i}.$$

If we define the symbol $s_{\overline{n}|i}$ by the equation

$$s_{\overline{n}|i} = \frac{(1 + i)^n - 1}{i},$$

then we can write

$$S = Rs_{\overline{n}|i}.$$

The symbol $s_{\overline{n}|i}$ is read "s angle n at i," and for certain values of n and i, its value is listed in Table V of the Appendix.

The present value A of the annuity is given by

$$A = R(1 + i)^{-1} + R(1 + i)^{-2} + R(1 + i)^{-3} + \cdots$$
$$+ R(1 + i)^{-(n-1)} + R(1 + i)^{-n}.$$

The right-hand side of this equation is the sum of the first n terms of a geometric progression with common ratio $(1 + i)^{-1}$. Using the formula for the sum of the first n terms of a geometric progression, we have

$$A = \frac{R(1 + i)^{-1}(1 - (1 + i)^{-n})}{1 - (1 + i)^{-1}}$$

$$= R\frac{(1 + i)^{-1} - (1 + i)^{-n-1}}{1 - (1 + i)^{-1}}.$$

If we multiply the numerator and denominator of this last expression by $(1 + i)$, we have

$$A = R\frac{1 - (1 + i)^{-n}}{(1 + i) - 1}$$

$$= R\frac{1 - (1 + i)^{-n}}{i}.$$

If we define the symbol $a_{\overline{n}|i}$ by the equation

$$a_{\overline{n}|i} = \frac{1 - (1 + i)^{-n}}{i},$$

then we can write

$$A = Ra_{\overline{n}|i}.$$

The symbol $a_{\overline{n}|i}$ is read "a angle n at i," and for certain values of n and i, its value is given in Table VI of the Appendix.

We conclude this section with some examples.

Example 2 Find the amount and present value of an ordinary annuity of $500 quarterly for 10 years if money is worth 8% compounded quarterly.

Solution For this annuity we have $R = \$500$, $n = 40$, and $i = 2\%$. The amount S of the annuity is given by

$$S = Rs_{\overline{n}|i} = \$500s_{\overline{40}|2\%}.$$

Using Table V, we have

$$S = \$500(60.401983) = \$30{,}200.99.$$

The present value A of the annuity is given by

$$A = Ra_{\overline{n}|i} = \$500a_{\overline{40}|2\%}.$$

Using Table VI, we have

$$A = \$500(27.355479) = \$13{,}677.74.$$

Example 3 A man wishes to place in a bank a deposit sufficient to enable his son to withdraw $200 per month for each of the four years (48 months) he will be in college. The first withdrawal is to be made one month after the deposit is made. The bank will pay 4% compounded monthly on the balance remaining in the bank. How much should the father deposit?

Solution We wish to know the present value A of an ordinary annuity with periodic payments of $200, having 48 payment periods. Since $i = \frac{1}{3}\%$, we have

$$A = \$200a_{\overline{48}|\frac{1}{3}\%}.$$

Using Table VI, we find that

$$A = \$200(44.288833) = \$8857.77.$$

Therefore, the father must deposit $8857.77 in the bank to enable his son to withdraw $200 per month for each of the 48 months he is in college.

Example 4 A man receives a royalty check for $120 every six months from an oil company. He deposits this money in a bank on January 1 and July 1 each year for 15 years. If the bank pays 5% compounded semiannually, how much will the man have in his account after 15 years?

Solution The man makes a deposit at the end of a six-month period for 30 periods. We shall assume that he made his first deposit at the end of a six-month period during which he had no money in the bank. Thus the series of deposits is an ordinary annuity with $R = \$120$ and $n = 30$, and we seek the amount of such an annuity. Since $i = 2\frac{1}{2}\%$, we have

$$S = Rs_{\overline{n}|i} = \$120s_{\overline{30}|2\frac{1}{2}\%}.$$

Using Table V, we have

$$S = \$120(43.902703) = \$5268.32.$$

Therefore the man will have $5268.32 in his account after 15 years.

Problems

1 Find the amount and present value of an ordinary annuity of $2000 per year for 25 years, calculating interest at 5% compounded annually.

2 Find the amount and present value of an ordinary annuity of $500 quarterly for $11\frac{1}{2}$ years, calculating interest at 10% compounded quarterly.

3 A man deposits $50 on the first of each month in a bank that pays 9% compounded monthly. How much does he have in his account at the end of 2 years? 4 years?

4 Find the amount of an ordinary annuity of $100 per month for 3 years if money is worth 4% compounded monthly.

5 Find the present value of an ordinary annuity of $300 per quarter for 6 years if money is worth 10% compounded quarterly.

6 Find the present value of an ordinary annuity of $250 every six months for 25 years if money is worth 8% compounded semiannually.

7 Find the amount of an ordinary annuity of $1500 every six months for 15 years if money is worth 8% compounded semiannually.

8 A man buys a house for $5000 down and $150 per month for 4 years. If interest is 9% compounded monthly, what is the equivalent cash price of the house?

9 A man buys a house for $2500 down and $500 every six months for 25 years. If money is worth 5% compounded semiannually, what is the equivalent cash price of the house?

10 Every three months for 10 years, Amanda's father deposited $100 in the Security Savings and Loan Company which paid interest at the rate of 5% compounded quarterly. At the end of the 10-year period, the money in the account was presented to Amanda as a graduation gift. How much did she receive?

11 A debt is paid by monthly installments of $90 per month for 36 months. If interest is figured at 9% compounded monthly, what is the debt?

12 To buy a car, Mr. Joyner saved $60 per month for 2 years. If his money earned interest at 4% compounded monthly, how much did he have for his down payment at the end of 2 years?

13 Prove that $(1 + i)a_{\overline{n}|i} = a_{\overline{n-1}|i} + 1$.

11.6 THE PERIODIC PAYMENT

If we solve the equations

$$S = Rs_{\overline{n}|i} \qquad \text{and} \qquad A = Ra_{\overline{n}|i} \qquad \text{for } R,$$

we have the formulas

$$R = S\frac{1}{s_{\overline{n}|i}} \qquad \text{and} \qquad R = A\frac{1}{a_{\overline{n}|i}}$$

for determining the periodic payment of an annuity. The values of $1/s_{\overline{n}|i}$ and $1/a_{\overline{n}|i}$ could be found from Tables V and VI of the Appendix by performing a problem in long division. However, this will not be necessary because certain values of $1/a_{\overline{n}|i}$ can be read from Table VII in the Appendix, and the equation

$$\frac{1}{s_{\overline{n}|i}} = \frac{1}{a_{\overline{n}|i}} - i$$

allows us to readily obtain the value of $1/s_{\overline{n}|i}$, provided the value of $1/a_{\overline{n}|i}$ is known. This equation can be derived from the definitions of $a_{\overline{n}|i}$ and $s_{\overline{n}|i}$. Using these definitions, we have

$$\frac{1}{s_{\overline{n}|i}} + i = \frac{i}{(1 + i)^n - 1} + i$$

$$= \frac{i}{(1 + i)^n - 1} \cdot \frac{(1 + i)^{-n}}{(1 + i)^{-n}} + i$$

$$= \frac{i(1 + i)^{-n}}{1 - (1 + i)^{-n}} + i$$

$$= \frac{i(1 + i)^{-n} + i - i(1 + i)^{-n}}{1 - (1 + i)^{-n}}$$

$$= \frac{i}{1 - (1 + i)^{-n}}$$

$$= \frac{1}{a_{\overline{n}|i}}.$$

Solving the equation

$$\frac{1}{s_{\overline{n}|i}} + i = \frac{1}{a_{\overline{n}|i}} \qquad \text{for} \qquad \frac{1}{s_{\overline{n}|i}},$$

we obtain the desired result.

Example 1 Find the value of $1/s_{\overline{25}|2\%}$.

Solution From Table VII, we find that

$$\frac{1}{a_{\overline{25}|2\%}} = .051220.$$

The decimal equivalent of $i = 2\%$ is .02. Hence

$$\frac{1}{s_{\overline{25}|2\%}} = .051220 - .02 = .031220.$$

Example 2 Monthly deposits are made in a savings account for three years. If money is worth 4% compounded monthly, how much should be deposited in the account each month for the account to have $3000 just after the final deposit?

Solution We seek the periodic payment R of an annuity for which $S = \$3000$, $n = 36$, and $i = \frac{1}{3}\%$. Thus,

$$R = S\frac{1}{s_{\overline{n}|i}} = \$3000\,\frac{1}{s_{\overline{36}|\frac{1}{3}\%}}.$$

From Table VII we find that

$$\frac{1}{a_{\overline{36}|\frac{1}{3}\%}} = .029523.$$

Hence

$$\frac{1}{s_{\overline{36}|\frac{1}{3}\%}} = .029523 - .003333 = .026190,$$

and

$$R = 3000(.026190) = \$78.57.$$

Example 3 To provide for his son's college expenses, a man deposits $5000 in a bank that pays interest at the rate of 5% compounded quarterly. If the son makes equal withdrawals at the end of the next 16 quarters, the first withdrawal being made one quarter after the money has been deposited, how much can he withdraw each quarter?

11.6 THE PERIODIC PAYMENT

387

Solution We seek the periodic payment R of an annuity for which $A = \$5000$, $n = 16$, and $i = 1\frac{1}{4}\%$. Thus

$$R = A\,\frac{1}{a_{\overline{n}|i}} = \$5000\,\frac{1}{a_{\overline{16}|1\frac{1}{4}\%}}.$$

From Table VII we find that

$$\frac{1}{a_{\overline{16}|1\frac{1}{4}\%}} = .069346, \quad \text{and hence} \quad R = 5000(.069346) = \$346.73.$$

Therefore the son can withdraw \$346.73 at the end of each quarter.

Problems

1 Find the value of

$$\frac{1}{s_{\overline{42}|4\%}}.$$

2 Find the value of

$$\frac{1}{s_{\overline{25}|\frac{3}{4}\%}}.$$

3 Annual deposits are made into a savings account for 30 years. If interest is computed at the rate of 5% compounded annually, what annual deposit is necessary if the account is to contain \$8000 just after the last deposit has been made?

4 A man wishes to have \$6000 available in 18 years when his son enters college. If he can invest his money at 5% compounded semiannually, how much should he deposit at the end of each six-month period?

5 Miss Long agrees to pay a debt of \$2000 by making equal payments at the end of each month for 36 months. If money is worth 9% compounded monthly, what should her payments be?

6 Mr. Henry buys a house worth \$12,000 by making a down payment of \$5000 and agreeing to pay the balance in 40 equal quarterly installments, the first to be made 3 months from now. If money is worth 8% compounded quarterly, what should his quarterly payment be?

7 Mr. Hughes wishes to have \$800 available in 2 years to purchase a color television set. If he can invest his money at 4% compounded monthly at the First National Bank, what monthly deposit should he make in order to pay cash for the television set at the end of 2 years?

8 A man deposits \$4000 in a bank that pays 5% compounded semiannually. He wishes to make equal withdrawals at the end of each six-month period for the next 10 years. How much can be withdrawn each time?

Chapter 12

COMPUTERS AND
COMPUTER PROGRAMMING

12.1 INTRODUCTION

Through the years there have been ever increasing demands that numerical computations be performed with greater speed and accuracy. These demands have been met with some remarkable inventions. Among these was the Hindu-Arabic numeration system (see Chapter 3). In this chapter we shall discuss the development and use of an invention of more recent vintage, the electronic digital computer.

Blaise Pascal, a French mathematician, is credited with the invention of the first mechanical calculating machine. In 1642, Pascal, at the age of nineteen, devised an adding machine to assist his father in the auditing of some government accounts. Pascal's machine could be used to find the sum of numbers not exceeding six digits. It was operated by turning a series of dials very similar to the dial of a telephone, that is marked with the digits 0 through 9 around the circumference. The "carrying" process was handled mechanically through the use of a ratchet mechanism that advanced a dial one digit whenever the dial to its right made a complete revolution. The answer to a problem appeared on indicators located above the dials.

The next big step forward in the development of calculating machines was made by the German mathematician, philosopher, writer and diplomat, Gottfried Wilhelm Leibniz. He wanted to mechanize the compilation of certain tables in order to free scientists from the labor of calculation. In his words, "It is unworthy of excellent men to lose hours like slaves in the labor of calculation." In 1671 he invented a machine that would not only add but also multiply and divide. The main contribution made by Leibniz to the development of modern calculating machinery was not his machine but his recognition of the advantages of using the binary numeration system (base 2) instead of the denary numeration system (base 10). The basic code used in most of today's computers is based on the binary numeration system.

About 1812 an English mathematician named Charles Babbage began to design a machine to aid in the calculation of mathematical tables. His first machine, called a Difference Engine, was built in 1822 and it could generate tables to an accuracy of six decimal places. He began work on a bigger engine capable of twenty-place accuracy, but because of the lack of finances only a part of this machine was ever constructed. Babbage abandoned his project and began to design a more versatile machine, which he called an Analytical Engine. It was to be steam-powered and was to work from a planned program of operating instructions stored on punched cards. He intended to make the machine capable of tabulating the values of any function and printing the results. Only part of the Analytical Engine was ever constructed. This was partially due to the lack of finances, but more probably to the lack of necessary precision tools. It was not until the twentieth century that a machine was built that incorporated all the concepts that the Analytical Engine was to have.

The first large-scale automatic digital computer was the IBM Automatic Sequence Control Calculator (ASCC) which was completed at Harvard in 1944. This machine was the result of work started in 1937 by Howard H. Aiken, a Harvard University Ph.D. candidate in physics, and supported by International Business Machines Corporation. The ASCC, later called the Mark I, weighed 5 tons and was 51 feet long and 8 feet high. It consisted of a complex of 78 devices linked by 500 miles of wiring. The Mark I was controlled by a program of instructions punched into a roll of paper tape. It could perform 23-digit additions and subtractions in three-tenths of a second and multiply two 23-digit numbers in about six seconds.

The first electronic digital calculator was the Electronic Numerical Integrator and Calculator (ENIAC). This machine was completed at the University of Pennsylvania in 1946 by J. Presper Eckert and Dr. John W. Mauchly. The ENIAC was developed for the U.S. Army. In this machine a number of mechanically moving parts were eliminated by making use of electronic pulses. This was a tremendous step forward, for electronic pulses can move thousands of times faster than electromechanical devices.

In the late forties and early fifties, several computers were developed which stored the operating instructions as well as the data inside the computer memory. This development, the idea of Dr. John von Neuman, completes the concept of today's stored program computer.

Since the appearance of the first electronic digital computer (ENIAC in 1946), the number and diversity of computer applications have increased sharply. In the beginning, the electronic digital computer was a specialized calculating tool for use by mathematicians and scientists. Today computers can be used to print out bank statements as well as make mathematical calculations. They can be used to make decisions as to the optimum route for a salesman as well as to control a space capsule orbiting the moon. They can read, write, and do arithmetic, all at rates of speed millions of times faster than a human. More and more our lives will be influenced by the electronic digital computers as they are bringing about a revolution based on the transformation and transmission of information.

We conclude this section with the remark that it is a struggle, even for computer specialists, to keep up with the progress being made with computers. Continuing improvement in both the equipment and the programming have made it possible for more people to use a computer to solve more problems. Even as this book is being written, new and improved machines are being developed and manufactured. In this section, we have tried to give the reader some idea of the significant steps in the development of the electronic digital computer and the diversity of its uses.

12.2 COMMUNICATING WITH A COMPUTER

A modern-day computer consists of a *central processing unit* (CPU) and an *input-output* (I-O) device. The CPU is a complex electronic mechanism which stores and processes data. The I-O device feeds data to the CPU and produces answers after the data have been processed. The inner structure of the CPU will not be discussed in this chapter. Instead, we shall describe some of the most common I-O devices and develop a language for communicating with a computer.

Perhaps the simplest of the I-O devices is the typewriter. By typing in the usual way, the operator can transmit instructions to the CPU. So that the operator can read what he has typed, the typewriter prints ordinary typewritten copy. After the problem has been solved by the CPU, the CPU directs the typewriter to print out the solution.

Another familiar method for exchanging information with the CPU is by use of an I-O device called a card read-punch. Information is transmitted to the CPU by a sequence of punched cards. After processing the data the CPU produces new punched cards with the output information. Many other I-O devices are available. A system often has several: one device for input and another for output. For example, information is frequently fed into the CPU by punched paper tape, magnetic tape, or magnetic disk. Output is often recorded on magnetic tapes or magnetic disks. Many computing systems have a high-speed printer which produces output in report form, printing an entire line of information at one time. Since output can be most easily interpreted in printed form, we shall assume throughout this chapter that a high-speed printer is available, and this method of output will be used exclusively. The punched card will be used exclusively for input purposes.

Input consists of *data* (in number form) and a set of instructions called a *program* directing the CPU to perform certain operations with the data. Output consists of answers to problems solved by the CPU. To use the computers of the 40's and 50's, it was necessary to feed instructions to the machine in a coded form called *machine language*. Writing a program in machine language is a highly specialized task, since everything must be set forth in a code which has little, if any, relationship to the English language. To eliminate the necessity of machine coding, special programs called *compilers* have been developed that can convert language consisting of English words into machine language acceptable to the computer. The invention of the compiler made programming available to the layman.

To process a program written in an artificial language, the compiler for that language is first stored in the CPU. The artificial language program is then converted by the compiler to a program in machine language. Following this translation process, often called *compilation*, the machine language program is then executed, using any required data to produce the final results. These final results are then produced in report form by the printer.

12.3 THE FORTRAN LANGUAGE

There are several artificial computer languages in common use. We shall study a computer language called FORTRAN, a language particularly well suited to mathematical problems. The name FORTRAN is an abbreviation for FORmula TRANslation. There are several different FORTRAN compilers available, but for the most part the basic instructions to be discussed here can be translated by any FORTRAN compiler.

The methods for programming mathematical problems with FORTRAN closely resemble ordinary algebraic methods. Like any language, FORTRAN has an alphabet, a specialized vocabulary, and rules of grammar and punctuation. The FORTRAN alphabet consists of the following characters, classified as indicated.

Alphameric characters:

Alphabetic characters	$A, B, C, \ldots, X, Y, Z$
Numeric characters	$0, 1, 2, \ldots, 8, 9$

Special characters (a partial list) $+ - * / , . ( ) =$

The reader should take special note of the fact that the alphabetic characters used in FORTRAN are all capital letters. The special characters $+$ and $-$ denote the operations of addition and subtraction, respectively. The character $*$ denotes the operation of multiplication, and the character $/$ denotes the operation of division. The double asterisk $**$ is the symbol used in FORTRAN to indicate exponentiations.

One way to specify a quantity in FORTRAN language is to represent the quantity by the number itself. When a quantity is specified in this way, it is called a FORTRAN *constant*. For example, 3.14159 and 12 are both FORTRAN constants.

In FORTRAN, as in ordinary algebra, certain symbols or combinations of symbols are used to represent unspecified quantities, quantities which are specified when the data are read and computation begins. These symbols are called FORTRAN *variables* and consist of from one to five alphameric characters. Although numeric characters may be used in a variable, the *first* character in a variable must be *alphabetic*. Special characters are never used in FORTRAN variables. To avoid confusing the letter O with the number zero, we shall use the symbol Ø to represent the letter O when using the FORTRAN language.

Example 1   Each of the following is a FORTRAN variable.

a) RØØT1   b) X
c) ØRD   d) ANSWR
e) P1Q23   f) NAME
g) PI

Example 2   The following are not FORTRAN variables for the reason given.

a) A + B   (+ is a special character)
b) FØRTRAN   (too many letters)
c) 713B   (first character not alphabetic)
d) F(X)   (the parenthesis is a special character)

Another rule regarding variable names is that a variable name cannot have blanks between any of its letters or numbers. For example, ABP is an acceptable variable name, but AB P is not because it contains a blank between B and P.

The rules of FORTRAN often allow the programmer to make use of mnemonic names in naming variables. For example, instead of calculating a variable which will be assumed by the programmer to mean ordinate, he may calculate a variable whose name is ØRD.

In FORTRAN, numbers are classified in two different ways: *fixed-point* numbers and *floating-point* numbers. A fixed-point number is an integer (i.e. a number which does not contain a decimal point). A floating-point number is any number which contains a decimal point. Incidentally, commas are not permitted in numbers of either type. For example, the number 10,000 is not permitted as a FORTRAN constant.

Example 3   The numbers

$$5143, \ 8, \ 1000000$$

are examples of fixed-point numbers. The numbers

$$5143., \quad 5143.0, \quad .00047, \quad 10.781, \quad 3.14159, \quad .5$$

are examples of floating-point numbers.

FORTRAN can direct the CPU to perform two different types of arithmetic: *fixed-point arithmetic* and *floating-point arithmetic*. These two types of arithmetic are called *modes* of arithmetic. Fixed-point arithmetic deals with fixed-point numbers and floating-point arithmetic deals with floating-point numbers. In floating-point arithmetic, the correct position of the decimal point in the result is determined automatically. Floating-point arithmetic is used for nearly all computations. It is carried out by the CPU as one would expect, usually expressing the answer to 8 significant figures with the decimal point in the appropriate place. In fixed-point arithmetic, sums, differences, and products are also computed in the usual way. However, fixed-point division often exhibits a slight peculiarity. For example, if 5 is divided by 2 using fixed-point arithmetic, the result is 2 not $2\frac{1}{2}$. If a fixed-point division problem results in a number with a fractional part, the fraction is simply dropped. The result is *not* rounded to the nearest integer.

FORTRAN variables must also be identified with one of the two modes of arithmetic and classified as fixed-point or floating-point variables. The mode of a variable is determined by the *first* letter of the variable name. If the first letter in the name of a variable is $I, J, K, L, M,$ or N, it is a fixed-point variable. The name of a floating-point variable begins with some other letter. The reader will note that this rule is consistent with our habit in algebra of using one of the letters *i* through *n* to represent an integer.

Example 4   Each of the following is a permissible fixed-point variable.

a) MIRV   b) INT
c) JØB   d) N
e) KAPPA

Example 5   Each of the following is a permissible floating-point variable.

a) ALPHA   b) X
c) ØRD   d) GØGØ
e) ST111

Problems

1   Which of the following symbols are acceptable as FORTRAN variables? What is wrong with those that are not?

a) MANDY   b) 3MAT
c) A1B2   d) H
e) I8*J   f) TUESDAY
g) INTG   h) ØRD 1
i) H(A)   j) NERØ
k) ANS   l) ANSWER

2 Classify each of the following numbers as a fixed-point or a floating-point number. If the number is not permitted in FORTRAN, explain why not.

a) 496.82   b) 38   c) −57.   d) 570,862
e) 570862   f) 0.   g) 0   h) 57.00
i) −.00001   j) 18,762.5   k) −.85   l) 1

3 Classify each of the following variables as a fixed-point or a floating-point variable.

a) MARIE   b) IBM   c) BM17   d) PT109
e) RHØ   f) INTG   g) M2ØØ   h) F177
i) JØ   j) MATT   k) A   l) ZERØ

4 Use fixed-point division to calculate the values of each of the following quotients.

a) $\frac{6}{3}$ b) $\frac{7}{4}$ c) $\frac{3}{4}$

d) $\frac{23}{5}$ e) $\frac{999}{1000}$ f) $\frac{47}{8}$

12.4 ARITHMETIC ASSIGNMENT STATEMENTS AND LIBRARY FUNCTIONS

A FORTRAN *expression* is any meaningful combination of constants, variables, functions (to be discussed later) and operation signs. According to this definition an expression may consist of a single constant or a single variable. Some examples of expressions are

$$A$$
$$X + Y**2$$
$$.47$$
$$I*J/M*N$$

Because the CPU handles fixed-point and floating-point numbers in different ways, the quantities used in an expression must be of the same mode. One exception to this rule is in exponentation. A floating-point number may be raised to a power of either mode. However, a fixed-point number can only be raised to a fixed-point power. For example, the expressions A**2 and A**2. and I**2 are acceptable, but the expressions J**2. and K**1.5 are not. Fixed-point exponents are always permissible and we shall use fixed-point values whenever possible.

A computer evaluates a FORTRAN expression in the same way a mathematician would evaluate the corresponding algebraic expression. Reading an expression from left to right, a computer first performs exponentations in the order they are encountered. Again reading from left to right, the computer next performs multiplications and divisions in the order in which they appear in the expression. After performing exponentations, multiplications, and divisions, the computer performs the additions and subtractions as it encounters them, again scanning the expression from left to right. Some examples follow.

Example 1 To evaluate the FORTRAN expression A*B + C*D a computer would perform the two multiplications first, and then add the two products.

Example 2 To evaluate the FORTRAN expression A*B**2 + C*D + E a computer would perform the following calculations in the order given.

1) Compute B**2
2) Compute the product of A with the result obtained in (1) and then compute C*D
3) Find the sum of the two numbers obtained in (2) and E

Example 3 Write a FORTRAN expression that can be used to compute the value of $3x^2 - 5x + 4$.

Solution The desired FORTRAN expression is

$$3.*X**2 - 5.*X + 4.$$

The reader will notice that we have expressed the constants 3, 4, and 5 in floating-point notation to agree with the mode of the variable X. The exponent 2 may be expressed in either mode, but for simplicity we wrote it as a fixed-point number.

Parentheses are used in FORTRAN the same way they are used in algebra, as symbols of grouping. To write

$$\frac{I + J}{K}$$

as a FORTRAN expression we would have $(I + J)/K$. This expression tells the computer to first find the sum $I + J$ and then divide this sum by K.

Example 4 Write the expression $((a + b)(x + y))^{n+1}$ in FORTRAN notation.

Solution The desired FORTRAN expression is

$$((A + B)*(X + Y))**(N + 1)$$

Parentheses may be used even when not necessarily required so long as each left parenthesis is balanced by a right parenthesis. For example, the expressions $(A + B)*C$ is equivalent to the expression $((A + B)*C)$. However, the expression $((A + B)*C$ is not valid because of the unbalanced parenthesis.

An *arithmetic assignment statement* is a statement that instructs the CPU to compute the value of a FORTRAN expression and assign the value to a given variable. An arithmetic assignment statement consists of a variable, an equals sign, and a FORTRAN expression. For example,

$$X = -.52$$
$$ØRD = W$$
$$Y = A + B$$
$$Z = A + B**C$$

are all arithmetic assignment statements. The CPU executes an arithmetic assignment statement in two steps: the value of the FORTRAN expression is computed and this computed value is assigned to the variable on the left of the equals sign. In an arithmetic assignment statement only one variable may appear on the left side of the equals sign. We remind the reader that the expression on the right of the equals sign must contain, except for exponents, quantities that are all of the same mode. However, the quantities on opposite sides of the equals sign may be of opposite modes if desired. For example, a statement such as $I = A*B + C$ is legitimate under FORTRAN rules, but one should be aware that the value of $A*B + C$ will be converted to a fixed-point value when it is assigned to the fixed-point variable I. If the value of $A*B + C$ has a fractional part, the conversion would result in the loss of the fractional part. In general, we remark that the value of the expression in an arithmetic assignment statement is converted to the same mode as the variable to the left of the equals sign.

From its use here the reader will notice that the special character $=$ is not an equality symbol in the algebraic sense. For example, the statement $Y = A + B$ means to compute the value of $A + B$ and assign this value to Y. We cannot write the statement $Y = A + B$ in the form $A + B = Y$. The latter statement does not qualify under FORTRAN rules to be called an arithmetic assignment statement and will not be translated by the compiler.

Available to FORTRAN users is a collection of special programs called *library functions*. Although there is some variation from one compiler to another, the following library functions are available with most compilers.

SQRTF	square root
ABSF	absolute value
SINF	sine (argument in radians)
CØSF	cosine (argument in radians)
LØGF	logarithm (base *e*)
EXPF	exponential (base *e*)

Library functions are easy to use and often save the programmer considerable time. If we want to compute the square root of the nonnegative number X

and set this value equal to Y, we place in the program the arithmetic assignment statement

$$Y = SQRTF(X)$$

In the above statement the variable X is called the *argument* of the function SQRTF. Parentheses are used with all library functions just as in algebra.

We may also consider a function whose argument contains another function. For example,

$$Y = SQRTF(ABSF(A + B**2))$$

is an acceptable arithmetic assignment statement.

The library functions described here are written to use floating-point arguments and yield floating-point values as results. Even though they meet the specifications, library function names may *not* be used as variable names.

Example 5 Write an arithmetic assignment statement to compute the value of

$$\left(\frac{x^2 + 3}{x + 1}\right)^4.$$

Solution If the value of the expression is stored in the variable Y, then the desired arithmetic assignment statement is

$$Y = ((X**2 + 3.)/(X + 1.))**4$$

Example 6 Write an arithmetic assignment statement to compute the value of

$$\frac{1}{\sqrt{5A + A^3}}.$$

Solution In this problem we can use the library function SQRTF. If the value of the expression is stored in the variable B, then the desired arithmetic assignment statement is

$$B = 1./SQRTF(5.*A + A**3)$$

Problems

1 Which of the following expressions are legitimate FORTRAN expressions? If the expression is unacceptable, explain why.

a) A**I + B

b) 3*A + C/D

c) X**3 + Y**5.2

d) I + J/Q

e) K**3.1 - L*M

f) (-3./X**2 + A/(.2*X)

In Problems 2 through 8 write FORTRAN expressions to compute the given expression.

2 x^3

3 $\dfrac{a+b}{c+d}$

4 $\dfrac{3xy}{x+y}$

5 $\dfrac{a+b}{c} + d$

6 $\dfrac{a+b}{c+\dfrac{d}{e}}$

7 $\dfrac{6x^2 - 5x + 4}{x^2 + 1}$

8 $a + b[c + d(a + c^2)]$

9 Find the value that will be assigned to M by each of the following statements.

a) M = 8*4/2   b) M = 8*(4/2)
c) M = 2**3/3   d) M = 10.*.5/6.0
e) M = 12*2/6*3   f) M = (12*2)/(6*3)

10 Find the value that will be assigned to A by each of the following statements.

a) A = 8*4/3   b) A = 8/4*3
c) A = 6.8*2.1/.01   d) A = (2**3)**2
e) A = SQRTF(5.*10./2.)   f) A = ABSF(-2.**3 + 5.)

In Problems 11 through 15 write an arithmetic assignment statement to compute the given expression.

11 $x = 2a^2 - 3a + 4$

12 $x = \dfrac{a+b}{a-b}$

13 $x = \left(\dfrac{38}{ab}\right)^{1/2}$

14 $x = 3^{-\sqrt{ab/2}}$

15 $x = \dfrac{7}{\sqrt{a^2 + b^2 - c^2}}$

16 Identify the error(s) in the following arithmetic assignment statements.

a) ANSWR = 15.(X + Y)   b) A + 2 = B**2/.1
c) BØ = B + C + 5*D   d) IMP = (B + 5)**6
e) SCA = B/*2.0   f) A = 16,543.*B
g) 3*A = 4 + B**2   h) NAIL = 3X**2. - 6

12.5 I-O STATEMENTS

We recall that a program is a set of instructions directing the CPU to perform certain operations. In this text, a program is transmitted to the CPU by a sequence of cards. The message on a single card is referred to as a *statement*.

In the preceding section, we learned how to write arithmetic statements in FORTRAN. In this section, we turn our attention to I-O (input-output) statements and other statements which will equip us to write FORTRAN programs.

It is essential that every program contain I-O statements. These statements will vary with the different kinds of I-O devices in use. We have agreed to use punched cards for input, and output will be in printed form. Corresponding to these types of input and output we have READ and WRITE statements, respectively.

To illustrate the use of the READ statement, consider the following example.

$$\text{READ}(1,101)A,B,K$$

In this statement, READ indicates to the computer that data are to be entered into the memory of the computer. Immediately following the word READ is the pair of numbers 1 and 101 included within parentheses. The first of these numbers, 1, specifies the type of input unit which is to be used. We shall assume that the punched card input has been assigned the number 1. Since we are using this method of input exclusively, the number in this position of a READ statement will always be 1. The number 101 refers to the number of a FØRMAT statement associated with this READ statement. The three variables listed in the READ statement have names A, B, and K. These variables are assigned values from the data cards when the READ statement is executed.

The FØRMAT statement referred to above might appear as follows.

$$101 \quad \text{FØRMAT}(\text{F}10.3,\text{F}10.5,\text{I}10)$$

The number preceding the word FØRMAT is the number of the FØRMAT statement. FØRMAT statements are used to describe to the computer the form of the numbers being read. They may appear anywhere in the program, but as a matter of convenience, they are usually placed near the corresponding I-O statement. From the READ statement, we see that the computer is to read in order the variables A, B, and K. The FØRMAT statement gives the number conversion code of these three variables as F10.3, F10.5, and I10, respectively. The number conversion code of the first variable, A, is F10.3. The F indicates that A is a floating-point variable. The 10 indicates that the value of A will be found in the first 10 columns of the input data card, and the .3 indicates that three places will be found to the right of the decimal point. F10.5 indicates that the second variable, B, is also a floating-point variable whose value will be found in the next ten columns (11–20), and five places will be found to the right of the decimal point. I10 indicates that the third variable in the list, K, is a fixed-point variable, and its value will be found in the next ten columns (21–30).

To summarize, the READ statement tells the computer *what* is to be read and the FØRMAT statement signifies *how* and *where* the numbers will be found.

Example 1 Interpret the following READ and corresponding FØRMAT statements.

                    READ(1,105)C,J,D,E
        105   FØRMAT(F10.2,I10,F10.3,F10.2)

Solution The READ statement indicates that the computer is to read in order the variables C,J,D, and E. The FØRMAT statement indicates that the variable C is a floating-point variable found in columns 1–10, and it has two places to the right of the decimal point. The variable J is a fixed-point variable found in columns 11–20. The variable D is a floating-point variable found in columns 21–30, and it has three places to the right of the decimal point. The variable E is a floating-point variable found in columns 31–40, and it has two places to the right of the decimal point.

Example 2 Construct a READ and corresponding FØRMAT statement that will indicate that the five floating-point variables A, B, C, D, and E are to be read, each with number conversion code F12.3.

Solution

                READ (1,101)A,B,C,D,E
        101   FØRMAT(F12.3,F12.3,F12.3,F12.3,F12.3)

The FØRMAT statement in Example 2 could be written equivalently

                    101 FØRMAT(5F12.3)

The number 5 before F12.3 indicates that the number conversion code is to be repeated five times.

Before going on to a discussion of output statements, it is appropriate to illustrate how the input data and program are punched on cards. The punched card in Fig. 12.1 illustrates the typical FORTRAN character code. This punched code varies slightly depending on the specific computer. This card has 80 vertical columns and thus can hold 80 characters of information.

When used with a statement combination such as

                    READ(1,101)A,B,K
        101   FØRMAT(F10.3,F10.5,I10)

the card in Fig. 12.2, when read, would result in the following values for the variables: A would have the value 732.539; B the value 23.72816; and

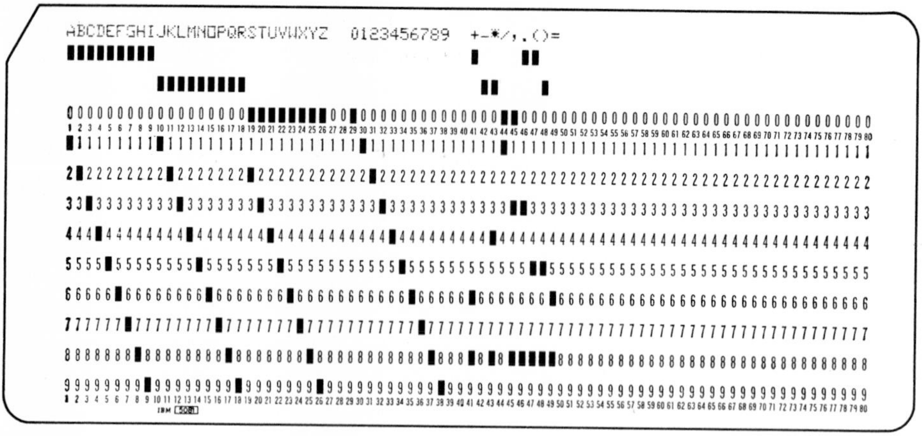

Figure 12.1

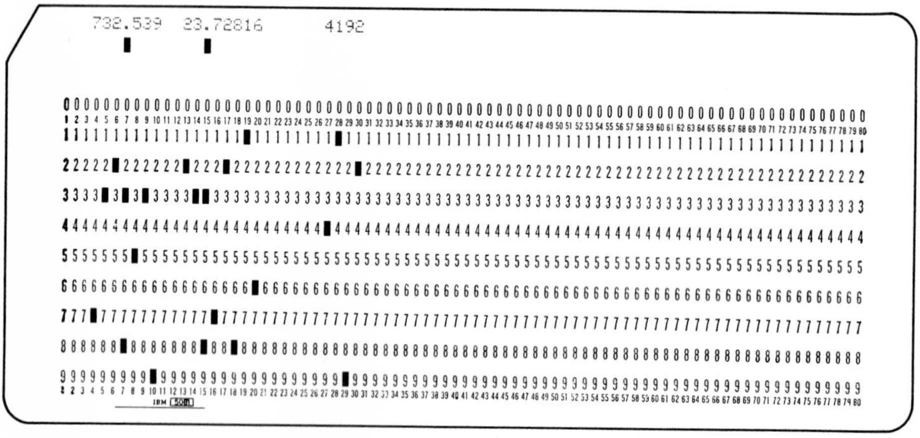

Figure 12.2

K the value 4192. Note that all quantities are punched in the rightmost portion of the allotted columns. For some computers, it is essential that this procedure, called *right justify*, be followed in punching input data cards; other computers do not require it. Our position will be to follow the right justify procedure since those computers which do not require it will accept cards in that form.

The punched card in Fig. 12.3 corresponds to the FORTRAN statement

101   FØRMAT(F10.3,F10.5,I10)

In punching cards for FORTRAN statements certain rules concerning column use must be observed. The first five columns are used for statement

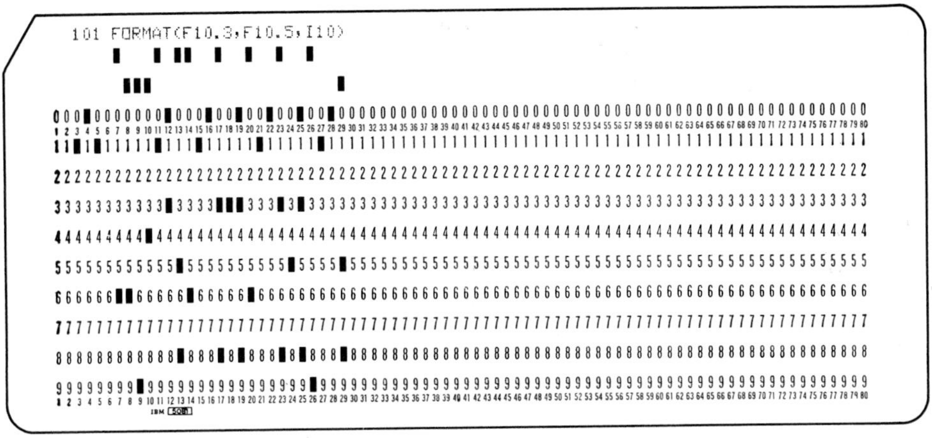

Figure 12.3

numbers. It is not necessary that all statements have a statement number, nor is it necessary for statement numbers to follow any specific order. The actual FORTRAN statement begins in the seventh column with each and every character of the statement in its own individual column. It is acceptable to leave blank columns in writing arithmetic assignment statements, and we often leave blanks to aid in the interpretation of such statements. Even though the card contains 80 spaces, the FORTRAN compiler ignores everything beyond space 72. If the statement is too long to get on a single card, it can be continued on other cards, and this information is coded in column 6. We will *not* discuss this procedure in this text, and all statements to be considered will be such that they can be punched on a single card.

After the input data and program have been punched on cards, the cards are stacked for feeding to the computer. In stacking the input cards, the data cards always follow the program cards in the deck.

The general procedures for constructing output statements are much the same as input statements. Since we have agreed that output will be in printed form, our output statement will be designated WRITE. FØRMAT output statements are constructed in the same way as FØRMAT input statements. We shall assume that the printing device has been assigned the number 3. Each line in the printed output contains 120 character spaces, and we must keep this limitation in mind when constructing our FØRMAT statements. Generally, enough spaces are allotted for each written number so as to make reading the results as easy as possible.

Example 3 Interpret the following WRITE and corresponding FØRMAT statements.

$$\text{WRITE}(3,107)\text{A},\text{B},\text{K}$$
$$107 \quad \text{FØRMAT}(2\text{F}20.2,\text{I}20)$$

Solution The WRITE statement indicates that the computer is to write out in order the variables A, B, and K. From the FØRMAT statement, A is a floating-point variable found in columns 1–20, and A has two decimal places. B is a floating-point variable found in columns 21–40, and B has two decimal places. K is a fixed-point variable found in columns 41–60.

We are now prepared to write a simple program. The following program instructs the computer to find and print out the sum of the three variables A, B, and C.

```
        READ(1,101)A,B,C
101     FØRMAT(3F10.2)
        E = A + B + C
        WRITE(3,102)E
102     FØRMAT(F20.2)
        STØP
        END
```

The END statement is always the last statement in a FORTRAN program. The STØP statement tells the compiler it is through compiling and the program is ready for execution. Once the STØP statement has been executed, the compiler cannot be conveniently made to continue within the same program. This problem can be overcome by using the PAUSE statement, which stops the computer, but allows restarting within the same program.

Problems

In Problems 1 through 4, construct a READ statement and a corresponding FØRMAT statement that will instruct the computer to read in the given variables. Assume all floating-point variables have number conversion code F10.2 and all fixed-point variables have number conversion code I10.

1 A, B, C, and D

2 J, K, and L

3 A, K, B, C, and M

4 ABY, JØAN, MARY, and TØM

In Problems 5 through 8, construct a WRITE statement and a corresponding FØRMAT statement that will instruct the computer to print out the given variables. Assume all floating-point variables have number conversion code F20.2 and all fixed-point variables have number code I20.

5 AB, J, and K

6 ALPHA, BETA, and GAMMA

7 ZERØ, IN, and ØUT

8 NØ, YES, and MAYBE

In Problems 9 through 12, write a FORTRAN program to compute the given expression. Assume all floating-point variables have number conversion code F10.2, and all fixed-point variables have number conversion code I10.

9 $\dfrac{a + b}{4}$

10 $(x - 3y)^4$

11 $\left(\dfrac{m^2 + 3}{m + 1}\right)^3$

12 $\dfrac{1}{\sqrt{5a + a^3}}$

12.6 CONTROL STATEMENTS

In each of the programs we have seen thus far, the computer will follow the instruction statements of the program in the order they appear. We now introduce some statements, called *control statements*, which will instruct the computer to interrupt the natural sequence of statement execution.

One of the simplest of the control statements is the GØ TØ statement. This statement consists of the words GØ TØ followed by a statement number. When a GØ TØ statement is executed, the computer is instructed to next execute the statement indicated by the GØ TØ statement. For example, the statement

GØ TØ 30

when executed, instructs the computer to next execute statement 30 in the program.

An extension of the GØ TØ statement (which refers the computer to a single statement in the program) is the *computed* GØ TØ statement. This statement can be used to refer the computer to any one of a number of different statements in the program, depending on the value of a fixed-point variable. The computed GØ TØ statement begins with the words GØ TØ followed by a pair of parentheses containing any desired number of statement numbers separated by commas. The closed parentheses are followed by a comma and a fixed-point variable. An example of a computed GØ TØ statement is the statement

GØ TØ (5,10,15,20),N

This statement instructs the computer as follows: If the value of N is 1, go to statement 5; if the value of N is 2, go to statement 10; if the value of N is 3, go to statement 15; if the value of N is 4, go to statement 20. The list of statement numbers in the computed GØ TØ statement may be as long as desired and certain statement numbers may be repeated. However, care must be taken that the control fixed-point variable on the right does *not* have a value larger than the number of statement numbers in the list. For example, in the statement

$$GØ \ TØ \ (5,7,3,5,6,8,9),M$$

we must be sure that M does not have a value larger than 7. Note that if M has value 7, the computer goes to statement 9 — *not* statement 7.

Another control statement, called the IF statement, is based on the ability of the computer to distinguish between negative, zero, and positive results. The following statement is an example of an IF statement.

$$IF \ (X \ - \ Y)10,20,30$$

This statement is interpreted as follows.

$$IF \ (X \ - \ Y) \begin{cases} <0, \text{ go to statement 10,} \\ =0, \text{ go to statement 20,} \\ >0, \text{ go to statement 30.} \end{cases}$$

Clearly, an IF statement can be used to direct the computer to any one of three different statements.

In an IF statement, the expression in the parentheses is an arithmetic statement, and thus the rules pertaining to operation hierarchy and mode must be observed. Further caution is given to the reader that certain problems may arise in using floating-point numbers with an IF statement. Because of rounding-off errors, an *exact* floating-point zero is hardly ever achieved. This particular problem is not encountered whenever fixed-point variables are used.

Consider the following problem. Three variables m, n, and l are to be read into a computer. If $mn/3 < l$, we want to set $j = 5$; if $mn/3 = l$, set $j = 7$; and if $mn/3 > l$, then set $j = 9$. The following program, which makes use of control statements, will accomplish the desired result.

```
  1   READ(1,101)M,N,L
101   FØRMAT(3I10)
      K = M*N/3
      IF (K - L)2,3,4
  2   J = 5
      WRITE(3,102)M,N,L,J
102   FØRMAT(4I10)
      GØ TØ 1
  3   J = 7
      WRITE(3,102)M,N,L,J
      GØ TØ 1
```

```
4    J = 9
     WRITE(3,102)M,N,L,J
     GØ TØ 1
     END
```

Note that in the printout, the values of the variables *m*, *n*, and *l* as well as *j* (which is determined by comparing $mn/3$ and *l*) are listed.

As a second illustration of the use of control statements, we write a program designed to find the roots of a quadratic equation $ax^2 + bx + c = 0$. The formula for the solutions of such an equation is

$$x = \frac{-b \pm \sqrt{b^2 - 4ac}}{2a}.$$

Recall that the roots of the equation are real if $b^2 - 4ac \geq 0$ and complex if $b^2 - 4ac < 0$. If the roots are real, we want the roots to be written out and if they are complex, we wish to have the quantities $-b/2a$ and $\sqrt{4ac - b^2}/2a$ written out. Of course in the latter case, the roots of the equation are

$$x = \frac{-b \pm \sqrt{4ac - b^2}\, i}{2a}.$$

In either case (real or complex roots), the computer will write out two numbers. Thus we will code these cases by using $I = 1$ and $I = 2$ for real and complex roots, respectively. The program follows.

```
  1   READ(1,101)A,B,C
101   FØRMAT(3F10.2)
      REAL1 = -B/(2.*A)
      DISCR = B**2 - 4.*A*C
      REAL2 = SQRTF(ABSF(DISCR))/(2.*A)
      IF (DISCR)2,3,3
  2   I = 2
      WRITE(3,102)I,REAL1,REAL2
102   FØRMAT(I10,2F10.2)
      GØ TØ 1
  3   I = 1
      RØØT1 = REAL1 + REAL2
      RØØT2 = REAL1 - REAL2
      WRITE(3,102)I,RØØT1,RØØT2
      GØ TØ 1
      END
```

The above program will continue to solve quadratic equations so long as data cards giving the coefficients of the equations are supplied to the computer.

Problems

1 Write a GØ TØ statement which would instruct a computer to go to statement 50.

2 Write a computed GØ TØ statement which would be used to instruct a computer to go (in the given order) to statement 7, 15, 30, 14, 7, 26, or 35 according to the value of the fixed-point variable N.

3 In Problem 2, if $N = 3$, what statement is the computer instructed to go to? What if $N = 5$? $N = 7$?

4 Given the two variables A and B. Write an IF statement instructing the computer to go to statement 10 if A — B is negative, statement 15 if A — B is zero, and statement 30 if A — B is positive.

5 Given the two variables A and B. Write an IF statement instructing the computer to go to statement 5 if A = B, statement 15 if A > B, and statement 17 if B > A.

6 Write a program which will instruct the computer to compare two un-equal fixed-point variables, print out the two variables, and designate the larger of the two.

7 Write a program which will instruct the computer to read the fixed-point variables j, k, l, and m, print out the variables, and designate the larger of the two expressions

$$\frac{j + k}{3} \quad \text{and} \quad \frac{l - m}{4}.$$

In the printout, code the results of the comparison 1, 2, or 3, respectively, according to whether $(j + k)/3$ is greater than, equal to, or less than $(l - m)/4$.

8 Write a program that will read three fixed-point variables, no two of which are equal, and write them out from least to greatest.

12.7 DO LOOPS

When a single variable name is used to refer to a list of numbers, there must be some means of referring to a specific number of that list. In mathematics this is done by use of subscripts. For example, if one chooses to represent a number of the list

$$5, 3, -1, 0, 6, 2, 9, 8$$

by the variable x, then the third number, -1, would be denoted by the symbol x_3. The 3 printed to the right and below x is called a *subscript*. In FORTRAN we cannot print lowered numbers, so some other method must be devised for writing subscripts. This is done by use of parentheses. To illustrate, we would write $X(3)$ in a FORTRAN program instead of x_3. In FORTRAN, $X(6)$ is equivalent to x_6, $X(8)$ is equivalent to x_8, etc.

There are certain rules governing the use of subscripted variables in FORTRAN. A subscripted variable may be either a floating-point variable or a fixed-point variable. A subscript may be a constant or a variable (or a simple FORTRAN expression). However, the subscript must *always* be written in the fixed-point mode. A constant or variable used as a subscript can never be zero or have a negative value. Furthermore, a subscript can never have a value greater than the number of items in the list being referred to.

Example 1 Let us consider a list consisting of 100 numbers. The following subscripted variables are permissible in referring to numbers of this list.

$$X(41)$$
$$ARF(98)$$
$$NAME(N + 1) \qquad \text{(if } 0 \leq N \leq 99)$$
$$F(4*J) \qquad \text{(if } 1 \leq J \leq 25)$$

The following subscripted variables are not permissible for the reason given.

$$Y(358) \qquad (358 > 100)$$
$$BEEF(-2) \qquad \text{(negative subscripts not allowed)}$$
$$SAM(B + 1) \qquad \text{(B + 1 is a floating-point expression)}$$

Whenever subscripted variables are used in a program, there must be a specification statement in the program to provide the computer with information about the size of the arrays being referenced. This is the purpose of the DIMENSIØN statement. An example of a DIMENSIØN statement is

$$DIMENSIØN \ A(100),J(300)$$

The compiler will interpret this statement to mean that the program will contain two subscripted variables A and J, the subscript on A possibly running as high as 100 and the subscript on J possibly running as high as 300. After this statement is read, the computer will reserve storage for 100 floating-point A's and 300 fixed-point J's whose values may be required later in the program. If more than one subscripted variable is used in a program, the size of all arrays may be specified in a single DIMENSIØN statement or more than one DIMENSIØN statement may be used if desired. It is important that all DIMENSIØN statements appear in the program *before* any statement using the arrays being described.

Many problems require that identical or very similar calculations be performed several times. In FORTRAN the DØ statement provides us with a very convenient method of solving such problems. The DØ statement consists of the word DØ followed by a statement number, which in turn is followed by a nonsubscripted fixed-point variable, an equals sign, and two fixed-point quantities separated by a comma. An example of a DØ statement is

$$DØ \ 20 \ J \ = \ 1,100$$

This statement instructs the computer to set J = 1 and proceed through the program until statement 20 has been executed. After executing statement 20, the computer returns to the first statement after the DØ statement, sets J = 2, and again proceeds through the "loop" until statement 20 has been executed a second time. This process continues until statement 20 has been executed with J = 100, and then the computer proceeds to the statement in the program which follows 20.

The fixed-point quantities after the equals sign in a DØ statement may be fixed-point constants or fixed-point variables whose values have been determined earlier in the program. Consider the following example.

Example 2 Each of the following is a permissible DØ statement.

DØ 50 I = 1,1000	DØ 200 K = 1,M
DØ 74 JØB = 10,25	DØ 13 N = M,MØØ

The following are not permissible DØ statements for the reason indicated.

DØ 42 A = 1,10	(A is not a fixed-point variable)
DØ,87 M = 1,N	(no comma permitted after DØ)
DØ 20,J = 4,8	(no comma permitted after 20)
DØ A1 MAY = 1,50	(a statement number must be numeric only)

The following example will illustrate how a DO-loop can be used to find the sum of an array of numbers.

Example 3 Write a program to find the sum of 100 floating-point numbers.
Solution

```
       DIMENSIØN A(100)
       DØ 10 I = 1,100
  10   READ(1,20)A(I)
  20   FØRMAT(F10.2)
       SUM = 0.
       DØ 30 I = 1,100
```

```
      30  SUM = SUM + A(I)
          WRITE(3,20)SUM
          STØP
          END
```

In the fifth statement of the program of Example 3, the reader will note that the value of the variable SUM was initialized to 0. This had to be done so that statement 30 of the program could be executed on the first pass through the DO-loop. Remember that each variable of an arithmetic expression must be specified before the expression can be evaluated. The variable SUM is used as an accumulator in the summing process.

Example 4   Given two sets of floating-point numbers

$$x_1, x_2, \ldots, x_{50} \quad \text{and} \quad y_1, y_2, \ldots, y_{50}.$$

Write a program to evaluate

$$\sum_{i=1}^{50} \text{Min}(x_i, y_i) = \text{Min}(x_1, y_1) + \text{Min}(x_2, y_2) + \cdots + \text{Min}(x_{50}, y_{50}).$$

The expression $\text{Min}(x_i, y_i)$ is the smaller of the numbers x_i and y_i or the common value if the two numbers are equal.

Solution   The following program will accomplish the desired result.

```
          DIMENSIØN X(50),Y(50)
          DØ 10 I = 1,50
      10  READ(1,20)X(I),Y(I)
      20  FØRMAT(2F10.2)
          SUM = 0.
          DØ 60 I = 1,50
          IF (X(I) − Y(I))40,40,50
      40  SUM = SUM + X(I)
          GØ TØ 60
      50  SUM = SUM + Y(I)
      60  CØNTINUE
          WRITE(3,70)SUM
      70  FØRMAT(F20.2)
          STØP
          END
```

In the program of Example 4 we note that the DO-loop is sometimes completed at statement 40 and sometimes at statement 50. The CØNTINUE statement in our program is a dummy statement used to provide a common finishing point for the DO-loop. The CØNTINUE statement doesn't actually do anything in the execution of the program; it simply provides us with a convenient finishing point for the DO-loop.

We should also note that a DO-loop must never end with a control statement (such as IF or GØ TØ). Another use for the CØNTINUE statement is to provide the DØ statement with a reference number in a loop that might otherwise end with a control statement.

In concluding this section, we remark that the IF statement can be used to accomplish the same feats as a DO-loop, but the latter is much more convenient.

Problems

1 Suppose we have a list consisting of 1000 numbers. Which of the following subscripted variables are permissible in referring to numbers of this list? Which are not permissible? Give reasons.

a) CREF(991)
b) JIG(M + 3.5) $(0 \leq M \leq 996)$
c) JUMP(5*J + 1) $(0 \leq J \leq 199)$
d) X48(342)
e) GIGI(-8)
f) FLØAT(F + 80.) $(0 \leq F \leq 420)$
g) P38Q(512)
h) M(2348)

2 Write a DIMENSIØN statement which will be interpreted to mean that a program will contain two floating-point variables A and B and a fixed-point variable J, the subscripts on A and B possibly running as high as 1000 and the subscript on J possibly running as high as 500.

3 Which of the following DØ statements are permissible and which are not? For those which are not permissible, explain what rule is violated.

a) DØ 2 A = 1,20   b) DØ, 50 J = 5,10
c) DØ 3 I = 1,M   d) DØ P3 K = 1,100
e) DØ 20 MØ3 = 1,1000   f) DØ 12 L = NEW,NEWS
g) DØ 55 MØAT = 1,100

4 What does the DØ statement

$$DØ \ 13 \ I = 5,21$$

instruct a computer to do?

5 Write a FORTRAN program to find the sum of 200 fixed-point numbers. Assume each number has conversion code I10.

6 Write a FORTRAN program to find the average of a set of 500 floating-point numbers. Assume each number has conversion code F10.2.

7 Given two sets of floating-point numbers

$$a_1, a_2, \ldots, a_{100} \quad \text{and} \quad b_1, b_2, \ldots, b_{100}.$$

Write a FORTRAN program to evaluate

$$\sum_{i=1}^{100} \text{Max}(a_i, b_i).$$

The expression $\text{Max}(a_i, b_i)$ is the larger of the numbers a_i and b_i or the common value if the two numbers are equal. Assume each number has conversion code F10.2.

12.8 SUMMARY

As we have observed throughout this chapter, a computer program is a sequence of statements giving the computer information and directing it to perform certain operations. In this section we give two examples of programs which incorporate several of the different kinds of statements discussed in this chapter.

In preparing a program for a keypunch operator, whose job it is to punch the cards to be used in the program, it is necessary for the programmer to

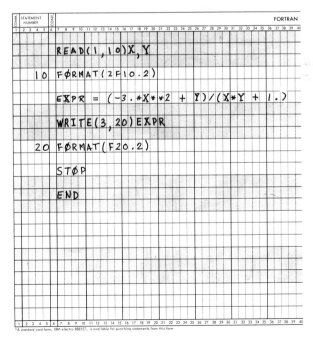

Figure 12.4

write the program on a *coding form*. A typical FORTRAN coding form is shown in Fig. 12.4. Each row on the coding form corresponds to a single card to be punched. Since the purpose of the coding form is to present a clear picture of the statements to be punched, spacing of symbols on the form should be exactly the same as that required on the cards. We shall use a coding form for each of the following two programs.

Example 1 Write a program to compute the value of the expression

$$\frac{-3x^2 + y}{xy + 1}.$$

Solution The desired program appears on the coding form in Fig. 12.4

Example 2 Write a program to find the number with the smallest absolute value in a block of 1000 nonzero numbers called x.

Solution We shall use the variable SMALX to denote the desired number. The program appears on the coding form in Fig. 12.5.

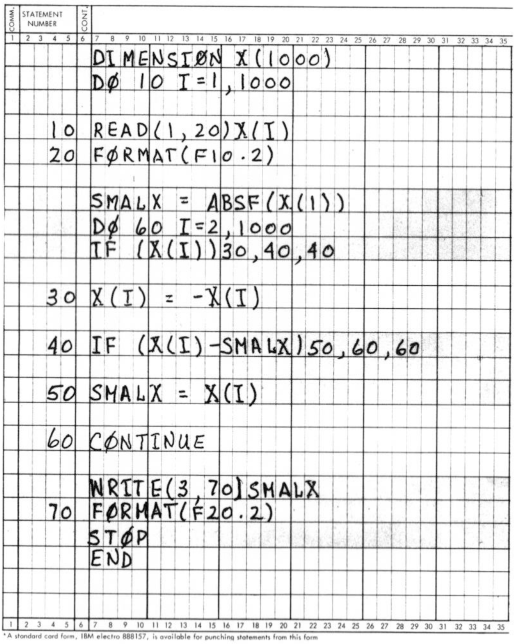

```
      DIMENSIØN X(1000)
      DØ 10 I=1,1000
   10 READ(1,20)X(I)
   20 FØRMAT(F10.2)
      SMALX = ABSF(X(1))
      DØ 60 I=2,1000
      IF (X(I))30,40,40
   30 X(I) = -X(I)
   40 IF (X(I)-SMALX)50,60,60
   50 SMALX = X(I)
   60 CØNTINUE
      WRITE(3,70)SMALX
   70 FØRMAT(F20.2)
      STØP
      END
```

*A standard card form, IBM electro 888157, is available for punching statements from this form

Figure 12.5

A CØNTINUE statement has been inserted in the program of Example 2 to avoid ending a DO-loop with an IF statement.

It has been our purpose in this chapter to introduce the reader to a procedure for communicating with a computer. We wish to emphasize that as far as computer programming is concerned, we have only scratched the surface. The statements we have discussed are rudimentary and the programs we have written using these statements will work for almost any computer with a FORTRAN compiler. However, each computer and each artificial language has peculiarities of its own which the programmer must know to use the computer efficiently.

Problems

In Problems 1 through 4 write a program to compute the value of the given expression.

1 $|x^2 - 3x|$

2 $\dfrac{5x^3 - 3x + 2}{x + 10}$

3 $\dfrac{-2x^2y + 1}{y^3 - xy}$

4 $\sqrt{\dfrac{3x + 1}{2x - 5}}$

5 Write a program to compute the value of

$$\sum_{i=1}^{50} (i^2 + 1).$$

6 Write a program for finding the standard deviation of a set of 1000 numbers (see Section 10.14). Assume all numbers are floating-point numbers.

7 Write a program to find the number with the largest absolute value in a block of 5000 nonzero numbers called x.

8 Given a block of 500 numbers, write a program to determine how many of these numbers are greater than 15.3.

BIBLIOGRAPHY

Banks, J. H., *Elements of Mathematics*, 2nd ed. Boston: Allyn and Bacon, 1961.

Bell, E. T., *The Development of Mathematics,* 2nd ed. New York: McGraw-Hill, 1945.

Bell, E. T., *Men of Mathematics*. New York: Simon and Schuster, 1937.

Eves, H., *An Introduction to the History of Mathematics*, 3rd ed. New York: Holt, Rinehart and Winston, 1969.

Fraleigh, J. B., *Mainstreams of Mathematics*. Reading, Mass.: Addison-Wesley, 1969.

Landau, E., *Foundations of Analysis*. New York: Chelsea, 1951.

McCoy, N. H., *Introduction to Modern Algebra*. Boston: Allyn and Bacon, 1960.

Meserve, B. E., and M. A. Sobel, *Introduction to Mathematics*, 2nd ed. Englewood Cliffs, New Jersey: Prentice-Hall, 1969.

Munroe, M. E., *Ideas in Mathematics*. Reading, Mass.: Addison-Wesley, 1968.

Murrill, P. W., and C. L. Smith, *Fortran IV Programming*. Scranton, Penn.: International Textbook Company, 1968.

Osborn, R., *The Mathematics of Investment*. New York: Harper & Brothers, 1957.

Vance, E. P., *Modern College Algebra*, 2nd ed. Reading, Mass.: Addison-Wesley, 1967.

Wade, T. L., and H. E. Taylor, *Fundamental Mathematics*, 3rd ed. New York: McGraw-Hill, 1967.

Ward, M., and C. E. Hardgrove, *Modern Elementary Mathematics*. Reading, Mass.: Addison-Wesley, 1964.

Wheeler, R. E., *Modern Mathematics: An Elementary Approach.* Belmont, Calif.: Brooks/Cole, 1968.

Whitesitt, J. E., *Principles of Modern Algebra.* Reading, Mass.: Addison-Wesley, 1964.

APPENDIX

Table I American Experience Table of Mortality

Age	Number living	Number dying	Yearly probability of dying	Yearly probability of living	Age	Number living	Number dying	Yearly probability of dying	Yearly probability of living
10	100 000	749	0.007 490	0.992 510	53	66 797	1 091	0.016 333	0.983 667
11	99 251	746	0.007 516	0.992 484	54	65 706	1 143	0.017 396	0.982 604
12	98 505	743	0.007 543	0.992 457	55	64 563	1 199	0.018 571	0.981 429
13	97 762	740	0.007 569	0.992 431	56	63 364	1 260	0.019 885	0.980 115
14	97 022	737	0.007 596	0.992 404	57	62 104	1 325	0.021 335	0.978 665
15	96 285	735	0.007 634	0.992 366	58	60 779	1 394	0.022 936	0.997 064
16	95 550	732	0.007 661	0.992 339	59	59 385	1 468	0.024 720	0.975 280
17	94 818	729	0.007 688	0.992 312	60	57 917	1 546	0.026 693	0.973 307
18	94 089	727	0.007 727	0.992 273	61	56 371	1 628	0.028 880	0.971 120
19	93 362	725	0.007 765	0.992 235	62	54 743	1 713	0.031 292	0.968 708
20	92 637	723	0.007 805	0.992 195	63	53 030	1 800	0.033 943	0.966 057
21	91 914	722	0.007 855	0.992 145	64	51 230	1 889	0.036 873	0.963 127
22	91 192	721	0.007 906	0.992 094	65	49 341	1 980	0.040 129	0.959 871
23	90 471	720	0.007 958	0.992 042	66	47 361	2 070	0.043 707	0.956 293
24	89 751	719	0.008 011	0.991 989	67	45 291	2 158	0.047 647	0.952 353
25	89 032	718	0.008 065	0.991 935	68	43 133	2 243	0.052 002	0.947 998
26	88 314	718	0.008 130	0.991 870	69	40 890	2 321	0.056 762	0.943 238
27	87 596	718	0.008 197	0.991 803	70	38 569	2 391	0.061 993	0.938 007
28	86 878	718	0.008 264	0.991 736	71	36 178	2 448	0.067 665	0.932 335
29	86 160	719	0.008 345	0.991 655	72	33 730	2 487	0.073 733	0.926 267
30	85 441	720	0.008 427	0.991 573	73	31 243	2 505	0.080 178	0.919 822
31	84 721	721	0.008 510	0.991 490	74	28 738	2 501	0.087 028	0.912 972
32	84 000	723	0.008 607	0.991 393	75	26 237	2 476	0.094 371	0.905 629
33	83 277	726	0.008 718	0.991 282	76	23 761	2 431	0.102 311	0.897 689
34	82 551	729	0.008 831	0.991 169	77	21 330	2 369	0.111 064	0.888 936
35	81 822	732	0.008 946	0.991 054	78	18 961	2 291	0.120 827	0.879 173
36	81 090	737	0.009 089	0.990 911	79	16 670	2 196	0.131 734	0.868 266
37	80 353	742	0.009 234	0.990 766	80	14 474	2 091	0.144 466	0.855 534
38	79 611	749	0.009 408	0.990 592	81	12 383	1 964	0.158 605	0.841 395
39	78 862	756	0.009 586	0.990 414	82	10 419	1 816	0.174 297	0.825 703
40	78 106	765	0.009 794	0.990 206	83	8 603	1 648	0.191 561	0.808 439
41	77 341	774	0.010 008	0.989 992	84	6 955	1 470	0.211 359	0.788 641
42	76 567	785	0.010 252	0.989 748	85	5 485	1 292	0.235 552	0.764 448
43	75 782	797	0.010 517	0.989 483	86	4 193	1 114	0.265 681	0.734 319
44	74 985	812	0.010 829	0.989 171	87	3 079	933	0.303 020	0.696 980
45	74 173	828	0.011 163	0.988 837	88	2 146	744	0.346 692	0.653 308
46	73 345	848	0.011 562	0.988 438	89	1 402	555	0.395 863	0.604 137
47	72 497	870	0.012 000	0.988 000	90	847	385	0.454 545	0.545 455
48	71 627	896	0.012 509	0.987 491	91	462	246	0.532 468	0.467 532
49	70 731	927	0.013 106	0.986 894	92	216	137	0.634 259	0.365 741
50	69 804	962	0.013 781	0.986 219	93	79	58	0.734 177	0.265 823
51	68 842	1 001	0.014 541	0.985 459	94	21	18	0.857 143	0.142 857
52	67 841	1 044	0.015 389	0.984 611	95	3	3	1.000 000	0.000 000

Table II The Number of Each Day of the Year

DAY OF MONTH	Jan.	Feb.	Mar.	April	May	June	July	Aug.	Sept.	Oct.	Nov.	Dec.	DAY OF MONTH
1	1	32	60	91	121	152	182	213	244	274	305	335	1
2	2	33	61	92	122	153	183	214	245	275	306	336	2
3	3	34	62	93	123	154	184	215	246	276	307	337	3
4	4	35	63	94	124	155	185	216	247	277	308	338	4
5	5	36	64	95	125	156	186	217	248	278	309	339	5
6	6	37	65	96	126	157	187	218	249	279	310	340	6
7	7	38	66	97	127	158	188	219	250	280	311	341	7
8	8	39	67	98	128	159	189	220	251	281	312	342	8
9	9	40	68	99	129	160	190	221	252	282	313	343	9
10	10	41	69	100	130	161	191	222	253	283	314	344	10
11	11	42	70	101	131	162	192	223	254	284	315	345	11
12	12	43	71	102	132	163	193	224	255	285	316	346	12
13	13	44	72	103	133	164	194	225	256	286	317	347	13
14	14	45	73	104	134	165	195	226	257	287	318	348	14
15	15	46	74	105	135	166	196	227	258	288	319	349	15
16	16	47	75	106	136	167	197	228	259	289	320	350	16
17	17	48	76	107	137	168	198	229	260	290	321	351	17
18	18	49	77	108	138	169	199	230	261	291	322	352	18
19	19	50	78	109	139	170	200	231	262	292	323	353	19
20	20	51	79	110	140	171	201	232	263	293	324	354	20
21	21	52	80	111	141	172	202	233	264	294	325	355	21
22	22	53	81	112	142	173	203	234	265	295	326	356	22
23	23	54	82	113	143	174	204	235	266	296	327	357	23
24	24	55	83	114	144	175	205	236	267	297	328	358	24
25	25	56	84	115	145	176	206	237	268	298	329	359	25
26	26	57	85	116	146	177	207	238	269	299	330	360	26
27	27	58	86	117	147	178	208	239	270	300	331	361	27
28	28	59	87	118	148	179	209	240	271	301	332	362	28
29	29		88	119	149	180	210	241	272	302	333	363	29
30	30		89	120	150	181	211	242	273	303	334	364	30
31	31		90		151		212	243		304		365	31

Table III   Values of $(1 + i)^n$

n	1/3%	1/2%	2%	2 1/2%	3%	5%	n
1	1.0033 33	1.0050 00	1.0200 00	1.0250 00	1.0300 00	1.0500 00	1
2	1.0066 77	1.0100 25	1.0404 00	1.0506 25	1.0609 00	1.1025 00	2
3	1.0100 33	1.0150 75	1.0612 08	1.0768 90	1.0927 27	1.1576 25	3
4	1.0134 00	1.0201 50	1.0824 32	1.1038 12	1.1255 08	1.2155 06	4
5	1.0167 78	1.0252 51	1.1040 80	1.1314 08	1.1592 74	1.2762 81	5
6	1.0201 67	1.0303 77	1.1261 62	1.1596 93	1.1940 52	1.3400 95	6
7	1.0235 67	1.0355 29	1.1486 85	1.1886 85	1.2298 73	1.4071 00	7
8	1.0269 79	1.0407 07	1.1716 59	1.2184 02	1.2667 70	1.4774 55	8
9	1.0304 03	1.0459 10	1.1950 92	1.2488 62	1.3047 73	1.5513 28	9
10	1.0338 37	1.0511 40	1.2189 94	1.2800 84	1.3439 16	1.6288 94	10
11	1.0372 83	1.0563 95	1.2433 74	1.3120 86	1.3842 33	1.7103 39	11
12	1.0407 41	1.0616 77	1.2682 41	1.3448 88	1.4257 60	1.7958 56	12
13	1.0442 10	1.0669 86	1.2936 06	1.3785 11	1.4685 33	1.8856 49	13
14	1.0476 91	1.0723 21	1.3194 78	1.4129 73	1.5125 89	1.9799 31	14
15	1.0511 83	1.0776 82	1.3458 68	1.4482 98	1.5579 67	2.0789 28	15
16	1.0546 87	1.0830 71	1.3727 85	1.4845 05	1.6047 06	2.1828 74	16
17	1.0582 03	1.0884 86	1.4002 41	1.5216 18	1.6528 47	2.2920 18	17
18	1.0617 30	1.0939 28	1.4282 46	1.5596 58	1.7024 33	2.4066 19	18
19	1.0652 69	1.0993 98	1.4568 11	1.5986 50	1.7535 06	2.5269 50	19
20	1.0688 20	1.1048 95	1.4859 47	1.6386 16	1.8061 11	2.6532 97	20
21	1.0723 83	1.1104 20	1.5156 66	1.6795 81	1.8602 94	2.7859 62	21
22	1.0759 57	1.1159 72	1.5459 79	1.7215 71	1.9161 03	2.9252 60	22
23	1.0795 44	1.1215 52	1.5768 99	1.7646 10	1.9735 86	3.0715 23	23
24	1.0831 42	1.1271 59	1.6084 37	1.8087 25	2.0327 94	3.2250 99	24
25	1.0867 53	1.1327 95	1.6406 05	1.8539 44	2.0937 77	3.3863 54	25
26	1.0903 75	1.1384 59	1.6734 18	1.9002 92	2.1565 91	3.5556 72	26
27	1.0940 10	1.1441 51	1.7068 86	1.9478 00	2.2212 89	3.7334 56	27
28	1.0976 57	1.1498 72	1.7410 24	1.9964 95	2.2879 27	3.9201 29	28
29	1.1013 16	1.1556 21	1.7758 44	2.0464 07	2.3565 65	4.1161 35	29
30	1.1049 87	1.1614 00	1.8113 61	2.0975 67	2.4272 62	4.3219 42	30
31	1.1086 70	1.1672 07	1.8475 88	2.1500 06	2.5000 80	4.5380 39	31
32	1.1123 66	1.1730 43	1.8845 40	2.2037 56	2.5750 82	4.7649 41	32
33	1.1160 73	1.1789 08	1.9222 31	2.2588 50	2.6523 35	5.0031 88	33
34	1.1197 94	1.1848 02	1.9606 76	2.3153 22	2.7319 05	5.2533 47	34
35	1.1235 26	1.1907 26	1.9998 89	2.3732 05	2.8138 62	5.5160 15	35
36	1.1272 71	1.1966 80	2.0398 87	2.4325 35	2.8982 78	5.7918 16	36
37	1.1310 29	1.2026 63	2.0806 85	2.4933 48	2.9852 26	6.0814 06	37
38	1.1347 99	1.2086 77	2.1222 98	2.5556 82	3.0747 83	6.3854 77	38
39	1.1385 82	1.2147 20	2.1647 44	2.6195 74	3.1670 26	6.7047 51	39
40	1.1423 77	1.2207 94	2.2080 39	2.6850 63	3.2620 37	7.0399 88	40
41	1.1461 85	1.2268 98	2.2522 00	2.7521 90	3.3598 98	7.3919 88	41
42	1.1500 06	1.2330 32	2.2972 44	2.8209 95	3.4606 95	7.7615 87	42
43	1.1538 39	1.2391 97	2.3431 89	2.8915 20	3.5645 16	8.1496 66	43
44	1.1576 85	1.2453 93	2.3900 53	2.9638 08	3.6714 52	8.5571 50	44
45	1.1615 44	1.2516 20	2.4378 54	3.0379 03	3.7815 95	8.9850 07	45
46	1.1654 16	1.2578 78	2.4866 11	3.1138 50	3.8950 43	9.4342 58	46
47	1.1693 01	1.2641 68	2.5363 43	3.1916 97	4.0118 95	9.9059 71	47
48	1.1731 98	1.2704 89	2.5870 70	3.2714 89	4.1322 51	10.4012 69	48
49	1.1771 09	1.2768 41	2.6388 11	3.3532 76	4.2562 19	10.9213 33	49
50	1.1810 33	1.2832 25	2.6915 88	3.4371 08	4.3839 06	11.4673 99	50

Table IV Values of $(1 + i)^{-n}$

n	1/2%	1 1/4%	2%	3 1/2%	4%	5%	n
1	0.9950 24	0.9876 54	0.9803 92	0.9661 83	0.9615 38	0.9523 80	1
2	0.9900 74	0.9754 61	0.0611 68	0.9335 10	0.9245 56	0.9070 29	2
3	0.9851 48	0.9634 18	0.9423 22	0.9019 42	0.8889 96	0.8638 37	3
4	0.9802 47	0.9515 24	0.9238 45	0.8714 42	0.8548 04	0.8227 02	4
5	0.9753 70	0.9397 77	0.9057 30	0.8419 73	0.8219 27	0.7835 26	5
6	0.9705 18	0.9281 74	0.8879 71	0.8135 00	0.7903 14	0.7462 15	6
7	0.9656 89	0.9167 15	0.8705 60	0.7859 90	0.7599 17	0.7106 81	7
8	0.9608 85	0.9053 98	0.8534 90	0.7594 11	0.7306 90	0.6768 39	8
9	0.9561 04	0.8942 20	0.8367 55	0.7337 30	0.7025 86	0.6446 08	9
10	0.9513 47	0.8831 80	0.8203 48	0.7089 18	0.6755 64	0.6139 13	10
11	0.9466 14	0.8722 77	0.8042 63	0.6849 45	0.6495 80	0.5846 79	11
12	0.9419 05	0.8615 08	0.7884 93	0.6617 83	0.6245 97	0.5568 37	12
13	0.9372 19	0.8508 72	0.7730 32	0.6394 04	0.6005 74	0.5303 21	13
14	0.9325 56	0.8403 68	0.7578 75	0.6177 81	0.5774 75	0.5050 67	14
15	0.9279 16	0.8299 93	0.7430 14	0.5968 90	0.5552 64	0.4810 17	15
16	0.9233 00	0.8197 46	0.7284 45	0.5767 05	0.5339 08	0.4581 11	16
17	0.9187 06	0.8096 26	0.7141 62	0.5572 03	0.5133 73	0.4362 96	17
18	0.9141 36	0.7996 30	0.7001 59	0.5383 61	0.4936 28	0.4155 20	18
19	0.9095 88	0.7897 58	0.6864 30	0.5201 55	0.4746 42	0.3957 33	19
20	0.9050 62	0.7800 08	0.6729 71	0.5025 65	0.4563 86	0.3768 89	20
21	0.9005 60	0.7703 78	0.6597 75	0.4855 70	0.4388 33	0.3589 42	21
22	0.8960 79	0.7608 67	0.6468 39	0.4691 50	0.4219 55	0.3418 49	22
23	0.8916 21	0.7514 74	0.6341 55	0.4532 85	0.4057 26	0.3255 71	23
24	0.8871 85	0.7421 97	0.6217 21	0.4379 57	0.3901 21	0.3100 67	24
25	0.8827 71	0.7330 34	0.6095 30	0.4231 46	0.3751 16	0.2953 02	25
26	0.8783 79	0.7239 84	0.5975 79	0.4088 37	0.3606 89	0.2812 40	26
27	0.8740 09	0.7150 46	0.5858 62	0.3950 12	0.3468 16	0.2678 48	27
28	0.8696 61	0.7062 18	0.5743 74	0.3816 54	0.3334 77	0.2550 93	28
29	0.8653 34	0.6974 99	0.5631 12	0.3687 48	0.3206 51	0.2429 46	29
30	0.8610 29	0.6888 88	0.5520 70	0.3562 78	0.3083 18	0.2313 77	30
31	0.8567 46	0.6803 83	0.5412 45	0.3442 30	0.2964 60	0.2203 59	31
32	0.8524 83	0.6719 84	0.5306 33	0.3325 89	0.2850 57	0.2098 66	32
33	0.8482 42	0.6636 87	0.5202 28	0.3213 42	0.2740 94	0.1998 72	33
34	0.8440 22	0.6554 94	0.5100 28	0.3104 76	0.2635 52	0.1903 54	34
35	0.8398 23	0.6474 01	0.5000 27	0.2999 76	0.2534 15	0.1812 90	35
36	0.8356 44	0.6394 09	0.4902 23	0.2898 32	0.2436 68	0.1726 57	36
37	0.8314 87	0.6315 15	0.4806 10	0.2800 31	0.2342 96	0.1644 35	37
38	0.8273 50	0.6237 18	0.4711 87	0.2705 61	0.2252 85	0.1566 05	38
39	0.8232 34	0.6160 18	0.4619 48	0.2614 12	0.2166 20	0.1491 47	39
40	0.8191 38	0.6084 13	0.4528 90	0.2525 72	0.2082 89	0.1420 45	40
41	0.8150 63	0.6009 02	0.4440 10	0.2440 31	0.2002 77	0.1352 81	41
42	0.8110 08	0.5934 83	0.4353 04	0.2357 79	0.1925 74	0.1288 39	42
43	0.8069 73	0.5861 56	0.4267 68	0.2278 05	0.1851 68	0.1227 04	43
44	0.8029 58	0.5789 20	0.4184 00	0.2201 02	0.1780 02	0.1168 61	44
45	0.7989 64	0.5717 72	0.4101 96	0.2126 59	0.1711 98	0.1112 96	45
46	0.7949 89	0.5647 13	0.4021 53	0.2054 67	0.1646 13	0.1059 96	46
47	0.7910 33	0.5577 42	0.3942 68	0.1985 19	0.1582 82	0.1009 49	47
48	0.7870 98	0.5508 56	0.3865 37	0.1918 06	0.1521 94	0.0961 42	48
49	0.7831 82	0.5440 55	0.3789 58	0.1853 20	0.1463 41	0.0915 63	49
50	0.7792 86	0.5373 39	0.3715 27	0.1790 53	0.1407 12	0.0872 03	50

Table V Values of $s_{\overline{n}|i}$

n	1/3%	3/4%	1 1/4%	2%	2 1/2%	4%	5%	n
1	1.0000 00	1.0000 00	1.0000 00	1.0000 00	1.0000 00	1.0000 00	1.0000 00	1
2	2.0033 33	2.0075 00	2.0125 00	2.0200 00	2.0250 00	2.0400 00	2.0500 00	2
3	3.0100 11	3.0225 56	3.0376 56	3.0604 00	3.0756 25	3.1216 00	3.1525 00	3
4	4.0200 44	4.0452 25	4.0756 26	4.1216 08	4.1525 15	4.2464 64	4.3101 25	4
5	5.0334 44	5.0755 64	5.1265 72	5.2040 40	5.2563 28	5.4163 22	5.5256 31	5
6	6.0502 22	6.1136 31	6.1906 54	6.3081 20	6.3877 36	6.6329 75	6.8019 12	6
7	7.0703 90	7.1594 83	7.2680 37	7.4342 83	7.5474 30	7.8982 94	8.1420 08	7
8	8.0939 58	8.2131 79	8.3588 88	8.5829 69	8.7361 15	9.2142 26	9.5491 08	8
9	9.1209 38	9.2747 78	9.4633 74	9.7546 28	9.9545 18	10.5827 95	11.0265 64	9
10	10.1513 41	10.3443 39	10.5816 66	10.9497 21	11.2033 81	12.0061 07	12.5778 92	10
11	11.1851 78	11.4219 21	11.7139 37	12.1687 15	12.4834 66	13.4863 51	14.2067 87	11
12	12.2224 62	12.5075 86	12.8603 61	13.4120 89	13.7955 52	15.0258 05	15.9171 26	12
13	13.2632 04	13.6013 93	14.0211 15	14.6803 31	15.1404 41	16.6268 37	17.7129 82	13
14	14.3074 15	14.7034 03	15.1963 79	15.9739 38	16.5189 52	18.2919 11	19.5986 31	14
15	15.3551 06	15.8136 79	16.3863 34	17.2934 16	17.9319 26	20.0235 87	21.5785 63	15
16	16.4062 90	16.9322 81	17.5911 63	18.6392 85	19.3802 24	21.8245 31	23.6574 91	16
17	17.4609 77	18.0592 73	18.8110 53	20.0120 70	20.8647 30	23.6975 12	25.8403 66	17
18	18.5191 81	19.1947 18	20.0461 91	21.4123 12	22.3863 48	25.6454 12	28.1323 84	18
19	19.5809 11	20.3386 78	21.2967 68	22.8405 58	23.9460 07	27.6712 29	30.5390 03	19
20	20.6461 81	21.4912 18	22.5629 78	24.2973 69	25.5446 57	29.7780 78	33.0659 54	20
21	21.7150 01	22.6524 03	23.8450 15	25.7833 17	27.1832 74	31.9692 01	35.7192 51	21
22	22.7873 85	23.8222 96	25.1430 78	27.2989 83	28.8628 55	34.2479 69	38.5052 14	22
23	23.8633 43	25.0009 63	26.4573 66	28.8449 63	30.5844 27	36.6178 88	41.4304 75	23
24	24.9428 87	26.1884 70	27.7880 84	30.4218 62	32.3490 37	39.0826 04	44.5019 98	24
25	26.0260 30	27.3848 84	29.1354 35	32.0302 99	34.1577 63	41.6459 08	47.7270 98	25
26	27.1127 84	28.5902 70	30.4996 28	33.6709 05	36.0117 08	44.3117 44	51.1134 53	26
27	28.2031 60	29.8046 97	31.8808 73	35.3443 23	37.9120 00	47.0842 14	54.6691 26	27
28	29.2971 70	31.0282 33	33.2793 84	37.0512 10	39.8598 00	49.9675 82	58.4025 82	28
29	30.3948 27	32.2609 44	34.6953 76	38.7922 34	41.8562 95	52.9662 86	62.3227 11	29
30	31.4961 43	33.5029 01	36.1290 68	40.5680 79	43.9027 03	56.0849 37	66.4388 47	30
31	32.6011 31	34.7541 73	37.5806 82	42.3794 40	46.0002 70	59.3283 35	70.7607 89	31
32	33.7098 01	36.0148 29	39.0504 40	44.2270 29	48.1502 77	62.7014 68	75.2988 29	32
33	34.8221 67	37.2849 41	40.5385 71	46.1115 70	50.3540 34	66.2095 27	80.0637 70	33
34	35.9382 41	38.5645 78	42.0453 03	48.0338 01	52.6128 85	69.8579 08	85.0669 59	34
35	37.0580 35	39.8538 12	43.5708 69	49.9944 77	54.9282 07	73.6522 24	90.3203 07	35
36	38.1815 62	41.1527 16	45.1155 05	51.9943 67	57.3014 12	77.5983 13	95.8363 22	36
37	39.3088 34	42.4613 61	46.6794 49	54.0342 54	59.7339 47	81.7022 46	101.6281 38	37
38	40.4398 63	43.7798 21	48.2629 42	56.1149 39	62.2272 96	85.9703 36	107.7095 45	38
39	41.5746 63	45.1081 70	49.8662 29	58.2372 38	64.7829 79	90.4091 49	114.0950 23	39
40	42.7132 45	46.4464 81	51.4895 57	60.4019 83	67.4025 53	95.0255 15	120.7997 74	40
41	43.8556 22	47.7948 30	53.1331 76	62.6100 22	70.0876 17	99.8265 36	127.8397 62	41
42	45.0018 08	49.1532 91	54.7973 41	64.8622 23	72.8398 07	104.8195 97	135.2317 51	42
43	46.1518 14	50.5219 41	56.4823 08	67.1594 67	75.6608 03	110.0123 81	142.9933 38	43
44	47.3056 53	51.9008 55	58.1883 36	69.5026 57	78.5523 23	115.4128 76	151.1430 05	44
45	48.4633 39	53.2901 12	59.9156 91	71.8927 10	81.5161 31	121.0293 92	159.7001 55	45
46	49.6248 83	54.6897 87	61.6646 37	74.3305 64	84.5540 34	126.8705 67	168.6851 63	46
47	50.7902 99	56.0999 61	63.4354 45	76.8171 75	87.6678 85	132.9453 90	178.1194 21	47
48	51.9596 00	57.5207 11	65.2283 88	79.3535 19	90.8595 82	139.2632 06	188.0253 92	48
49	53.1327 99	58.9521 16	67.0437 43	81.9405 89	94.1310 71	145.8337 34	198.4266 62	49
50	54.3099 08	60.3942 57	68.8817 89	84.5794 01	97.4843 48	152.6670 83	209.3479 95	50

Table VI Values of $a_{\overline{n}|i}$

n	1/3%	3/4%	1 1/4%	2%	2 1/2%	4%	5%	n
1	0.9966 77	0.9925 55	0.9876 54	0.9803 92	0.9756 09	0.9615 38	0.9523 80	1
2	1.9900 44	1.9777 22	1.9631 15	1.9415 60	1.9274 24	1.8860 94	1.8594 10	2
3	2.9801 10	2.9555 56	2.9265 33	2.8838 83	2.8560 23	2.7750 91	2.7232 48	3
4	3.9668 87	3.9261 10	3.8780 57	3.8077 28	3.7619 74	3.6298 95	3.5459 50	4
5	4.9503 86	4.8894 39	4.8178 35	4.7134 59	4.6458 28	4.4518 22	4.3294 76	5
6	5.9306 17	5.8455 97	5.7460 09	5.6014 30	5.5081 25	5.2421 36	5.0756 92	6
7	6.9075 92	6.7946 37	6.6627 25	6.4719 91	6.3493 90	6.0020 54	5.7863 73	7
8	7.8813 21	7.7366 13	7.5681 24	7.3254 81	7.1701 37	6.7327 44	6.4632 12	8
9	8.8518 15	8.6715 76	8.4623 44	8.1622 36	7.9708 65	7.4353 31	7.1078 21	9
10	9.8190 84	9.5995 79	9.3455 25	8.9825 85	8.7520 63	8.1108 95	7.7217 34	10
11	10.7831 41	10.5206 74	10.2178 03	9.7868 48	9.5142 08	8.7604 76	8.3064 14	11
12	11.7439 94	11.4349 12	11.0793 11	10.5753 41	10.2577 64	9.3850 73	8.8632 51	12
13	12.7016 55	12.3423 45	11.9301 84	11.3483 73	10.9831 84	9.9856 47	9.3935 72	13
14	13.6561 35	13.2430 22	12.7705 52	12.1062 48	11.6909 12	10.5631 22	9.8986 40	14
15	14.6074 43	14.1369 94	13.6005 45	12.8492 63	12.3813 77	11.1183 87	10.3796 58	15
16	15.5555 91	15.0243 12	14.4202 92	13.5777 09	13.0550 02	11.6522 95	10.8377 69	16
17	16.5005 89	15.9050 24	15.2299 18	14.2918 71	13.7121 97	12.1656 68	11.2740 66	17
18	17.4424 48	16.7791 81	16.0295 48	14.9920 31	14.3533 63	12.6592 96	11.6895 06	18
19	18.3811 77	17.6468 29	16.8193 07	15.6784 62	14.9788 91	13.1339 39	12.0853 20	19
20	19.3167 88	18.5080 19	17.5993 16	16.3514 33	15.5891 62	13.5903 26	12.4622 10	20
21	20.2492 90	19.3627 98	18.3696 94	17.0112 09	16.1845 48	14.0291 59	12.8211 52	21
22	21.1786 95	20.2112 14	19.1305 62	17.6580 48	16.7654 13	14.4511 15	13.1630 02	22
23	22.1050 11	21.0533 14	19.8820 37	18.2922 04	17.3321 10	14.8568 41	13.4885 73	23
24	23.0282 50	21.8891 46	20.6242 34	18.9139 25	17.8849 85	15.2469 63	13.7986 41	24
25	23.9484 22	22.7187 55	21.3572 68	19.5234 56	18.4243 76	15.6220 79	14.0939 44	25
26	24.8655 37	23.5421 89	22.0812 52	20.1210 35	18.9506 11	15.9827 69	14.3751 85	26
27	25.7796 05	24.3594 92	22.7962 99	20.7068 97	19.4640 10	16.3295 85	14.6430 33	27
28	26.6906 36	25.1707 12	23.5025 17	21.2812 72	19.9648 88	16.6630 63	14.8981 27	28
29	27.5986 41	25.9758 93	24.2000 17	21.8443 84	20.4535 49	16.9837 14	15.1410 73	29
30	28.5036 29	26.7750 80	24.8889 06	22.3964 55	20.9302 92	17.2920 33	15.3724 51	30
31	29.4056 10	27.5683 17	25.5692 90	22.9377 01	21.3954 07	17.5884 93	15.5928 10	31
32	30.3045 95	28.3556 50	26.2412 74	23.4683 34	21.8491 77	17.8735 51	15.8026 76	32
33	31.2005 93	29.1371 22	26.9049 62	23.9885 63	22.2918 80	18.1476 45	16.0025 49	33
34	32.0936 14	29.9127 76	27.5604 56	24.4985 91	22.7237 86	18.4111 97	16.1929 04	34
35	32.9836 68	30.6826 56	28.2078 58	24.9986 19	23.1451 57	18.6646 13	16.3741 94	35
36	33.8707 66	31.4468 05	28.8472 67	25.4888 42	23.5562 51	18.9082 81	16.5468 51	36
37	34.7549 16	32.2052 65	29.4787 82	25.9694 53	23.9573 18	19.1425 78	16.7112 87	37
38	35.6361 29	32.9580 80	30.1025 01	26.4406 40	24.3486 03	19.3678 64	16.8678 92	38
39	36.5144 14	33.7052 90	30.7185 19	26.9025 88	24.7303 44	19.5844 84	17.0170 40	39
40	37.3897 82	34.4469 38	31.3269 33	27.3554 79	25.1027 75	19.7927 73	17.1590 86	40
41	38.2622 41	35.1830 65	31.9278 35	27.7994 89	25.4661 22	19.9930 51	17.2943 67	41
42	39.1318 02	35.9137 12	32.5213 18	28.2347 93	25.8206 06	20.1856 26	17.4232 07	42
43	39.9984 73	36.6389 20	33.1074 75	28.6615 62	26.1664 45	20.3707 94	17.5459 11	43
44	40.8622 66	37.3587 30	33.6863 95	29.0799 63	26.5038 49	20.5488 41	17.6627 73	44
45	41.7231 89	38.0731 81	34.2581 68	29.4901 59	26.8330 23	20.7200 39	17.7740 69	45
46	42.5812 51	38.7823 14	34.8228 82	29.8923 13	27.1541 69	20.8846 53	17.8800 66	46
47	43.4364 63	39.4861 67	35.3806 24	30.2865 81	27.4674 82	21.0429 36	17.9810 15	47
48	44.2888 33	40.1847 81	35.9314 80	30.6731 19	27.7731 53	21.1951 30	18.0771 57	48
49	45.1383 72	40.8781 95	36.4755 36	31.0520 78	28.0713 69	21.3414 72	18.1687 21	49
50	45.9850 89	41.5664 47	37.0128 75	31.4236 05	28.3623 11	21.4821 84	18.2559 25	50

Table VII Values of $\dfrac{1}{a_{\overline{n}|i}}$

n	1/3%	3/4%	1 1/4%	2%	2 1/2%	4%	5%	n
1	1.0033 33	1.0075 00	1.0125 00	1.0200 00	1.0250 00	1.0400 00	1.0500 00	1
2	0.5025 01	0.5056 32	0.5093 94	0.5150 49	0.5188 27	0.5301 96	0.5378 04	2
3	0.3355 58	0.3383 45	0.3417 01	0.3467 54	0.3501 37	0.3603 48	0.3672 08	3
4	0.2520 86	0.2547 05	0.2578 61	0.2626 23	0.2658 17	0.2754 90	0.2820 11	4
5	0.2020 04	0.2045 22	0.2075 62	0.2121 58	0.2152 46	0.2246 27	0.2309 74	5
6	0.1686 16	0.1710 68	0.1740 33	0.1785 25	0.1815 49	0.1907 61	0.1970 17	6
7	0.1447 68	0.1471 74	0.1500 88	0.1545 11	0.1574 95	0.1666 09	0.1728 19	7
8	0.1268 82	0.1292 55	0.1321 33	0.1365 09	0.1394 67	0.1485 27	0.1547 21	8
9	0.1129 71	0.1153 19	0.1181 70	0.1225 15	0.1254 56	0.1344 92	0.1406 90	9
10	0.1018 42	0.1041 71	0.1070 03	0.1113 26	0.1142 58	0.1232 90	0.1295 04	10
11	0.0927 37	0.0950 50	0.0978 68	0.1021 77	0.1051 05	0.1141 49	0.1203 88	11
12	0.0851 49	0.0874 51	0.0902 58	0.0945 59	0.0974 87	0.1065 52	0.1128 25	12
13	0.0787 29	0.0810 21	0.0838 21	0.0881 18	0.0910 48	0.1001 43	0.1064 55	13
14	0.0732 27	0.0755 11	0.0783 05	0.0826 01	0.0855 36	0.0946 68	0.1010 23	14
15	0.0684 58	0.0707 36	0.0735 26	0.0778 25	0.0807 66	0.0899 41	0.0963 42	15
16	0.0642 85	0.0665 58	0.0693 46	0.0736 50	0.0765 98	0.0858 20	0.0922 69	16
17	0.0606 03	0.0628 73	0.0656 60	0.0699 69	0.0729 27	0.0821 98	0.0886 99	17
18	0.0573 31	0.0595 97	0.0623 84	0.0667 02	0.0696 70	0.0789 93	0.0855 46	18
19	0.0544 03	0.0566 67	0.0594 55	0.0637 81	0.0667 60	0.0761 38	0.0827 45	19
20	0.0517 68	0.0540 30	0.0568 20	0.0611 56	0.0641 47	0.0735 81	0.0802 42	20
21	0.0493 84	0.0516 45	0.0544 37	0.0587 84	0.0617 87	0.0712 80	0.0779 96	21
22	0.0472 17	0.0494 77	0.0522 72	0.0566 31	0.0596 46	0.0691 98	0.0759 70	22
23	0.0452 38	0.0474 98	0.0502 96	0.0546 68	0.0576 96	0.0673 09	0.0741 36	23
24	0.0434 24	0.0456 84	0.0484 86	0.0528 71	0.0559 12	0.0655 86	0.0724 70	24
25	0.0417 56	0.0440 16	0.0468 22	0.0512 20	0.0542 75	0.0640 11	0.0709 52	25
26	0.0402 14	0.0424 76	0.0452 87	0.0496 99	0.0527 68	0.0625 67	0.0695 64	26
27	0.0387 90	0.0410 51	0.0438 66	0.0482 93	0.0513 76	0.0612 38	0.0682 91	27
28	0.0374 66	0.0397 28	0.0425 48	0.0469 89	0.0500 87	0.0600 12	0.0671 22	28
29	0.0362 33	0.0384 97	0.0413 22	0.0457 78	0.0488 91	0.0588 79	0.0660 45	29
30	0.0350 83	0.0373 48	0.0401 78	0.0446 49	0.0477 77	0.0578 30	0.0650 51	30
31	0.0340 07	0.0362 73	0.0391 09	0.0435 96	0.0467 39	0.0568 55	0.0641 32	31
32	0.0329 98	0.0352 66	0.0381 07	0.0426 10	0.0457 68	0.0559 48	0.0632 80	32
33	0.0320 50	0.0343 20	0.0371 67	0.0416 86	0.0448 59	0.0551 03	0.0624 90	33
34	0.0311 58	0.0334 30	0.0362 83	0.0408 18	0.0440 06	0.0543 14	0.0617 55	34
35	0.0303 18	0.0325 91	0.0354 51	0.0400 02	0.0432 05	0.0535 77	0.0610 71	35
36	0.0295 23	0.0317 99	0.0346 65	0.0392 32	0.0424 51	0.0528 86	0.0604 34	36
37	0.0287 72	0.0310 50	0.0339 22	0.0385 06	0.0417 40	0.0522 39	0.0598 39	37
38	0.0280 61	0.0303 41	0.0332 19	0.0378 20	0.0410 70	0.0516 31	0.0592 84	38
39	0.0273 86	0.0296 68	0.0325 53	0.0371 71	0.0404 36	0.0510 60	0.0587 64	39
40	0.0267 45	0.0290 30	0.0319 21	0.0365 55	0.0398 36	0.0505 23	0.0582 78	40
41	0.0261 35	0.0284 22	0.0313 20	0.0359 71	0.0392 67	0.0500 17	0.0578 22	41
42	0.0255 54	0.0278 44	0.0307 49	0.0354 17	0.0387 28	0.0495 40	0.0573 94	42
43	0.0250 00	0.0272 93	0.0302 04	0.0348 89	0.0382 16	0.0490 89	0.0569 93	43
44	0.0244 72	0.0267 67	0.0296 85	0.0343 87	0.0377 30	0.0486 64	0.0566 16	44
45	0.0239 67	0.0262 65	0.0291 90	0.0339 09	0.0372 67	0.0482 62	0.0562 61	45
46	0.0234 84	0.0257 84	0.0287 16	0.0334 53	0.0368 26	0.0478 82	0.0559 28	46
47	0.0230 22	0.0253 25	0.0282 64	0.0330 17	0.0364 06	0.0475 21	0.0556 14	47
48	0.0225 79	0.0248 85	0.0278 30	0.0326 01	0.0360 05	0.0471 80	0.0553 18	48
49	0.0221 54	0.0244 62	0.0274 15	0.0322 03	0.0356 23	0.0468 57	0.0550 39	49
50	0.0217 46	0.0240 57	0.0270 17	0.0318 23	0.0352 58	0.0465 50	0.0547 76	50

ANSWERS TO SELECTED PROBLEMS

Chapter 1

1.2 MATHEMATICAL SYSTEMS

5 Parts (a) and (c) would be of concern to a scientist. Parts (b), (d), and (e) would be of concern to a mathematician.

1.4 DIRECT PROOF

5 Hypothesis: $3x - 4 = x + 8$. Conclusion: $x = 6$.

7 The converse is "If $x = 8$, then $2x - 5 = x + 3$." The converse is true.

9 The converse is "If $x = 1$, then $5x + 4 = x + 8$." The converse is true.

11 Hypothesis: a person lives in Chicago. Conclusion: he lives in North America. The converse is "If a person lives in North America, then he lives in Chicago." The converse is not true because a person living in New York lives in North America but not in Chicago.

13 Hypothesis: two lines are parallel to the same line. Conclusion: the two lines are parallel to each other.

1.5 INDIRECT PROOF

1 Show that Bill is not in room 101 or room 103.

Chapter 2

2.1 SETS AND SET NOTATION

1 b) $\{6, 7, 8, 9\}$; $\{x \mid x$ is a positive integer between 5 and 10$\}$

  c) $\{51, 52, 53, \ldots\}$; $\{x \mid x$ is a positive integer greater than 50$\}$

  d) $\{1, -1\}$; $\{x \mid x^2 = 1\}$

  e) $\varnothing$ or $\{\ \}$;
  $\{x \mid x$ is a woman who has served as President of the United States$\}$

3 $\{a, b\}; \{a\}; \{\ \}; \{1, 2, 3, \ldots\}$

5 Yes. Each set consists of the numbers 1, 2, and 3.

7 a) $\{2, 3, 4\} = B$ b) $\{2, 3, 4, 5\}$ c) $\{2, 4\}$

9 Parts (a), (d), (e), (g), (i), and (j) are true.

11 Parts (b), (c), (e), and (h) are true.

13 $\varnothing$

15 $\varnothing, \{1\}, \{2\}, \{1, 2\}$

17 $\varnothing, \{1\}, \{\{2\}\}, \{3\}, \{1, \{2\}\}, \{1, 3\}, \{\{2\}, 3\}, \{1, \{2\}, 3\}$

2.2 SPECIAL SETS

1 a) An appropriate universal set would be the set of all courses offered for credit on your campus.

  b) An appropriate universal set would be the set $\{0, 1, 2, 3, 4, 5, 6, 7, 8, 9\}$.

  c) $\{6, 7, 8, 9, 10, 11\}$; an appropriate universal set would be the set of positive integers.

  d) An appropriate universal set would be the set $\{0, 1, 2, 3, 4, 5, 6, 7, 8, 9\}$.

3 The equations in parts (a) and (c)

5 $\{1, \{2\}, 3\}, \{1, 2, 3, \{2\}\}$ and $\{1, 2, 3, \{3\}, \{2\}\}$

7 a) $\{1, 2, 3, 4, 5\} = A$ b) $\{2, 3, 4, 5, 6\}$

  c) $\{6, 7, 8, 9\} = D$ d) $\{1, 2, 3\}$

  e) $\varnothing$ f) $\{4, 5\}$

  g) $\varnothing$ h) $\{1, 6, 7, 8, 9\}$

  i) $\{1\}$ j) $\{1, 2, 3, 6, 7, 8, 9\}$

  k) $\{6, 7, 8, 9\} = D$ l) $\{1, 2, 3, 4, 5, 6, 7, 8, 9\} = U$

9 a) U b) $\{i\}$

  c) $\varnothing$ d) $\{a, e, i, o, u, f, g, h, j, k\}$

  e) V f) $\{f, g, h, j, k\}$

  g) U h) C i) F

11 a) X b) U c) X

  d) $\varnothing$ e) X f) X

  g) $\varnothing$ h) $\varnothing$ i) U

13 Parts (a) and (d)

2.3 ONE-TO-ONE CORRESPONDENCE

1 $A \leftrightarrow B$ means there exists a one-to-one correspondence between A and B. $A = B$ means A and B have the same elements.

3 Tom ↔ Mary   Tom ↔ Jane   Tom ↔ Alice
    Bob ↔ Jane   Bob ↔ Mary   Bob ↔ Jane
    Bill ↔ Alice   Bill ↔ Alice   Bill ↔ Mary

5 There are 24 such one-to-one correspondences. Three of them are:

$a \leftrightarrow 1$	$a \leftrightarrow 4$	$a \leftrightarrow 3$
$b \leftrightarrow 2$	$b \leftrightarrow 3$	$b \leftrightarrow 1$
$c \leftrightarrow 3$	$c \leftrightarrow 2$	$c \leftrightarrow 2$
$d \leftrightarrow 4$	$d \leftrightarrow 1$	$d \leftrightarrow 4$

7 No. The sets do not have the same number of elements.

9 $5, 10, 15, \ldots, 5n, \ldots$
    ↕ ↕ ↕   ↕
    $10, 20, 30, \ldots, 10n, \ldots$

11 The sets in parts (a), (c), (d), and (e) are finite. The sets in the other
parts are infinite.

2.4 VENN DIAGRAMS

1 a)

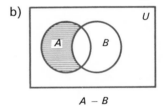

$A \cap B'$ b) $A - B$

c)

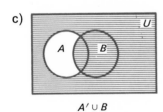

$A' \cup B$ d) $A \cap (B \cap C)$

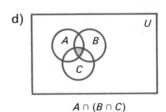

e)

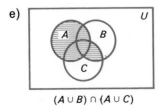

$(A \cup B) \cap (A \cup C)$ f) $U \cap A'$

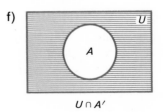

g)

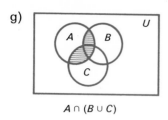

$A \cap (B \cup C)$

h)

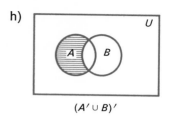

$(A' \cup B)'$

i)

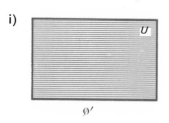

$\emptyset'$

3 The Venn diagrams for $A \cup B$ and $B \cup A$ suggest $A \cup B = B \cup A$.

7

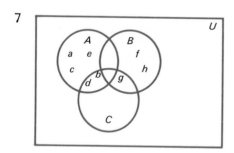

2.5 THE CARTESIAN PRODUCT

1 $A \times B = \{(a, r), (a, s), (a, t), (b, r), (b, s), (b, t)\}$
$B \times A = \{(r, a), (r, b), (s, a), (s, b), (t, a), (t, b)\}$

3 $X \times Y = \{(5, a), (5, b), (5, c)\}$
$Y \times X = \{(a, 5), (b, 5), (c, 5)\}$

5 $A \times B = \{(\$, \cent), (\$, *), (\#, \cent), (\#, *), (\cent, \cent), (\cent, *), (@, \cent), (@, *)\}$
$B \times A = \{(\cent, \$), (\cent, \#), (\cent, \cent), (\cent, @), (*, \$), (*, \#), (*, \cent), (*, @)\}$

7 $A \times A = \{(\#, \#), (\#, \cent), (\#, *), (\cent, \#), (\cent, \cent), (\cent, *), (*, \#), (*, \cent), (*, *)\}$

9 $(A \times B) \times C = \{((1, 3), 5), ((1, 4), 5), ((2, 3), 5), ((2, 4), 5)\}$

11 Let $A = \{\text{white, yellow, blue}\}$ and $B = \{\text{green, brown}\}$.
$A \times B = \{(\text{white, green}), (\text{white, brown}), (\text{yellow, green}),$
$\qquad\qquad\qquad (\text{yellow, brown}), (\text{blue, green}), (\text{blue, brown})\}$

13 $A = B$

Chapter 3

3.2 THE EGYPTIAN SYSTEM

1. a) ?????∩||||||

   b) £££????∩∩∩∩∩∩∩||||||||

   c) ∩∩∩∩|||||

   d) ⌒⌒⌒⌒⌒⌒ £££££?∩∩∩∩|||

   e) ⌒⌒⌒⌒⌒⌒⌒⌒ £££££?∩∩|||||

   f) ££££££££?????????∩∩∩∩||

3. ???????∩∩∩∩∩∩||||

5. ££££££?∩∩∩|

7. ??||||||||||

9. £££???∩∩∩||||

11. ???????∩|||||||||

13. No

3.3 THE ROMAN SYSTEM

1. a) MMMDCXVII b) CMXCIX c) CDXLIX
   d) DCCLXXXVII e) MMMMCCCLVI f) DCCCVII
3. MCCLXXVII 5 DCLXXXIII
7. LXV 9 MCMLXX (1970)
11. CXXII 13 DCXXVI; CCXLVIII

3.4 THE GREEK SYSTEM

1. a) 478 b) 8920 c) 691
3. a) NH b) SJD c) YA
5. TOM
7. a) A'#MI b) YNF
   c) A'UKB d) B'TA

3.5 INTEGRAL EXPONENTS

1 a) a^7 b) x^{18} c) a^7

  d) a^{24} e) 1   f) x^7

  g) y^{54} h) y^{66} i) b^9

3.6 THE BABYLONIAN SYSTEM

1 a)   <<< << ||

      b)   < <<|||

  c) ||| ||| |||| || |

  d) ||| ||| ||| <<||| || |

  e) ||| || ||| << ||| ||| |

  f)   <<| <<< <<<

3 <<<|| <<<| <

5 ||| <||| | <||| |

7 <<< <<<

3.7 THE MAYAN SYSTEM

1 a) ·· · ⩵   b) · ⊙ —   c) ⩵ ⊙ ⩶   d) ···· ··· ···· ⩵

3 ··· · ⩶ · ⩶ · ⩶   5 ···· ···· — ···   7 — · ⩶ ····

3.8 THE HINDU-ARABIC SYSTEM

1 a) $4 \cdot 10^2 + 7 \cdot 10^1 + 6 \cdot 10^0$

  b) $3 \cdot 10^0 + 4 \cdot 10^{-1} + 0 \cdot 10^{-2} + 4 \cdot 10^{-3}$

c) $8 \cdot 10^3 + 0 \cdot 10^2 + 9 \cdot 10^1 + 6 \cdot 10^0$

d) $9 \cdot 10^3 + 8 \cdot 10^2 + 7 \cdot 10^1 + 1 \cdot 10^0$

e) $4 \cdot 10^3 + 8 \cdot 10^2 + 9 \cdot 10^1 + 3 \cdot 10^0$

f) $0 \cdot 10^{-1} + 0 \cdot 10^{-2} + 0 \cdot 10^{-3} + 5 \cdot 10^{-4} + 2 \cdot 10^{-5}$

g) $6 \cdot 10^2 + 5 \cdot 10^1 + 1 \cdot 10^0 + 6 \cdot 10^{-1} + 3 \cdot 10^{-2}$

h) $6 \cdot 10^{-1} + 1 \cdot 10^{-2} + 2 \cdot 10^{-3}$

i) $4 \cdot 10^6 + 0 \cdot 10^5 + 2 \cdot 10^4 + 0 \cdot 10^3 + 3 \cdot 10^2 + 1 \cdot 10^1$
   $+ 6 \cdot 10^0 + 2 \cdot 10^{-1} + 2 \cdot 10^{-2}$

3.9 BASES OTHER THAN TEN

1 1, 2, 3, 4, 10, 11, 12, 13, 14, 20, 21, 22, 23, 24, 30, 31, 32, 33, 34, 40, 41, 42, 43, 44, 100, 101, 102, 103, 104, 110

3 1, 10, 11, 100, 101, 110, 111, 1000, 1001, 1010, 1011, 1100, 1101, 1110, 1111, 10000, 10001, 10010, 10011, 10100, 10101, 10110, 10111, 11000, 11001, 11010, 11011, 11100, 11101, 11110

5 a) 1001001_2 b) 1100110_2 c) 1001101001_2

7 a) 39_{12} b) tte_{12} c) $173e4_{12}$

9 14414_7

11 If b is any positive integer greater than 4, 42_b is an even integer when converted to base ten. There is no value for b such that 41_b is an even integer when converted to base ten.

3.10 COMPUTATION IN OTHER BASES

1 a) 1011_2 b) 100000_2 c) 1312_5
   d) 14445_9 e) 15844_{12} f) 2034_7

3 a) 1423_5 b) 1210_3 c) 5954_{12}
   d) 6132_8 e) 204311_5 f) 360500_7

3.11 ALGORITHMS

1 a)

*	1	44
	2	88
	4	176
	8	352
*16		704
		748

d)

*	1	281
*	2	562
	4	1124
	8	2248
*	16	4496
	32	8992
	64	17984
*128		35968
		41307

3 a)

c)

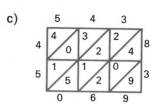

e)   5

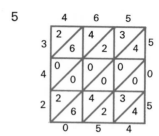

7   0 3
   3 $\not{3}$ $\not{2}$
  $\not{2}$ $\not{2}$ $\not{3}$ 1
      $\not{4}$ $\not{3}$
  $\not{3}$ $\not{2}$ $\not{2}$
     $\not{3}$

Chapter 4

4.1 COUNTING AND NATURAL NUMBERS

1 (Jan., Feb., Mar., Apr., May, June, July, Aug., Sept., Oct., Nov., Dec.); {Jan., Feb., Mar., Apr., May, June, July, Aug., Sept., Oct., Nov., Dec.}

3 The cardinal number is 6. The appropriate reference set is $\{0, 1, 2, 3, 4, 5\}$.

5 a) 8   b) 7   c) 0   d) 3

7 $n(s) = 50$; 1; 2; according to population

9 6; the same

11 a) Ordinal, cardinal   b) Cardinal, cardinal, ordinal

   c) Cardinal, ordinal   d) Ordinal, cardinal, cardinal

   e) Cardinal, ordinal   f) Ordinal, cardinal, cardinal

4.2 ADDITION OF NATURAL NUMBERS

1 a) Let $A = \{a, b\}$ and $B = \{c, d, e\}$. Then $n(A) = 2$, $n(B) = 3$, $A \cap B = \varnothing$, $A \cup B = \{a, b, c, d, e\}$, and $n(A \cup B) = 5$. Therefore, $2 + 3 = 5$.

3 $a + b$ means add b to a, and $b + a$ means add a to b; yes; property A3.

7 *a*

9 No; $1 + 1 = 2$ and $2 \notin S$.

4.3 MULTIPLICATION OF NATURAL NUMBERS

1 a) $3 \times 2 = 2 + 2 + 2 = 6$

  b) $5 \times 6 = 6 + 6 + 6 + 6 + 6 = 30$

5 a) Associative   b) Commutative   c) Associative

  d) Commutative   e) Associative

4.4 THE DISTRIBUTIVE PROPERTY

3 No; a counterexample is obtained by choosing $a = 1$, $b = 2$, and $c = 3$.

5 a) $5 \cdot 35 = 5(30 + 5) = 5 \cdot 30 + 5 \cdot 5$

  b) $7 \cdot 42 = 7(40 + 2) = 7 \cdot 40 + 7 \cdot 2$

  c) $15 \cdot 25 = 15(20 + 5) = 15 \cdot 20 + 15 \cdot 5$

  d) $4 \cdot 136 = 4(100 + 30 + 6) = 4 \cdot 100 + 4 \cdot 30 + 4 \cdot 6$

7 $a = 0, b = 0, c = 1$

4.5 THE EQUALITY RELATION

1 Symmetric

3 Transitive

5 Student A could be taking English and mathematics; student B could be taking English and history; and student C could be taking history and biology.

7 Any line n is parallel to itself (reflexive). If m is parallel to n, then n is parallel to m (symmetric). If m is parallel to n and n is parallel to l, then m is parallel to l (transitive).

9 Let A be related to B if A is the father of B.

4.6 THE ORDER RELATION

1 a) $6 < 15$ because $6 + 9 = 15$.

  b) $1 < 7$ because $1 + 6 = 7$.

  c) $8 > 5$ because $5 < 8$.

  d) $4 \nless 3$ because there is not a natural number n such that $4 + n = 3$.

  e) $1 \leqq 5$ because $1 < 5$.

  f) $10 > 8$ because $8 < 10$.

  g) $6 < 7$ because $6 + 1 = 7$.

  h) $0 < 5$ because $0 + 5 = 5$.

3 $A = \{4, 5, 6, \ldots\}$; $B = \{0, 1, 2, \ldots, 11\}$; $A \cap B = \{x \mid 4 \leq x \leq 11\}$;
   $A \cup B = \{x \mid 0 \leq x\}$.

5 $8 + x < 12 + x$.

7 No; no; yes; no

4.7 A SUMMARY OF THE PROPERTIES OF THE NATURAL NUMBERS

1 a) Commutative property of addition

   b) Associative property of addition

   c) Distributive property

   d) Commutative property of multiplication

   e) Commutative property of multiplication

   f) Commutative property of addition

   g) Closure property of addition

   h) Commutative property of addition

   i) Cancellation property of multiplication

   j) Associative property of multiplication

4.8 THE NATURAL NUMBERS AND SUBTRACTION

1 a) 5   b) 3   c) 25   d) 7

   e) 23   f) 8   g) 0   h) 75

3 No; $4 - 2 = 2$, whereas $2 - 4$ is meaningless in the set of natural numbers.

4.9 INTEGERS

1 a) -3 b) $+6$ c) -7

   d) -7 e) 0   f) $+13$

   g) $+10$ h) 0   i) -37

3 a) 5   b) 15   c) 12

   d) 1   e) 11   f) 66

4.10 ADDITION OF INTEGERS

1 a) $(11, 5)$ b) $(9, 10)$ c) $(18, 15)$

   d) $(11, 24)$ e) $(14, 14)$ f) $(22, 29)$

5 9

4.11 SUBTRACTION OF INTEGERS

1 a) $(5, 11)$ b) $(11, 16)$ c) $(14, 11)$

   d) $(20, 12)$ e) $(18, 11)$ f) $(29, 8)$

3 Symmetric property

5 a) (9, 16)   b) (22, 15)   c) (12, 15)

   d) (14, 14)   e) (7, 12)   f) (16, 10)

7 $a = b$

4.12 MULTIPLICATION OF INTEGERS

1 a) (48, 33)   b) (61, 89)   c) (124, 156)

   d) (30, 34)   e) (338, 338)   f) (630, 666)

5 a) Associative property of multiplication

   b) Cancellation property of multiplication

   c) 1 is the multiplicative identity

   d) Commutative property of multiplication

   e) Closure property of addition

   f) Cancellation property of multiplication

4.13 THE DISTRIBUTIVE PROPERTY

1 a) −16   b) 0   c) 56

   d) −18   e) 20   f) 6

   g) −24   h) 210   i) 12

4.14 THE INTEGERS AND ORDER

1 a) (3, 7) < (7, 2)   since $3 + 2 < 7 + 7$.

   b) (4, 11) < (2, 8)   since $4 + 8 < 11 + 2$.

   c) (11, 4) < (13, 2) since $11 + 2 < 4 + 13$.

   d) (15, 3) < (20, 6) since $15 + 6 < 3 + 20$.

3 a) $\{-2, -1, 0, 1, 2, 3, 4, 5, 6, 7, 8\}$

   b) $\{-2, -1, 0, 1, 2, 3, 4\}$

   c) $\{-4, 4\}$

   d) $\varnothing$

   e) $\{4\}$

   f) $\{0\}$

5 Yes; 1

4.15 THE INTEGERS AND DIVISION

1 a) 2   b) Doesn't exist   c) 0

   d) Doesn't exist   e) −3   f) −4

   g) Doesn't exist   h) Doesn't exist   i) 2

3 a) 8   b) 10   c) No solution
   d) 9   e) No solution   f) −1
   g) −3   h) −3

4.16 THE FUNDAMENTAL THEOREM OF ARITHMETIC

1 1, 2, 4, 5, 10, 20
3 No; a divisor must be nonzero.
5 a) $2^7 \cdot 3^2 \cdot 5^3$ b) $7 \cdot 11 \cdot 13^2$ c) $13 \cdot 17 \cdot 29$
7 One; 2 is the only even prime.
9 11 and 13; 17 and 19; 29 and 31
11 $7! + 2 = 5042$
    $7! + 3 = 5043$
    $7! + 4 = 5044$
    $7! + 5 = 5045$
    $7! + 6 = 5046$
    $7! + 7 = 5047$

4.17 THE GREATEST COMMON DIVISOR AND THE LEAST COMMON MULTIPLE

1 1, 2, 3, 4, 6, 8, 12, 24; 24
3 a) GCD is 6; LCM is 7344
   b) GCD is 3; LCM is 27,432
   c) GCD is 24; LCM is 864
   d) GCD is 7; LCM is 420
5 4 and 15
7 28

Chapter 5

5.1 RATIONAL NUMBERS

1 a) (10, 12), (15, 18), (20, 24)
   b) (−6, 8), (−9, 12), (−12, 16)
   c) (0, 16), (0, 24), (0, 32)
   d) (−14, −16), (−21, −24), (−28, −32)
   e) (22, −26), (33, −39), (44, −52)
   f) (14, 8), (21, 12), (28, 16)
3 a) 9   b) −9   c) −4
   d) 2   e) 0   f) 8

5 a) (5, 1) b) (1, 4) c) (10, −3)

   d) (0, 1) e) (−3, 7) f) (4, 3)

7 (−a, b) = (a, −b)

9 No; the second element of the ordered pair of integers is 0.

11 No, because (n, −1) = (−n, 1) for every integer n.

5.2 ADDITION AND SUBTRACTION OF RATIONAL NUMBERS

1 a) (5, 6) b) (−4, 32) c) (27, 18)

   d) (−42, 98) e) (15, 27) f) (68, 96)

5 a) (−3, 7) b) (2, 3)

   c) (6, −9) d) (−11, −13)

7 a) (28, 98) b) (−1, 6) c) (−44, 32)

   d) (−8, −128) e) (56, −128) f) (16, 512)

9 0

5.3 MULTIPLICATION OF RATIONAL NUMBERS

1 a) Commutative property of multiplication

   b) Distributive property

   c) Commutative property of addition

   d) Closure property of multiplication

   e) Associative property of multiplication

   f) Associative property of addition

3 a) $\frac{1}{2}$ b) $-\frac{20}{21}$ c) $\frac{21}{80}$

   d) $\frac{56}{99}$ e) $-\frac{1}{2}$ f) 0

7 a) (7, 2) b) (8, −3)

   c) (−11, −4) d) (1, 8)

5.4 DIVISION OF RATIONAL NUMBERS

1 a) (6, 8) b) (0, 12) c) (28, −48)

   d) (25, −49) e) (117, 117) f) (21, −32)

3 a) $\frac{3}{4}$ b) 0 c) $-\frac{7}{12}$

   d) $-\frac{25}{49}$ e) 1 f) $-\frac{21}{32}$

5 a) 2 b) 6 c) $\frac{4}{5}$ d) −1

7 No; $2 \div 3 = \frac{2}{3}$, but $3 \div 2 = \frac{3}{2}$.

5.5 THE RATIONAL NUMBERS AND ORDER

1 a) $(1, 2) < (2, 3)$ since $1 \cdot 3 < 2 \cdot 2$.

   b) $(5, 7) < (8, 9)$ since $5 \cdot 9 < 7 \cdot 8$.

   c) $(-3, 8) < (1, 8)$ since $(-3) \cdot 8 < 8 \cdot 1$.

   d) $(5, -7) < (-1, 2)$ since $(-5) \cdot 2 < (7) \cdot (-1)$.

   e) $(0, -3) > (2, -3)$ since $(2, -3) < (0, -3)$.

   f) $(-5, -9) > (3, 8)$ since $(3, 8) < (-5, -9)$.

3 $x < \frac{5}{3}$ 5 $\frac{5}{12}$

5.6 THE DECIMAL FORM OF A RATIONAL NUMBER

1 a) $.2$ b) $.8\overline{3} \cdots$ c) $.875$

   d) $25.\overline{0} \cdots$ e) $.\overline{142857} \cdots$ f) $.7\overline{14285} \cdots$

   g) $.\overline{153846} \cdots$ h) $.04286$

   i) $.\overline{6470588235294117} \cdots$

3 a) $\frac{265}{1000}$ b) $\frac{7}{9}$ c) $\frac{137}{99}$

   d) $\frac{29}{99}$ e) $\frac{5758}{999}$ f) $\frac{1}{999}$

   g) $\frac{714285}{999999}$ h) $\frac{2322}{990}$ i) $\frac{58851}{99990}$

5.9 THE REAL NUMBER SYSTEM

1 No; this is neither a terminating nor a repeating decimal.

3 3.162   5 2.2361

5.10 THE REAL NUMBERS AND ORDER

1 $3x < 3y; -2x > -2y$

3 $x = y$ 5 $x + y < -2$

5.11 THE NUMBER LINE

1

3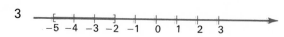

5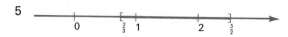

7

9 $x > y$

5.12 ABSOLUTE VALUE AND DISTANCE

1. a) 8   b) 5   c) 0
   d) π e) $\frac{14}{3}$ f) 3
3. 0
7. a) 5   b) 8   c) 4
   d) 4   e) 0   f) 7
9. None

5.13 THE COMPLEX NUMBERS

1. a) $1 + 4i$ b) $-8 - 4i$
   c) $2 - 4i$ d) $-3 + 11i$
   e) $-i$ f) $-2 + 2i$
   g) i h) $-\frac{6}{25} - \frac{17}{25}i$
   i) $\frac{1}{3} + \frac{\sqrt{2}}{3} i$ j) $-i$

3. a) $\pm 2i$ b) ± 4
   c) $\pm 4i$ d) $\pm 3i$

5. a) $-\dfrac{i}{2}$ b) $\frac{1}{2} - \frac{1}{2}i$
   c) $\frac{2}{13} + \frac{3}{13}i$ d) $-\frac{1}{5}$
   e) $-\frac{4}{41} - \frac{5}{41}i$ f) $\dfrac{1}{3} - \dfrac{\sqrt{2}}{3} i$

11. $\bar{\bar{z}} = a + bi$

Chapter 6

6.1 THE CONCEPT OF A RELATION

1. $A \times B = \{(a, 2), (a, 3), (b, 2), (b, 3), (c, 2), (c, 3)\}$; the following five relations are among the 64 different relations from A to B.

   $r = \{(a, 2)\}, D(r) = \{a\}, R(r) = \{2\}$
   $s = \{(a, 2), (b, 3)\}, D(s) = \{a, b\}, R(s) = \{2, 3\}$
   $t = \{(a, 3), (b, 3)\}, D(t) = \{a, b\}, R(t) = \{3\}$
   $u = \{(b, 2), (c, 2), (c, 3)\}, D(u) = \{b, c\}, R(u) = \{2, 3\}$
   $v = \{(a, 3), (b, 3), (c, 3)\}, D(v) = \{a, b, c\}, R(v) = \{3\}$

3. $S \times S = \{(\#, *), (\#, \#), (*, \#), (*, *)\}$; the following five relations are among the 16 different relations on S.

   $r = \{(\#, *)\}, D(r) = \{\#\}, R(r) = \{*\}$
   $s = \{(\#, \#), (*, *)\}, D(s) = \{\#, *\}, R(s) = \{\#, *\}$

$t = \{(*, *)\}, D(t) = \{*\}, R(t) = \{*\}$
$u = \{(\#, *), (*, \#)\}, D(u) = \{\#, *\}, R(u) = \{*, \#\}$
$v = \{(\#, *), (\#, \#), (*, *), (*, \#)\}, D(v) = \{\#, *\}, R(v) = \{\#, *\}$

5 $\{(\text{Little Rock, Arkansas}), (\text{Austin, Texas}), (\text{Denver, Colorado})\}$

7 $\{(2, 1), (4, 1), (4, 3), (6, 1), (6, 3), (6, 5), (8, 1), (8, 3), (8, 5), (8, 7)\}$

9 Yes

11 a) $r = \{(1, 3), (3, 5), (1, 5)\}$
    b) $s = \{(1, 1), (3, 3), (5, 5), (1, 3), (3, 1), (3, 5), (5, 3)\}$
    c) $t = \{(1, 3), (3, 1)\}$
    d) $u = \{(1, 3), (3, 1), (1, 5)\}$

6.2 THE CONCEPT OF A FUNCTION

1 a) Function
   b) Function
   c) Not a function; $D(t) \neq S$ and 0 is paired with both 2 and 4.
   d) Not a function; $D(u) \neq S$
   e) Function
   f) Not a function; $D(w) \neq S$

3 $\{(2, 3), (4, 3), (6, 3)\}$

5 $\{(\text{Little Rock, Arkansas}), (\text{Austin, Texas}), (\text{Denver, Colorado})\}$; yes.

7 $f(-1) = 2; f(5) = 44; f(0) = -1; f(-8) = 135; f(\frac{1}{2}) = -1; f(.1) = -1.08; f(-\frac{1}{2}) = -\frac{1}{4}; f(100) = 19{,}899; f = \{(x, y) \mid x \in R \text{ and } y = 2x^2 - x - 1\}.$

9 No; $\{(1, 2), (2, 2)\}$ is a function from $\{1, 2\}$ to $\{2\}$, but $\{(2, 1), (2, 2)\}$ is not a function.

6.3 THE CARTESIAN COORDINATE SYSTEM

1 a)

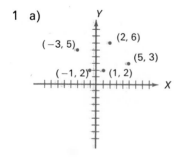

   b)

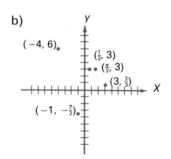

c)

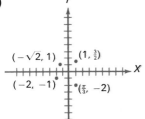

$(-\sqrt{2}, 1)$ $(1, \frac{3}{2})$

$(-2, -1)$ $(\frac{\pi}{3}, -2)$

3 a) 0

b) 0

5 a)

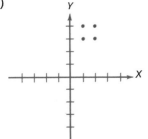

b)

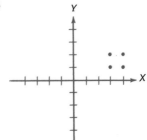

c)

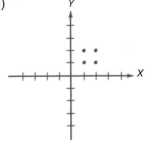

d)

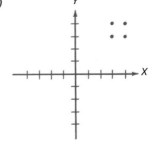

7 v is not a function.

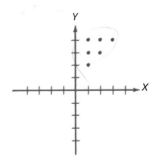

9 No; the points of intersection of the vertical line and the graph of the relation have the same x-coordinates but different y-coordinates.

6.4 LINEAR FUNCTIONS AND GRAPHS

1 a) 5   b) $\frac{1}{2}$ c) 2   d) -46

3 a) 1   b) 4   c) $\frac{5}{2}$ d) $-\frac{1}{2}$

5 a)

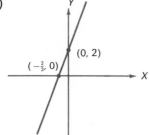

b)

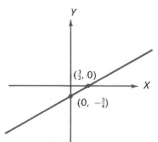

c)

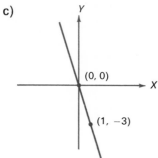

d)

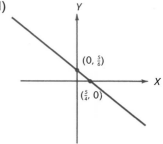

e)

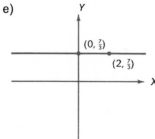

f)

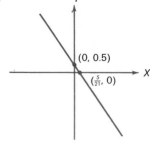

7

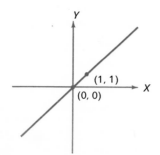

6.5 LINEAR EQUATIONS

1 a) $-\frac{5}{3}$ b) 5

   c) $-13\frac{1}{2}$ d) 12

3 -3 5 4 7 10

9 $-\frac{23}{18}$ 11 $-\frac{31}{2}$ 13 5

15 1 17 $\dfrac{d}{t}$ 19 $\dfrac{2s - gt^2}{2t}$

21 $\dfrac{f - a}{n - 1}$ 23 $(-4, 0)$

6.6 LINEAR EQUATIONS IN TWO VARIABLES

1 $\{(1, 1)\}$ 3 $\{(0, 3)\}$ 5 $\{(\frac{3}{19}, \frac{14}{19})\}$

7 $\{(3, \frac{3}{2})\}$ 9 $\{(-\frac{1}{2}, 1)\}$ 11 $\{(2, -1)\}$

13 $\{(-\frac{5}{3}, \frac{2}{3})\}$ 15 $\varnothing$ 17 $\{(\frac{1}{11}, \frac{4}{11})\}$

19 $\{(3, -1)\}$

21 $\{(x, y) \mid 2x - 3y = 12\}$

23 $\{(2, 5)\}$

25 $x = \dfrac{b_2 c_1 - b_1 c_2}{a_1 b_2 - a_2 b_1}$, $y = \dfrac{a_1 c_2 - a_2 c_1}{a_1 b_2 - a_2 b_1}$

27 $x = \frac{1}{4}, y = -\frac{1}{6}$

6.7 LINEAR EQUATIONS AND APPLICATIONS

1 26, 130 3 129, 130, 131 5 17 by 22

7 8 years old

9 Shannon is 4 years old, and Amanda is 20 years old.

11 39 13 55 dimes and 30 quarters

15 6.5 hours after the first car starts 17 75 miles per hour

19 a) 10:36 a.m. b) 10:40 a.m.

21 217.5 mph; 22.5 mph; 17.5 mph 23 $13\frac{1}{3}$ days

25 $4\frac{2}{3}$ hours 27 40 hours 29 40 pounds

31 30 quarts 33 $4\frac{8}{13}$ quarts 35 $3\frac{1}{3}$ quarts

6.8 EXPONENTS AND RADICALS

1 a) 8 b) $\frac{1}{9}$ c) 2

   d) 4 e) $\frac{1}{8}$ f) $-\frac{1}{3}$

   g) 16 h) $\frac{1}{16}$ i) $\frac{1}{64}$

3 a) $\frac{1}{4}$ b) 729   c) 6561

  d) $x^5 y^4$ e) a^3 f) 1

5 a) x^6 b) $x^{3/8}$

  c) 117,649   d) -2187

6.9 QUADRATIC FUNCTIONS AND GRAPHS

1 Minimum value is -9

3 Minimum value is 2

5 Maximum value is 3

7 Minimum value is $-\frac{5}{4}$

9 Minimum value is -3

11 Both numbers are 35

13 300 ft by 300 ft

6.10 QUADRATIC EQUATIONS

1 4, -1 3 -5, 3   5 3, -8

7 3, 5   9 -3, -5 11 $-\frac{1}{2}$, 1

13 3, -1 15 -7, 4   17 $\frac{5}{2}$, -2

19 $\frac{3}{2}$, -1

21 a) Roots are imaginary

   b) One distinct real root

   c) Two real roots

6.11 THE QUADRATIC FORMULA

1 4, -1 3 7, -5 5 $\dfrac{-1 \pm \sqrt{3}\,i}{2}$

7 -7, 6   9 $-2 \pm \sqrt{3}$ 11 $\dfrac{-1 \pm \sqrt{3}}{2}$

13 $-\frac{1}{2}$ 15 -7, 6

19 The product of the roots is -8 and sum of the roots is 7.

21 8, 9   23 25 rows   25 5 or $-\frac{1}{3}$

6.12 INEQUALITIES

1 $\{x \mid x < 5\}$ 3 $\{z \mid z > -\frac{17}{5}\}$ 5 $\{w \mid w < \frac{2}{3}\}$

7 $\{x \mid -\frac{1}{2} \leqq x \leqq 1\}$ 9 $\{x \mid -3 < x < \frac{1}{2}\}$

11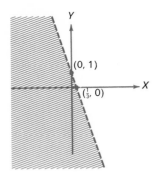

13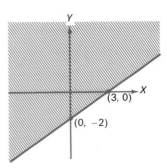

15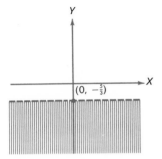

17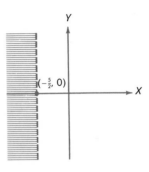

19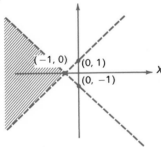

21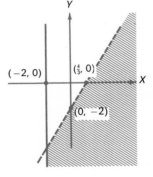

23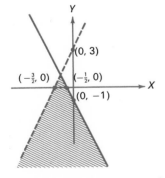

25 $\{x \mid x > 3\} \cup \{x \mid x < -2\}$

27

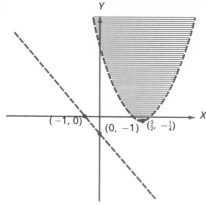

$(-1, 0)$ $(0, -1)$ $(\frac{5}{2}, -\frac{1}{4})$

6.13 STATISTICAL GRAPHS

1 a) 71   b) 64   c) July
   d) 7   e) 7

3 a) Individual income tax   b) 9 cents   c) 27 cents

5 a) October and November   b) July and August
   c) 48   d) 7

7

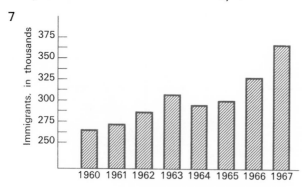

9 A suggested family budget for a family of four with $8000 annual income
   (after taxes)

11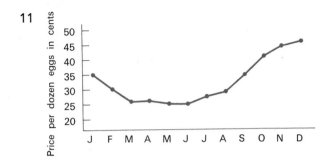

Chapter 7

7.1 NUMBER CONGRUENCES

1 8 o'clock; 15 o'clock

3 9 o'clock; 8 o'clock

5 3, 10, 17, 24, 31

7 16, 5, 86, −19, −54

9 815, 821, 827, 833, 839

11 5, 12, 19, 26, 33

13 $\{7 + 5n \mid n$ is an integer$\}$

15 $\{x \mid x$ is an integer$\}$

17 $\{5n \mid n$ is an integer$\}$

7.2 PROPERTIES OF NUMBER CONGRUENCES

1 3, 8, 13, and 18

3 21, 24, 27, and 30

5 −14, −8, −2, and 4

7 −12, 0, 12, and 24

9 −3, 5, 13, and 21

11 −31, −24, −17, and −10

13 0, 5, 10, and 15

15 a) 11   b) 13

7.3 ARITHMETIC MODULO 5

1 a) 4   b) 3   c) 3   d) 1

e) 3   f) 4   g) 1   h) 0

i) 1   j) 4   k) 4   l) 4

3 The multiplicative inverse for 2 is 3 and the multiplicative inverse for 4 is 4.

5 a) 2   b) 3   c) 3   d) 4

e) 4   f) 3   g) 0   h) 2

i) 2   j) 2   k) 2   l) 0

7 The operation of division on I_5 is not commutative since $2 \div 4 = 3$ and $4 \div 2 = 2$. The operation is not associative since $(2 \div 4) \div 3 = 1$ and $2 \div (4 \div 3) = 4$.

9 3   11 3   13 3   15 4

7.4 ARITHMETIC MODULO 6

1. a) 5   b) 3   c) 1   d) 2
   e) 0   f) 0   g) 3   h) 3
   i) 0   j) 4   k) 4   l) 3
3. 4 is the only other zero divisor.
5. a) 3   b) 3   c) 5
   d) 4   e) 3   f) 5
   g) 4   h) 5   i) 4
7. 1   9. 5   11. 2 and 5
13. No solution in I_6 15. 1, 3, and 5   17. 1 and 5

7.6 THE CHECK OF NINES

1.
$$761 \equiv 14 \equiv 5 \bmod 9$$
$$\underline{592 \equiv 16 \equiv 7 \bmod 9}$$
$$1353 \qquad 12 \equiv 3 \bmod 9 \qquad 1 + 3 + 5 + 3 \equiv 12 \equiv 3 \bmod 9$$

7.
$$6981 \equiv 24 \equiv 6 \bmod 9$$
$$\underline{-4793 \equiv 23 \equiv 5 \bmod 9}$$
$$2188 \qquad 1 \qquad 2 + 1 + 8 + 8 \equiv 19 \equiv 10 \equiv 1 \bmod 9$$

11.
$$63 \equiv 9 \equiv 0 \bmod 9$$
$$\underline{\times 29 \equiv 11 \equiv 2 \bmod 9}$$
$$1827 \qquad 0 \qquad 1 + 8 + 2 + 7 \equiv 18 \equiv 9 \equiv 0 \bmod 9$$

7.7 TESTS FOR DIVISIBILITY

1. 942 is divisible by 2, 3, and 6.
3. 417,565 is divisible by 5.
5. 79,783 is divisible by 11.
7. 21,437 is not divisible by any of the numbers.
9. 123,120   11. 834,132   13. 365,231

Chapter 8

8.1 OPERATIONS ON A SET

1. The two binary operations $*$ and $\#$ defined by the following tables are binary operations from $A = \{0, 5, 10\}$ into $B = \{2, 4, 6\}$.

*	0	5	10
0	2	4	6
5	4	6	2
10	6	2	4

#	0	5	10
0	6	4	2
5	4	2	6
10	2	6	4

3 The binary operation ∗ given by the following table is the *only* binary operation from $C = \{1, 2, 3\}$ into set $D = \{0\}$.

∗	1	2	3
1	0	0	0
2	0	0	0
3	0	0	0

5 The two binary operations ∗ and # defined by the following tables are binary operations on the set $Y = \{0, 3, 6\}$ such that Y is closed with respect to the operation.

∗	0	3	6
0	0	3	6
3	3	6	0
6	6	0	3

#	0	3	6
0	3	6	3
3	6	3	6
6	3	6	3

7 The set of even integers is closed with respect to both addition and multiplication.

9 The set $S = \{-1, 0, 1\}$ is not closed with respect to addition since $1 + 1 = 2 \notin S$. The following table verifies that S is closed with respect to multiplication.

·	−1	0	1
−1	1	0	−1
0	0	0	0
1	−1	0	1

11 512

13 The mileage chart defines an operation since it is a function from $C \times C$ into M, where C is the set of cities under consideration and M the set of different mileages between the cities.

8.2 BINARY OPERATIONS AND THEIR PROPERTIES

1 a) Yes   b) No   c) No   d) No

e) None of the elements have inverses since there is no identity.

3 a) Yes   b) Yes   c) Yes

d) 1 is the identity element.

e) For any integer a, its inverse is $2 - a$.

5 a) Yes   b) Yes   c) Yes

d) $-\frac{1}{2}$ is the identity element.

e) The inverse for any rational number a is $-a - 1$.

7	a) No	b) No	c) No
	d) No	e) No inverses	
9	a) Yes	b) No	c) Yes
	d) No	e) No inverses	
11	a) Yes	b) Yes	c) Yes
	d) No	e) No inverses	
13	a) Yes	b) No	c) No
	d) No	e) No inverses	
15	a) Yes	b) No	c) No
	d) No	e) No inverses	

17 Yes; yes   19 No; yes

8.3 THE CONCEPT OF A GROUP

3 Group   5 Group

7 This is not a group since 0 has no inverse.

9 Group

11 This is not a group since there is no identity.

13 Group

15 This is not a group since there is no identity.

8.4 FURTHER EXAMPLES OF GROUPS

7 Not a group   9 Group

13 Group   15 Not a group

8.5 PERMUTATION GROUPS

1 a) $\begin{bmatrix} 1 & 2 & 3 & 4 & 5 \\ 5 & 4 & 2 & 1 & 3 \end{bmatrix}$ b) $\begin{bmatrix} 1 & 2 & 3 & 4 & 5 \\ 3 & 4 & 5 & 2 & 1 \end{bmatrix}$ c) $\begin{bmatrix} 1 & 2 & 3 & 4 & 5 \\ 5 & 3 & 4 & 2 & 1 \end{bmatrix}$

d) $\begin{bmatrix} 1 & 2 & 3 & 4 & 5 \\ 3 & 4 & 1 & 2 & 5 \end{bmatrix}$ e) $\begin{bmatrix} 1 & 2 & 3 & 4 & 5 \\ 4 & 5 & 1 & 3 & 2 \end{bmatrix}$ f) $\begin{bmatrix} 1 & 2 & 3 & 4 & 5 \\ 5 & 1 & 2 & 4 & 3 \end{bmatrix}$

g) $\begin{bmatrix} 1 & 2 & 3 & 4 & 5 \\ 5 & 1 & 2 & 3 & 4 \end{bmatrix}$ h) $\begin{bmatrix} 1 & 2 & 3 & 4 & 5 \\ 5 & 4 & 1 & 3 & 2 \end{bmatrix}$ i) $\begin{bmatrix} 1 & 2 & 3 & 4 & 5 \\ 1 & 3 & 4 & 5 & 2 \end{bmatrix}$

3 From Table 8.13 we obtain the following table showing all possible combinations of α, ϵ, and δ under the operation of multiplication of permutations. Multiplication of permutations is an associative operation. From the table, it is clear that we have closure, α is the identity element, and each element has an inverse (α is its own, and ϵ and δ are inverses of each other). Thus $\{\alpha, \epsilon, \delta\}$ under multiplication of permutations is a group.

○	α	ϵ	δ
α	α	ϵ	δ
ϵ	ϵ	δ	α
δ	δ	α	ϵ

5 From Table 8.14 we obtain the table below showing all possible combinations of R_0 and X under multiplication of permutations. Multiplication of permutations is an associative operation. From the table it is clear that we have closure, R_0 is the identity element, and each element is its own inverse. Thus, $\{R_0, X\}$ under multiplication of permutations is a group.

○	R_0	X
R_0	R_0	X
X	X	R_0

8.6 SUBGROUPS

1 Since $V \subset S$ and V was shown to be a group in Problem 5 of Section 8.5, V is a subgroup of S.

3 Clearly the set of multiples of 5 is a subset of the set of integers. If $5n$ and $5m$ are any two multiples of 5,

$$5n + 5m = 5(n + m)$$

is a multiple of 5, and thus we have closure. Addition on the set of integers is associative, and therefore addition on the set of multiples of 5 is associative. Zero is a multiple of 5 ($5 \cdot 0$) and is the identity. Each multiple of 5, $5n$, has as its inverse $-5n$, which is a multiple of 5. Therefore the set of multiples of 5 under addition is a subgroup of the set of integers.

5 1, 2, 3, 4, 6, 8, 12, 24

7 The set H is a subset of G and from the accompanying table we observe that H is closed with respect to multiplication. Since the operation is associative on G and $H \subset G$, the operation is associative on H. The identity element is 6, and each element is its own inverse. Therefore $H = \{4, 6\}$ under multiplication mod 10 is a subgroup of $G = \{2, 4, 6, 8\}$.

$\cdot$	6	4
6	6	4
4	4	6

9 4

11 No; the group has 5 elements, and the number of elements in any subgroup must divide 5. Since 5 is prime, the only possible subgroups are those with 1 or 5 elements.

1 This is not a field because the set is not closed under addition. Further, 1 has no additive inverse.

3 Field　　　　　5 Field　　　　　7 Field　　　　　9 Field

15 2

Chapter 9

9.2 POINTS, LINES, PLANES, AND SPACE

1 a) $\overrightarrow{DE}$　　　b) $\overline{BD}$　　　c) $\overline{BD}$　　　d) $\overline{BD}$　　　e) $\overrightarrow{BD}$

　f) $\varnothing$　　　g) $\overline{BC}$　　　h) $\overline{AB}$　　　i) $\overleftrightarrow{AE}$　　　j) $\overrightarrow{BC}$

3 a) $\{P\}$　　　　b) $\{B\}$　　　　c) $\overrightarrow{BD}$　　　d) $\{B, D\}$

　e) $\varnothing$　　　　f) $\{P\}$　　　　g) $\{A, C\}$

5 a) True　　　b) True　　　c) False　　　d) True

　e) False　　　f) True　　　g) True　　　h) False

7 6　　　　　　　　　　　　　　　9 No

9.3 ANGLES

1 ρ and γ are adjacent angles; θ and ϕ are adjacent angles.

3 ρ and γ are supplementary angles; θ and ϕ are supplementary angles.

5 a) $\overline{BC}$　　　　　　　　　　b) $\{A, C\}$

　c) $\{A, B\}$　　　　　　　　　d) $\{A, \overline{BC}\}$

7 No; the rays do not have a common endpoint.

9 $\angle APB$ and $\angle BPC$ are adjacent angles. $\angle APB \cup \angle BPC$ is not an angle because it is the union of *three* rays with a common endpoint.

11 a)

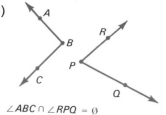

$\angle ABC \cap \angle RPQ = \varnothing$

b)

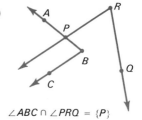

$\angle ABC \cap \angle PRQ = \{P\}$

c)

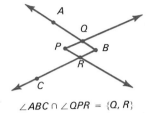

$\angle ABC \cap \angle QPR = \{Q, R\}$

d)

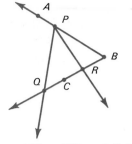

$\angle ABC \cap \angle RPQ = \{P, R, Q\}$

e)

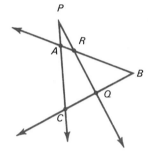

$\angle ABC \cap \angle CPQ = \{A, C, R, Q\}$

f)

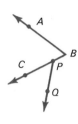

$\angle ABC \cap \angle CPQ = \overrightarrow{PC}$

g)

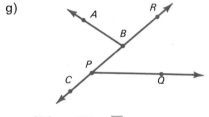

$\angle ABC \cap \angle RPQ = \overline{PB}$

9.4 CURVES

1 (b), (e), (g), and (h) are closed; (a), (c), (d), and (f) are open.

3 (e), (h)

5 The intersection of these two simple closed curves (triangle and circle) is $\{P\}$. The union of these two curves is *not* simple, but it is closed.

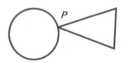

7 *U, R,* and *V* are exterior; *Q* and *W* are interior; *P* and *T* are on the curve; the curve is not convex.

9 This curve is closed but not simple.

11 This curve is closed and simple but not convex.

9.5 POLYGONS

1 (b) and (d) are polygons; (a), (c), (e), and (f) are not polygons.

3 None of the curves are triangles.

5 a) $\{B\}$ b) $\overline{AB}$ c) $\{A, C\}$ d) $\overline{AC}$

     e) $\{A, C\}$ f) $\overline{BC}$ g) $\varnothing$ h) $\{\overline{AB}, C\}$

7

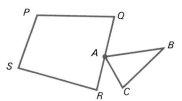

$ABC \cap PQRS = \{A\}$

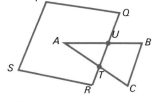

$ABC \cap PQRS = \{U, T\}$

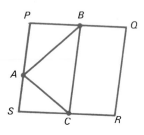

$ABC \cap PQRS = \{A, B, C\}$

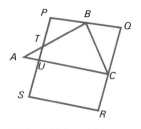

$ABC \cap PQRS = \{U, T, B, C\}$

9 2

11

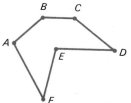

9.6 CIRCLES

1 a) O b) $\overline{OB}$ or $\overline{OA}$

  c) $\overrightarrow{AB}$ d) $\overline{AB}$

  e) $\overleftrightarrow{PQ}$ f) P

  g) $\overleftrightarrow{AB}$ h) O

  i) Q j) $\overparen{APB}$

3

5 $\{B\}$ 7 $\{P\}$; $\varnothing$; $\overrightarrow{PQ} - \{P\}$

9 Ring; a coin better illustrates a circular region.

9.7 SIMPLE CLOSED SURFACES

1 Vertices are: $A, B, C, D, E, F, G, H.$ Sides are: $ADHE, DCGH, GFBC,$ $ABFE, ABCD, EFGH.$ Edges are: $\overline{AB}, \overline{DC}, \overline{EF}, \overline{HG}, \overline{AE}, \overline{DH}, \overline{BF}, \overline{CG},$ $\overline{EH}, \overline{FG}, \overline{AD}, \overline{BC}.$ There are 8 vertices, 6 sides, and 12 edges. Thus $8 + 6 - 12 = 2$, and Euler's formula is satisfied.

3 Vertices are: $A, B, C, D, E.$ Sides are: $ABCD, ABE, BEC, CED, AED.$ Edges are: $\overline{AB}, \overline{BC}, \overline{CD}, \overline{DA}, \overline{EA}, \overline{EB}, \overline{EC}, \overline{ED}.$ There are 5 vertices, 5 sides, and 8 edges. Thus $5 + 5 - 8 = 2$, and Euler's formula is satisfied.

5 Triangle   7 Circle   9 Circle

11 There are 20 vertices, 12 sides, and 30 edges. Thus $20 + 12 - 30 = 2$, and Euler's formula is satisfied.

9.9 THE METRIC SYSTEM

1 a) 0.005 kilometer   b) 1,500,000 centimeters

  c) 30 liters   d) 140 milliliters

  e) 3 hectograms   f) 150,000 decigrams

  g) 0.001750 kiloliter   h) 0.3475 hectometer

  i) 615,000,000 milligrams   j) 3.27 dekameters

3 0.15 kilogram   5 30 liters

7 7.35 pints   9 30 cents   11 65 mph

9.10 MEASUREMENT OF POLYGONS AND POLYGONAL REGIONS

1 6 meters   3 2.5 feet

7 35; 20; 70

9.11 MEASUREMENT OF CIRCLES AND CIRCULAR REGIONS

1 $c = 28\pi$ inches; $A = 196\pi$ square inches

3 $c = 6\pi$ meters; $A = 9\pi$ square meters

5 $c = 12\pi$ yards; $A = 36\pi$ square yards

7 The circle with radius measure $2r$ has circumference twice that of the circle with radius measure r.

9 Approximately 25,120 miles   11 2π units

9.12 MEASUREMENT OF SURFACES AND SOLIDS

1 158 square meters; 1,580,000 square centimeters

3 308π square inches; $77\pi/36$ square feet

5 784π square centimeters; $10976\pi/3$ cubic centimeters

7 $189\pi/2$ square inches

9 Let r be the radius of the base of the can. The height of the can is $2r$ and it has lateral surface area of $4\pi r^2$. If the ball just fits into the can, it s radius is r and it has surface area $4\pi r^2$.

Chapter 10

10.1 COUNTING PROBLEMS

1 8;

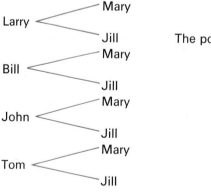

The possible committees are:
Larry — Mary
Larry — Jill
Bill — Mary
Bill — Jill
John — Mary
John — Jill
Tom — Mary
Tom — Jill

3 280   5 125   7 75

9 16;

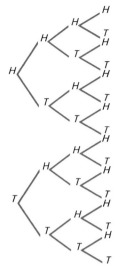

HHHH,	*HHHT*
HHTH,	*HHTT*
HTHH,	*HTHT*
HTTH,	*HTTT*
THHH,	*THHT*
THTH,	*THTT*
TTHH,	*TTHT*
TTTH,	*TTTT*

11 17,576,000   13 40,320

10.2 PERMUTATIONS

1 a) 720   b) 5040   c) 40,320   d) 362,880   e) 3,628,800

3 $P(10, 5)$ means the number of permutations of 10 things taken 5 at a time; $P(10, 5) = 30,240$.

5 $P(8, 1)$ means the number of permutations of 8 things taken 1 at a time; $P(8, 1) = 8$.

7 720   9 120; 720   11 7920

13 1440   15 3360   17 34,650

10.3 COMBINATIONS

1 $C(5, 3)$ means the number of combinations of 5 things taken 3 at a time; $C(5, 3) = 10$.

3 $C(10, 8)$ means the number of combinations of 10 things taken 8 at a time; $C(10, 8) = 45$.

5 $C(8, 8)$ means the number of combinations of 8 things taken 8 at a time; $C(8, 8) = 1$.

7 8568   9 635,013,559,600   11 4620

13 103,950   15 63

10.5 SAMPLE SPACES AND EVENTS

1 $\{HH, TT, HT, TH\}$ and $\{2, 1, 0\}$

3 a) Sample space

   b) $\{2, 4, 5\}$ is not a sample space because the outcomes 1, 3, and 6 are not listed.

   c) $\{1, 2, 3, \text{odd}\}$ is not a sample space for two reasons: an outcome of an experiment could result in two elements of this set, and the outcomes 4 and 6 are not listed.

   d) Sample space　　　e) Sample space　　　f) Sample space

5 $S = \{H1, H2, H3, H4, H5, H6, T1, T2, T3, T4, T5, T6\}; E = \{T1, T2, T3, T4, T5, T6\}$

7 $\emptyset, \{R\}, \{B\}, \{Y\}, \{G\}, \{R, B\}, \{R, Y\}, \{R, G\}, \{B, Y\}, \{B, G\}, \{Y, G\},$ $\{R, B, Y\}, \{B, Y, G\}, \{R, B, G\}, \{R, Y, G\}$ and S

9 $E_1 = \{1, 4\}$

11 E and $\emptyset$ are always disjoint.

10.6 PROBABILITY MEASURES

1 $\frac{1}{2}; \frac{2}{3}$　　　　　　　　　　　3 $Pr(R) = \frac{3}{4}$ and $Pr(B) = \frac{1}{4}$

5 $Pr(1) = Pr(2) = Pr(3) = Pr(4) = Pr(5) = Pr(6) = \frac{1}{6}; Pr(7) = Pr(8) = 0$

7 $Pr(P) = \frac{1}{2}, Pr(N) = \frac{1}{6},$ and $Pr(Q) = \frac{1}{3}; \frac{5}{6}; \frac{1}{2}$

9 If $S = \{R, B\}$, an appropriate probability measure is $Pr(R) = \frac{1}{2}$ and $Pr(B) = \frac{1}{2}$, and thus the probability that the card drawn is black is $\frac{1}{2}; \frac{1}{4}; \frac{3}{4}$.

10.7 THE EQUIPROBABLE MEASURE

1 $\frac{1}{4}; \frac{5}{12}$　　　　　　3 $\frac{1}{9}$　　　　　　5 $\frac{2}{9}$

7 $\frac{3}{22}; \frac{19}{22}$　　　　　9 $\frac{1}{2}$　　　　　11 $\frac{19}{34}; \frac{15}{34}$

13 $\frac{91}{285}; \frac{91}{190}; \frac{194}{285}$

10.8 CONDITIONAL PROBABILITY

1 1　　　　　　　　　3 $\frac{1}{2}$　　　　　　5 $\frac{22}{105}; \frac{2}{35}$

7 $\frac{1}{6}$　　　　　　　　9 $\frac{1}{48}; \frac{1}{12}$　　　　11 $\frac{1}{4}$

13 $\frac{1}{4}$　　　　　　　　15 $\frac{64}{169}; \frac{80}{169}$　　　17 $\frac{1}{52}$

10.9 EMPIRICAL PROBABILITY

1 $\frac{1}{12}$　　　　　　3 $\dfrac{3}{25,000}$　　　　5 $\frac{1}{44}$

7 $\dfrac{38,569}{91,914}$　　　9 $\dfrac{10,419}{14,474}$

10.10 ODDS AND MATHEMATICAL EXPECTATION

1   $\frac{3}{10}$; $\frac{10}{3}$ 3 $\frac{5}{11}$; $\frac{13}{3}$ 5   \$40; \$5

7   \$2.50   9   \$5

10.12 MEASURES OF CENTRAL TENDENCY

1   28   3   44   5   262

9   4.54; 4.6; 4.6   11   43.2; 43.15; 43.1   13   6 ft; 6 ft 1 in.

15   \$2.80 per hour; \$2.50 per hour; \$2.50 per hour; mean.

17   No; this conclusion would be based on the assumption that there are the same number of professional and nonprofessional workers.

19   91; $88\frac{1}{3}$

10.13 FREQUENCY DISTRIBUTIONS

1

Class interval	Tally	Frequency
221.5–238.5	II	2
206.5–221.5	⊁⊦⊦⊤	5
191.5–206.5	⊁⊦⊦⊤ IIII	9
176.5–191.5	⊁⊦⊦⊤ ⊁⊦⊦⊤ IIII	14
161.5–176.5	⊁⊦⊦⊤ II	7
146.5–161.5	⊁⊦⊦⊤ IIII	9
131.5–146.5	IIII	4

3

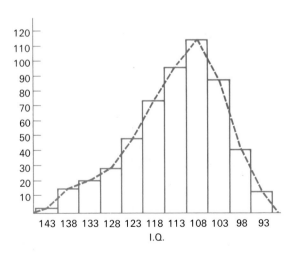

5   a) 44

b)

Class interval	Tally	Frequency
92.5–103.5	|||	3
81.5– 92.5	ЖHT	5
70.5– 81.5	ЖHT ЖHT		11
59.5– 70.5	ЖHT |||	8
48.5– 59.5	|||	3

c)

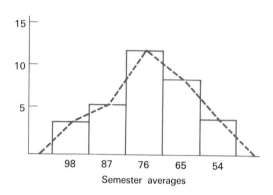

Semester averages

d) 74.9; the actual mean is 74.67.

e) The median is 75, and there are 5 modes, 96, 85, 79, 73, and 70.

7 a) 22

b)

Class interval	Tally	Frequency
35.5–40.5	ЖHT	5
30.5–35.5	ЖHT ||||	9
25.5–30.5	ЖHT ЖHT ||||	14
20.5–25.5	ЖHT |||	8
15.5–20.5	||||	4

c)

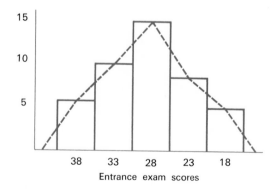

Entrance exam scores

d) 28.375; the actual mean is 28.6.

10.14 MEASURES OF DISPERSION

1 10; MD $= 3.44$; $\sigma = 3.87$

3 15; MD $= 4.62$; $\sigma = 4.93$

5 $\sigma = 9.43$ (using $\bar{x} = 74.9$ and the frequency distribution in Problem 5 of Section 10.13).

7 a) 98   b) MD $= 8.24$ c) $\sigma = 10.5$ d) 326

10.15 THE BINOMIAL THEOREM

1 $a^7 + 7a^6b + 21a^5b^2 + 35a^4b^3 + 35a^3b^4 + 21a^2b^5 + 7ab^6 + b^7$

3 $2^5 + 5 \cdot 2^4 \cdot 3 + 10 \cdot 2^3 \cdot 3^2 + 10 \cdot 2^2 \cdot 3^3 + 5 \cdot 2 \cdot 3^4 + 3^5 = 3125$

5 $a^7 - 7a^6b + 21a^5b^2 - 35a^4b^3 + 35a^3b^4 - 21a^2b^5 + 7ab^6 - b^7$

7 $100^3 - 3 \cdot 100^2 \cdot 1 + 3 \cdot 100 \cdot 1^2 - 1^3 = 970{,}299$

10.16 BINOMIAL AND NORMAL DISTRIBUTIONS

1 The expected frequencies of 1, 2, 3, 4 5, 6, or 7 heads are 1, 7, 21, 35, 35, 21, 7, and 1, respectively.

3 $\frac{1}{128}$, $\frac{21}{128}$, $\frac{35}{128}$, $\frac{35}{128}$

7 $\frac{1}{2}$, $\frac{3}{16}$, $\frac{5}{16}$

10.17 CORRELATION

1 3.4; 2.4; 2.9

3
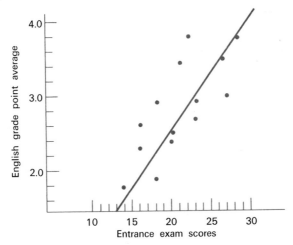

5 a) .95   b) .75   c) .7

Chapter 11

11.1 SIMPLE INTEREST

1 $1500; $6500   3 $45.69; $1045.69   5 $6.67

7 $83.75   9 7.7%   11 50%

13 $3125   15 $528.17

11.2 COMPOUND INTEREST

1 $1213.63; $713.63; $450   3 $4195.13

5 $999.89   7 $34,891.18

9 $2361.29   11 $2313.77

11.3 ARITHMETIC PROGRESSIONS

1 15, 19, 23; 105   3 $2, \frac{5}{2}, 3; 85\frac{1}{2}$

5 −1, 2, 5; 18   7 $a_{15} = 87; S_{15} = 675$

9 $a_1 = 1; a_7 = 5$ 11 $a_1 = -11; S_{15} = 150$

13 3   15 1275   17 2500

11.4 GEOMETRIC PROGRESSIONS

1 54, 162, 486; 2186   3 $2, 4, 8; \frac{63}{4}$

5 1, −1, 1; 0   7 $a_6 = 64; S_6 = 126$

9 $a_1 = 1; S_3 = \frac{3}{4}$ 11 $a_1 = \frac{1}{125}; S_3 = \frac{21}{125}$

13 3   15 288

17 $a_7 = \frac{1}{9}$ 19 $\frac{1}{2}$

11.5 ORDINARY ANNUITIES

1 $S = \$95,454.20; A = \$28,187.89$

3 $1309.42; $2876.04

5 $5365.50   7 $84,127.41

9 $16,681.16   11 $2830.21

11.6 THE PERIODIC PAYMENT

1 0.009540   3 $120.41

5 $63.60   7 $32.07

Chapter 12

12.3 THE FORTRAN LANGUAGE

1 a) Acceptable

   b) 3MAT is not acceptable because it starts with a numeric character.

c) Acceptable

d) Acceptable

e) I8*J is not acceptable because it contains a special character.

f) TUESDAY is not acceptable because it contains too many characters.

g) Acceptable

h) ØRD 1 is not acceptable because of the space between D and 1.

i) H(A) is not acceptable because it contains special characters.

j) Acceptable

k) Acceptable

l) ANSWER is not acceptable because it contains too many characters.

3 a) Fixed-point   b) Fixed-point   c) Floating-point

d) Floating-point   e) Floating-point   f) Fixed-point

g) Fixed-point   h) Floating-point   i) Fixed-point

j) Fixed-point   k) Floating-point   l) Floating-point

12.4 ARITHMETIC ASSIGNMENT STATEMENTS AND LIBRARY FUNCTIONS

1 a) Acceptable

b) 3*A + C/D is not acceptable because 3 is a fixed-point number.

c) Acceptable

d) I + J/Q is not acceptable because it contains variables of different modes.

e) K**3.1 − L*M is not acceptable because a fixed-point variable cannot be raised to a floating-point power.

f) (−3./X**2 + A/(.2*X) is not acceptable because of the un-balanced parenthesis.

3 (A + B)/(C + D)

5 (A + B)/C + D

7 (6.*X**2 − 5.*X + 4.)/(X**2 + 1.)

9 a) 16   b) 16   c) 2

d) 0   e) 12   f) 1

11 X = 2.*A**2 − 3.*A + 4.

13 X = (38./A*B)**.5

15 X = 7./SQRTF(A**2 + B**2 − C**2)

12.5 I-O STATEMENTS

1   READ(1,101)A,B,C,D
    101 FØRMAT(4F10.2)

```
  3        READ(1,20)A,K,B,C,M
      20 FØRMAT(F10.2,I10,2F10.2,I10)
  5        WRITE(3,105)AB,J,K
     105 FØRMAT(F20.2,2I20)
  7        WRITE(3,30)ZERØ,IN,ØUT
      30 FØRMAT(F20.2,I20,F20.2)
  9        READ(1,101)A,B
     101 FØRMAT(2F10.2)
           X = (A + B)/4.
           WRITE(3,102)X
     102 FØRMAT(F10.2)
           STØP
           END
 11        READ(1,101)M
     101 FØRMAT(I10)
           J = ((M**2 + 3)/(M + 1))**3
           WRITE(3,102)J
     102 FØRMAT(I10)
           STØP
           END
```

12.6 CONTROL STATEMENTS

```
  1 GØ TØ 50          3 30; 7; 35     5 IF (A − B)17,5,15
  7    1 READ(1,101)J,K,L,M
     101 FØRMAT(4I10)
           JAKE = (J + K)/3
           LUKE = (L − M)/4
           IF (JAKE−LUKE)2,3,4
       2 MAX = 3
           WRITE(3,102)J,K,L,M,MAX
     102 FØRMAT(5I20)
           GØ TØ 1
       3 MAX = 2
           WRITE(3,102)J,K,L,M,MAX
           GØ TØ 1
       4 MAX = 1
           WRITE(3,102)J,K,L,M,MAX
           GØ TØ 1
           END
```

12.7 DO LOOPS

1 a) Permissible

b) JIG(M + 3.5) is not permissible because 3.5 is a floating-point number.

c) Permissible   d) Permissible

e) GIGI(−8) is not permissible because the subscript is negative.

f) FLØAT(F + 80.) is not permissible because 80. is a floating-point number.

g) Permissible

h) M(2348) is not permissible because the subscript is greater than 1000.

3 a) DØ 2 A = 1,20 is not permissible because A is a floating-point variable.

    b) DØ, 50 J = 5,10 is not permissible because of the comma after DØ.

    c) Permissible

    d) DØ P3 K = 1,100 is not permissible because P3 is not a legitimate statement number.

    e) Permissible   f) Permissible   g) Permissible

```
5         DIMENSIØN J(200)
          DØ 10 I = 1,200
      10  READ(1,101)J(I)
     101  FØRMAT(I10)
          K = 0
          DØ 20 I = 1,200
      20  K = K + J(I)
          WRITE(3,102)K
     102  FØRMAT(I20)
          STØP
          END
7         DIMENSIØN X(100),Y(100)
          DØ 10 I = 1,100
      10  READ(1,101)X(I),Y(I)
     101  FØRMAT(2F10.2)
          SUM = 0.
          DØ 40 I = 1,100
          IF (X(I) − Y(I))20,20,30
      20  SUM = SUM + Y(I)
          GØ TØ 40
      30  SUM = SUM + X(I)
      40  CØNTINUE
          WRITE(3,101)SUM
          STØP
          END
```

```
1       READ(1,10)X
    10 FØRMAT(F10.2)
        Y = ABSF(X**2 - 3.*X)
        WRITE(3,20)Y
    20 FØRMAT(F20.2)
        STØP
        END

3       READ(1,10)X,Y
    10 FØRMAT(2F10.2)
        W = (-2.*X**2*Y + 1.)/(Y**3 - X*Y)
        WRITE(3,20)W
    20 FØRMAT(F20.2)
        STØP
        END

5       DIMENSIØN J(50)
        DØ 10 I = 1,50
    10 READ(1,101)J(I)
    101 FØRMAT(I10)
        L = 0
        DØ 20 I = 1,50
        K = J(I)**2 + 1
    20 L = L + K
        WRITE(3,102)L
    102 FØRMAT(I20)
        STØP
        END

7       DIMENSIØN X(5000)
        DØ 10 I = 1,5000
    10 READ (1,101)X(I)
    101 FØRMAT(F10.2)
        BIGX = ABSF(X(1))
        DØ 50 I = 2,5000
        IF (X(I))20,30,30
    20 X(I) = -X(I)
    30 IF (X(I) - BIGX)50,40,40
    40 BIGX = X(I)
    50 CØNTINUE
        WRITE(3,102)BIGX
    102 FØRMAT(F20.2)
        STØP
        END
```

INDEX

INDEX

BCDE79876543210